ADVANCED
ENGINEERING
MATHEMATICS

ADVANCED ENGINEERING MATHEMATICS

Dr H. S. Govinda Rao

Viva Books

New Delhi | Mumbai | Chennai | Kolkata | Bangalore | Hyderabad | Kochi | Guwahati

VIVA BOOKS PRIVATE LIMITED

* 4737/23, Ansari Road, Daryaganj, New Delhi 110 002
  Tel. 42242200, 23258325, 23283121 E-mail: vivadelhi@vivagroupindia.net

* Plot No. 76, Service Industries, Shirvane, Sector 1, Nerul, Navi Mumbai 400 706
  Tel. 27721273, 27721274 E-mail: vivamumbai@vivagroupindia.net

* Jamals Fazal Chambers, 26 Greams Road, Chennai 600 006
  Tel. 28294241, 28290304 E-mail: vivachennai@vivagroupindia.net

* B-103, Jindal Towers, 21/1A/3 Darga Road, Kolkata 700 017
  Tel. 22816713 E-mail: vivakolkata@vivagroupindia.net

* 7, GF, Sovereign Park Aptts., 56-58, K. R. Road, Basavanagudi, Bangalore 560 004
  Tel. 26607409 E-mail: vivabangalore@vivagroupindia.net

* 101-102, Moghal Marc Apartments, 3-4-637 to 641, Narayanguda, Hyderabad 500 029
  Tel. 27564481 E-mail: vivahyderabad@vivagroupindia.net

  http://www.vivagroupindia.com

Every possible effort has been made to ensure that the information contained in this book is accurate at the time of going to press, and the publisher and author cannot accept responsibility for any errors or omissions, however caused. No responsibility for loss or damage occasioned to any person acting, or refraining from action, as a result of the material in this publication can be accepted by the editor, the publisher or the author.

ISBN 81-309-0009-2

Published by Vinod Vasishtha for Viva Books Private Limited,
4737/23 Ansari Road, Daryaganj, New Delhi 110 002.

Printed & bound by Raj Press, R-3 Inderpuri, New Delhi-110 012.

CONTENTS

Acknowledgements   *vii*

Preface   *ix*

1. ORDINARY DIFFERENTIAL EQUATIONS OF FIRST ORDER   1

2. POWER SERIES SOLUTIONS OF DIFFERENTIAL EQUATIONS   83

3. LAPLACE TRANSFORM   149

4. LINEAR ALGEBRA: VECTORS   267

5. OPTIMIZATION   399

ACKNOWLEDGEMENTS

I am grateful to Dr V. Seenappa, Principal, Dr Ambedkar Institute of Technology, Bangalore – formerly Director of Technical Education, Government of Karnataka – for his constant encouragement. I am extremely grateful to Shri K.R. Krishnamurthy, Administrative officer, Dr Ambedkar Institute of Technology, Bangalore, for his kind gesture and support. My thanks are also due to Mr Vinod Vasishtha, the Managing Director of Viva Books for publishing this book. I am extremely grateful to Mr Sudharshan Shetty P. and Mr T. V. Madhu of Viva Books, Bangalore, for offering me a proposal to publish this book, which encouraged me to complete this task in time.

PREFACE

In this book my aim has been to give an extensive treatment to some of the advanced areas of mathematics that have applications in engineering. Topics are chosen according to the frequency of their occurrence in applications. I have attempted to develop an understanding of the mathematical principles and practices that today's engineers need to know.

Features

- Solutions to problems in advance mathematics are depicted in step-by-step detail

- A large number of examples and exercises

- Organized logically to present each mathematical topic as a complete conceptual and visual unit

- Approaches mathematical concepts from a practical – use perspective

I shall appreciate constructive suggestions from the readers, which will help to make the book more useful to students in subsequent editions.

H. S. Govinda Rao

1

ORDINARY DIFFERENTIAL EQUATIONS OF FIRST ORDER

An equation containing at most two variables, and derivatives of the first or higher order of one of the variables with respect to the other, such as

$$F\left[x, y, \frac{dy}{dx}, \frac{dy^2}{dx^2}, \dots \frac{dy^n}{dx^n}\right] = 0,$$ is called a differential equation.

The order of a differential equation is the order of the highest order derivative which appears. When an equation contains only derivatives of the first order, it is frequently written in terms of differentials. This is permissible because the first derivative may be treated as the quotient of the differentials. For example, if the given differential equation is $y\frac{dy}{dx} + 2x = 0,$ we can write $ydy + 2xdx = 0$.

The degree of an equation is the degree of the highest order differential coefficient present in the equation.

In a differential equation of first order, the only differential coefficient that occurs is $\left(\frac{dy}{dx}\right)$, and so the equation can be written in the form:

$$F\left(x, y, \left(\frac{dy}{dx}\right)\right) = 0$$

In the equation of the first order and first degree, the derivative $\left(\frac{dy}{dx}\right)$ occurs in the first degree in

$$F\left(x, y, \left(\frac{dy}{dx}\right)\right) = 0$$

So it can be easily separated out, and written as

$$f_2(x, y)\left(\frac{dy}{dx}\right) + f_1(x, y) = 0$$

or $\quad f_1(x, y)dx + f_2(x, y)dy = 0$

More usually, $f_1(x, y)$ is put equal to $P(x, y)$ or P and

$$f_2(x, y) = Q(x, y) = Q$$

Thus an equation of the first order and first degree is written in the standard form:

$$Pdx + Qdy = 0$$

Formation of Differential Equations

Differential equations are formed by the elimination of constant parameter in the equation.

For example, consider $x^2 + y^2 = 0$

Differentiating w.r.t to x, $2xdx + 2ydy = 0$,

or $\quad \left(\dfrac{dy}{dx}\right) + \left(\dfrac{x}{y}\right) = 0$. Here, the constant parameter is automatically eliminated;

$\left[y\left(\dfrac{dy}{dx}\right) + x\right] = 0$ is the differential equation of the primitive $(x^2 + y^2) = a$

Also, $(x^2 + y^2) = a$, is the solution of the equation $y\left(\dfrac{dy}{dx}\right) + x = 0$.

Arbitrary Constants

Consider $y = a\cos x + b\sin x$, where 'a' and 'b' are constant parameters. Since there are two constants, we require two more relations to eliminate 'a' and 'b'.

Differentiating successively, we get:

$$\left(\frac{dy}{dx}\right) = -a\sin x + b\cos x$$

$$\left(\frac{d^2 y}{dx^2}\right) = -a\cos x - b\sin x$$

$$= -(a\cos x + b\sin x) = -y$$

Hence, $\left(\dfrac{d^2 y}{dx^2}\right) + y = 0$. This is the result of eliminating 'a' and 'b'. Thus, $\left(\dfrac{d^2 y}{dx^2}\right) + y = 0$ is the differential equation of $y = a\cos x + b\sin x$.

Also, $y = a\cos x + b\sin x$ is the solution of the equation $\left(\dfrac{d^2 y}{dx^2}\right) + y = 0$.

We know that a general solution of an equation of the first order involves one and only one arbitrary constant. Thus, the solution of an equation

$$F\left(x, y, \left(\frac{dy}{dx}\right)\right) = 0,$$

can be written $f(x, y, c) = 0$. In the solution of an equation of the first order and first degree, the constant occurs in the first degree. Hence, c occurs in the first degree in $f(x, y, c) = 0$.

The general solution of $F\left[x, y, \left(\frac{dy}{dx}\right)\right] = 0$, is $f(x, y, c) = 0$. Any particular solution is derived from $f(x, y, c) = 0$ by obtaining the appropriate value of c, to satisfy the conditions.

Thus, let the equation be

$$\left(\frac{dy}{dx}\right) = 2x$$

So, we get $y = \int 2x \, dx = x^2$ and the general solution is

$$y = \left(x^2 + c\right)$$

If it should be required to find the solution satisfying the condition that $y = 5$, when $x = 2$, we substitute and see that

$$5 = 2^2 + c;$$

$\therefore \quad c = 1$ (in particular)

The particular solution is

$$y = x^2 + c, \quad \text{where} \quad c = 1;$$

$\therefore \quad y = x^2 + 1$

Suitable forms of constants: Sometimes the solution can be represented in an elegant form by suitable adjustments in the form of the constant. Also any manipulated form of a constant is another constant.

EXAMPLE

Let the solution be obtained in the form,

$$2 \log x + \log \tan y = \text{constant} = c$$

We can put it in a more compact form as follows:

$$2\log x + \log \tan y = c$$

$$\log\left(x^2 \tan y\right) = c$$

$$\therefore \quad x^2 \tan y = e^c$$

Now e^c is also another constant and so may be put in the form k.

Hence, the solution is: $x^2 \tan y = k$

It can also be written directly. Thus

$$2\log x + \log \tan y = \text{constant}$$

$$\log x^2 + \log \tan y = \text{constant}$$

i.e., $\quad \log\left(x^2 \tan y\right) = \text{constant}$

$\therefore \quad x^2 \tan y = \text{constant} = k \ \left(\text{say}\right)$

$$x^2 \tan y = k$$

Separable Equations

If $\qquad P = f(x) = a$ function of x only, and

$\qquad Q = \phi(y) = a$ function of y only,

We have the equation $Pdx + Qdy = 0$

or, $\qquad f(x)dx + \phi(y) = 0$ [1]

Evidently, the variables are separated, and the solution is found by direct integration

$$\int \left(f(x)dx + \phi(y)dy\right) = \text{constant} \qquad [2]$$

EXAMPLE

Consider $\cos x\,dx + \sec^2 y\,dy = 0$ Here the variables are separated. So, integrating

$$\int \cos x dx + \int \sec^2 y dy = \text{constant}$$

i.e., $\quad \sin x + \tan y = \text{constant}$

Note: Sometimes the variables may not be separated, but may become so by some small manipulation. In this case the variables can be separated, or are separable. The solution can then be found.

EXAMPLE

Consider the equation

$$\sqrt{(1+y^2)}\,dx + y(x^2+1)\,dy = 0 \qquad\qquad [3]$$

Here, the variables cannot be separated.

Dividing by $(x^2+1)\sqrt{(1+y^2)}$,

[the product of $\sqrt{(1+y^2)}$ and (x^2+1)]

we have,

$$\frac{dx\sqrt{(1+y^2)}}{(x^2+1)\sqrt{(1+y^2)}} + \frac{y(x^2+1)dy}{(x^2+1)\sqrt{(y^2+1)}} = 0$$

$$\Rightarrow \quad \frac{dx}{(x^2+1)} + \frac{ydy}{\sqrt{(1+y^2)}} = 0 \qquad\qquad [4]$$

Integrating $\displaystyle\int \frac{dx}{(x^2+1)} + \int \frac{ydy}{\sqrt{(y^2+1)}} = \text{constant}$ $\qquad\qquad [5]$

$$\because \quad \frac{dx}{x^2+a^2} = \frac{1}{a}\tan^{-1}\left(\frac{x}{a}\right)$$

$$\int \frac{xdx}{\sqrt{a^2+x^2}} = \left(\sqrt{a^2+x^2}\right)$$

Clearly, the variables are separated now. Integrating, the solution:

$$\tan^{-1}(x) + \sqrt{(1+y^2)} = C$$

Grouping arrangements: Sometimes the variables x and y as such cannot be separated. But by introducing another quantity u we can group together,

(a) Functions of x with dx;

(b) Functions of y with dy and

(c) Functions of u with du.

We then have the variables x, y and u separated. Integration completes the solution.

EXAMPLE

$$(\sec^2 x + 2xy^3)dx + (\cos y + 3x^2 y^2)dy = 0$$

Here, $P = (\sec^2 x + 2xy^3)$ and

$$Q = (\cos y + 3x^2 y^2)$$

Clearly, the variables, x and y as such are not separated, nor are they easily separable. Sort out the functions of x and take them with dx, those of y with dy and regroup the rest.

Then we have

$$(\sec^2 x + 2xy^3)dx + (\cos y + 3x^2 y^2)dy = 0 \qquad [1]$$

$$\Rightarrow \quad \sec^2 xdx + \cos ydy + (2xy^3 dx + 3x^2 y^2 dy) = 0 \qquad [2]$$

Now, $(2xy^3 dx + 3x^2 y^2 dy)$

$$= y^3(2xdx) + x^2(3y^2 dy)$$

$$= y^3 d(x^2) + x^2 d(y^3)$$

$$= d(x^2 y^3) \qquad [3]$$

Put $u = (x^2 y^3)$

then $(2xy^3 dx + 3x^2 y^2 dy) = d(x^2 y^3) = du \qquad [4]$

From [2] and [4],

$$\sec^2 xdx + \cos ydy + du = 0 \qquad [5]$$

Clearly the variables x, y and u are separated.

∴ Solution is given by:

$$\int \sec^2 xdx + \int \cos ydy + \int du = c$$

$$\Rightarrow \quad \tan x + \sin y + u = \text{constant}$$

or, $\tan x + \sin y + x^2 y^3 = \text{constant}$

(A) EXAMPLES

1. Find the curve which satisfies the differential equation
    $(y^2 + 1)xdx + (x^2 + 1)dy = 0$, and passes through the origin. [1]

Solution: Given, $(y^2+1)xdx+(x^2+1)ydy = 0$

Dividing by $[(x^2+1)(y^2+1)]$, the equation reduces to

$$\frac{x}{(x^2+1)}dx+\frac{y}{(v^2+1)}dy = 0 \hspace{3cm} [2]$$

Evidently the variables are separated.
The solution is given by

$$\int\frac{x}{(x^2+1)}dx+\int\frac{y}{(y^2+1)}dy = \text{constant} = \frac{c}{2}\text{(say)}$$

So, $\quad \left(\frac{1}{2}\right)\log(x^2+1)+\left(\frac{1}{2}\right)\log(y^2+1)=\frac{c}{2}$

$$\left(\because\int\frac{x}{x^2+a^2}dx=\frac{1}{2}\log(x^2+a^2)\right)$$

$$\left[\log(x^2+1)+\log(y^2+1)\right]=c=\log(k)\text{(say)};$$

i.e., $\quad \log\left[(x^2+1)(y^2+1)\right]=\log(k);$

$\therefore \quad (x^2+1)(y^2+1)=k \hspace{3.5cm} [3]$

The curve is to pass through the origin (0, 0). Hence,
$$(0+1)\ (0+1)\ =\ k;$$
or $\quad k\ =\ 1$

So, the solution is
$$(x^2+1)(y^2+1)=1;$$

or $\quad x^2y^2+(x^2+y^2)=0 \hspace{3cm} [4]$

2. Solve: the initial value problem $(x^2+1)\dfrac{dy}{dx}+y^2+1=0,\quad y(0)=1$

Solution: Given, $(x^2+1)\dfrac{dy}{dx}+y^2+1=0 \hspace{2cm} [1]$

Separating variables, we find

$$\frac{dy}{1+y^2} = -\frac{dx}{1+x^2}$$

Integrating,

$$\int \frac{dy}{1+y^2} = -\int \frac{dx}{1+x^2} + c$$

or $\tan^{-1}(y) = -\tan^{-1}(x) + c$

i.e., $\arctan y + \arctan x = c$

Taking the tangent on both sides, we have

$$\tan(\arctan y + \arctan x) = \tan c \qquad\qquad [2]$$

Now, the addition formula for the tangent is

$$\tan(a+b) = \frac{\tan a + \tan b}{1 - \tan a \tan b}$$

$$\tan^{-1}(y) + \tan^{-1}(x) = c$$

For $a = \arctan y$ and $b = \arctan x$ this becomes

$$\tan(\arctan y + \arctan x) = \frac{y+x}{1-xy}$$

∴ Equation [2] may be written as:

$$\frac{y+x}{1-xy} = \tan c \qquad\qquad [3]$$

We find c from the initial condition.

Setting $x = 0$ and $y = 1$ in [3], we have

$$1 = \tan c, \text{ so that}$$

$$\frac{y+x}{1-xy} = 1$$

$$\Rightarrow \quad y = \frac{1-x}{1+x}$$

3. $\sec^2 x \tan y\, dx + \sec^2 y \tan x\, dy = 0$

Solution: Given, $\sec^2 x \tan y\, dx + \sec^2 y \tan x\, dy = 0$

Dividing by $\tan x \tan y$, we get

$$\frac{\sec^2 x}{\tan x}dx + \frac{\sec^2 y}{\tan y}dy = 0$$

$$\therefore \quad \int \frac{\sec^2 x}{\tan x}dx + \int \frac{\sec^2 y}{\tan y}dy = \text{constant}$$

i.e., $\quad \log \tan x + \log \tan y = \text{constant}$

$$\left(\because \int \frac{f'(x)}{f(x)}dx = \log f(x) \right)$$

i.e., $\quad \log(\tan x \cdot \tan y) = \text{constant}$

Hence $\tan x \cdot \tan y = \text{constant}$ is the solution.

---

4. $\left(e^x + 1\right)ydy = (y+1)e^x dx$

Solution: Given, $\left(e^x + 1\right)ydy - (y+1)e^x dx = 0$ $\hfill$ [1]

Divide by $\left(e^x + 1\right)(y+1)$

$$\therefore \quad \frac{\left(e^x + 1\right)ydy}{\left(e^x + 1\right)(y+1)} - \frac{(y+1)e^x dx}{\left(e^x + 1\right)(y+1)} = 0;$$

The equation reduces to variable separable form

$$\frac{ydy}{(y+1)} - \frac{e^x dx}{\left(1 + e^x\right)} = 0$$

Then put $e^x = t$;

$$\therefore \quad e^x dx = dt$$

or $\quad \dfrac{ydy}{(y+1)} - \dfrac{dt}{(t+1)} = 0$

$$\left[1 - \frac{1}{1+y} \right]dy - \frac{1}{(t+1)}dt = 0$$

So $\quad \displaystyle\int\left[1 - \frac{1}{1+y} \right]dy - \int \frac{dt}{(1+t)} = \text{constant}$ $\hfill$ [2]

i.e., $\quad y - \log(1+y) - \log(1+t) = \text{constant}$

or $\quad y - \log\left[(1+y)(1+t)\right] = \text{constant} = C$

or $y - \log\left[(1+y)(1+e^x)\right] = C.$ [3]

or $\log e^y - \log\left[(1+y)(1+e^x)\right] = C$

or $\log\left[\dfrac{e^y}{(1+y)(1+e^x)}\right] = C$

or $\dfrac{e^y}{(1+y)(1+e^x)} = e^C = k$

or $\dfrac{e^y}{(1+y)} = k(1+e^x)$

5. $(x+1)\left(\dfrac{dy}{dx}\right) + 1 = 2e^{-y}$

Solution: Given, equation is: $(x+1)\left(\dfrac{dy}{dx}\right) + 1 = 2e^{-y}$ [1]

[1] can be written as

$$(x+1)\dfrac{dy}{dx} = \left(2e^{-y} - 1\right) = \left(\dfrac{2}{e^y} - 1\right) = \dfrac{(2 - e^y)}{e^y}$$

$\therefore$ $\dfrac{e^y dy}{(2 - e^y)} = \dfrac{dx}{(x+1)}$

This is evidently a case where the variables are separated.

Put $e^y = t$, so, $e^y dy = dt$ [2]

So, equation is

$$\dfrac{dx}{x+1} + \dfrac{dt}{(t-2)} = \text{constant}$$

$\log(x+1) + \log(t-2) = C$

$\Rightarrow$ $\log\left[(x+1)(t-2)\right] = \text{constant} = \log k \text{ (say)}$

$(x+1)(t-2) = k;$

$(x+1)(e^y - 2) = k$

6. $\left(\dfrac{dy}{dx}\right) = e^{x-y} + x^2 e^{-y}$

Solution: Multiplying by e^y, we get

$$e^y \, dy = e^x \, dx + x^2 \, dx \quad \text{(variables separable)}$$

$\therefore \quad \int e^y \, dy = \int e^x \, dx + \int x^2 \, dx + \text{constant}$

$\Rightarrow \quad e^y = e^x + \dfrac{x^3}{3} + \text{constant}$

$\therefore \quad x^3 + 3\left(e^x - e^y\right) = \text{constant}$

7. $\left(\dfrac{dy}{dx}\right) = e^{x+y} + x^2 e^{y}$

Solution: $\left(\dfrac{dy}{dx}\right) = e^x \cdot e^y + x^2 e^{y}$

$$= e^y \left(e^x + x^2\right)$$

$\therefore \quad e^{-y} \, dy = \left(x^2 + e^x\right) dx$

$\therefore \quad \left(-e^{-y}\right) = \left[\left(\dfrac{x^3}{3}\right) + e^x\right] + C$

$$x^3 + 3\left(e^x + e^{-y}\right) = \text{constant}$$

8. $\dfrac{dy}{dx} = e^{2x-y} + x^3 e^{-y}$

Solution: $\dfrac{dy}{dx} = e^{-y}\left(e^{2x} + x^3\right)$

$\Rightarrow \quad e^y \, dy = \left(e^{2x} + x^3\right) dx$

$\therefore \quad e^y = \dfrac{e^{2x}}{2} + \dfrac{x^4}{4} + C$

9. $\left(\dfrac{dy}{dx}\right) = e^{x+y} + x^2 e^{x^3+y}$

> ***Solution:*** $e^{-y}dy = \left(e^x + x^2 e^{x^3}\right)dx$
>
> $\therefore \qquad -e^{-y} = e^x + \int x^2 e^{x^3}\,dx + C$
>
> Put $\quad x^3 = t; \quad \therefore \; 3x^2 dx = dt$
>
> $\therefore \qquad I = \dfrac{1}{3}\int e^t dt = \dfrac{1}{3}e^t = \dfrac{1}{3}e^{x^3}$
>
> $\therefore \qquad -e^{-y} = e^x + \dfrac{1}{3}e^{x^2} + C$

10. $e^{x-y}dy + e^{y-x}dx = 0$

> ***Solution:*** $e^{-2x}dx + e^{-2y}dy = 0$
>
> $\therefore \qquad e^{-2x} + e^{-2y} = \text{constant}$

11. $\dfrac{ds}{dx} + x^2 = x^2 e^{3s}$

> ***Solution:*** $\dfrac{ds}{dx} = x^2\left(e^{3s}-1\right);$
>
> $\Rightarrow \qquad \dfrac{ds}{dx} + x^2 = x^2 e^{3s}$
>
> $\Rightarrow \qquad \dfrac{ds}{dx} = x^2(e^{3s}-1)$
>
> $\Rightarrow \qquad \displaystyle\int \dfrac{ds}{e^{3s}-1} = \int x^2 dx$
>
> $\Rightarrow \qquad \displaystyle\int \dfrac{e^{-3s}ds}{1-e^{3s}} = \int x^2 dx$
>
> $\Rightarrow \qquad \dfrac{1}{3}\log(1-e^{-3s}) = \dfrac{x^3}{3} + C$
>
> $\Rightarrow \qquad \log(1-e^{-3s}) = x^3 + \text{constant}$
>
> $\Rightarrow \qquad (1-e^{-3s}) = e^{x^3+k}$

Integrating,

$$\frac{1}{3}\log\left(1-e^{-3s}\right) = \frac{x^3}{3} + C;$$

$$\log\left(1-e^{-3s}\right) = x^3 + k$$

or, $$\left(1-e^{-3s}\right) = e^{x^3+k}$$

$$= e^{x^3} \cdot e^k$$

$$= Ae^{x^3}$$

12. $\left(1-x^2\right)\left(1-y\right)dx = xy\left(1+y\right)dy$

Solution: $\dfrac{\left(1-x^2\right)}{x}dx = \dfrac{y(1+y)}{1-y}dy$

$$\frac{\left(1-x^2\right)}{x}dx = \frac{y+y^2}{1-y} = \frac{(y^2+y-2)+2}{1-y}$$

$$= \frac{(y-1)(y+2)+2}{1-y}$$

$$= \left[-(y+2)+\frac{2}{1-y}\right]$$

$$= \left[-(y-2)+\frac{2}{1-y}\right]$$

$$\left[\frac{1}{x}-x\right]dx = \left[-y-2+\frac{2}{1-y}\right]dy \quad \text{(by division)} \qquad [1]$$

Actual division in an elegant form

$1-y)\ \ y+y^2\ (-y-2$

$\dfrac{-(-y+y^2)}{2}$

$\dfrac{-(-2+2y)}{2}$

$\therefore \quad y\dfrac{(1+y)}{1-y} = \dfrac{y+y^2}{1-y} = -y-2+\dfrac{2}{1-y}$

Integrating [1], we get

$$\log x - \frac{x^2}{2} = -\frac{y^2}{2} - 2y - 2\log(1-y) + K$$

13. $a\left(x\dfrac{dy}{dx} + 2y\right) = xy\dfrac{dy}{dx}$

Solution:

or $\quad \dfrac{(a-y)}{y}dy = -\dfrac{2a}{x}dx$

or $\quad \dfrac{a}{y}dy + \dfrac{2a}{x}dx = dy$

Integrating we get,

$$a\log y + 2a\log x = 4 + C$$

$$\log yx^2 = \frac{y+c}{a}$$

$\therefore \qquad yx^2 = e^{\frac{(y+c)}{a}} = ke^{\frac{y}{a}}$

$$yx^2 = ke^y \cdot e^{\frac{1}{a}}$$

$$yx^2 = ce^y$$

14. $y - x\dfrac{dy}{dx} = a\left(y^2 + \dfrac{dy}{dx}\right)$

Solution:

or $\quad (y - ay^2) = (x+a)\dfrac{dy}{dx}$

$\therefore \qquad \dfrac{dy}{y(1-ay)} = \dfrac{dx}{x+a}$

$\Rightarrow \qquad \left[\dfrac{1}{y} + \dfrac{a}{1-ay}\right]dy = \dfrac{dx}{x+a}$

Integrating we get,

$$\log y - \log(1-ay) = \log(x+a) + c$$

$$\log \frac{y}{1-ay} = \log k(x+a);$$

$$= \log k$$

$$\therefore \quad y = k(1-ay)(x+a)$$

15. $\dfrac{dy}{dx} = \dfrac{xy+y}{xy+x}$

Solution: $\dfrac{y+1}{y} dy = \dfrac{x+1}{x} dx$

or $\quad \left(1+\dfrac{1}{y}\right) dy = \left(1+\dfrac{1}{x}\right) dx$

$$y + \log y = x + \log x + \log k \ ;$$

$$\therefore \quad y - x = \log \frac{kx}{y}$$

16. $\left(x^2 - yx^2\right)\dfrac{dy}{dx} + \left(y^2 + xy^2\right) = 0$

Solution: $x^2(1-y)\dfrac{dy}{dx} + y^2(1+x) = 0$

$$\frac{1-y}{y^2} dy + \frac{1+x}{x^2} dx = 0$$

or $\quad \left(\dfrac{1}{y^2} - \dfrac{1}{y}\right) dy + \left(\dfrac{1}{x^2} + \dfrac{1}{x}\right) dx = 0$

Integrating, $\log x - \log y - \left(\dfrac{1}{x} + \dfrac{1}{y}\right) = C$

or $\quad \log \dfrac{x}{ky} = \dfrac{x+y}{xy}$

17. $\left(\dfrac{dy}{dx}\right) = \sin^2(x-y+1)$

Solution: $\left[\text{Put}\quad z = x - y + 1, \quad \text{so}\quad \dfrac{dz}{dx} = 1 - \dfrac{dy}{dx} + 0\right]$

$\therefore$ Differential Equation becomes $\left(1 - \dfrac{dz}{dx}\right) = \sin^2 z$

or $\quad \dfrac{dz}{dx} = 1 - \sin^2 z = \cos^2 z$

or $\quad \sec^2 dz = dx$

Integrating, $\tan z = x + c$

or $\quad \tan(x - y + 1) = x + c$

18. Show that the particular solution of $\left(x^2 + 1\right)\dfrac{dy}{dx} + \left(y^2 + 1\right) = 0$, $y(0) = 1$, is $y = \dfrac{1-x}{1+x}$

Solution: $\dfrac{dy}{y^2 + 1} + \dfrac{dx}{x^2 + 1} = 0$

Integrating we get,

$\tan^{-1}(y) + \tan^{-1}(x) = C$

Use $\tan^{-1} a + \tan^{-1} b = \tan^{-1}\left[\dfrac{a+b}{1-ab}\right]$

$\tan\left(\tan^{-1}(y) + \tan^{-1}(x)\right) = \tan c$

$\left[\therefore\quad \tan(a+b) = \dfrac{\tan a + \tan b}{1 - \tan a \tan b}\right]$

$\Rightarrow\quad \dfrac{y+x}{1-xy} = \tan c$ [1]

When $x = 0$, $y = 1$ then

$\dfrac{1+0}{1-0} = \tan c$

$\therefore\quad \dfrac{y+x}{1-xy} = 1 \qquad$ Using [1]

$\Rightarrow\quad y = \dfrac{1-x}{1+x}$

19. $\cos(x+y+1)dx - dy = 0$

Solution: We have $\dfrac{dy}{dx} = \cos(x+y+1)$

$$\left[\text{Put } (x+y+1) = t, \text{ then } 1 + \frac{dy}{dx} = \frac{dt}{dx}\right]$$

Given equation becomes

or $\dfrac{dt}{dx} - 1 = \cos t$

$\therefore$ $\displaystyle\int \dfrac{dt}{1+\cos t} = \int dx + c$

$\dfrac{1}{2} \cdot \displaystyle\int \sec^2 \dfrac{t}{2}\, dt = x + c;$

or $\dfrac{t}{2} + \sec\dfrac{t}{2} = x + c$

Substituting for t, we get the required solution as

$$\frac{1}{2}(x+y+1) + \sec\left(\frac{x+y+1}{2}\right) = x + c$$

20. The stress p in thick cylinders of radius r is given by $r\left(\dfrac{dr}{dp}\right) + 2p = 2c$. Find p in terms of r.

Solution: $r\left(\dfrac{dr}{dp}\right) = 2c - 2p;$

$rdr = 2(c-p)dp$

$rdr + 2(p-c)dp = 0$

$\therefore$ $\displaystyle\int rdr + \int 2(p-c)dp = \text{constant}$

$\left(\dfrac{r^2}{2}\right) + (p-c)^2 = \text{constant} = \left(\dfrac{a^2}{2}\right)(\text{say})$

$(p-c)^2 = \dfrac{(a^2 - r^2)}{2}$ i.e., $2(p-c)^2 = (a^2 - r^2)$

Homogeneous Differential Equations

Any function $f(x, y)$ is said to be homogeneous of degree n, if $f(x, y)$ can be written as

$$f(x,y) = x^n g\left(\frac{y}{x}\right)$$

A differential equation of the form

$$\frac{dy}{dx} = \frac{f(x,y)}{g(x,y)}$$

is called a homogeneous equation if both $f(x, y)$ and $g(x, y)$ are homogeneous of the same degree in x and y.

For example $\dfrac{dy}{dx} = \dfrac{3xy + y^2}{3x^2 + xy}$ is a homogeneous differential equation.

Working Rule

To solve a homogeneous differential equation, we put $y = vx$ and $\dfrac{dy}{dx} = v + x\dfrac{dv}{dx}$

The reduced equation involves v and x only. This new differential equation can be solved by variables separable method.

(B) EXAMPLES

1. Solve : $\left(x^2 + y^2\right) dx - 2xy\, dy = 0$

Solution: The given equation is homogeneous.

Putting $y = vx$; $dy = v\,dx + x\,dv$

we get, $(x^2 + v^2 x^2)dx - 2x \cdot vx(x\,dv + v\,dx) = 0$

$\Rightarrow \quad x^2(1 + v^2)dx - 2x \cdot vx(x\,dv + v\,dx) = 0$

(dividing by x^2)

$\Rightarrow \quad dx\left[(1 + v^2) - 2v^2\right] - 2vx\,dv = 0$

$\Rightarrow \quad \left(\dfrac{dx}{x}\right) - \left[\dfrac{2v}{(1 - v^2)}\right]dv = 0$

$\Rightarrow \quad \displaystyle\int\left(\dfrac{dx}{x}\right) - \int\left[\dfrac{2v}{1} - v^2\right]dv = \text{constant}$

$\Rightarrow \qquad \log x + \log(1 - v^2) = \text{constant}$

$\therefore \qquad \log[x(1 - v^-)] = \text{constant}$

Putting $v = \dfrac{y}{x}$

$\Rightarrow \qquad x\left(1 - \dfrac{y^2}{x^2}\right) = e^c = \text{another constant} = A$

$\therefore \qquad x^2 - y^2 = Ax$

2. Solve $(x^2 + y^2)dx + 2xy\,dy = 0$

  Solution: Putting $y = vx$; $dy = vdx + xdv$

  $\therefore \qquad (x^2 + v^2x^2)dx + 2xvx(vdx + xdv) = 0$

  $\therefore \qquad dx(1 + v^2 + 2v^2) + 2vxdv = 0$

  or, $\qquad \dfrac{dx}{x} + \dfrac{2v}{1 + 3v^2} = C;$

  or $\qquad \log x + \left(\dfrac{1}{3}\right)\log(1 + 3v^2) = \text{constant}$

  $\qquad 3\log x + \log(1 + 3v^2) = \text{constant}$

  $\qquad x^3\left[1 + \dfrac{3y^2}{x^2}\right] = C;$

  $\qquad x(x^2 + 3y^2) = C$

3. Solve $(x^2y - 2xy^2)dx - (x^3 - 3x^2y)dy = 0$

  Solution: The given equation can be written as

  $$\dfrac{dy}{dx} = \dfrac{x^2y(x - 2y)}{x^2(x - 3y)} = \dfrac{y}{x}\dfrac{\left(1 - \dfrac{2y}{x}\right)}{\left(1 - \dfrac{3y}{x}\right)}$$

  which is homogeneous. Putting $y = vx$ we get

  $$v + x\dfrac{dv}{dx} = \dfrac{v(1 - 2v)}{1 - 3v} = v\left[1 + \dfrac{v}{1 - 3v}\right]$$

$\Rightarrow \qquad x\dfrac{dv}{dx} = \dfrac{v}{1-3v}$

$\Rightarrow \qquad \dfrac{1-3v}{v}dv = \dfrac{dx}{x}$

Hence $\displaystyle\int\left[\dfrac{1}{v}-3\right]dv = \int\dfrac{dx}{x}+C$

or $\qquad \log v - 3v = \log x + C$

$\therefore \qquad \log\dfrac{y}{x} - 3\dfrac{y}{x} = \log x + C$

4. Solve $\dfrac{dy}{dx} = \dfrac{y^3 + 3x^2 y}{x^3 + 3xy^2}$

Solution: The given equation is homogeneous. Putting $y = vx$, we get

$$\dfrac{dy}{dx} = v + x\left(\dfrac{dv}{dx}\right)$$

$\therefore \qquad v + x\dfrac{dv}{dx} = \dfrac{v^3 + 3v}{1 + 3v^2}$

$\therefore \qquad x\dfrac{dv}{dx} = \dfrac{v^3 + 3v}{1 + 3v^2} - v.$

$\qquad\qquad = \dfrac{2v(1-v^2)}{1+3v^2}$

$\therefore \qquad \dfrac{1+3v^2}{v(1-v^2)}dv = 2\left(\dfrac{dx}{x}\right)$

$\therefore \qquad 2\left(\dfrac{dx}{x}\right) = \dfrac{1}{v} - \dfrac{2}{1+v} + \dfrac{2}{1-v}$ (by Partial Fractions)

$\therefore \qquad 2\log x = \log v - 2\log(1+v) - 2\log(1-v) + \log C$

$\therefore \qquad x^2 = \dfrac{Cv}{(1+v)^2 (1-v)^2}$

$\therefore \qquad x^2[1+v]^2[1-v]^2 = Cv$

Hence $\quad x^2(1-v^2)^2 = Cv$

$\therefore \qquad x^2\left(1-\dfrac{y^2}{x^2}\right)^2 = C\left(\dfrac{y}{x}\right)$

$$\therefore \qquad \left(x^2 - y^2\right)^2 = Cxy$$

5. Solve $\left(x^2 - y^2\right)dx = xy\,dy$

Solution: The given equation can be written as

$$\frac{dy}{dx} = \frac{x^2 - y^2}{xy}$$

Putting $y = vx$ and $\dfrac{dy}{dx} = v + x\dfrac{dv}{dx}$

$\therefore$ Given equation becomes $v + x\dfrac{dv}{dx} = \dfrac{x^2\left(1 - v^2\right)}{x^2 v}$

i.e., $\qquad x\dfrac{dv}{dx} = \dfrac{1 - v^2}{v} - v$

or $\qquad x\dfrac{dv}{dx} = \dfrac{1 - 2v^2}{v}$

$\Rightarrow \qquad \dfrac{v}{1 - 2v^2}dv = \dfrac{dx}{x}$

$\Rightarrow \qquad \displaystyle\int \frac{v}{1 - 2v^2}dv - \int \frac{dx}{x} = \text{constant}$

$\Rightarrow \qquad -\dfrac{1}{4}\log\left(1 - 2v^2\right) - \log x = \text{constant}$

$\Rightarrow \qquad \log\left(1 - 2v^2\right) + 4\log x = -4(\text{constant}) = -4C$

$\Rightarrow \qquad \log\left[\left(1 - 2v^2\right)x^4\right] = \log C\,(\text{say})$

$\qquad \left(\because 4\log x = \log {}_x 4\right)$

$\Rightarrow \qquad \left(1 - 2v^2\right)x^4 = C, \text{where } v = \dfrac{y}{x}$

$\Rightarrow \qquad \left(1 - \dfrac{2y^2}{x^2}\right)x^4 = C$

$\Rightarrow \qquad x^2\left(x^2 - 2y^2\right) = C$

$\therefore \qquad x^4 - 2x^2 y^2 = C$

6. $xdy - ydx = \left(\sqrt{x^2 + y^2}\right)dx$

Solution: Given, $xdy - ydx = \left(\sqrt{x^2 + y^2}\right)dx$

$\Rightarrow$ $xdy = \left[y + \sqrt{x^2 + y^2}\right]dx$

$\Rightarrow$ $\dfrac{dy}{dx} = \dfrac{y + \sqrt{x^2 + y^2}}{x}$

Now, putting $y = vx$ and $\dfrac{dy}{dx} = v + x\dfrac{dv}{dx}$

Given equation becomes: $v + x\dfrac{dv}{dx} = \dfrac{vx + \sqrt{x^2 + v^2 x^2}}{x}$

$\Rightarrow$ $v + x\dfrac{dv}{dx} = \dfrac{x\left(v + \sqrt{1 + v^2}\right)}{x}$

$\Rightarrow$ $x\dfrac{dv}{dx} = \sqrt{1 + v^2}$

$\therefore$ $\dfrac{dv}{\sqrt{1 + v^2}} = \dfrac{dx}{x}$

Integrating, we get

$$\int \dfrac{dv}{\sqrt{1 + v^2}} - \int \dfrac{dx}{x} = \text{constant}$$

$\Rightarrow$ $\sinh^{-1} v - \log x = C$

where $v = \dfrac{y}{x}$

Note: $\int \dfrac{dv}{\sqrt{1 + v^2}} = \log\left(v + \sqrt{1 + v^2}\right)$

Hence the solution is:

$$\log\left[\dfrac{y}{x} + \sqrt{1 + \left(\dfrac{y^2}{x^2}\right)}\right] - \log x = \text{constant}$$

$\Rightarrow \qquad \log\left[\dfrac{y+\sqrt{x^2+y^2}}{x}\cdot\dfrac{1}{x}\right] = \text{constant} = \log c, \text{(say)}$

$\Rightarrow \qquad \dfrac{y+\sqrt{x^2+y^2}}{x^2} = C$

$\therefore \qquad y+\sqrt{x^2+y^2} = Cx^2$

7. Solve $dy = \left(1+\dfrac{y}{x}+\dfrac{y^2}{x^2}\right)dx$

Solution: The given equation can be written as

$$\dfrac{dy}{dx} = 1+\dfrac{y}{x}+\dfrac{y^2}{x^2}$$

Putting $\dfrac{y}{x} = v$; or $y = vx$ and $\dfrac{dy}{dx} = v+x\dfrac{dv}{dx}$

$\therefore$ Given equation becomes $v+x\dfrac{dv}{dx} = 1+v+v^2$ or $x\dfrac{dv}{dx} = 1+v^2$

$\Rightarrow \qquad \dfrac{dv}{1+v^2} = \dfrac{dx}{x}$

$\Rightarrow \qquad \displaystyle\int\dfrac{dv}{1+v^2} - \int\dfrac{dx}{x} = \text{constant}$

$\Rightarrow \qquad \tan^{-1}(v) - \log x = C, \text{ where } v = \dfrac{y}{x}$

$\therefore \qquad \tan^{-1}\left(\dfrac{y}{x}\right) - \log x = C$

8. Solve $x\dfrac{dy}{dx}+\dfrac{y^2}{x} = y$

Solution: Given, $x\dfrac{dy}{dx}+\dfrac{y^2}{x} = y$

$\Rightarrow \qquad x\dfrac{dy}{dx} = y-\dfrac{y^2}{x}$

$$\Rightarrow \quad \frac{dy}{dx} = \frac{xy - y^2}{x^2}$$

Now, putting $y = vx$ and $\dfrac{dy}{dx} = v + x\dfrac{dv}{dx}$

$\therefore$ Given equation becomes $v + x\dfrac{dv}{dx} = \dfrac{x \cdot vx - v^2 x^2}{x^2}$

$$\Rightarrow \quad v + x\frac{dv}{dx} = \frac{x^2(v - v^2)}{x^2}$$

$$\Rightarrow \quad x\frac{dv}{dx} = -v^2$$

$$\Rightarrow \quad \frac{dv}{v^2} = -\frac{dx}{x},$$

Integrating, we get,

$$\int \frac{dv}{v^2} + \int \frac{dx}{x} = \text{constant}$$

$$-\frac{1}{v} + \cos x = C,$$

where $v = \dfrac{y}{x}$, is the solution.

9. Solve $\dfrac{dy}{dx} = \dfrac{y}{x} + \sin\dfrac{y}{x}$

Solution: Given, $\dfrac{dy}{dx} = \dfrac{y}{x} + \sin\dfrac{y}{x}$ [1]

Putting $y = vx$

$$\Rightarrow \quad \frac{dy}{dx} = v + x\frac{dv}{dx}$$

$\therefore$ [1] becomes

$$v + x\frac{dv}{dx} = v + \sin v$$

$$\Rightarrow \quad x\frac{dv}{dx} = \sin v$$

$\Rightarrow \qquad \text{cosec } v dv = \dfrac{1}{x} dx$

Integrating we get,

$$\int \text{cosec } v dv = \int \dfrac{dx}{x} + \text{constant}$$

$\Rightarrow \qquad \log \tan \dfrac{v}{2} = \log x + \log c$

$\Rightarrow \qquad \log \tan \dfrac{y}{2x} = \log cx;$

or $\qquad \tan \dfrac{y}{2x} = cx$ is the solution.

10. Solve $\dfrac{dy}{dx} = \dfrac{y}{x} + \tan \dfrac{y}{x}$

Solution: Given, $\dfrac{dy}{dx} = \dfrac{y}{x} + \tan \dfrac{y}{x}$ [1]

Now, putting $y = vx$ then,

$$\dfrac{dy}{dx} = v + x \dfrac{dv}{dx}$$

$\therefore$ [1] becomes $v + x \dfrac{dv}{dx} = v + \tan v$

$\Rightarrow \qquad x \dfrac{dv}{dx} = \tan v$

$\Rightarrow \qquad \cot v dv = \dfrac{dx}{x}$

Integrating we get,

$$\int \cot v dv = \int \dfrac{dx}{x} + \text{constant}$$

$\log \sin v = \log x + \text{constant}$

$\Rightarrow \qquad \log \sin \dfrac{y}{x} = \log x + \log c = \log cx$

$$\therefore \quad \sin\frac{y}{x} = cx$$

11. Solve $\dfrac{dy}{dx} = \dfrac{y}{x + \sqrt{xy}}$

Solution: Given, $\dfrac{dy}{dx} = \dfrac{y}{x + \sqrt{xy}}$

$$\Rightarrow \quad \frac{dy}{dx} = \frac{\dfrac{y}{x}}{1 + \sqrt{\dfrac{y}{x}}} \qquad\qquad [1]$$

This is homogeneous.

Putting $y = vx$, and $\dfrac{dy}{dx} = v + x\dfrac{dv}{dx}$

$$v + x\frac{dv}{dx} = \frac{v}{1 + \sqrt{v}}$$

$$x\frac{dv}{dx} = \frac{v}{1 + \sqrt{v}} - v = -\frac{v\sqrt{v}}{1 + \sqrt{v}}$$

Separating the variables we get,

$$-\frac{dx}{x} = \frac{1 + \sqrt{v}}{v\sqrt{v}}\,dv = \left(\frac{1}{v\sqrt{v}} + \frac{1}{v}\right)dv$$

Integrating we get,

$$-\log x + C = -\frac{2}{\sqrt{v}} + \log v,$$

or $\quad \log(vx) = \dfrac{2}{\sqrt{v}} + C$

$$\therefore \quad \log y = 2\frac{\sqrt{x}}{\sqrt{y}} + c$$

12. Solve $x\dfrac{dy}{dx} = y - x\cos^2\left(\dfrac{y}{x}\right)$

Solution: Given, $x\dfrac{dy}{dx} = y - x\cos^2\left(\dfrac{y}{x}\right)$

or, $\dfrac{dy}{dx} = \dfrac{y}{x} - \cos^2\left(\dfrac{y}{x}\right)$

Putting $y = vx$, then

$$\dfrac{dy}{dx} = v + x\dfrac{dv}{dx}$$

Given equation becomes

$$v + x\dfrac{dv}{dx} = v - \cos^2 v$$

$\Rightarrow \quad x\dfrac{dv}{dx} = -\cos^2 v$

$\Rightarrow \quad \sec^2 v\, dv = -\dfrac{dx}{x}$

Integrating both sides we get,

$$\tan v = -\log x + c$$

$$\tan\left(\dfrac{y}{x}\right) + \log x = C$$

13. Solve $x\dfrac{dy}{dx} = y(\log y - \log x + 1)$

Solution: Given, $x\dfrac{dy}{dx} = y(\log y - \log x + c)$

$\Rightarrow \quad \dfrac{dy}{dx} = \dfrac{y}{x}\left(\log\dfrac{y}{x} + 1\right)$ \hfill [1]

Putting $y = vx$, we get,

$$\dfrac{dy}{dx} = v + x\dfrac{dv}{dx}$$

$\therefore$ [1] becomes

$$v + x\dfrac{dv}{dx} = v(\log v + 1) = v\log v + v$$

or $\quad x\dfrac{dv}{dx} = v\log v$

$$\dfrac{1}{v\log v}dv = \dfrac{dx}{x}$$

$\Rightarrow \quad \dfrac{\left(\dfrac{1}{v}\right)}{\log v}dv = \dfrac{1}{x}dx$

Integrating we get,

$$\int \dfrac{\left(\dfrac{1}{v}\right)}{\log v}dv = \int \dfrac{dx}{x} + \text{constant}$$

$$\log(\log v) = \log x + \log c = \log cx$$

$\Rightarrow \quad \log v = cx$

$\therefore \quad \log\dfrac{y}{x} = cx$

14. Solve $\left[x\tan\left(\dfrac{y}{x}\right) - y\sec^2\left(\dfrac{y}{x}\right)\right]dx + x\sec^2\left(\dfrac{y}{x}\right)dy = 0$ $\qquad$ [VTU, March, 1999]

Solution: Given, $\left[x\tan\left(\dfrac{y}{x}\right) - y\sec^2\left(\dfrac{y}{x}\right)\right]dx + x\sec^2\left(\dfrac{y}{x}\right)dy = 0$

$\Rightarrow \quad \dfrac{dy}{dx} = \dfrac{\left[\dfrac{y}{x}\right]\sec^2\left(\dfrac{y}{x}\right) - \tan\left(\dfrac{y}{x}\right)}{\sec^2\left(\dfrac{y}{x}\right)}$ $\qquad$ [1]

This is a homogeneous differential equation.

Hence, putting $y = vx$ and $\dfrac{dy}{dx} = v + x\dfrac{dv}{dx}$

$\therefore$ [1] becomes, $\quad v + x\dfrac{dv}{dx} = \dfrac{v\sec^2 v - \tan v}{\sec^2 v}$

$$= v - \dfrac{\tan v}{\sec^2 v}$$

$\Rightarrow \quad x\dfrac{dv}{dx} = -\dfrac{\tan v}{\sec^2 v}$

$$\Rightarrow \quad \frac{\sec^2 v}{\tan v}dv = -\frac{dx}{x}$$

Integrating, we get

$$\log \tan v = -\log x + \log c$$

$$\Rightarrow \quad x \tan v = C$$

$$\Rightarrow \quad x \tan\left(\frac{y}{x}\right) = C$$

15. Solve $(x+y)dx + (y-x)dy = 0$ [VTU, August, 2001]

Solution: Given, $(x+y)dx + (y-x)dy = 0$ [1]

Putting $y = vx$; we get

$$\Rightarrow \quad (x+vx)dx + (vx-x)(vdx + xdv) = 0$$

$$\Rightarrow \quad x[(1+v)dx + (v-1)](vdx + xdv) = 0$$

$$\Rightarrow \quad [(1+v)dx + (v-1)](vdx + xdv) = 0$$

$$\Rightarrow \quad dx(1+v^2) + (v-1)xdv = 0$$

$$\Rightarrow \quad \frac{dx}{x} + \frac{(v-1)}{1+v^2}dv = 0 \qquad [2]$$

Integrating, we get

$$\int \frac{dx}{x} + \int \frac{v-1}{v^2+1}dv = \text{constant}$$

$$\Rightarrow \quad \log x + \left[\int \left\{\frac{v}{(v^2+1)} - \frac{1}{(v^2+1)}\right\}dv\right]$$

$$\Rightarrow \quad \log x + \frac{1}{2}\log(v^2+1) - \tan^{-1}(v) = \log k$$

$$\Rightarrow \quad \log x^2 + \log(v^2+1) - 2\tan^{-1}(v) = 2\log k$$

$$\Rightarrow \quad \log\left[x^2 + (v^2+1)\right] - 2\tan^{-1}(v) = \text{constant} = C$$

$$\Rightarrow \quad \tan^{-1}\left(\frac{y}{x}\right) - \frac{1}{2}\log\left[(x^2)\left(\frac{y^2}{x^2}+1\right)\right] = C$$

$$\therefore \quad \tan^{-1}\left(\frac{y}{x}\right) - \frac{1}{2}\log(x^2+y^2) = C$$

16. Solve $y^2 + (x^2 - xy)\dfrac{dy}{dx} = 0$

Solution: Given, $y^2 + (x^2 - xy)\dfrac{dy}{dx} = 0$

$$\Rightarrow \quad \frac{dy}{dx} = \frac{xy - x^2}{y^2} = \frac{y}{x} = \frac{x^2}{y^2} \qquad \qquad [1]$$

We note that R.H.S. is a homogeneous function and hence this is a homogeneous differential equation.

So we put, $x = v(y)$ \qquad\qquad [2]

$$\left(v = v(y) \text{ and } \frac{dx}{dy} = y\frac{dv}{dy} + v \right)$$

$\therefore$ [1] becomes

$$y = \frac{dv}{dy} + v = v - v^2; \text{ or, } -\frac{dv}{v^2} = \frac{dy}{y}$$

Integrating we get, $-\dfrac{1}{v} = \log y + \text{constant}$

or $\quad \dfrac{y}{x} = \log y + C$ Using [2] in the solution.

17. Solve $\left(x + y\cot\dfrac{x}{y} \right) dy - y\,dx = 0$

Solution: Given, $\left(x + y\cot\dfrac{x}{y} \right) dy - y\,dx = 0$

$$\Rightarrow \quad \frac{dx}{dy} = \frac{x}{y} + \cot\frac{x}{y} \qquad\qquad [1]$$

This is a homogeneous differential equation.

$\therefore$ Putting $x = vy$; $\dfrac{dx}{dy} = v + y\dfrac{dv}{dy}$

Hence [1] becomes

$$v + y\frac{dv}{dy} = v + \cot v \text{ or } \tan v \, dv = \frac{dy}{y}$$

Integrating, we get

$$\log \sec v = \log y + \text{constant}$$

$$\Rightarrow \quad \log \frac{\sec v}{y} = \text{constant}$$

$$\Rightarrow \quad \frac{\sec v}{y} = C,$$

Substituting for v we get;

$$\sec \frac{x}{y} = Cy$$

18. Solve $\left(1 + e^{\frac{x}{y}}\right) dx + e^{\frac{x}{y}} \left(1 - \frac{x}{y}\right) dy = 0$

Solution: Given, $\left(1 + e^{\frac{x}{y}}\right) dx + e^{\frac{x}{y}} \left(1 - \frac{x}{y}\right) dy = 0$

$$\Rightarrow \quad \frac{dx}{dy} = \frac{-e^{\frac{x}{y}}\left(1 + \frac{x}{y}\right)}{1 + e^{\frac{x}{y}}}$$

which is a homogeneous equation.

We put $x = vy; \quad \dfrac{dx}{dy} = y\dfrac{dv}{dy} + v = vy; \quad \dfrac{dx}{dy} = y\dfrac{dv}{dy} + v$

$$v + y\frac{dv}{dy} = -\frac{e^v(1-v)}{1+e^v}$$

or $\quad y\dfrac{dv}{dy} = -\dfrac{e^v(1-v)}{1+e^v} - v = -\dfrac{v + e^v}{1+e^v}$

$$\Rightarrow \quad -\frac{dy}{y} = \frac{1+e^v}{v+e^v}dv \qquad \text{(variable separable form)}$$

Integrating, we get,

$$-\log y = \log(v + e^v) + \text{constant}$$

$$\Rightarrow \quad \log y = (v + e^v) = \text{constant} = C$$

$$\Rightarrow \quad \log y(v + e^v) = \text{another constant} = e^c = A$$

$$\therefore \quad x + ye\frac{x}{y} = A$$

EXERCISES

1. $\dfrac{dy}{dx} = \dfrac{x^2 + 3y^2}{2xy}$;
$\qquad\qquad\qquad\qquad \left[Ans.\ x^2 + y^2 = cx^3 \right]$

2. $\dfrac{dy}{dx} = \dfrac{x^3 + 3y^3}{2xy^2}$;
$\qquad\qquad\qquad\qquad \left[Ans.\ 2y^3 = 3x^3 (\log x + c) \right]$

3. $\dfrac{x}{y}\dfrac{dy}{dx} = \dfrac{x\cos\left(\dfrac{y}{x}\right) + y\sin\left(\dfrac{y}{x}\right)}{y\sin\left(\dfrac{y}{x}\right) - x\cos\left(\dfrac{y}{x}\right)}$;
$\qquad \left[Ans.\ xy\cos\left(\dfrac{y}{x}\right) = C \right]$

4. $x^2 + x^2\dfrac{dy}{dx} = xy\dfrac{dy}{dx}$;
$\qquad\qquad\qquad \left[Ans.\ y^2 = 2x\left[y + x\log(x) \right] \right]$

5. $ye^{\frac{x}{y}}dx\left(xe^{\frac{x}{y}} + y^2 \right)dy$;
$\qquad\qquad\qquad \left[Ans.\ e^{\frac{x}{y}} = y + c \right]$

6. $y - x\dfrac{dy}{dx} = x + y\dfrac{dy}{dx}$;
$\qquad\qquad \left[Ans.\ \log\sqrt{x^2 + y^2} + \tan^{-1}\dfrac{y}{x} = C \right]$

7. $xdx + \sin^2\left(\dfrac{y}{x}\right)(ydx - xdy) = 0$;
$\qquad \left[Ans.\ \log x = \dfrac{1}{2}\left\{ \dfrac{y}{x} - \dfrac{1}{2}\sin\left(\dfrac{2y}{x}\right) \right\} + C \right]$

8. $xy\log\left(\dfrac{x}{y}\right)dx + \left[y^2 - x^2\log\left(\dfrac{x}{y}\right) \right]dy = 0$;
$\quad \left[Ans.\ \log y - \left(\dfrac{x^2}{4y^2}\right)\left[2\log\left(\dfrac{y}{x}\right) + 1 \right] = C \right]$

9. $\dfrac{dy}{dx} = \dfrac{6x^2 + 2y^2}{x^2 + 4xy}$;
$\qquad\qquad\qquad \left[Ans.\ (2x + y)(2y - 3x) = Cx \right]$

10. $\left(x^2 + 2xy - y^2 \right)dx + \left(y^2 + 2xy - x^2 \right)dy = 0$;
$\qquad \left[Ans.\ x + y = c\left(x^2 + y^2 \right) \right]$

11. $(x-y)dx = (2x+3y)dy;$

$$\left[Ans. \ \log\left(3y^2 + 3xy - x^2\right) + \frac{1}{\sqrt{21}} \log\left[\frac{2\sqrt{3}y + x\left(\sqrt{3} - \sqrt{7}\right)}{2\sqrt{3}y + x\left(\sqrt{3} + \sqrt{7}\right)} \right] = C \right]$$

12. $x\dfrac{dy}{dx} y(\log y - \log x + 1);$ $\left[Ans. \ x = c\log\left(\dfrac{y}{x}\right) \right]$

Equations Reducible to the Homogeneous Form

Let us consider the differential equation in the form:

$$(ax + by + c)dx + (a'x + b'y + c')dy = 0 \Bigg\}$$
or $\quad\quad (ax + by + c)dx - (a'x + b'y + c')dy = 0 \Bigg\}$ [1]

We can write the equation [1] as:

$$\frac{dy}{dx} = \frac{ax + by + c}{a'x + b'y + c'} \ ; \ \left(\frac{a}{a'} \neq \frac{b}{b'} \right)$$ [2]

This can be solved by reducing it to homogeneous from using the transformations $x = X + h; \ y = Y + k$, then $dx = dX \ ; \ dy = dY$

hence $\quad \dfrac{dy}{dx} = \dfrac{dY}{dX}$

∴ the given equation reduces to

$$\frac{dY}{dX} = \frac{a(X + h) + b(Y + k) + c}{a'(X + h) + b'(Y + k) + c'}$$

$$\frac{dy}{dx} = \frac{ax + by + (ah + bk + c)}{a'x + b'y + (a'h + b'K + c')}$$

We choose h and k such that $ah + bk + c = 0$ and

$$a'h + b'k + c' = 0$$

By solving these equations for h and k we get

$$h = \frac{bc' - b'c}{ab' - a'b} \ ; \quad k = \frac{a'c - ac'}{ab' - a'b}$$

∴ when $\dfrac{a}{a'} \neq \dfrac{b}{b'}$ i.e., when $ab' - a'b \neq 0$; for these values of h and k, the given

equation reduces to $\quad \dfrac{dY}{dX} = \dfrac{ax + by}{a'x + b'y}$

This is homogeneous and can be solved by putting $Y = VX$ and in the solution replace $X = x - h$ and $Y = y - k$, to get the solution of the given equation.

When $\quad \dfrac{a}{a'} = \dfrac{b}{b'}$ (a case of failure)

we put $\quad \dfrac{a}{a'} = \dfrac{b}{b'} = m$, (say),

Then, $\quad \dfrac{dy}{dx} = \dfrac{ax + by + c}{a'x + b'y + c'}$ becomes

$$\dfrac{dy}{dx} = \dfrac{ax + by + c}{m(ax + by) + c'}$$

Now, by putting $ax + by = u$, the equation can be brought to variable separable form.

(C) EXAMPLES

1. Solve: $\quad \dfrac{dy}{dx} = \dfrac{x + 2y - 3}{2x + y - 3}$

Solution: We have $\left(\dfrac{a}{a'} \neq \dfrac{b}{b'} \right)$ i.e., $\left(\dfrac{1}{2} \neq \dfrac{2}{1} \right)$

Put $\quad x = (X + h); y = (Y + k)$

$\therefore \quad \dfrac{dY}{dX} = \dfrac{X + 2Y + h + 2k - 3}{2X + Y + 2h + k - 3}$

Choose h and k such that $h + 2k - 3 = 0$, $2h + k - 3 = 0$

On solving we get, $h = 1$; $k = 1$

$\therefore$ Putting $Y = VX$; $\quad \therefore \dfrac{dY}{dX} = V + X \dfrac{dV}{dX}$

$\therefore \quad V + X\dfrac{dV}{dX} = \dfrac{X + 2VX}{2X + VX}$

$\Rightarrow \quad V + X\dfrac{dV}{dX} = \dfrac{1 + 2V}{2 + V}$

$\Rightarrow \quad X\dfrac{dV}{dX} = \dfrac{1 + 2V}{2 + V} - V = \dfrac{1 + 2V - 2V - V^2}{2 + V}$

$$= \frac{1-V^2}{2+V}$$

$$\Rightarrow \quad \frac{(2+V)dV}{1-V^2} = \frac{dX}{X}$$

Integrating, $\quad 2\int \frac{1}{1-V^2}dV + \int \frac{V}{1-V^2}dV = \int \frac{dX}{X} + \text{constant}$

$$\Rightarrow \quad 2\frac{1}{2}\log\left(\frac{1+V}{1-V}\right) - \frac{1}{2}\log\left(1-V^2\right) = \log X + \log C$$

$$\Rightarrow \quad \log\left(\frac{1+V}{1-V}\right) - \frac{1}{2}\log\left(1-V^2\right) = \log CX$$

$$\Rightarrow \quad \frac{1+\dfrac{Y}{X}}{1-\dfrac{Y}{X}} = CX\sqrt{1-\frac{Y^2}{X^2}}$$

$$\Rightarrow \quad \frac{X+Y}{X-Y} = C\sqrt{X^2 - Y^2}$$

$$\Rightarrow \quad \frac{x-y+y-1}{x-1-y+1} = C\sqrt{(x-1)^2 - (y-1)^2}$$

$$\Rightarrow \quad \frac{x+y-2}{x-y} = C\sqrt{(x+y-2)(x-y)}$$

Squaring, $\quad \dfrac{(x+y-2)^2}{(x-y)^2} = C^2(x+y-2)(x-y)$

$$\Rightarrow \quad (x+y-2) = C^2(x-y)^3$$

$$\Rightarrow \quad (x+y-2) = K(x-y)^3$$

2. Solve: $\dfrac{dy}{dx} = \dfrac{x+y-1}{x-y+1}$

Solution: Here, $\left(\dfrac{a}{a'} \neq \dfrac{b}{b'}\right)$ i.e., $\left(\dfrac{1}{1} \neq \dfrac{1}{-1}\right)$

Put $\quad x = X + h; \, y = Y + k$

$$\therefore \quad \frac{dy}{dx} = \frac{X+Y+(h+k-1)}{X-Y+(h-k+1)}$$

Choose h and k such that $h+k-1=0$, $h-k+1=0$

On solving, we get $h = 0$; $k = 1$

$$\therefore \quad \frac{dY}{dX} = \frac{X+Y}{X-Y} = \frac{\left(1+\dfrac{Y}{X}\right)}{\left(1-\dfrac{Y}{X}\right)}$$

This is homogeneous.

Putting $Y = VX$;

$$\Rightarrow \quad V+X\frac{dV}{dX} = \frac{1+V}{1-V}$$

$$\Rightarrow \quad X\frac{dV}{dX} = \frac{1+V}{1-V}-V = \frac{1+V^2}{1-V}$$

$$\Rightarrow \quad \frac{1-V}{1+V^2}dV = \frac{dX}{X}$$

Integrating we get,

$$\tan^{-1}(V)-\frac{1}{2}\log(1+V^2) = \log X + \text{constant}$$

$$\Rightarrow \quad \tan^{-1}(V)-\log X\sqrt{1+V^2} = \text{constant}$$

Substituting for V and then for X and Y, we get

$$\tan^{-1}\left(\frac{Y}{X}\right)-\log\sqrt{X^2+Y^2} = C,$$

$$\Rightarrow \quad \tan^{-1}\left(\frac{y-1}{x}\right)-\log\sqrt{x^2+(y-1)^2} = C$$

3. Solve: $(3y-7x+7)\ dx + (7y-3x+3)\ dy = 0$

Solution: Given, $\dfrac{dy}{dx} = \dfrac{7x-3y-7}{7y-3x+3}$ [1]

Put $\quad x = (X+h);\ y = (Y+k)$

$$\therefore \quad \frac{dy}{dx} = \frac{(Y+K)-(X+h)+1}{(Y+K)+(X+h)+5} \qquad [2]$$

Choose h and k such that $7h - 3k - 7 = 0$, $7k - 3h + 3 = 0$

On solving, we get $h = 1$; $k = 0$ [3]

$$\therefore \quad \frac{dY}{dX} = \frac{7X - 3Y}{7Y - 3X}$$

Putting $Y = VX$;

$$\therefore \quad V + X\frac{dV}{dX} = \frac{7 - 3V}{7V - 3}$$

$$\Rightarrow \quad X\frac{dV}{dX} = \frac{7 - 3V}{7V - 3} - V = \frac{7(1 - V^2)}{7V - 3}$$

$$\Rightarrow \quad \frac{dX}{X} = \frac{7V - 3}{7(1 - V^2)} dv = -\frac{1}{7}\left[\frac{5}{V + 1} + \frac{2}{V - 1}\right] dv$$

Integrating, $\log X = -\dfrac{1}{7}\left[5\log(V + 1) + 2\log(V - 1)\right] + C'$

$$\Rightarrow \quad \log X^7 (V + 1)^5 (V - 1)^2 = C'$$

$$\Rightarrow \quad X^7 (V + 1)^5 (V - 1)^2 = C$$

but $\quad V = \dfrac{Y}{X}$

$$\Rightarrow \quad (Y + X)^5 (Y - X)^2 = C$$

$$\Rightarrow \quad (y + x - 1)^5 (y - x + 1)^2 = C$$

4. Solve: $\quad \dfrac{dy}{dx} = \dfrac{y - x + 1}{y + x + 5}$

Solution: Here, $\dfrac{dy}{dx} = \dfrac{2x + y + 6}{y - x - 3}$ i.e., $\left(\dfrac{1}{1} \neq \dfrac{-1}{1}\right)$

Putting $\quad x = X + h$; $y = Y + k$

$$\therefore \quad \frac{dY}{dX} = \frac{2X + Y + 2h + k + 6}{Y - X + K - h - 3} \tag{1}$$

or $\quad \dfrac{dY}{dX} = \dfrac{(Y - X) + (k - h + 1)}{(Y + X) + (k + h + 5)} \cdots$ [2]

Choose h and k such that $k-h+1=0$, $k+h+5=0$

On solving, we get $(h=-2;\ k=-3)$ [3]

$$\therefore \quad \frac{dY}{dX} = \frac{(Y-X)}{(Y+X)}$$

Putting $Y = VX$

$$\therefore \quad V + X\frac{dV}{dX} = \frac{V-1}{V+1} \qquad\qquad [4]$$

$$\Rightarrow \quad X\frac{dV}{dX} = \frac{V-1}{V+1} - V$$

$$\Rightarrow \quad X\frac{dV}{dX} = \frac{V-1-V^2-V}{V+1} = -\frac{1+V^2}{V+1}$$

$$\Rightarrow \quad \frac{dX}{X} = -\frac{1}{2}\cdot\frac{2V}{V^2+1}\ dV = -\frac{1}{V^2+1}dV$$

Integrating we get,

$$\Rightarrow \quad \log X = -\frac{1}{2}\log(V^2+1) - \tan^{-1}(V) + C$$

$$\Rightarrow \quad \log(V^2+1)^{\frac{1}{2}}\ X + \tan^{-1}(V) = C$$

$$\Rightarrow \quad \log(X^2+Y^2)^{\frac{1}{2}} + \tan^{-1}\left(\frac{Y}{X}\right) = C \qquad \text{Using [4]}$$

$$\Rightarrow \quad \log\left\{(x+2)^2+(y+3)^2\right\}^{\frac{1}{2}} + \tan^{-1}\left\{\frac{y+3}{x+2}\right\} = C \ \text{ is the required solution.}$$

5. Solve: $\dfrac{dy}{dx} = \dfrac{2x+y+6}{y-x-3}$ when $x=0,\ y=0$

Solution: Here $\left(\dfrac{a}{a'} \neq \dfrac{b}{b'}\right)$ i.e., $\left(\dfrac{2}{-1} \neq \dfrac{1}{1}\right)$

Put $x = X+h;\ y = Y+k$

$$\therefore \quad \frac{dy}{dx} = \frac{2X+Y+2h+k+6}{Y-X+k-h-3}$$

Choose h and k such that $2h+k+6=0$, $k-h-3=0$

Solving, we get $h = -3$ and $k = 3$.

$$\therefore \quad \frac{dy}{dx} = \frac{2X + Y}{Y - X}$$

Putting $Y = VX$

$$\therefore \quad V + X\frac{dV}{dX} = \frac{2X + VX}{VX - X} = \frac{2 + V}{V - 1}$$

$$\Rightarrow \quad X\frac{dV}{dX} = \frac{2 + V}{V - 1} - V = \frac{2 + V - V^2 + V}{V - 1}$$

$$\Rightarrow \quad \frac{V - 1}{2 + 2V - V^2}\, dV = \frac{dX}{X}$$

Integrating,we get

$$-\frac{1}{2}\int \frac{2 - 2V}{2 + 2V - V^2}\, dV = \int \frac{dX}{X} + \text{constant}$$

$$\Rightarrow \quad -\frac{1}{2}\log\,(2 + 2V - V^2) = \log\,X + \log\,C$$

$$\Rightarrow \quad \frac{1}{\sqrt{2 + 2V - V^2}} = CX$$

$$\Rightarrow \quad \frac{1}{\sqrt{2 + \dfrac{2Y}{X} - \dfrac{Y^2}{X^2}}} = CX$$

$$\Rightarrow \quad \frac{X}{\sqrt{2X^2 + 2XY - Y^2}} = CX$$

$$\Rightarrow \quad 2X^2 + 2XY - Y^2 = \frac{1}{C^2}$$

$$\Rightarrow \quad 2(x + 3)^2 + 2(x + 3)y - y^2 = \frac{1}{C^2}$$

$$\Rightarrow \quad 2x^2 + 2xy - y^2 + 12x + 6y + 18 = \frac{1}{C^2}$$

When $x = 0;\ y = 0$, we get $\dfrac{1}{C^2} = 18$

$$\therefore \quad 2x^2 + 2xy - y^2 + 12x + 6y = 0.$$

6. Solve: $\dfrac{dy}{dx} = \dfrac{x-y+1}{x+2y-3}$

Solution: Here $\left(\dfrac{a}{a'} \neq \dfrac{b}{b'}\right)$ i.e., $\left(\dfrac{1}{1} \neq \dfrac{-1}{2}\right)$

Put $\quad x = X + h; \; y = Y + '$

$\therefore \quad \dfrac{dY}{dX} = \dfrac{(X+h)-(Y+k+1)}{(X+h)+2(Y+k)-3}$

or $\quad \dfrac{dY}{dX} = \dfrac{X-Y+h-k+1}{X+2Y+h+2k+3}$

Choose h and k such that $h-k+1=0, \; h+2k-3=0$

Solving we get, $h = \dfrac{1}{3}; \; k = \dfrac{4}{3}$

$\therefore \quad \dfrac{dY}{dX} = \dfrac{X-Y}{X+2Y}$

Putting $Y = VX; \; \therefore \; \dfrac{dY}{dX} = V + X\dfrac{dV}{dX}$

$\therefore \quad V + X\dfrac{dV}{dX} = \dfrac{X-VX}{X+2X} = \dfrac{1-V}{1+2V}$

$\Rightarrow \quad X\dfrac{dV}{dX} = \dfrac{1-V}{1+2V} - V$

$\qquad = \dfrac{1-V-V-2V^2}{1+2V} = \dfrac{1-2V-2V^2}{1+2V}$

$\therefore \quad \dfrac{(1+2V)dV}{1-2V-2V^2} = \dfrac{dX}{X}$

$\qquad -\dfrac{1}{2}\displaystyle\int \dfrac{-2-4V}{1-2V-2V^2}\,dV = \int \dfrac{dX}{X} + \text{constant}$

$\Rightarrow \quad -\dfrac{1}{2}\log(1-2V-2V^2) = \log X + \log C$

$\Rightarrow \quad \dfrac{1}{\sqrt{1-2V-2V^2}} = CX$

$$\Rightarrow \quad \frac{X}{\sqrt{X^2 - 2XY - 2Y^2}} = CX$$

$$\Rightarrow \quad X^2 - 2XY - 2Y^2 = \frac{1}{C^2}$$

$$\Rightarrow \quad \left(x - \frac{1}{3}\right)^2 - 2\left(x - \frac{1}{3}\right)\left(y - \frac{4}{3}\right) - 2\left(y - \frac{4}{3}\right)^2 = K \text{ is the required solution.}$$

In the following examples, $\dfrac{dy}{dx} = \dfrac{ax + by + c}{a'x + b'y + c'}$, the equations are of the type: $\dfrac{a}{b} = \dfrac{a'}{b'}$

7. Solve: $(4x + 6y + 3)\,dx = (6x + 9y + 2)\,dy$

Solution: Given, $\dfrac{dy}{dx} = \dfrac{4x + 6y + 3}{6x + 9y + 2}$ $\qquad$ [1]

Here, $a = 4$; $a' = 6$; $b = 6$; $b' = 9$

$$\therefore \quad \left(\frac{a}{a'} = \frac{b}{b'}\right) \Rightarrow \left(\frac{4}{6} = \frac{6}{9}\right) \Rightarrow \left(\frac{2}{3} = \frac{2}{3}\right)$$

$\Rightarrow$ a case of failure

$$\therefore \quad \frac{dy}{dx} = \frac{2(2x + 3y) + 3}{3(2x + 3y) + 2} \qquad [2]$$

Putting $2x + 3y = u$; then $2 + 3\dfrac{dy}{dx} = \dfrac{du}{dx}$

or $\quad \dfrac{dy}{dx} = \dfrac{1}{3}\left[\dfrac{du}{dx} - 2\right]$

$\therefore$ From [2], $\dfrac{1}{3}\left[\dfrac{du}{dx} - 2\right] = \dfrac{2u + 3}{3u + 2}$

$$\frac{du}{dx} - 2 = \frac{6u + 9}{3u + 2} \quad \text{or} \quad \frac{du}{dx} = \frac{6u + 9}{3u + 2} + 2$$

$$= \frac{12u + 13}{3u + 2}$$

$$\Rightarrow \quad \frac{34+2}{124+13} \, du = dx \text{ (variable separable)}$$

$$\Rightarrow \quad \left[\frac{1}{4} - \frac{5}{4} \frac{1}{12u+13} \right] du = dx \qquad\qquad [3]$$

∴ by actual division in an elegant form

$$
\begin{array}{r}
1/4 \\
12u+13 \overline{)3u+2} \\
-\left(3u+\dfrac{13}{4}\right) \\
\hline
-\dfrac{5}{4}
\end{array}
$$

Integrating [3] we get,

$$\frac{u}{4} - \frac{5}{4} \cdot \frac{1}{12} \log (12u+13) = x + c_1$$

$$\Rightarrow \quad 12(2x + 3y) - 5 \log(24x + 36y + 13) = 48x + c$$

$$\Rightarrow \quad 12(3y - 2x) - 5 \log(24x + 36y + 13) = c$$

8. Solve: $\dfrac{dy}{dx} = \dfrac{x-2y+3}{x-2y+5}$

Solution: Put $x - 2y + 3 = Y$; ∴ $x - 2y + 5 = Y + 2$

Also, $1-2 \dfrac{dy}{dx} = \dfrac{dY}{dX}$; ∴ $\dfrac{dy}{dx} = \left(1-\dfrac{dY}{dX}\right)\dfrac{1}{2}$

∴ $\dfrac{1}{2}\left(1-\dfrac{dY}{dX}\right) = \dfrac{Y}{Y+2}$;

$$1 - \frac{dY}{dX} = \frac{2Y}{Y+2}$$

$$\frac{dY}{dX} = 1 - \frac{2Y}{Y+2} = \frac{Y+2-2Y}{Y+2} = \frac{2-Y}{Y+2}$$

∴ $dx + \dfrac{Y+2}{Y-2} dY = 0$

$$dx + \left[1+\frac{4}{Y-2}\right] dY = 0$$

Integrating, $\int dx - \int dY + 4 \int \dfrac{dY}{Y-2} = $ constant

$\quad x + Y + 4 \, \log(Y - 2) = $ constant

$\quad (2x - 2y + 3) + 4 \, \log(x - 2y + 1) = $ constant

9. **Solve:** $(x + y + 2)dx + (2x - 2y - 1)dy = 0$

Solution: Let $(x - y + 2) = Y;$ $(2x - 2y - 1) = (2Y - 5)$

Also, $dx - dy = dY;$ $dy = (dx - dY)$

$\therefore \quad Ydx + (2Y - 5)(dx - dy) = 0$

$\quad (Y + 2Y - 5)dx - (2Y - 5)dY = 0$

$$dx - \left[\frac{(2Y - 5)}{(3Y - 5)}\right]dY = 0$$

Integrating, we get,

$$\int dx - \int \frac{(2Y - 5)}{(3Y - 5)}dy = \text{constant}$$

Putting $(3Y - 5) = u;$

$$Y = 2\left[\frac{(u + 5)}{3}\right] - 5$$

$$= \left[\frac{(2u - 5)}{3}\right]$$

$$\int dx - \int \frac{2u - 5}{u}du = \text{constant};$$

$$x = \int\left[2 - \frac{5}{u}\right]du = \text{constant}$$

$\Rightarrow \quad x - 2u + 5\log u = $ constant, is the solution, where $u = 3(x - y + 2) - 5$

10. **Solve:** $(x - 2y + 3)dx + (4y - 2x + 7)dy = 0$

Solution: Putting $x - 2y + 3 = Y;$

Then $4y - 2x + 7 = -2Y + 13$

$\quad dx - 2dy = dY;$

$$\therefore \quad dy = \frac{1}{2}(dx - dY)$$

$\therefore$ Given equation becomes

$$Y \cdot dx + (-2Y + 13) \frac{1}{2}(dx - dY) = 0$$

$$dx(2Y - 2Y + 13) + (2Y - 13)dY = 0$$

$$13dx + [2Y - 13]dY = 0$$

$$\int 13\, dx + \int (2Y - 13)\, dY = \text{constant}$$

$$13x + y^2 - 13Y = \text{constant}$$

$$13x + y^2 - 13Y = \text{constant}$$

Putting $Y = x - 2y + 3$

$$\therefore \quad (x - 2y + 3)^2 - 13(x - 2y + 3) + 13x = \text{constant}$$

$$(x - 2y + 3)^2 + (2y - 3)\,13 = c$$

11. Solve: $(x + y + 1)dx + (2x + 2y + 3)dy = 0$

Solution: Put $(x + y + 1) = u$; $(dx + dy) = du$;

$$dy = (du - dx) \text{ and } 2x + 2y + 2 = 2u;$$

$$(2x + 2y + 3) = (2u + 1)$$

$\therefore$ The equation becomes :

$$udx + (2u + 12)(du - dx) = 0$$

$$udx + (2u + 1)\, du - (2u + 1)dx = 0$$

$$(2u + 1)du + dx(u - 2u - 1) = 0$$

$$(2u + 1)du - (u + 1)dx = 0$$

$$\left[(2u + 1)/(u + 1)\right] du - dx = 0$$

$$\int \frac{2u + 1}{u + 1}\, du - \int dx = C;$$

$$\int \left[2 - \frac{1}{u + 1}\right] du = x + C$$

$$\therefore \quad 2u - \log(u + 1) = x + c$$

12. Solve: $(2x + y - 1)dx = (4x + 2y + 5)dy$

Solution: Putting $(2x + y - 1) = u$; $\therefore dy = (du - 2dx)$

$$4x + 2y + 5 = (4x + 2y - 2) + 7 = (2u + 7)$$

$\therefore \quad udx = (2u + 7)(du - 2dx)$

$$= (2u + 7)du - 2(2u + 7)dx$$

$$dx[u + 2(2u + 7)] = (2u + 7)du$$

$$dx = \frac{(2u+7)}{5u+14}; \quad (x + c) = \int \frac{(2u+7)}{5u+14} du$$

Putting $5u + 14 = t$;

$$u = \left[\frac{t-14}{5}\right]; \quad du = \left(\frac{1}{5}\right)dt$$

$$x + c = \int \frac{2\left[\dfrac{t-14}{5}\right]+7}{t} \frac{dt}{5}$$

$$= \frac{1}{25}\int \frac{2t+7}{t} dt$$

$$= \left(\frac{1}{25}\right)\left[\int 2dt + 7\int \frac{1}{t}dt\right]$$

$$= \left(\frac{1}{25}\right)[2t + 7 \log t]$$

$\therefore \quad 25(x + c) = [2t + 7 \log t] = [2(5u + 14) + 7 \log(5u + 14)]$

EXERCISES

1. $(2x + 3y{-}6)\dfrac{dy}{dx} + 2x + 3y + 1 = 0$;

   Ans: $x + y - \dfrac{29}{12} = C$

2. $(2x + 3y - 8) dx = (x + 2y - 3) dy$

   Ans: $(y + 2)2 - (x - 7)(y + 2) - (x - 7)2 = \left[\dfrac{2yx + 11 + \sqrt{5}(x-7)}{2yx + 11\sqrt{5}(x-7)}\right]^2$

3. $\dfrac{(3x+5y+6)}{(x+7y+2)} \cdot \dfrac{dy}{dx} = 1$

   Ans: $(x + 2)2 + 4(x + 2)y - 5y^2 \cdot \left[\dfrac{5y-5x-10}{5y+x+2}\right]^{7/3} = C$

4. $\dfrac{dy}{dx} + \dfrac{3x+2y-5}{2x+3y-5} = 0$

   Ans: $3(x - 1)^2 + 4(x - 1)(y - 1) + 3(y - 1)^2 = C$

5. $(4x - 6y - 1)dx - (2x - 3y + 2)dy = 0$

   Ans: $x = -\dfrac{1}{4}\left[2x-3y+\dfrac{15}{4}\log\left(2x-3y-\dfrac{7}{4}\right)+C\right]$

6. Solve: $(x + 2y)(dx - dy) = dx + dy$

   Ans: $x = \dfrac{1}{3}\left[x+2y+\dfrac{4}{3}\log\left(x+2y\dfrac{1}{3}\right)\right]+C$

7. $(x + y)(dx - dy) = dx + dy$

   Ans: $x - y = \log(x + y) + C$

8. $(x - 2y + 5)dx - (2x + y - 1)dy = 0$

   Ans: $x^2 - y^2 - 4xy + 10X + 2y = C$

9. $(2x + 9y - 20)dx - (6x + 2y - 10)dy = 0$

   Ans: $x + 2y - 5 = C(2x - y)^2$

10. $(2x - 4y + 3)\,dy + (x - 2y + 1)\,dx = 0$

    Ans: $\log\{4(x-2y)+5\} = 4(x + 2y) + C$

11. $(3x + 2y - 5)dx + (2x + 3y - 5)dy = 0$

    Ans: $3(x^2 + y^2) + 4xy - 10(x + y) = C$

12. $(3x - y - 2)\dfrac{dy}{dx} = x + 3y - 4$

$$Ans: \log\left[(x+1)^2 + (y-1)^2\right] = 6\tan^{-1}\left(\frac{y-1}{x-1}\right) + C$$

Solve the following differential equations

13. $(x-y-2)dx - (2x-2y-3)dy = 0$

$\quad$ *Ans*: $2(y + 2) - x - \log(x-y-1) = C$

14. $dy(3x-y + 4) = dx(6x - 2y-7)$

$\quad$ *Ans*: $15 \log(3x-y + 19) + (y - 2x - 4) = C$

15. $(x + 2y + 1) = (2x + 4y + 3)\dfrac{dy}{dx}$

$\quad$ *Ans*: $8x - (4u + 1) - \log(1 + 4u) = C$

$\quad$ Where $u = x + 2y + 1$

16. $(2x - 6y + 7)\,dx = (x-3y + 4\,)dy$

$\quad$ *Ans*: $25x + 3\left[(5x-15y+17)+3\log(5x-15y+17)=\text{constant}\right]$

Linear Equations

A differential equation of the form $\dfrac{dy}{dx} + Py = Q$, where $P = P(x)$; $Q = Q(x)$ is called a linear differential equation of first order.

To solve $\dfrac{dy}{dx} + Py = Q$ $\hspace{4cm}$ [1]

Multiply [1] by $e^{\int Pdx}$, then we get

$$\frac{dy}{dx}e^{\int Pdx} + Pye^{\int Pdx} = Qe^{\int Pdx}$$

The L.H.S can be written as

$$\frac{d}{dx}\left(ye^{\int Pdx}\right)$$

$$\therefore \quad \frac{d}{dx}\left(ye^{\int Pdx}\right) = Qe^{\int Pdx}$$

Integrating we get,

$$ye^{\int Pdx} = \int\left[Qe^{\int Pdx}\right]dx + C$$

which is the required solution.

$e^{\int Pdx}$ is called the Integrating factor (*I.F.*)

Working Rule:

(i) Find $I.F. = e^{\int Pdx}$

(ii) The solution is: $y(I.F.) = \int Q(I.F.)dx + C$

It should be noted that if equation $\dfrac{dx}{dy} + Px = Q$ where P and Q are functions of y alone, is also a linear differential equation and *I.F.*, than in this case in $e^{\int Pdy}$ the solution is $x(I.F.) = \int Q(I.F.)dy + c$

(D) EXAMPLES

1. Solve: $\sec^2 y\left(\dfrac{dy}{dx}\right) + 2x\tan y = x^3$

   Solution: put $\tan y = u$;

   $$\therefore \quad \sec^2 y\left(\frac{dy}{dx}\right) = \frac{du}{dx}$$

   The equation now becomes,

   $$\frac{du}{dx} + 2x \cdot u = x^3 \qquad\qquad [1]$$

   This equation is linear

   $$\frac{du}{dx} + Pu = Q$$

   The solution is

   $$ue^{\int Pdx} = A + \int Qe^{\int Pdx}dx \qquad\qquad [2]$$

   Here, $P = 2x;\ e^{\int Pdx} = e^{x^2} \qquad\qquad [3]$

$$\int Q e^{\int P dx} dx = \int x^3 e^{x^2} dx;$$

$$\left(x^2 = t; \ 2x dx = dt\right)$$

$$= \int x^2 \cdot e^{x^2} x dx = \int t e^t \cdot \frac{1}{2} dt$$

$$= \frac{1}{2}\left\{e^t t - \int e^t 1 dt\right\} = \frac{1}{2}(e^t \cdot t - e^t)$$

$$= \frac{1}{2} e^{x^2} (x^2 - 1); \ u = \tan y$$

$\therefore$ The solution is, $\tan y e^{x^2} = u e^{x^2} = A + \left(\dfrac{1}{2}\right) e^{x^2} (x^2 - 1)$

2. Solve: $\dfrac{dy}{dx} - \dfrac{\tan y}{1 + x} = (1 + x) e^x \sec y$

Solution: Multiply by $\cos y$ (or divide by $\sec y$)

$$\cos y \frac{dy}{dx} - \frac{1}{1 + x} \cdot \frac{\sin y \cos y}{\cos y} = (1 + x) e^x$$

Putting $\sin y = u;$ $\therefore \cos y \left(\dfrac{dy}{dx}\right) = \dfrac{du}{dx}$

$\Rightarrow \qquad \dfrac{du}{dx} - \dfrac{1}{1 + x} u = (1 + x) e^x$

$\therefore \qquad U(L) = A + (R)$

$$P = -\frac{1}{(1 + x)}; \ (L) = e^{\int P dx} = e^{-\log(1 + x)} = \frac{1}{(1 + x)}$$

$$(R) = \int (1 + x) e^x \cdot \left[\frac{1}{1 + x}\right] dx = \int e^x dx = e^x$$

$\therefore \qquad \sin y \left[\dfrac{1}{(1 + x)}\right] = A + e^x$

3. Solve: $\sin y \left(\dfrac{dy}{dx}\right) = \cos y (1 - x \cos y)$

Solution: Multiplying by $\sec^2 y$; (or dividing by $\cos^2 y$)

$$\frac{\sin y}{\cos^2 y}\frac{dy}{dx} = \frac{\cos y}{\cos^2 y} - \frac{x\cos^2 y}{\cos^2 y}$$

$$\sec y \tan y\left(\frac{dy}{dx}\right) - \sec y = -x$$

Putting $\sec y = u$; $\therefore \sec y \tan y\left(\frac{dy}{dx}\right) = \frac{du}{dx}$

$$\left(\frac{du}{dx}\right) - u = -x \quad \text{(standard form)}$$

$$ue^{-x} = A + \int -xe^{-x}dx = A + (x+1)e^{-x}$$

$\therefore \qquad \sec ye^{-x} = A + (x+1)e^{-x}$

4. Solve: $\left(x^2 + y^2 + 1\right)dx - 2xy dy = 0$

Solution: $\left(x^2 + 1\right) + y^2 - 2xy\left(\frac{dy}{dx}\right) = 0$

Putting $y^2 = u$; $\left(\frac{dy}{dx}\right)(2y) = \frac{du}{dx}$

$\therefore \qquad \left(x^2 + 1\right) + u - x\left(\frac{dv}{dx}\right) = 0$

$$x\left(\frac{dy}{dx}\right) - u = x^2 + 1$$

or $\qquad \dfrac{du}{dx} + \left(\dfrac{-1}{x}\right)u = \dfrac{x^2 + 1}{x} \quad \text{(standard form)}$

$$(L) = e^{\int Pdx}; \quad (R) = \int Qe^{\int Pdx}dx$$

$\therefore \qquad U(L) = A + (R)$

Here, $P = \dfrac{-1}{x}$; $\int Pdx = \int\left(-\dfrac{1}{x}\right)dx$

$$= -\log x = \log\left(\frac{1}{x}\right);$$

$$L = \left(\frac{1}{x}\right)$$

$$\therefore \quad (R) = \int Q(L)\,dx = \int \frac{x^2+1}{x}\left(\frac{1}{x}\right)dx = \int \left[1+\left(\frac{1}{x^2}\right)\right]dx + A$$

$$= x + \left(\frac{-1}{x}\right) = \frac{(x^2-1)}{x} + A$$

$$\therefore \quad u \cdot \frac{1}{x} = A + \frac{x^2-1}{x};$$

$$y^2 = Ax + x^2 - 1$$

5. Solve: $\dfrac{dy}{dx} + y\cot x = \sin x$

Solution: Given, $\dfrac{dy}{dx} + y\cot x = \sin x$

This is a linear differential equation.

$$\therefore \quad I.F. = e^{\int \cot x\,dx}$$

$$\Rightarrow \quad I.F. = e^{\log(\sin x)} = \sin x$$

$\therefore$ complete solution is

$$y\sin x = \int \sin^2 x\,dx + c$$

$$y\sin x = \frac{1}{2}\int (1-\cos 2x)\,dx + c$$

$$\therefore \quad y\sin x = \frac{1}{2}\left[x - \frac{\sin 2x}{2}\right] + c$$

6. Solve: $\dfrac{dy}{dx} + y\tan x = \sin 2x$

Solution: Given, $\dfrac{dy}{dx} + y\tan x = \sin 2x$

This is a linear differential equation.

$$\therefore \quad I.F. = e^{\int \tan x\,dx}$$

$$\Rightarrow \quad e^{\log \sec x} = I.F.$$

$$\Rightarrow \quad I.F. = \sec x$$

∴ General solution is

$\Rightarrow \quad y\sec x = \int \sin 2x \sec x\,dx + k$

$\Rightarrow \quad y\sec x = \int 2\sin x\cos x \sec x\,dx + k$

$\Rightarrow \quad y\sec x = 2\int \sin x\,dx + k$

$\Rightarrow \quad y\sec x = -2\cos x + k$

$\therefore \quad y\sec x + 2\cos x = k$

7. Solve: $\dfrac{dy}{dx} + y\cot x = 4x\operatorname{cosec} x$ at $x = \dfrac{\pi}{2}$, $y = 0$

Solution: Given $\dfrac{dy}{dx} + y\cot x = 4x\operatorname{cosec} x$

This is a linear differential equation.

∴ $\quad I.F. = e^{\int \cot x\,dx} = e^{\log(\sin x)} = \sin x$

∴ $\quad$ the general solution is

$y\sin x = \int 4x\operatorname{cosec} x \cdot \sin x\,dx + c$

$\Rightarrow \quad y\sin x = \int 4x\,dx + c$

$\Rightarrow \quad y\sin x = 2x^2 + c$

By data, $x = \dfrac{\pi}{2}$, $y = 0$

∴ $\quad 0 = \dfrac{\pi^2}{2} + c$

$\Rightarrow \quad c = -\dfrac{\pi^2}{2}$

∴ The required particular solution is $y\sin x = 2x^2 - \dfrac{\pi^2}{2}$.

8. Solve: $\left(x^3 + xy^4\right)dx + 2y^3 dy = 0$

Solution: $4y^3\left(\dfrac{dy}{dx}\right) + 2x \cdot y^4 = -2x$ (Multiply by 2)

Putting $y^4 = u$; $4y^3\left(\dfrac{dy}{dx}\right) = \left(\dfrac{dv}{dx}\right)$

$\therefore \quad \left(\dfrac{dv}{dx}\right) + 2xu = -2x^3$ (standard form)

$ue^{\int Pdx} = A + \int Qe^{\int Pdx} dx$

Putting $P = 2x;\ \therefore \int Pdx = \int 2x\,dx = x^2$

$e^{\int pdx} = e^{x^2}$

$\int Qe^{\int Pdx} = \int -2x^3 e^{x^2} dx$

$= -\int x^2 \cdot e^{x^2} 2x\,dx$

$= -\int te^t \cdot dt \ \left(x^2 = t;\ 2x\,dx = dt\right)$

$= -\left[te^t - \int e^t \cdot 1 dt\right] = -\left[te^t - e^t\right]$

$= e^t (1-t) = e^{x^2}\left(1 - x^2\right)$

$\therefore \quad ue^{x^2} = y^4 e^{x^2} = A + e^{x^2}\left(1 - x^2\right)$

9. Solve: $\dfrac{dy}{dx} + \dfrac{2y}{x} = \dfrac{x^3}{y^2}$

Solution: $y^2 \dfrac{dy}{dx} + \dfrac{2y^3}{x} = x^3$

$3y^2\left(\dfrac{dy}{dx}\right) + \left(\dfrac{6}{x}\right)y^3 = 3x^3$ [1]

Putting $y^3 = u;\ 3y^2\left(\dfrac{dy}{dx}\right) = \left(\dfrac{du}{dx}\right)$ [2]

$\dfrac{du}{dx} + \left(\dfrac{6}{x}\right)u = 3x^3$ (standard form)

$P = \dfrac{6}{x};\ \int Pdx = 6\log x = \log x^6$

$(L) = e^{\int Pdx} = e^{6\log x} = x^6$ [3]

$$(R) = \int Q e^{\int P dx} dx = \int 3x^3 \cdot x^6 dx = 3\int x^9 dx = 3\left(\frac{x^{10}}{10}\right) \qquad [4]$$

$$\therefore \quad u(L) = A + (R);$$

$$\Rightarrow \quad y^3 x^6 = A + \left(\frac{3}{10}\right)x^{10}$$

EXERCISES

Solve the following differential equations:

1. $(1-x^2)\left(\dfrac{dy}{dx}\right) + 2xy = x\sqrt{(1-x^2)};$ $\left[Ans. \ y = A(1-x^2) + \sqrt{(1-x^2)}\right]$

2. $\dfrac{dy}{dx} + \dfrac{n}{x}y = \dfrac{a}{x^n};$ $\left[Ans. \ yx^n = A + ax\right]$

3. $\dfrac{dy}{dx} + \dfrac{3y}{x} = \dfrac{1}{x^2};$ $\left[Ans. \ yx^3 = A + \dfrac{x^2}{2}\right]$

4. $2\cos x\left(\dfrac{dy}{dx}\right) + 4 \cdot y\sin x = \sin 2x;$ $\left[\text{Given that } y = 0, \text{ when } x = \left(\dfrac{\pi}{3}\right)\right]$

$\left[Ans. \ y\sec^2 x = -2 + \sec x\right]$

5. $x\left(\dfrac{dy}{dx}\right) - y = x^2 \sin x;$ $\left[Ans. \ y\left(\dfrac{1}{x}\right) = A - \cos x\right]$

Bernoulli's Linear Form

Let the equation to be solved is of the form

$$\frac{dy}{dx} + Py = Qy^n \qquad [1]$$

where $P = P(x); Q = Q(x)$,

Dividing by y^n, we get

$$y^{-n}\frac{dy}{dx} + Py^{1-n} = Q. \qquad [2]$$

To solve [2]

We put $y^{1-n} = v$

$$\Rightarrow \qquad (1-n)y^{-n}\frac{dy}{dx} = \frac{dv}{dx}$$

$\therefore$ [2] becomes

$$\frac{1}{(1-n)}\frac{dv}{dx} + Pv = Q$$

i.e., $\qquad \dfrac{dv}{dx} + (1-n)Pv = (1-n)Q$

This is linear in v and x which can be solved by finding $I.F. = e^{\int(1-n)Pdx}$

Replacing y^{1-n} by v, we get the required solution.

It should be noted that if the equation to be solved is of the form $\dfrac{dx}{dy} + Px = Qx^n$ where P and Q are functions of y alone, is also a Bernoulli's equation.

Dividing by x^n,

we get $\quad x^{-n}\dfrac{dx}{dy} + Px^{1-n} = Q$

Putting $x^{1-n} = v$;

$$\Rightarrow \qquad (1-n)x^{-n}\frac{dx}{dy} = \frac{dv}{dy}$$

$\therefore \qquad \dfrac{1}{(1-n)}\dfrac{dv}{dy} + Pv = Q$

or $\qquad \dfrac{dv}{dy} + (1-n)Pv = (1-n)Q$

This is linear in v and y which can be solved by finding $I.F. = e^{\int(1-n)Pdy}$. Solution is $v(I.F.) = \int (1-n)Q(I.F)dy + c$

Putting down x^{1-n} for v, we get the required solution.

(E) EXAMPLES

1. Solve: $\dfrac{dy}{dx} + xy = xy^3$

Solution: Given, $\dfrac{dy}{dx} + xy = xy^3$

Dividing by y^3,

Given equation becomes, $\dfrac{1}{y^3} \cdot \dfrac{dy}{dx} + \dfrac{1}{y^2}x = x$ [1]

Putting $\dfrac{1}{y^2} = v$ [2]

so that $-\dfrac{2}{y^3}\dfrac{dy}{dx} = \dfrac{dv}{dx}$

$\therefore$ [1] becomes

$$\left[-\dfrac{1}{2}\right]\dfrac{dv}{dx} + vx = x$$

or $\dfrac{dv}{dx} - 2xv = -2x$ [3]

This is a linear equation in v and x with $P = -2x$
and $Q = -2x$;

$\therefore$ $\displaystyle\int Pdx = \int -2xdx = -x^2$;

and $I.F. = e^{\int Pdx} = e^{-x^2}$

Hence, the solution of the equation [3] is

$$ve^{\int Pdx} = \int Qe^{\int Pdx} + c$$

or $ve^{-x^2} = \displaystyle\int (-2x)e^{-x^2}dx + c = \int e^t dt + c$, where $t = -x^2$

$\qquad = e^t + c = e^{-x^2} + c$

Using [2], this becomes

$$\dfrac{1}{y^2} = 1 + ce^{x^2}$$

2. Solve: $\dfrac{dy}{dx}(x^2 y^3 + xy) = 1$

Solution: Given, $\dfrac{dy}{dx}(x^2 y^3 + xy) = 1$

$\Rightarrow \qquad \dfrac{dx}{dy} = x^2 y^3 + xy$

$\Rightarrow \qquad \dfrac{dx}{dy} - yx = x^2 y^3$

This is a Bernoulli's equation in which y is independent variable and x is the dependent variable.

Dividing by x^2 we get,

$$\frac{1}{x^2}\frac{dx}{dy} - \frac{1}{x}y = y^3$$

Putting $\quad -\dfrac{1}{x} = v \Rightarrow \dfrac{1}{x^2}\dfrac{dx}{dy} = \dfrac{dv}{dy}$

we have $\dfrac{dv}{dy} + vy = y^3$

This is a linear differential equation.

$$I.F = e^{\int y\, dy} \Rightarrow I.F = e^{\frac{y^2}{2}}$$

The general solution is

$$ve^{\frac{y^2}{2}} = \int y^3 e^{\frac{y^2}{2}}\, dy + c$$

Consider $\int y^3 \cdot e^{\frac{y^2}{2}}\, dy$

Putting $\dfrac{y^2}{2} = t \Rightarrow y\, dy = dt$

$= \int 2t \cdot e^t\, dt$

$= 2\int t e^t\, dt$

$= 2\left[t e^t - \int e^t\, dt \right]$

$= 2(t e^t - e^t)$

$\therefore$ solution is: $ve^{\frac{y^2}{2}} = 2e^t(t-1) + c$

or $\quad -\dfrac{1}{x}e^{\frac{y^2}{2}} = 2e^{\frac{y^2}{2}}\left[\dfrac{y^2}{2} - 1\right] + c$

$\left(\text{Since } v = -\dfrac{1}{x} \text{ and } t = \dfrac{y^2}{2}\right)$

or $\quad y^2 - 2 + ce^{-\frac{y^2}{2}} = \dfrac{1}{x}$

or $\quad \boxed{x\left(y^2 - 2 + ce^{-\frac{y^2}{2}}\right) = 1}$

3. Solve: $3y^2\dfrac{dy}{dx} + 2xy^3 = 4xe^{-x^2}$

Solution: Given, $3y^2\dfrac{dy}{dx} + 2xy^3 = 4xe^{-x^2}$

Putting $y^3 = v$

$\Rightarrow \quad 3 \cdot y^2\dfrac{dy}{dx} = \dfrac{dv}{dx}$

The given equation becomes

$\dfrac{dv}{dx} + 2x \cdot v = 4xe^{-x^2}$

This is a linear differential equation.

$\therefore \quad I.F = e^{\int 2x\,dx} = e^{x^2}$

$\therefore$ The general solution is

$ve^{x^2} = \int 4x \cdot e^{-x^2} \cdot e^{x^2}\,dx + c$

$\Rightarrow \quad ve^{x^2} = \int 4x\,dx + c$

$\Rightarrow \quad \boxed{y^3 e^{x^2} = 2x^2 + c}$

4. Solve: $\cos\theta\left(\dfrac{dr}{d\theta}\right) - r\sin\theta = -r^2$

Solution: Given, $\cos\theta\left(\dfrac{dr}{d\theta}\right) - r\sin\theta = -r^2$

$$\dfrac{\cos\theta}{r^2}\cdot\dfrac{dr}{d\theta} - \dfrac{1}{r}\sin\theta = -1$$

Putting $\left(\dfrac{1}{r}\right) = u;$

$$\left(\dfrac{1}{r^2}\right)\left(\dfrac{dr}{d\theta}\right) = -\left(\dfrac{du}{d\theta}\right)$$

$$-\cos\theta\dfrac{du}{d\theta} - u\sin\theta = -1;$$

$$\dfrac{du}{d\theta} + \tan\theta\cdot u = \sec\theta$$

$$P = \tan\theta; \quad \int P d\theta = \int \tan\theta d\theta = \log\sec\theta$$

$$e^{\int Pd\theta} = e^{\log\sec\theta} = \sec\theta;$$

$$\int Q e^{\int Pd\theta} = \int \sec^2\theta d\theta = \tan\theta$$

$$\Rightarrow \quad u\sec\theta = A + \tan\theta$$

5. Solve: $xdy = \left(y + xy^3\left(1 + \log x\right)\right)dx = 0$

Solution: $\left(\dfrac{dy}{dx}\right) - y = xy^3\left(1 + \log x\right)$

$$\dfrac{x}{y^3}\dfrac{dy}{dx} - \dfrac{1}{y^2} = x\left(1 + \log x\right) \qquad \text{(dividing by } y^3\text{)}$$

Putting $\dfrac{1}{y^2} = u; \quad \dfrac{-2}{y^3}\dfrac{dy}{dx} = \dfrac{du}{dx}$

$$\dfrac{1}{y^3}\dfrac{dy}{dx} = -\dfrac{1}{2}\dfrac{du}{dx}$$

$$x\left(-\dfrac{1}{2}\right)\left(\dfrac{du}{dx}\right) - u = x\left(1 + x\log x\right);$$

$$\left(\dfrac{du}{dx}\right) + \left(\dfrac{2}{x}\right)u = -2\left(1 + \log x\right) \quad \text{(dividing by } -\dfrac{x}{2}\text{)}$$

$$P = \left(\frac{2}{x}\right); \quad \int P dx = \int \left(\frac{2}{x}\right) dx = 2 \log x;$$

$$e^{\int P dx} = x^2$$

$$\int Q e^{\int P dx} dx = -2 \int (1 + \log x) x^2 dx \qquad \text{(Integrating by parts)}$$

$$= -2 \left[\left(\frac{x^3}{3}\right)(1 + \log x) - \int \left(\frac{x^3}{3}\right)\left(\frac{1}{x}\right) dx \right]$$

$$= -2 \left[\left(\frac{x^3}{3}\right)(1 + \log x) - \left(\frac{1}{3}\right)(x^2 dx) \right]$$

$$= -\left(\frac{2}{3}\right) \left[x^3 (1 + \log x) - \left(\frac{x^3}{3}\right) \right]$$

$$\therefore \quad \left(\frac{x^2}{y^2}\right) = A - \left(\frac{2}{3}\right) \left[x^3 (1 + \log x) \right] - \left[\frac{x^3}{3} \right]$$

6. Solve: $\left(\dfrac{dy}{dx}\right) - xy = xy^5$

Solution: Given, $\dfrac{dy}{dx} - xy = xy^5$

Dividing by y^5 and

Putting $\left(\dfrac{1}{y^4}\right) = u$;

$$\left(\frac{1}{y^5}\right)\left(\frac{dy}{dx}\right) = -\left(\frac{1}{4}\right)\left(\frac{dy}{dx}\right)$$

$$\frac{1}{y^5}\left(\frac{dy}{dx}\right) = -\left(\frac{1}{4}\right)\left(\frac{dy}{dx}\right)$$

$$\frac{1}{y^5}\left(\frac{dy}{dx}\right) - \frac{1}{y^4} x = x$$

$$-\frac{1}{4}\frac{du}{dx} - u \cdot x = x$$

$$\left(\frac{dy}{dx}\right) + 4xu = -4x$$

Put $P = 4x$; $\int P dx = \int 4x dx = 2x^2$

$$e^{\int P dx} = e^{2x^2}$$

$$\int Q e^{\int P dx} dx = \int -4x e^{2x^2 dx} \quad (2x^2 = t; \ 4x dx = dt)$$

$$= \int -e^t dt = e^t$$

$$\therefore \quad \left(\frac{1}{x^4}\right) e^{2x^2} = A - e^{2x^2}$$

7. Solve: $\dfrac{dy}{dx} + y = y^2 (\cos x - \sin x)$

Solution: Given, $\dfrac{dy}{dx} + y = y^2 (\cos x - \sin x)$

Dividing by y^2,

$$\frac{1}{y^2} \frac{dy}{dx} + \frac{1}{y} = (\cos x - \sin x)$$

Putting $\dfrac{1}{y} = v \Rightarrow -\dfrac{1}{y^2} \dfrac{dy}{dx} = \dfrac{dv}{dx}$

The equation becomes

$$-\frac{dv}{dx} + v = (\cos x - \sin x)$$

or $\quad \dfrac{dv}{dx} - v = (\sin x - \cos x)$

This is a linear equation.

$$\therefore \quad I.F. = e^{\int -dx} = e^{-x}$$

$$\therefore \quad v e^{-x} = \int (\sin x - \cos x) e^{-x} dx + c$$

Consider $I = \int (\sin x - \cos x) e^{-x} dx$

Integrating by parts

$$I = (\sin x - \cos x)(-e^{-x}) + \int (\cos x + \sin x) e^{-x} dx$$

$$= (\sin x - \cos x)(-e^{-x}) + (\cos x + \sin x)(-e^{-x})$$

$$+ \int (\cos x - \sin x)(-e^{-x}) \, dx$$

$$= -2e^{-x} \sin x - I$$

$$\therefore \quad 2I = -2e^{-x} \sin x$$

∴ The solution is

$$ve^{-x} = -e^{-x} \sin x + c$$

or $1 + y \sin x = cye^{x}$ is the required solution.

8. Solve: $\dfrac{dy}{dx} + \dfrac{y}{x-1} = x \cdot y^{\frac{1}{3}}$

Solution: Given $\dfrac{dy}{dx} + \dfrac{y}{x-1} = xy^{\frac{1}{3}}$

$$\Rightarrow \quad \frac{1}{y^{\frac{1}{3}}} \frac{dy}{dx} + \frac{1}{x-1} y^{\frac{2}{3}} = x$$

Putting $y^{\frac{2}{3}} = v \Rightarrow \dfrac{2}{3} y^{-\frac{1}{3}} \dfrac{dy}{dx} = \dfrac{dv}{dx}$

$$\Rightarrow \quad \frac{1}{y^{\frac{1}{3}}} \frac{dy}{dx} = \frac{3}{2} \frac{dv}{dx}$$

The given equation becomes

$$\frac{3}{2} \cdot \frac{dv}{dx} + \frac{1}{x-1} v = x$$

$$\Rightarrow \quad \frac{dv}{dx} + \frac{2}{3(x-1)} v = \frac{2}{3} x$$

This is a linear differential equation.

Consider $\displaystyle\int \frac{2}{3(x-1)} \, dx = \frac{2}{3} \log(x-1) = \log(x-1)^{\frac{2}{3}}$

$$\therefore \quad I.F = (x-1)^{\frac{2}{3}}$$

$$\therefore \quad v(x-1)^{\frac{2}{3}} = \frac{2}{3} \int x(x-1)^{\frac{2}{3}} \, dx + k$$

Integrating R.H.S by parts, we have

$$= \frac{2}{3}\left[\frac{3}{5}x(x-1)^{\frac{5}{3}} - \frac{3}{5}\int (x-1)^{\frac{5}{3}}\,dx\right] + k$$

$\therefore$ we have

$$y^{\frac{2}{3}}(x-1)^{\frac{2}{3}} = \frac{2}{3}\left[\frac{3}{5}x(x-1)^{\frac{5}{3}} - \frac{9}{40}(x-1)^{\frac{8}{3}}\,dx\right] + k$$

EXERCISES

1. $\sin x\left(\dfrac{dy}{dx}\right) - y\cos x + y^2 = 0;$
$\qquad\qquad\left[Ans.\ u\sin x = A + x\right]$

2. $\dfrac{dy}{dx} + \dfrac{y}{x} = x^2 y^2;$
$\qquad\qquad\left[Ans.\ \left(\dfrac{1}{y}\right)\left(\dfrac{1}{x}\right) = A - \dfrac{x^2}{2}\right]$

3. $x\left(\dfrac{dy}{dx}\right) + y = x^2 y^2;$
$\qquad\qquad\left[Ans.\ u\cdot\dfrac{1}{x} = A - x\ \ or\ \ \dfrac{1}{yx} = A - x\right]$

4. $\left(\dfrac{dy}{dx}\right) + 2xy = 2x^3 y^3;$
$\qquad\qquad\left[Ans.\ 2e^t = y^2\left[2A - e^t(t-1),\ where\ t = -x^2\right]\right]$

5. $\dfrac{dy}{dx} + y\tan x = x^2 y^2;$
$\qquad\qquad\left[Ans.\ \left(\dfrac{1}{y}\right)\cos x = A - \left[\sin x\cdot(x^2 - 2) + 2x\cos x\right]\right]$

6. $x^2\left(\dfrac{dy}{dx}\right) + y^2 = xy\left(\dfrac{dy}{dx}\right);$
$\qquad\qquad\left[Ans.\ \left(\dfrac{1}{x}\right)y = A + \log y\right]$

[Hint : Interchange the role of x and y]

7. $x\left(\dfrac{dy}{dx}\right) + y = x^2 y^2 \sin x;$
$\qquad\qquad\left[Ans.\ \left(\dfrac{1}{xy}\right) = \left(\dfrac{u}{x}\right) = A + \cos x\right]$

8. $x\left(\dfrac{dy}{dx}\right) + y = x^3 y^6;$
$\qquad\qquad\left[Ans.\ \dfrac{1}{x^5 y^5} = A + \dfrac{5}{2}x^2;\ or\ 2 = x^3 y^5\left(2Ax^2 + 5\right)\right]$

9. $2\left(\dfrac{dy}{dx}\right) - y\sec x = y^3 \tan x;$ $\qquad \left[\,Ans. \;\; \left(\dfrac{1}{y^2}\right)(\sec x + \tan x) = A + x - \tan x - \sec x\,\right]$

10. $\dfrac{dy}{dx} + y\cot x = 5e^{\cos x}$, given $y = 4$, when $x = \dfrac{\pi}{2}$; $\qquad \left[\,Ans. \;\; \sec x = -Ay + y\tan x\,\right]$

11. $\dfrac{dy}{dx} + y\cot x = 5e^{\cos x}$, given $y = 4$, when $x = \dfrac{\pi}{2}$; $\qquad \left[\,Ans. \;\; y\sin x + 5e^{\cos x} = 1\,\right]$

12. $\dfrac{dy}{dx} + x(x+y) = x^3(x+y)^3 - 1;$ $\qquad \left[\,Ans. \;\; 1 = (1+x^2)(x+y)^2 + C(x+y)^2 e^{x^2}\,\right]$

Exact Equations

Let us suppose that we wish to solve the equation of the form

$$P(x, y)\,dx + Q(x, y)\,dy = 0. \qquad [1]$$

where P and Q are functions of x and y such that

$$\frac{\partial P}{\partial y} = \frac{\partial Q}{\partial x} \qquad [2]$$

Putting $F = F(x, y)$

$$= \int_{y \text{ constant}} P(x, y)\,dx \qquad [3]$$

Then, $\qquad \dfrac{\partial F}{\partial x} = P \qquad\qquad [4]$

and $\qquad \dfrac{\partial}{\partial y}\left(\dfrac{\partial F}{\partial x}\right) = \dfrac{\partial P}{\partial y} = \dfrac{\partial Q}{\partial x}\;$ using equation [2]

$\Rightarrow \qquad \dfrac{\partial}{\partial x}\left(\dfrac{\partial F}{\partial y} - Q\right) = 0$

$\Rightarrow \qquad \dfrac{\partial F}{\partial y} - Q = \varphi'(y),\ \text{(say)} \qquad\qquad [5]$

where $\varphi'(y)$ is a function of y.

Since $F = F(x,y)$, we have

$$\partial F = \frac{\partial F}{\partial x} dx + \frac{\partial F}{\partial y} dy$$

$$\Rightarrow \quad dF = Pdx + \left[Q + \varphi'(y) \right] dy$$

Using equation [4] and [5]

$$\Rightarrow \quad Pdx + Qdy = dF - \varphi'(y)dy = dF - d\varphi$$

$$= d(F - \varphi)$$

Hence [1] is called an exact differential equation, then the equation can be rewritten as $d(F - \varphi) = 0$

Integrating $F - \varphi = C$ [7]

is the required solution.

Working rule

1. Verify $\dfrac{\partial P}{\partial y} = \dfrac{\partial Q}{\partial x}$

2. Integrate P with respect to x treating y as constant.

3. Integrate with respect to y, those terms in Q which do not contain x.

4. Equate the sum of the results of [2] and [3] to a constant C, which is the required solution.

Symbolically the solution is given by

$$\int_{y \text{ constant}} Pdx + \int \left(\text{terms in } Q \text{ not containing } x \right) dy = \text{constant}$$

$$\therefore \quad \int_{y \text{ constant}} Pdx + \int \left(\text{terms in } Q \text{ not containing } x \right) dy = C$$

(F) EXAMPLES

1. Solve: $y^2 e^{xy^2} + 4x^3 dx + \left(2xye^{xy^2} - 3y^2 \right) dy = 0$

    Solution: In the given equation we have,

$$P = y^2 e^{xy^2} + 4x^3 dx$$

$$Q = 2xye^{xy^2} - 3y^2$$

Now, $\dfrac{\partial P}{\partial y} = y^2 e^{xy^2} \cdot 2xy + 2ye^{xy^2} = e^{xy^2}\left(xy^2 + 1\right)2y$

$$\dfrac{\partial Q}{\partial x} = 2xye^{xy^2} \cdot y^2 + 2ye^{xy^2} = e^{xy^2}\left(xy^2 + 1\right)2y$$

$\Rightarrow \quad \dfrac{\partial P}{\partial y} = \dfrac{\partial Q}{\partial x}$

The equation is exact.

Now consider $\displaystyle\int_{y\text{-constant}} P dx = \int \left(y^2 e^{xy^2} + 4x^3\right) dx = e^{xy^2} + x^4$

and $\displaystyle\int (\text{term of } Q \text{ independent of } x) dy = \int \left(-3y^2 dy\right) = -y^3$

$\therefore \qquad e^{xy^2} + x^4 - y^3 = C$

2. Solve: $3x(xy-2)dx + \left(x^3 + 2y\right)dy = 0$

Solution: In the given equation, we have

$$P = 3x(xy-2); \quad Q = x^3 + 2y$$

Now, $\dfrac{\partial P}{\partial y} = 3x^2 = \dfrac{\partial Q}{\partial x} \qquad \therefore$ the equation is exact.

Now, consider $\displaystyle\int_{y\text{-constant}} P dx = \int_{y\text{-constant}} \left(3x^2 y - 6x\right) dx$

$$= x^3 y - 3x^2$$

and $\displaystyle\int (\text{term in } Q \text{ not containing } x) \, dy = \int 2y dy = y^2$

$\therefore \qquad x^3 y - 3x^2 + y^2 = C$

3. Solve: $\left(x^2 + y^2 - a^2\right)x dx + \left(x^2 - y^2 - b^2\right)y dy = 0$

Solution: In the given equation, we have

$$P = x\left(x^2 + y^2 - a^2\right); \quad Q = y\left(x^2 - y^2 - b^2\right)$$

Now, $\dfrac{\partial P}{\partial y} = 2xy = \dfrac{\partial Q}{\partial x}$ $\quad \therefore$ the equation is exact.

Now, consider $\displaystyle\int_{y\text{-constant}} P\,dx = \int_{y\text{-constant}} \left(x^3 + xy^2 - a^2 x\right) dx$

$$= \frac{x^4}{4} + \left(y^2 - a^2\right)\frac{x^2}{2}$$

and $\displaystyle\int (\text{terms in } Q \text{ not containing } x)\,dy$

$$= \int \left(-y^3 - b^2 y\right) dy = -\frac{y^4}{4} - b^2 \frac{y^2}{2}$$

$\therefore \qquad \dfrac{x^2}{4} + \left(y^2 - a^2\right)\dfrac{x^2}{2} - \dfrac{y^4}{4} - b^2 \dfrac{y^2}{2} = C$

or $\qquad x^4 + 2x^2\left(y^2 - a^2\right) - y^4 - 2b^2 y^2 = 2C$

4. **Solve:** $\left[y\left(1 + \dfrac{1}{x}\right) + \cos y\right] dx + \left[x + \log x - x\sin y\right] dy = 0$

Solution: In the given equation

$$P = y\left(1 + \frac{1}{x}\right) + \cos y; \quad Q = x + \log x - x\sin y$$

Now, $\dfrac{\partial P}{\partial y} = 1 + \dfrac{1}{x} - \sin y$

and $\dfrac{\partial Q}{\partial x} = 1 + \dfrac{1}{x} - \sin y$

$\therefore \qquad \dfrac{\partial P}{\partial y} = \dfrac{\partial Q}{\partial x}$

The given equation is exact.

Now, $\displaystyle\int_{y\text{-constant}} P\,dx = \int \left[y\left(1 + \frac{1}{x}\right) + \cos y\right] dx$

$$= y[x + \log x] + x\cos y$$

No term of Q is independent of x.

$\therefore \qquad y\left(x + \log x\right) + x\cos y = C$

5. Solve: $xdx + ydy = \dfrac{a^2(xdy - ydx)}{x^2 + y^2}$

Solution: Given, $xdx + ydy = \dfrac{a^2(xdy - ydx)}{x^2 + y^2}$

$\Rightarrow \quad \left[x + \dfrac{a^2 y}{x^2 + y^2}\right]dx + \left[y - \dfrac{a^2 x}{x^2 + y^2}\right]dy = 0$

$\therefore \quad P = \left[x + \dfrac{a^2 y}{x^2 + y^2}\right]; \ Q = \left[y - \dfrac{a^2 x}{x^2 + y^2}\right]$

$\therefore \quad \dfrac{\partial P}{\partial x} = \dfrac{(x^2 + a^2)a^2 - a^2 y(2y)}{(x^2 + y^2)^2} = \dfrac{a^2(x^2 - y^2)}{(x^2 + y^2)^2}$

$\dfrac{\partial Q}{\partial x} = \dfrac{-a^2(x^2 + y^2) + a^2 x(2x)}{(x^2 + y^2)^2} = \dfrac{a^2(x^2 - y^2)}{(x^2 + y^2)^2}$

$\Rightarrow \quad \dfrac{\partial P}{\partial y} = \dfrac{\partial Q}{\partial x}$

The given equation is exact.

$$\int_{y-\text{constant}} Pdx + \int (\text{those terms in } Q \text{ not containing } x)dy = C$$

$\Rightarrow \quad \int_{y-\text{constant}} \left[\left(x + \dfrac{a^2 y}{x^2 + y^2}\right)\right]dx + \int ydy = C$

$\Rightarrow \quad \dfrac{x^2}{2} + a^2 y \dfrac{1}{y}\tan^{-1}\left(\dfrac{x}{y}\right) + \dfrac{y^2}{2} = C$

$\therefore \quad \dfrac{x^2}{2} + a^2 \tan^{-1}\left(\dfrac{x}{y}\right) + \dfrac{y^2}{2} = C$

6. Solve: $(ax + hy + g)dx + (hx + by + f)dy = 0$

Solution: $P = (ax + hy + g); \ Q = (hx + by + f)$

$\dfrac{\partial P}{\partial y} = h; \ \dfrac{\partial Q}{\partial x} = h$

$\Rightarrow \quad \dfrac{\partial P}{\partial y} = \dfrac{\partial Q}{\partial x}$

The given equation is exact.

Hence, the solution is given by

$$\int_{y-\text{constant}} P\,dx + \int (\text{those terms in } Q \text{ not containing } x)\,dy = C$$

$$\Rightarrow \quad \int_{y-\text{constant}} (ax + hy + g)\,dx + \int (by + f)\,dy = \text{constant}$$

$$\Rightarrow \quad \frac{ax^2}{2} + hyx + gx + \frac{by^2}{2} + fy = \text{constant}$$

$$\Rightarrow \quad ax^2 + 2hxy + by^2 + 2gx + 2fy + c = 0$$

7. Solve: $x(x^2 + 3y^2)\,dx + y(y^2 + 3x^2)\,dy = 0$

Solution: $P = x(x^2 + 3y^2) = x^3 + 3xy^2; \left(\dfrac{\partial P}{\partial y}\right) = 6xy$

$$Q = y(y^2 + 3x^2) = y^3 + 3x^2 y; \left(\dfrac{\partial Q}{\partial x}\right) = 6xy$$

$$\Rightarrow \quad \left(\frac{\partial P}{\partial y}\right) = \left(\frac{\partial Q}{\partial x}\right)$$

The given equation is exact.

$$\therefore \quad \int P\,dx + \int Q\,dy = \text{constant}$$

$$\Rightarrow \quad \int_{y-\text{constant}} (x^3 + 3xy^2)\,dx$$

$$\int (\text{those terms in } Q \text{ not containing } x)\,dy = \text{constant}$$

$$= \int_{y-\text{constant}} (x^3 + 3xy^2)\,dx + \int y^3\,dy = \text{constant}$$

$$= \left(\frac{x^4}{4}\right) + 3y^2\left(\frac{x^2}{2}\right) + \left(\frac{y^4}{4}\right) = \text{constant}$$

$$\Rightarrow \quad (x^4 + 6x^2 y^2 + y^4) = C \text{ is the required solution.}$$

8. Solve: $(a^2 - 2xy - y^2)\,dx = (x + y)^2\,dy$

Solution: $P = (a^2 - 2xy - y^2); \left(\dfrac{\partial P}{\partial y}\right) = (-2x - 2y)$

$$Q = \left(-x^2 - 2xy - y^2\right); \left(\frac{\partial Q}{\partial x}\right) = \left(-2x - 2y\right)$$

The equation is exact

The solution is

$$\int_{y-\text{constant}} \left(a^2 - 2xy - y^2\right) dx - \int \left(0 + 0 + y^2\right) dy = \text{constant}$$

$$a^2x - x^2y - xy^2 - \left(\frac{y^3}{3}\right) = \text{constant}.$$

$$\left(3a^2x - 3x^2y - 3xy^2 - y^3\right) = \text{constant}$$

EXERCISES

Solve the following differential equations:

1. $\left(3x^2 + 8xy\right)dx + \left(4x^2 - 24y^3\right)dy = 0;$

$$\left[Ans. \ x^3 + 3xy + y^2 = C\right]$$

2. $3\left(x^2 + y\right)dx + \left(3x + 2y\right)dy = 0;$

$$\left[Ans. \ x^3 + 3xy + y^2 = C\right]$$

3. $\left(3x^2 + 2xy^2\right)dx + \left(3y^2 + 2x^2y\right)dy = 0;$

$$\left[Ans. \ \left(x^3 + x^2y^2 + y^3\right) = C\right]$$

4. $\left(x^2 - 2xy - y^2\right)dx = \left(x + y\right)^2 dy;$

$$\left[Ans. \ \left(x^3 - 3x^2y - 3xy^2 - y^3\right) = C\right]$$

5. $\left[x^4 - 2xy^2 + y^4\right]dx + \left[4xy^3 - 2x^2y - \sin y\right]dy = 0;$

$$\left[Ans. \ \left(x^5 - 5x^2y^2 + 5xy^4 + 5\cos y\right) = \text{constant}\right]$$

6. $\left(x + 2\sin y + 3\right)dx + \left(2x - 4\sin y - 3\right)\cos y \, dy = 0;$

$$\left[Ans. \ \left(\frac{x^2}{2}\right) + 2x\sin y + 3x - 2\sin^2 y - 3\sin y = C\right]$$

7. $\left(\sin x \cos y + e^{2x}\right) dx + \left(\cos x \sin y + \tan y\right) dy = 0;$

$$\left[Ans. \ \left(-\cos x \cos y + \left(\frac{1}{2}\right) e^{2x} + \log \sec y\right) = \text{constant} \right]$$

8. $\cos x \left(\cos x - \sin a \sin y\right) dx + \cos y \left(\cos y - \sin a \sin x\right) dy = x;$

$$\left[Ans. \ \left(2x + \sin 2x - 4\sin a \sin x \sin y + 2y + \sin 2y\right) = C \right]$$

9. $\left(2xy + y - \tan y\right) dx + \left(x^2 - x \tan^2 y + \sec^2 y\right) dy = 0;$

$$\left[Ans. \ xy(x+1) + \tan y(1-x) = C \right]$$

10. $\left(3x + 4y - 7\right) dx + 4\left(x + y - 2\right) dy = 0$ given $y = 3,$ when $x = 2;$

$$\left[Ans. \ 3x^2 + 8xy + 4y^2 - 14x - 16y = 20 \right]$$

11. $\left(2y \sin x + \cos y\right) dx - \left(x \sin y + 2\cos x + \tan y\right) dy = 0;$

$$\left[Ans. \ x \cos y - 2y \cos x - \log \sec y = C \right]$$

12. $\dfrac{dy}{dx} = \dfrac{\cos x - 3x^2 \tan y}{x^3 \sec^2 y};$

$$\left[Ans. \ x^3 \tan y - \sin x = C \right]$$

Equations Reducible to Exact Equations

We consider some differential equations of the form : $Pdx + Qdy = 0$ that are not exact but can be made exact by means of integrating factors (which can be obtained by multiplying the equation by appropriate functions of x and y).

(1) Integration factors using certain rules

    (a) If P and Q are homogeneous functions of the same degree and $Px + Qy \neq 0,$

    then $\dfrac{1}{Px + Qy}$ is an integrating factor.

    (b) If $\dfrac{1}{Q}\left(\dfrac{\partial P}{\partial y} - \dfrac{\partial Q}{\partial x}\right)$ is a function of x alone, say $f(x),$ then $e^{\int f(x) dx}$ dx is an integrating factor.

    (c) If $\dfrac{1}{P}\left(\dfrac{\partial Q}{\partial x} - \dfrac{\partial P}{\partial y}\right)$ is a function of y alone, say $g(y),$ then $e^{\int g(y) dy}$ is an integrating factor.

(d) If the equation is of the form $f_1(x, y)ydx + f_2(x, y)xdy = 0$, so that

$P = yf_1(x, y)$ and $Q = xf_2(x, y)$, and if $Px - Qy \neq 0$, then $\dfrac{1}{Px - Qy}$ is an integrating factor.

(e) If the equation is of the form $x^m y^n (aydx + bxdy) + x^p y^q (cydx + exdy) = 0$

where m, n, p, q, a, b, c, e are all constants, then $x^h y^k$ is an integrating factor. Here h and k are constants to be chosen so that the condition for exactness is satisfied.

(2) Integrating factors by inspection:

Many differential equation which can be made exact by means of integrating factors, can be determined by inspection. The following exact differentials are useful:

(a) $d(xy) = xdy + ydx$

(b) $d\left(\dfrac{x}{y}\right) = \dfrac{xdy - xdy}{y^2}$

(c) $d\left(\dfrac{x}{y}\right) = \dfrac{xdy - ydx}{x^2}$

(d) $d\left(\tan^{-1}\dfrac{y}{x}\right) = \dfrac{xdy - ydx}{x^2 + y^2}$

(e) $d\left(\tan^{-1}\dfrac{x}{y}\right) = \dfrac{ydx - xdy}{x^2 + y^2}$

(f) $d\left(\log\dfrac{x}{y}\right) = \dfrac{ydx - xdy}{xy}$

(g) $d\left(\log\dfrac{x}{y}\right) = \dfrac{xdy - ydx}{xy}$

(h) $d\left(\dfrac{e^x}{y}\right) = \dfrac{e^x(ydx - dy)}{y^2}$

(i) $d[\log(x^2 + y^2)] = \dfrac{2xdx + 2ydy}{x^2 + y^2}$

(j) $d\left(\dfrac{-1}{xy}\right) = \dfrac{ydx + xdy}{(xy)^2}$

(G) EXAMPLES

1. Solve: $x^2 ydx - (x^3 + y^3)dy = 0$

   Solution: Given, $x^2 ydx - (x^2 ydx - (x^3 + y^3)dy = 0$

   The given equation is homogeneous, $P = x^2 y$;

   $Q = -x^3 - y^3$

   $\therefore \quad \dfrac{\cdot \partial P}{\partial y} = x^2;$

$$\frac{\partial Q}{\partial x} = -3x^2$$

$$\Rightarrow \quad \frac{\partial P}{\partial y} \neq \frac{\partial Q}{\partial x}$$

$\therefore$ the equation is not exact.

Now, $Px + Qy = (x^2 y)x - (x^3 + y^3)y$

$$= x^3 y - x^3 y - y^4 = -y^4 \neq 0$$

$\therefore \quad \dfrac{1}{Px + Qy} = -\dfrac{1}{y^4}$ is an integrating factor of the equation [using Rule (1)]

Multiplying the given equation by $\dfrac{-1}{y^4}$

$$\therefore \quad \frac{-x^2}{y^3} dx + \left(\frac{x^3}{y^4} + \frac{1}{y} \right) dy = 0$$

Now, $\dfrac{\partial P}{\partial y} = \dfrac{3x^2}{y^4}; \quad \dfrac{\partial Q}{\partial x} = \dfrac{3x^2}{y^4} \Rightarrow \dfrac{\partial P}{\partial y} = \dfrac{\partial Q}{\partial x}$

The equation is exact

$$\therefore \quad \int_{y\ \text{constant}} \frac{-x^2}{y^3} dx + \int \frac{1}{y} dy = \text{constant}$$

$$\frac{-x^3}{3y^3} + \log y = c$$

2. Solve: $(x^2 + y^3 + 6x)dx + y^2 x dy = 0$

Solution: Given, $(x^2 + y^3 + 6x)dx + y^2 x dy = 0$

It is of the form: $Pdx + Qdy = 0$,

With $P = x^2 + y^3 + 6x, \quad Q = y^2 x;$

We find: $\dfrac{\partial P}{\partial y} - \dfrac{\partial Q}{\partial x} = 3y^2 - y^2 = 2y^2 \neq 0$

$\therefore$ the equation is not exact.

Now, $\dfrac{1}{Q}\left(\dfrac{\partial P}{\partial y}-\dfrac{\partial Q}{\partial x}\right)=\dfrac{2y^2}{y^2 x}=\dfrac{2}{x}=f(x)$ say.

$\therefore$ An integrating factor for the given equation by rule (2) is:

$$e^{\int f(x)dx}=e^{\int(2/x)dx}=e^{2\log x}=x^2$$

Multiplying the equation by this factor, we get the exact equation.

$$(x^4+x^2 y^3+6x^3)dx+y^2 x^3 dy=0$$

Hence, the solution is given by:

$$\int_{y\ \text{constant}}(x^4+x^2 y^3+6x^3)dx+6\int x^3 dx=c,$$

$$\Rightarrow\quad \dfrac{x^5}{5}+\dfrac{y^3 x^3}{3}+\dfrac{6x^4}{4}=c$$

$$\Rightarrow\quad 6x^5+10x^3 y^3+45x^4=30c.$$

3. Solve: $(y^4+2y)dx+(xy^3+2y^4-4x)dy=0$.

Solution: It is of the form: $Pdx+Qdy=0$

With $P=(y^4+2y):Q=(xy^3+2y^4-4x)$

We find $\left(\dfrac{\partial P}{\partial y}-\dfrac{\partial Q}{\partial x}\right)=4y^3+2-(y^3-4)$

$$=3(y^3+2)\neq 0$$

$\Rightarrow$ The given equation is not exact.

Now, $\dfrac{1}{P}\left(\dfrac{\partial Q}{\partial X}-\dfrac{\partial P}{\partial Y}\right)=-\dfrac{3(y^3+2)}{y^4+2y}=-\dfrac{3}{y}=g(y)$

$\therefore$ By rule (3), an integrating factor for the the given equation is

$$e^{\int g(y)dy}=e^{\int\left(\frac{-3}{y}\right)dy}=\dfrac{1}{y^3}$$

Multiplying the equation by the integrating factor, we get the equation

$$\left[y+\dfrac{2}{y^2}\right]dx+\left[x+2y-4\dfrac{x}{y^3}\right]dy=0$$

or $\quad\left[y+\dfrac{2}{y^2}\right]x+y^2=c$

4. Solve: $(xy^2 + 2x^2y^3)dx + (x^2y - x^3y^2)dy = 0$

Solution: Given, $(xy + 2x^2y^2)ydx + (xy - x^2y^2)xdy = 0$

It is of the form: $f_1(xy)ydx + f_2(xy)xdy = 0$.

Now, $Px - Qy = x^2y^2 + 2x^3y^3 - x^2y^2 + x^3y + 3x^3y^3 \neq 0$.

$\therefore$ By rule [4], $\dfrac{1}{Px - Qy} = \dfrac{1}{3x^3y^3}$ is an integrating factor of the equation.

$\therefore$ $\left(\dfrac{1}{3x^3y} + \dfrac{2}{3x}\right)dx + \left(\dfrac{1}{3xy^2} - \dfrac{1}{3y}\right)dy = 0$

$\dfrac{\partial P}{\partial Y} = \dfrac{-1}{3x^2y^2}; \quad \dfrac{\partial Q}{\partial x} = \dfrac{-1}{3x^2y^2}$

$\Rightarrow$ $\dfrac{\partial P}{\partial Y} = \dfrac{\partial Q}{\partial x} \Rightarrow$ The equation is exact.

$\therefore$ $\displaystyle\int\left[\dfrac{1}{3x^2y} - + \dfrac{2}{3x}dx\right] - \int\dfrac{1}{3y}dy = c$

$\Rightarrow$ $\dfrac{1}{3y}\left(\dfrac{-1}{x}\right) + \dfrac{2}{3}\log x - \dfrac{1}{3}\log y = c.$

5. Solve: $(y^2 + 2x^2y)dx + (2x^3 - xy)dy = 0$.

Solution: We may write the given equation as:

$$y(ydx - xdy) + 2x^2(ydx + xdy) = 0 \qquad [1]$$

Now, by rule (5), x^hy^k is an integrating factor, where h and k are constants to be determined.

Multiplying the equation by this factor, we get

$$x^hy^k(y^2 + 2x^2y)dx + x^hy^k(2x^3 - xy)dy = 0 \qquad [2]$$

Now, $P = x^hy^{k+2} + 2x^{h+2}y^{k+1}$,

$Q = 2x^{h+3}y^k - x^{h+1}y^{k+1}$

$\therefore$ $\dfrac{\partial P}{\partial y} = (k+2)x^hy^{k+1} + 2(k+1)x^{h+2}y^k$

$\dfrac{\partial Q}{\partial x} = 2(h+3)x^{h+2}y^k - (h+1)x^hy^{k+1}$

∴ For the equation [2], the condition

$$\frac{\partial P}{\partial y} = \frac{\partial Q}{\partial x} \text{ must hold}$$

if $(k+2) y + 2 (k+1) x^2 = 2(h+3)x^2 - (h+1)y,$

⇒ $k+2 = -(h+1); \quad k+1 = h+3,$

⇒ $h+k+3 = 0; \quad h-k+2 = 0.$

(Obtained on equating the corresponding coefficients)

Solving for h and k, we get

$$\left. \begin{aligned} h &= -\frac{5}{2}; \\ k &= -\frac{1}{2}; \end{aligned} \right\}$$

For these values of $h = -\dfrac{5}{2}$ and $k = \dfrac{-1}{2}$, the equation [2] is exact. Substituting these values of h and k into [2], we get the equation

$$\left(x^{\frac{-5}{2}} y^{\frac{3}{2}} + 2x^{\frac{-1}{2}} y^{\frac{1}{2}} \right) dx + \left(2x^{\frac{1}{2}} y^{\frac{-1}{2}} - x^{\frac{-3}{2}} y^{\frac{1}{2}} \right) dy = 0$$

∴ the solution of the exact equation is: $6x^{\frac{1}{2}}y^{\frac{1}{2}} - x^{\frac{-3}{2}} y^{\frac{3}{2}} = c$

6.   Solve: $(3xy + 8y^5)dx + (2x^2 + 24xy^4)dy = 0$

Solution: The equation can be written as

$$x(3ydx + 2xdy) + 8y^4 (ydx + 3xdy) = 0 \qquad [1]$$

This is of the form: $x^m y^n (aydx + bx\ dy) + x^p y^q (cydx + exdy) = 0$

Now, by rule (5), $x^h y^k$ be the integrating factor, where h and k are constants to be determined.

Multiplying the equation by $x^h y^k$, we get

∴ $(3x^{h+1}g^{k+1} + 8x^h y^{k+5})dx + (2x^{h+2}y^k + 24x^{h+1}y^{k+h})dy = 0$

If this is exact, $\dfrac{\partial P}{\partial y} = \dfrac{\partial Q}{\partial x}$

∴ $3x^{h+1}(k+1)y^k + 8x^h(k+5)y^{k+4} = 2(h+2)x^{h+1}y^k + 24(h+1)x^h y^{k+h}$

∴ $3(k+1) = 2(h+2) \Rightarrow 2h - 3k = -1$

$$8(k+5) = 24(h+1) \Rightarrow 3h - k = 2$$

Solving for (h, k) we get, $h = 1$; $k = 1$

Substituting these values, we get

$$(3x^2 y^2 + 8xy^6)dx + (2x^3 y + 24x^2 y^5)dy = 0$$

This is an exact equation.

$\therefore$ the solution is: $\displaystyle\int_{y \text{ constant}} (3x^2 y^2 + 8xy^6)dx = c$

$\Rightarrow \qquad x^3 y^2 + 4x^2 y^6 = c$

7. Solve: $ydx - xdy + (x^2 + 1)dx + x^2 \sin y \, dy = 0$

Solution: Given $(ydx - xdy) + (x^2 + 1)dx + x^2 \sin y \, dy = 0$

Dividing by x^2 or multiplying by $\left(\dfrac{1}{x^2}\right)$.

$\therefore \qquad \dfrac{ydx - xdy}{x^2} + \dfrac{(x^2 + 1)}{x^2}dx + \dfrac{x^2 \sin y}{x^2}dy = 0$

$\Rightarrow \qquad \left(1 + \dfrac{1}{x^2}\right)dx + \sin y dy - \dfrac{(xdy - ydx)}{x^2} = 0$

Each of the group is a differential.

$\therefore \qquad \displaystyle\int\left(1 + \dfrac{1}{x^2}\right)dx + \int \sin y dy - \int d\left(\dfrac{y}{x}\right) = c$

$\Rightarrow \qquad \left[x - \left(\dfrac{1}{x}\right)\right] - \cos y - \left(\dfrac{y}{x}\right) = c$

or $\qquad (x^2 - 1) - x \cos y - y = cx$

8. Solve: $[(1 + y \tan (xy)]dx + [x \tan (xy)]dy = 0$

Solution: Given, $[1 + y \tan (xy)]dx + [x \tan (xy)]dy = 0$

$\Rightarrow \qquad dx + \tan(xy)[ydx + xdy] = 0$

$\Rightarrow \qquad dx + \tan(xy)d(xy) = 0$

Integrating we get, $\displaystyle\int dx + \int \tan(xy)d(xy) = c; \; (xy = t)$

$\Rightarrow \qquad x + \log \sec(xy) = c$

$\because \qquad \int \tan t\, dt = \log(\sec t)$

$\therefore \qquad x + \log \sec(xy) = c$

9. Solve: $xdx = y(x^2 + y^2 - 1)dy$

   Solution: Given, $xdx = y(x^2 + y^2 - 1)dy$

   $\Rightarrow \qquad xdx + ydy = y(x^2 + y^2)dy$

   $\Rightarrow \qquad \dfrac{xdx + ydy}{x^2 + y^2} = ydy$

   or $\qquad d\left[\dfrac{1}{2}\log(x^2 + y^2)\right] = ydy$

   Integrating we get,

   $$\frac{1}{2}\log(x^2 + y^2) = \frac{y^2}{2} + c$$

   $\Rightarrow \qquad \log(x^2 + y^2) - y^2 = A$ is the solution (where $A = 2c$)

10. Solve: $xdx + ydy + \dfrac{xdy - ydx}{x^2 + y^2} = 0$

    Solution: Given, $xdx + ydy + d\left[\tan^{-1}\left(\dfrac{y}{x}\right)\right] = 0$

    Integrating we have, $\dfrac{x^2}{2} + \dfrac{y^2}{2} + \tan^{-1}\left(\dfrac{y}{x}\right) = A$

11. Solve: $\dfrac{ydx - xdy}{y^2} + (xdy + ydy) = 0$

    Solution: Given, $d\left(\dfrac{x}{y}\right) + xdx + ydy = 0$

    Integrating, $\dfrac{x}{y} + \dfrac{x^2}{2} + \dfrac{y^2}{2} = A$ or $\dfrac{x}{y} + \dfrac{1}{2}(x^2 + y^2) = A$

12. Solve: $(y - 2x^3)dx - x(1 - xy)dy = 0$

Solution: Given $ydx - xdy - 2x^3dx + x^2ydx = 0$

Divide by x^2 we get

$$\frac{-(xdy - ydn)}{x^2} - 2xdx + ydy = 0$$

$$\Rightarrow \quad -d\left(\frac{y}{x}\right) - 2x \cdot dx + ydy = 0$$

Integrating $\dfrac{-y}{x} - x^2 + \dfrac{y^2}{2} = c$

13. Solve: $ye^x dx - e^x dy + y^4 dy = 0$

Solution: Given $ye^x\, dx - e^x dy + y^4\, dy = 0$

Dividing by y^2 we get

$$\frac{e^x}{y}dx - \frac{e^x}{y^2}dy + y^2 dy = 0$$

or $\quad \dfrac{e^x(ydx - dy)}{y^2} + y^2 dy = 0$

$$d\frac{(e^x)}{y} + y^2 dy = 0$$

Integrating we get the solution as: $\dfrac{e^x}{y} + \dfrac{y^3}{3} = c$

14. Solve: $(1 + xy)ydx + (1 - xy)xdy = 0$

Solution: $ydx + xdy + xy^2 dx - x^2 ydy = 0$

Dividing by $x^2 y^2$ we get

$$\frac{ydx + xdy}{x^2 y^2} + \frac{1}{x}dx - \frac{1}{y}dy = 0$$

i.e., $\quad \dfrac{ydx + xdy}{(xy)^2} + \dfrac{1}{x}dx - \dfrac{1}{y}dy = 0$

i.e., $\quad d\left(\dfrac{-1}{xy}\right)+\dfrac{1}{x}dx-\dfrac{1}{y}dy=0$

Integrating we get, $\dfrac{-1}{xy}+\log x-\log y=c$

15. Solve: $(y^2e^x+2xy)dx-x^2dy=0$

Solution: Given $y^2e^xdx+2xy\,dx-x^2dy=0$

Dividing by y^2 we get,

$$e^x dx+\dfrac{2xydx-x^2dy}{y^2}=0$$

i.e., $\quad e^x dx+d\left(\dfrac{x^2}{y}\right)=0$

Integrating we get, $e^x+\dfrac{x^2}{y}=c$

16. Solve: $(x^2+y^2+x)dx-(2x^2+2y^2-y)dy=0$

Solution: Given $(x^2+y^2)(dx-2dy)+xdx+ydy=0$

Dividing by $\left(\dfrac{2}{x^2+y^2}\right)$;

$$2(dx-2dy)+\dfrac{2xdx+2ydy}{x^2+y^2}=0$$

i.e., $\quad 2dx-4dy+d[\log(x^2+y^2)]=0$

Integrating we get, $2x-4y+\log(x^2+y^2)=c$

17. Solve: $ye^{\frac{x}{y}}dx=(xe^{\frac{x}{y}}+y^2)dy$

Solution: Given $e^{\frac{x}{y}}(ydx-xdy)=y^2dy$

$\Rightarrow \quad e^{\frac{x}{y}}\left[\dfrac{ydx-xdy}{y^2}\right]=dy$

$$\Rightarrow \quad e^{\frac{x}{y}} d\left(\frac{x}{y}\right) = dy$$

Integration, yields $e^{\frac{x}{y}} = y + c;$

$$\left(\because \int e^t dt = e^t\right)$$

$$\Rightarrow \quad e^{\frac{x}{y}} - y = A$$

EXERCISES - I

Solve the following differential equations:

1. $(4xy + 3y^2 - x)dx + x(x + 2y)dy = 0;$ $\qquad \left[Ans. \ x^4 y + x^3 y^2 - \dfrac{x^4}{4} = A\right]$

2. $y(2x - y + 1)dx + x(3x - 4y + 3)dy = 0;$ $\qquad \left[Ans. \ x^2 y^3 - xy^4 + xy^3 = A\right]$

3. $y(2xy + 1)dx - xdy = 0;$ $\qquad \left[Ans. \ x^2 + \dfrac{x}{y} = A\right]$

4. $(xy + y^2)dx + (x + 2y - 1)dy = 0;$ $\qquad \left[Ans. \ e^x(xy + y^2 - y) = A\right]$

5. $(xy \sin xy + \cos xy)ydx + (xy \sin xy - \cos xy)xdy = 0;$ $\qquad \left[Ans. \ x \sec xy = Ay\right]$

6. $(xy^3 + y)dx + 2(x^2 y^2 + x + y4)dy = 0;$ $\qquad \left[Ans. \ 3x^2 y^4 + 6xy^2 + 2y^6 = c\right]$

7. $(1 + xy)y \, dx + (1 - xy)xdy = 0;$ $\qquad \left[Ans. \ \log\left(\dfrac{x}{y}\right) - \left(\dfrac{1}{xy}\right) = c\right]$

8. $y(xy + 2x^2 y^2)dx + x(xy - x^2 y^2)dy = 0;$ $\qquad \left(\dfrac{1}{xy}\right) = ct \log\left(\dfrac{x^2}{y}\right)$

9. $xdy - ydx + a(x^2 + y^2)dx = 0;$ $\qquad \left[Ans. \ ax + \tan^{-1}\left(\dfrac{y}{x}\right) = c\right]$

10. $(y^2 + 2x^2 y)dx + (3x^3 - xy)dy = 0;$

$$\left[Ans.\ \ 6\sqrt{xy} - \sqrt{\frac{y^3}{x^3}} = A \right]$$

11. $x(3ydx + 2xdy) + 8y^4(ydx + 3xdy) = 0;$

$$\left[Ans.\ \ x^3 y^2 + 4x^2 y^6 = A \right]$$

12. $x(4ydx + 2xdy) + y^3(3ydx + 5xdy) = 0;$

$$\left[Ans.\ \ x^4 y^2 + x^3 y^5 = A \right]$$

EXERCISES - II

Solve the following differential equations:

1. $(\cos 2y - 3x^2 y^2)\ dx + (\cos 2y - 2x \sin zy - 2x^3 y)\ dy = 0;$

$$\left[Ans.\ \ \frac{\sin 2y}{2} + \cos 2y - x^3 y^2 = c \right]$$

2. $\cos x(e^y + 1)dx + \sin x e^y dy = 0;$

$$\left[Ans.\ \ \sin x(e^y + 1) = c \right]$$

3. $xdy - ydx = \cos^2\left[\frac{y}{x}\right]dx;$

$$\left[Ans.\ \ \tan\left(\frac{y}{x}\right) + \frac{1}{x} \right]$$

4. $(3x^2 y^4 + 2xy)dx + (2x^3 y^3 - x^2)dy = 0;$

$$\left[Ans.\ \ x^3 y^3 + x^2 = y \right]$$

5. $[4x^3 y^2 + y\cos(xy)]dx + [2x^4 y + x\cos(xy)]dy = 0;$

$$\left[Ans.\ \ x^4 y^2 + \sin(xy) = c \right]$$

2

POWER SERIES SOLUTIONS OF DIFFERENTIAL EQUATIONS

Introduction

In Chapter 1, we have seen the solutions of ordinary differential equations which can be termed as closed form solutions.

Many differential equations arising from physical problems may be linear but it may not be possible to obtain their general solution in some particular form involving known functions, with the help of methods available to solve linear differential equations. In such cases we try to obtain the value of the dependent variable by methods of approximation. One method of approximation which is usually used is to find the solution in the form of an infinite convergent series and the method is outlined below:

The solutions of the differential equations $y'' - y = 0$ are

$$y = e^x = 1 + \frac{x}{1!} + \frac{x^2}{2!} + \frac{x^3}{3!} + ...$$

and

$$y = e^{-x} = 1 - \frac{x}{1!} + \frac{x^2}{2!} + \frac{x^3}{3!} + ...$$

These are Power Series solutions of the differential equation $y'' + y = 0$

$$y = \sin x = x - \frac{x^3}{3!} + \frac{x^5}{5!} + \frac{x^7}{7!} + ...$$

$$y = \cos x = 1 - \frac{x^2}{2!} + \frac{x^4}{4!} + \frac{x^6}{6!} + ...$$

In this Chapter, we will solve the differential equations of the first and the second order, namely

$$p_0(x)\frac{dy}{dx} + p_1(x)y = q(x) \qquad\qquad [1]$$

$$p_0(x)\frac{d^2y}{dx^2} + p_1(x)\frac{dy}{dx} + p_2(x)y = 0 \qquad [2]$$

or $$\frac{d^2y}{dx^2} + q_1(x)\frac{dy}{dx} + q_2(x)y = 0 \qquad [3]$$

where $$q_1(x) = \frac{p_1(x)}{p_0(y)} \text{ and } q_2(x) = \frac{p_2(x)}{p_0(x)}$$

Consider $$p_0(x)\frac{d^2y}{dx^2} + p_1(x)\frac{dy}{dx} + p_2(x)y = 0$$

such that $p_0(0) \neq 0$ and all p's are polynomials in x.

Let $y = a_0 + a_1x + a_2x^2 + ... + a_nx^n + ...$ [2] be a solution of [1]. Then substituting [2] in [1] we obtain the coefficients $a_2, a_3, a_4, ...$ in terms of a_0 and a_1 where a_0 and a_1 are arbitrary constants. If the equation is of the form

$$p_0(x)\frac{dy}{dx} + p_1(x)y = q(x). \qquad \text{(i.e. first order)}$$

then we have to obtain the coefficients $a_1, a_2, a_3, ...$ in terms of a_0. This procedure is illustrated in the examples which follow the working rule.

The Power Series Method

Working Rule

Step (1): Let $y = \displaystyle\sum_{n=0}^{\infty} a_n x^n$

$= a_0 + a_1x + a_2x^2 + ...$ be the solution of the given differential equation.

Step (2): Find y', y'', y''' etc.

Step (3): Substitute the values of y, y', y'' etc. in the given differential equation.

Step (4): Calculate $a_0, a_1, a_2, ...$, coefficients of various power of x by equating the coefficients to zero.

Step (5): Substitute the values of $a_0, a_1, a_2, ...$ in y to get the desired series solution.

1. Solve: $y' - y = 0$ using Power Series method.

   Solution: Given, $y' - y = 0 ...$ \qquad [1]

   Let us assume a solution of the form

$$y = a_0 + a_1 x + a_2 x^2 + \ldots$$

or, $\qquad y = \sum_{n=0}^{\infty} a_n x^n$ [2]

Substituting [2] into equation [1], we get

$$\left(a_1 + 2a_2 x + 3a_3 x^2 + \ldots\right) - \left(a_0 + a_1 x + \ldots\right) = 0$$

$$\Rightarrow \quad \left(a_1 - a_0\right) + \left(2a_2 - a_1\right)x + \left(3a_3 - a_2\right)x^2 + \ldots = 0$$

Equating to zero, the coefficients of each power of x, we get,

$$a_1 - a_0 = 0; \quad 2a_2 - a_1 = 0; \quad 3a_3 - a_2 = 0;$$

On solving, we find $a_1 = a_0; \quad a_2 = \dfrac{a_1}{2} = \dfrac{a_0}{2!}$

$$a_3 = \frac{a_2}{3} = \frac{a_0}{3!} \ldots$$

With these values, [2] becomes

$$y = a_0 + a_0 x + \frac{a_0}{2!} x^2 + \frac{a_0}{3!} x^3 + \ldots$$

or $\qquad y = a_0 \left(1 + x + \frac{x^2}{2!} + \frac{x^3}{3!} + \ldots \right)$

$$= a_0 e^x$$

2. Solve: $\dfrac{dy}{dx} = 2xy$ using Power Series method.

Solution: Given, $y' = 2xy$ [1]

Let us assume a solution of the form;

$$y = a_0 + a_1 x + \ldots + \ldots$$

$$= \sum_{n=0}^{\infty} a_n x^n$$ [2]

Substituting [2] into equation [1], we have

$$a_1 + 2a_2 x + 3a_3 x^2 + 4a_4 x^3 + 5a_5 x^4 + 6a_6 x^5 + \ldots$$

$$= 2a_0 x + 2a_1 x^2 + 2a_2 x^3 + 2a_3 x^4 + 2a_4 x^5 + \ldots$$

$$\Rightarrow \quad a_1 = 0$$

$\Rightarrow \qquad a_3 = 0, a_5 = 0$

and for the coefficients with even subscripts we get,

$$a_2 = a_0; \qquad a_4 = \frac{a_2}{2} = \frac{a_0}{2!}; \qquad a_6 = \frac{a_4}{3} = \frac{a_0}{3!} ....$$

where a_0 remains arbitrary.

With these values [2] becomes

$$y = a_0 \left[1 + x^2 + \frac{x^4}{2!} + \frac{x^6}{3!} + \frac{x^8}{4!} + ... \right]$$

$$= a_0 e^{x^2}$$

3. Solve: $y'' + y = 0, \quad y(0) = 0; \quad y'(0) = 1$ using Power Series method.

Solution: Given, $y'' + y = 0$ [1]

$\qquad y(0) = 0, \quad y'(0) = 1;$

Let $y = a_0 + a_1 x + a_2 x^2 + ...$

$$= \sum_{n=0}^{\infty} a_n x^n \qquad \{x = 0; \quad y = 0; \quad 0 = a_0\} \qquad [2]$$

Since $x = 0$ is the ordinary point of the given equation,

$$y' = \sum_{n=1}^{\infty} n a_n x^{n-1}$$

$$y'' = \sum_{n=2}^{\infty} n(n-1) a_n x^{n-2} \qquad \begin{bmatrix} y' = a_1 + 2a_2 + ... \\ y' = 1, \qquad x = 0 \\ 1 = a_1 \end{bmatrix}$$

Substituting the values of y'' and y in [1] we have

$$\sum n(n-1) a_n x^{n-2} + \sum a_n x^n = 0$$

Equating the coefficient of x^n, we get

$$(n+2)(n+1) a_{n+2} + a_n = 0$$

$$a_{n+2} = -\frac{1}{(n+1)(n+2)} a_n$$

If $n = 0; \quad a_2 = -\frac{1}{1 \times 2} a_0 = 0$ $(a_1 = 0)$

If $n = 1$; $\quad a_3 = -\dfrac{1}{2 \times 3} a_1 = -\dfrac{1}{2 \times 3}(1) = \dfrac{1}{2 \times 3}$; $\qquad (a_1 = 1)$

If $n = 2$, $\quad a_4 = -\dfrac{1}{3 \times 4} a_2 = 0$

If $n = 3$, $\quad a_5 = \dfrac{1}{4 \times 5} a_3 = -\dfrac{1}{4 \times 5}\left(-\dfrac{1}{2 \times 3}\right) = \dfrac{1}{5!}$

Substituting these values in [2] we get

$$y = x - \frac{x^3}{3!} + \frac{x^5}{5!} + \frac{x^9}{9!} - \ldots\ldots$$

4. Solve: $y' - y = 0$ using Power Series method

Solution: Let us assume a solution of the form;

$$y = a_0 + a_1 x + a_2 x^2 + a_3 x^3 + a_4 x^4 + \ldots \qquad [1]$$

$\therefore \qquad y' = a_1 + 2a_2 x + 3a_3 x^2 + 4a_4 x^3 + \ldots$

$y'' = 2a_2 + 6a_3 x + 12a_4 x^2 + \ldots$

From the given equation we obtain,

$$\left(2a_2 + 6a_3 x + 12a_4 x^2 + \ldots\right) - \left(a_0 + a_1 x + a_2 x^2 + a_3 x^3 + \ldots\right) = 0$$

$\Rightarrow \quad \left(2a_2 - a_0\right) + \left(6a_3 - a_1\right)x + \left(12a_4 - a_2\right)x^2 + \ldots = 0 \qquad [2]$

Equating each of the coefficients to zero we obtain,

$$\Rightarrow \quad a_2 = \frac{1}{2} a_0; \quad a_3 = \frac{1}{6} a_1; \quad a_4 = \frac{1}{12} a_2 = \frac{1}{24} a_0; \quad a_5 = \frac{1}{20} a_1, \ldots$$

Substituting these values into equation [1], we obtain the Power Series solution to the given equation

$$y = a_0 \left(1 + \frac{1}{2} x^2 + \frac{1}{24} x^4 + \ldots\right) + a_1 \left(x + \frac{1}{6} x^3 + \frac{1}{120} x^5 + \ldots\right)$$

$$= a_0 \left(1 + \frac{x^2}{2!} + \frac{x^4}{4!} + \ldots\ldots\right) + a_1 \left(x + \frac{x^3}{3!} + \frac{x^5}{5!} + \ldots\ldots\right)$$

$$= a_0 \cos x + a_1 \sin x$$

5. Find a Power Series Solution in powers of x of the differential Equation:

$$\frac{d^2y}{dx^2} + xy = 0$$

Solution: $\dfrac{d^2y}{dx^2} + xy = 0$ [1]

Let us assume a solution of [1] in the form

$$y = \sum_{n=0}^{\infty} a_n x^n$$

$$= a_0 + a_1 x + a_2 x^2 + \ldots + a_n x^n + \ldots \qquad [2]$$

Then $y' = a_1 + 2a^2 x + 3a_3 x^2 + \ldots + na_n x^{n-1} + \ldots$ [3]

$$y'' = 2a_2 + 3\cdot 2a_3 x + 4\cdot 3a_4 x^2 + \ldots + n(n-1)a_n x^{n-2} + \ldots + \ldots \qquad [4]$$

Substituting [4] and [2] in [1], we have

$$2a_2 + 3\cdot 2a_3 x + 4\cdot 3a_4 x^2 + \ldots + n(n-1)a_n x^{n-2} + \ldots$$

$$+x\left(a_0 + a_1 x + a_2 x^2 + \ldots + a_n x^n + \ldots\right) = 0$$

$$\Rightarrow \quad 2a_2 + \left(3\cdot 2a_3 + a_0\right)x + \left(4\cdot 3a_4 + a_1\right)x^2 + \ldots$$

$$+\left[n(n-1)a_n + a_{n-3}\right]x^{n-2} + \ldots = 0 \qquad [5]$$

Equate to zero, the coefficients of x, x^2,.... etc in [5] separately, we have $a_2 = 0$

$$3\cdot 2a_3 + a_0 = 0 \quad \text{and} \quad \therefore \quad a_3 = -\frac{a_0}{3!}$$

$$4\cdot 3a_4 + a_1 = 0 \quad \text{and} \quad \therefore \quad a_4 = -\frac{a_1}{3\cdot 4} = -\frac{2a_1}{4!}$$

$$5\cdot 4a_5 + a_2 = 0 \quad \text{and} \quad \therefore \quad a_5 = -\frac{a_2}{4\cdot 5} = 0$$

Equate to zero, the coefficient x^n, we have

$$(n+2)(n+1)a_{n+2} + a_{n-1} = 0$$

$$\Rightarrow \quad a_{n+2} = \frac{a_{n-1}}{(n+1)(n+2)} \qquad [6]$$

Equation [6] can be used to calculate additional constants, putting $n = 4, 5, 6,$.... in [6], we have

$$a_6 = -\frac{a_3}{5 \cdot 6} = -\frac{1}{5 \cdot 6} \cdot \frac{-a_0}{3!} = \frac{4a_0}{6!}$$

$$a_7 = -\frac{a_4}{6 \cdot 7} = -\frac{1}{6 \cdot 7} \cdot -\frac{2a_1}{4!} = \frac{5 \cdot 2}{7!} a_1$$

$$a_8 = -\frac{a_5}{7 \cdot 8} = 0$$

$$a_9 = -\frac{a_6}{8 \cdot 9} = -\frac{1}{8 \cdot 9} \cdot \frac{4a_0}{6!} = -\frac{7 \cdot 4}{9!} a_0 \text{ and so on.}$$

Substituting these values in [2], we have

$$y = a_0 + a_1 x - \frac{a_0}{3!} x^8 - \frac{2a_1}{4!} x^4 + \frac{4a_0}{6!} x^6 + \frac{5 \cdot 2}{7!} a_1 x^7 - \frac{7 \cdot 4}{9!} a_0 x^9 + \ldots$$

$$= a_0 \left(1 - \frac{1}{3!} x^2 + \frac{1 \cdot 4}{6!} x^6 - \frac{1 \cdot 4 \cdot 7}{9!} x^9 + \ldots \right)$$

$$+ a_1 \left(x - \frac{2}{4!} x^4 + \frac{2 \cdot 5 \cdot 7}{7!} - \frac{2 \cdot 5 \cdot 8}{10!} x^{10} + \ldots \right) \qquad [7]$$

6. Solve the Equation in Series: $\dfrac{d^2 y}{dx^2} - xy = 0$

Solution: Given $y'' - xy = 0$ $\qquad\qquad$ [1]

Let us assume a solution of [1] in the form

$$y = \sum_{n=0}^{\infty} a_n x^n = a_0 + a_1 x + a_2 x^2 + a_3 x^3 + a_4 x^3 + a_5 x^5 + \ldots$$

$$\therefore \quad y' = a_1 + 2a_2 x + 3a_3 x^2 + 4a_4 x^3 + 5a_5 x^4 + \ldots$$

$$y'' = 2a_2 + 6a_3 x + 12a_2 x^2 + 20a_5 x^3 + \ldots$$

From the given equation, we obtain

$$\left(2a_2 + 6a_3 x + 12a_4 x^2 + 20a_5 x^3 + \ldots \right) - x\left(a_0 + a_1 x + a_2 x^2 + a_3 x^3 + \ldots \right) = 0$$

$$\Rightarrow \quad 2a_2 + \left(6a_3 - a_0\right)x + \left(12a_4 - a_1\right)x^2 + \left(20a_5 - a_2\right)x^2 + \ldots = 0$$

Equating each of the coefficients to zero, we obtain the identities,

$$2a_2 = 0; \qquad 6a_3 - a_0 = 0; \qquad 12a_4 - a_1 = 0; \qquad 20a_5 - a_2 = 0; \ldots$$

$$\Rightarrow \quad a_2 = 0; \qquad a_3 = \frac{1}{6} a_0; \qquad a_4 = \frac{1}{12} a_1; \qquad a_5 = \frac{1}{20} a_2 = 0;$$

In general, $(n+2)(n+1)a_{n+2} - a_{n-1} = 0$

$$\Rightarrow \quad a_{n+2} = \frac{a_{n-1}}{(n+2)(n+1)}$$

For $n = 4, 5, 6,....$ we obtain

$$a_6 = \frac{a_3}{6 \cdot 5} = \frac{a_0}{6 \cdot 6 \cdot 5}, \qquad a_7 = \frac{a_4}{7 \cdot 6} = \frac{1}{12 \cdot 7 \cdot 6} a_1 \qquad a_8 = 0$$

$\therefore$ the general solution is

$$y = a_0 \left(1 + \frac{1}{6}x^3 + \frac{1}{180}x^6 + ...\right) + a_1 \left(x + \frac{x^4}{12} + \frac{x^7}{504} + ...\right)$$

7. Apply the Power Series method to solve the equation:

$y(0) = 0; \quad y'' + 4y = 0; \quad y'(0) = 1$

Solution: Given, $y'' + 4y = 0$ \hfill [1]

$\qquad y(0) = 0; y'(0) = 1$

Let $\quad y = \sum_{n=0}^{\infty} a_n x^n$

$\qquad = a_0 + a_1 x + a_2 x^2 + ...$ \hfill [2]

be the solution of equation [1]. Hence, find y', y'', to substitute in [1],

$$\frac{dy}{dx} = y' = \sum n a_n x^{x-1} \qquad \begin{bmatrix} \dfrac{dy}{dx} = a_1 + 2a_2 x + ... \\[2mm] \dfrac{dy}{dx} = 1, x = 0 \\[2mm] 0 - a_0, x = 0 \end{bmatrix}$$

$$\frac{d^2 y}{dx^2} = y'' = \sum n(n-1)a_n x^{n-2}$$

$\therefore \quad$ given equation is $\sum n(n-1)a_n x^{n-2} + 4\sum a_n x^n = 0$

Equating the coefficients of x^n, we get

$\qquad (n+2)(n+1)a_{n+2} + 4a_n = 0$

$$a_{n+2} = -\frac{4}{(n+1)(n+2)} a_n$$

If $n = 0$, $\quad a_2 = -\frac{4}{1 \times 2} a_0 = -2a_0 = 0;$ $\qquad (a_0 = 0)$

If $n = 1$, $\quad a_3 = -\frac{4}{2 \times 3} a_1 = -\frac{4}{2 \times 3}(1) = -\frac{2}{3};$ $\quad (a_1 = 1)$

If $n = 2$, $\quad a_4 = -\frac{4}{3 \times 4} a_2 = 0$

If $n = 3$, $\quad a_5 = \frac{-4}{4 \times 5} a_3 = -\frac{4}{4 \times 5}\left(-\frac{2}{3}\right)$

$$= \frac{2}{3 \cdot 5} = \frac{2}{15}$$

Putting these values in [2], we get

$$y = x - \frac{2}{3} \cdot x^3 + \frac{2}{15} x^5 - \dots$$

EXERCISES

Solve the following equations in Power Series

1. $(1 + x^2) y'' + xy' - y = 0$

2. $4y'' + 9xy = 0$

3. $y'' - 2xy' + 4y = 0, \quad y(0) = 1, \quad y'(0) = 0$

4. $y'' + xy' + y = 0$

5. $y' = y + x^2$

6. $(1 + x^2) y'' - 9y = 0$

7. $(1 - x^2) y'' - 4xy' + 2y = 0$

Method of Frobenius

Sometimes the Power Series method fails to yield a solution. For example, if we consider

$$x^2 y'' + xy' + y = 0 \qquad [1]$$

$$\Rightarrow \quad y'' + \frac{1}{x} y' + \frac{1}{x^2} y = 0 \qquad [2]$$

Neither of the terms $p_1(x) = \frac{1}{x}$ or $p_2(x) = \frac{1}{x^2}$ is defined at $x = 0$, so we cannot find a Power Series representation for $p_1(x)$ or $p_2(x)$ that converges in an open interval containing $x = 0$.

The following definitions and results help us in establishing the validity of the series method.

Ordinary Point A point $x = p$ is said to be an ordinary point of equation: $p_0(x)y'' + p_1(x)y' + p_2(x)y = 0$ if $p_0(p) \neq 0$. Ordinary point is also called the regular point of the equation.

Singular Point A point $x = p$ is said to be an ordinary point of equation

$$p_0(x)y'' + p_1(x)y' + p_2(x)y = 0$$

if $p_0(p) = 0$.

Example: $x = 0$ is a singular point of $x^2 y'' + xy' + y = 0$

Regular Singular Point A singular point $x = p$ is said to be regular when [1] is put in the form

$$\frac{d^2 y}{dx^2} + \frac{B_1(x)}{x - p} \cdot \frac{dy}{dx} + \frac{B_2(x)}{(x - p)^2} = 0$$

$B_1(x)$ and $B_2(x)$ possess derivative of all orders in a neighbourhood of $x = p$. In other words, the point $x = p$ is regular singular point of equation [1] if both the functions $(x - p)B_1(x)$ and $(x - p)^2 B_2(x)$ have Taylor series expansions about the point $x = p$. If $x = 0$ then both the functions $x.B_1(x)$ and $x^2.B_2(x)$ should have Maclaurin's series in an open interval containing $x = 0$.

In the equation, $y'' + \frac{1}{x} y' + \frac{1}{x^2}.y = 0$, both $x.B_1$ and $x^2 B_2(x)$ are equal to 1. Hence $x = 0$ is a regular singular point.

Irregular Singular Point A point which is not a regular singular point of the equation is known as an irregular singular point.

Example: $y'' + 4x(2-x)y' + x^2 y = 0$ [1]

$$y'' + \frac{10}{3x(2-x)} \cdot y' + \frac{11}{4x} y = 0 \qquad [2]$$

$$y'' + \frac{4}{x} y'' + \frac{5}{x^2} y = 0 \qquad [3]$$

[1] has no singularities, [2] has regular singularities at $x = 0$ and $x = 2$

[3] has singularity at $x = 0$ which is not regular. Hence it is not possible to obtain a solution of Equation [3] in a series of ascending powers of x. Let the Equation [3] be $y = a_0 + a_1 x + a_2 x^2 + ...$ On solving the differential equation [3] we get $a_0 = 0$, $a_1 = 0$, $a_2 = 0$, $a_3 = 0,....$ Hence there is no series solution of [3].

We see that if $x = 0$ it is a regular singularity of the equation

$$p_0(x)y'' + p_1(x)y' + p_2(x)y = 0 \qquad [1]$$

then, its series solution is,

$$y = x^m \left(a_0 + a_1 x + a_2 x^2 + ... \right)$$
$$= \sum_{r=0}^{\infty} a_r x^{m+r}$$

Find y, y' and y'' and substitute in [1], we get, on equating to zero, the lowest degree term of x, a quadratic equation in m (indicial equation) is obtained. Thus, we will get two values of m. The series solution of [1] will depend on the nature of the roots of the indicial equation.

	Nature of the roots of indicial equation	Corresponding complete solutions of the differential equation
Case (1)	Roots may be distinct and not differing by an integer, say (m_1, m_2) where $m_1 = \dfrac{1}{2}$ and $m_2 = 2$	$y = c_1(y)_{m_2} + c_2(y)_{m_2}$
Case (2)	Equal roots say $(m_1 = m_2)$	$y = c_1(y)_{m_1} + c_2\left(\dfrac{\partial y}{\partial m}\right)_{m_1}$
Case (3)	$(m_1 = m_2)$ may be distinct and differing by an integer. say $m_1 = \dfrac{3}{4}$; $m_2 = \dfrac{1}{2}$; $m_2 = 4$; $m_2 = 2$	If some of the coefficients of y series become infinite when $m = m_1$, then to overcome this difficulty replace a_0 by $b_0(m - m_2)$ $y = c_1(y)_{m_1} + c_2\left(\dfrac{\partial y}{\partial m}\right)_{m_1}$ is the complete solution. $y = c_1(y)_{m_1} + c_2(y)_{m_2}$
Case (4)	(m_1, m_2) are distinct and differing by an integer.	If the coefficients do not become infinite when $m = m_2$. complete solution is $y = c_1(y)_{m_1} + c_2(y)_{m_2}$

8. Solve the equation in Series:

$8x^2 y'' + 2xy' + y = 0$, $x > 0$

Solution: Given, $8x^2 y'' + 2xy' + y = 0$ [1]

or $y'' + \dfrac{1}{4x}y' + \dfrac{1}{8x^2}y = 0$

The point $x = 0$ is a regular singular point of the equation.

Let $y = \displaystyle\sum_{r=0}^{\infty} a_r x^{m+r}$ be the solution

Find y', y'' and substituting in the differential equation and simplifying we obtain:

$$8\sum_{r=0}^{\infty}(m+r)(m+r-1)a_r x^{m+r} +2\sum_{r=0}^{\infty}(m+r)a_r x^{m+r} +\sum_{r=0}^{\infty}a_r x^{m+r} = 0 \quad [2]$$

Equate to zero, the coefficients of lowest degree term of x in [2], i.e., coefficient of x^m, we get the indicial equation as

$$8(m)(m-1)+2m+1=0 \qquad \text{(take } a_0 =1 \text{)}$$

$$\Rightarrow \quad 8m^2 -6m+1=0$$

$$\Rightarrow \quad \left(m-\frac{1}{2}\right)\left(m-\frac{1}{4}\right)=0$$

$$\Rightarrow \quad m=\frac{1}{2}; \ m=\frac{1}{4}$$

Here the roots are distinct and do not differ by an integer. Let $m=\dfrac{1}{4}$ and assume a solution of the form

$$y = x^{\frac{1}{4}}\left(a_0 +a_1 x+a_2 x^2 +a_3 x^3 +.....\right) \qquad [3]$$

from [2], we obtain;

$$8\sum\left(\frac{1}{4}+r\right)\left(\frac{1}{4}+r-1\right)a_r x^{\frac{1}{4}+r} +2\sum\left(\frac{1}{4}+r\right)a_r x^{\frac{1}{4}+r} +\sum a_r x^{\frac{1}{4}+r} = 0$$

$$\Rightarrow \quad \sum_{r=0}^{\infty}\left[8\left(r+\frac{1}{4}\right)\left(r+\frac{1}{4}-1\right)+2\left(r+\frac{1}{4}\right)+1\right]a_r x^{r-\frac{1}{4}} = 0$$

$$\Rightarrow \quad \sum_{r=0}^{\infty}\left(r^2 -\frac{r}{4}\right)a_4 x^{r+\frac{1}{4}} = 0$$

Equate all terms of this series to zero we obtain $\left(r^2 -\dfrac{r}{4}\right)a_r = 0$

$$\Rightarrow \quad a_r =0 \text{ for } r \geq 0$$

$$a_1, \ a_2, \ a_3, ... \text{ are all zero.}$$

$$\therefore \quad y_1(x)=x^{\frac{1}{4}}, \qquad\qquad \text{from [3], using } a_0 =1$$

To find second solution,

Let $m = \dfrac{1}{2}$ and assume a solution of the form $y = x^{\frac{1}{2}}\left(b_0 + b_1 x + b_2 x^2 + ...\right)$. Then, from [2] we obtain,

$$8\sum\left(r+\frac{1}{2}\right)\left(r+\frac{1}{2}-1\right)b_r x^{r+\frac{1}{2}} + 2\sum\left(r+\frac{1}{2}\right)b_r x^{r+\frac{1}{2}} + b_r x^{r+\frac{1}{2}} = 0$$

after a minor simplification, we obtain, $\displaystyle\sum_{r=0}^{\infty}\left(r^2+\frac{r}{4}\right)b_r x^{r+\frac{1}{2}} = 0$

from which $\left(r^2+\dfrac{r}{4}\right)b_r = 0$ and so, $y_2(x) = x^{\frac{1}{2}}$

$\therefore$ the complete solution is : $y = Ax^{\frac{1}{4}} + Bx^{\frac{1}{2}}$.

9. Solve: $xy'' + y' - xy = 0$ by Frobenius Method.

Solution: Since $x = 0$ is a regular singular point of the equation.
$\therefore$ the method of Frobenius can be applied.

Let $\quad y = \displaystyle\sum_{r=0}^{\infty}a_r x^{m+r}$ 　　　　　　　　　　　　　　　　[1]

$\therefore \quad y' = \sum(m+r)a_r x^{m+r-1}; \quad$ and $\quad y'' = \sum(m+r)(m-r-1)a_r x^{m+r-2}$

Substituting in the equation we obtain

$$\sum(m+r)(m+r-1)a_r x^{m+r-1} + \sum(m+r)a_r x^{m+r-1} - \sum a_r x^{m+r+1} = 0$$

The lowest power of x is x^{m-1}.

$\therefore$ the indicial equation is $m(m-1)+m = 0$ 　　　　　(Choosing $a_0 = 1$)

$\Rightarrow \quad m^2 = 0$

$\Rightarrow \quad m = 0, 0,$ i.e., roots are equal

Let $\quad m = 0$ in equation [2]

$$\sum_{r=0}^{\infty}r(r-1)a_r x^{r-1} + \sum_{r=0}^{\infty}ra_r x^{r-1} - \sum_{r=0}^{\infty}a_r x^{r+1} = 0$$

$$\Rightarrow \quad \sum_{r=0}^{\infty} r^2 a_r x^{r-1} - \sum_{r=0}^{\infty} a_r x^{r+1} = 0$$

Equating the coefficients of like powers of x to obtain $a_1, a_2, \ldots$

i.e., $\quad a_1 = 0, \ 4a_2 - a_0 = 0 \Rightarrow a_2 = \dfrac{a_0}{4} = \dfrac{1}{4}$

$9a_3 - a_1 = 0 \Rightarrow a_3 = 0$

$16a_4 - a_2 = 0 \Rightarrow a_4 = \dfrac{a_2}{16} = \dfrac{1}{16 \cdot 4} = \dfrac{1}{4^2 \cdot 2^2}$

$25a_5 - a_3 = 0 \Rightarrow a_5 = 0$

$36a_6 - a_4 = 0 \Rightarrow a_6 = \dfrac{a_4}{36} = \dfrac{1}{6^2 \cdot 4^2 \cdot 2^2} \cdots$

Hence one solution is: $y_1 = a_0 + a_2 x^2 + a_4 x^4 + a_6 x^6 + \cdots$

$$= 1 + \frac{x^2}{2^2} + \frac{x^4}{4^2 \cdot 2^2} + \frac{x^6}{6^2 \cdot 4^2 \cdot 2^2} + \cdots \qquad\qquad [3]$$

To find the second solution, we have to express [3] in terms of m. So equating the coefficient of $x^m, x^{m+1}, \ldots$ from [2] to zero we obtain $a_1 = a_3 = a_5 = 0$

$$a_2 = \frac{1}{(m+2)^2}; \qquad a_4 = \frac{1}{(m+4)^2(m+2)^2};$$

$$a_6 = \frac{1}{(m+6)^2(m+4)^2(m+2)^2} \qquad \text{and so on,}$$

$\therefore \quad$ [3] is rewritten as:

$$y_1(x) = \left[1 + \frac{x^2}{(m+2)^2} + \frac{x^4}{(m+4)^2(m+2)^2} + \frac{x^6}{(m+6)^2(m+4)^2(m+2)^2} + \cdots \right]$$

(a solution for $m = 0$)

$\therefore \quad y_2(x) = \left(\dfrac{\partial y_1}{\partial m_1} \right)$ at $m = 0$

$$= y_1 \log x - x^m \left[\frac{x^2}{(m+2)^2} \frac{2}{(m+2)} + \frac{x^4}{(m+4)^2(m+2)^2} \left[\frac{2}{m+2} + \frac{2}{m+n} \right] + \cdots \right]$$

when $m = 0$.

$$y_2(x) = y_1 \log x - \left[\frac{x^2}{2^2} + \frac{x^4}{4^2 \cdot 2^2}\left(1 + \frac{1}{2}\right) + \frac{x^6}{6^2 \cdot 4^2 \cdot 2^2}\left(1 + \frac{1}{2} + \frac{1}{3}\right) + ... \right] \quad [4]$$

Hence the complete solution

$$y = A\, y_1(x) + B\, y_2(x)$$

Where $y_1(x)$ and $y_2(x)$ are given in [3] and [4] respectively.

10. Solve: $4xy'' + 2y' + y = 0$ using Power Series method.

Solution: Given, $4xy'' + 2y' + y = 0$.... $\qquad$ [1]

Let us assume a solution [1] in the form:

$$y = a_0 x^n + a_1 x^{n+1} + a_2 x^{n+2} + ...$$

$$= \sum_{r=0}^{\infty} a_r x^{n+r} \qquad [2]$$

Substituting in the given equation,

$4xy'' + 2y' + y = 0$, we get

$4a_0 n(n-1)x^{n-2} + 4a_1(n+1)nx^n + 4a_2(n+2)(n+1)4x^{n+1} + ...$

$+2a_0 nx^{n-1} + 2a_1(n+1)x^n + 2a_2(n+2)x^{n+1} + ...$

$+a_0 x^n + a_1 x^{n+2} + ... = 0.$

This gives, on equating to zero ,coefficients of

x^{n-1}, x^n....

$$\left. \begin{aligned} &2a_0 n(2n-1) = 0, \\ &2a_1(n+1)(2n+1) + a_0 = 0 \\ &2a_2(n+2)(2n+3) + a_1 = 0, \text{ and so on} \end{aligned} \right\}$$

The first of these is the indicial equation, giving $n = 0$ or $\frac{1}{2}$

The others give

$$a_1 = \frac{-a_0}{2(n+1)(2n+1)}$$

$$= \frac{-a_0}{2(n+1)(2n+1)}$$

$$a_2 = \frac{-a_1}{(2n+3)(2n+4)}$$

$$= + \frac{a_0}{(2n+1)(2n+2)(2n+3)(2n+4)}, \text{ and so on}$$

Taking $n = 0$, we get the first solution

$$y_1 = a_0 \left(1 - \frac{x}{1 \cdot 2} + \frac{x^2}{1 \cdot 2 \cdot 3 \cdot 4} - \frac{x^3}{6!} + ... \right)$$

$$= a_0 \cos \sqrt{x}$$

Taking $n = \frac{1}{2}$; we get the second solution

$$y_2 = a_0 x^{\frac{1}{2}} \left(1 - \frac{x}{1 \cdot 3} + \frac{x^2}{2 \cdot 3 \cdot 4 \cdot 5} - \frac{x^3}{7!} + ... \right)$$

$$= a_0 \sin \sqrt{x}$$

The general solution is : $y = Ay_1 + By_2$

11. Find the Power Series solution of $\left(1+x^2\right) \cdot \frac{d^2 y}{dx^2} + x \frac{dy}{dx} - y = 0$ about $x = 0$

Solution: Given, $(1+x^2)y'' + xy' - y = 0$ about $x = 0$

Let $y = \sum_{r=0}^{\infty} a_k x^{k+r} = a_0 + a_1 x + a_2 x^2 + a_3 x^3 + ...$ [2]

Find y', y'' we get

$$y' = a_1 + 2a_2 x + 3a_3 x^2 + 4a_4 x^3 + ...$$
$$y'' = 2a_2 + 6a_3 x + 12a_4 x^4 + 20a_5 x^3 + ...$$

Substitute for y, y' and y'' in the given equation, we have

$$(1+x^2)\left(2a_2 + 6a_3 + 12a_4 x^2 + 20a_5 x^3 + ...\right)$$
$$+ x(a_1 + 2a_2 x + 3a_3 x^2 + 4a_4 x^3 + ...)$$
$$- (a_0 + a_1 x + a_2 x^2 + a_3 x^3 + ...) + ... = 0$$
$$(2a_2 - a_0) + (6a_3 + a_1 - a_1)x + (2a_2 + 12a_4 + 2a_2 - a_2)x^2 +$$
$$(20a_5 + 6a_3 + 3a_3 - a_3)x^3 + ... = 0$$

Equate to zero, the various powers of x, we obtain

$$2a_2 - a_0 = 0 \text{ or } a_2 = \frac{1}{2}a_0 ;$$
$$6a_3 = 0 \qquad \text{or } a_3 = 0$$

$$12a_4 + 3a_2 = 0 \qquad \text{or} \qquad a_4 = \frac{-1}{4}a_2 = \frac{-1}{8}a_0$$

$$20a_5 + 8a_3 = 0 \qquad \text{or} \qquad a_5 = \frac{-2}{5}a_3 = 0$$

∴   solution is

$$y = a_0\left[1 + \frac{x^2}{2} - \frac{x^4}{8} \cdots\cdots\right] + a_1 x$$

12. Solve: $(x-1)^2 y'' + (x-1)y' - 4y = 0$ in powers of $(x-1)$ using Frobenius method.

Solution: Since $x = 1$ is a regular singular point

Let $y = \displaystyle\sum_{r=0}^{\infty} a_r (x-1)^{m+r}$

∴ $y' = \displaystyle\sum_{r=0}^{\infty} (m+r)a_r (x-1)^{m+r-1}$

$y'' = \displaystyle\sum_{r=0}^{\infty} (m+r)(m+r-1)a_r (x-1)^{m+r-2}$

Substituting y, y', y'' in the given equation, we get

$$\sum_{r=0}^{\infty} (m+r)(m+r-1)a_r (x-1)^{m+r}$$

$$+\sum_{r=0}^{\infty} (m+r)a_r (x-1)^{m+r} - 4\sum_{r=0}^{\infty} a_r (x-1)^{m+r} = 0$$

$\Rightarrow \quad \displaystyle\sum_{r=0}^{\infty}\left[(m+r)(m+r-1) + (m+r) - 4\right] a_r (x-1)^{m+r} = 0$

$\Rightarrow \quad \displaystyle\sum_{r=0}^{\infty}\left[(m+r)^2 - 4\right] a_r (x-1)^{m+r} = 0$ $\qquad\qquad$ [2]

The lower degree term is $(x-1)^m$.

∴   the indicial equation is $m^2 - 4 = 0$

$\Rightarrow \quad m = -2, 2$.

Here the roots are integral and different by an integer. Let us find the solution with the smallest root, i.e., $m = -2$.

∴   from [2] we obtain

$$\left[(r-2)^2 - 4\right]a_r = 0$$

for $r = 0,$ $0.a_0 = 0 \Rightarrow$ a_0 is arbitrary [3]

$r = 1,$ $-3.a_1 = 0 \Rightarrow$ $a_1 = 0$

$r = 2,$ $-4.a_2 = 0 \Rightarrow$ $a_2 = 0$

$r = 3,$ $-3.a_3 = 0 \Rightarrow$ $a_3 = 0$

$r = 4,$ $0.a_4 = 0 \Rightarrow$ $a_4 = 0$ is arbitrary

Similarly, $a_5 = a_6 = \dots = 0$

Hence, the general solution is

$$y = a_0(x-1)^{-2} + a_4(x-1)^4$$

13. Use the Power Series method to find the general solution of the differential equation: $(1-x^2)y'' + 2y = 0$ about $x = 0$

Solution: Given, $(1-x^2)y'' + 2y = 0$ [1]

When $x = 0$, coefficient of $y'' \neq 0$. So $x = 0$ is an ordinary point of [1].

Let us assume a solution of [1] in the form of

$$y = \sum_{n=0}^{\infty} a_n x^n$$

$$= a_0 + a_1 x + a_2 x^2 + \dots.$$ [2]

$\therefore$ $\dfrac{dy}{dx} = \displaystyle\sum_{r=0}^{\infty} a_n . n . x^{n-1}; \quad \dfrac{d^2 y}{dx^2} = \sum_{r=0}^{\infty} a_n n(n-1) x^{n-2}$ [3]

Putting the above values of y, y', y'' in [1] gives

$$\left(1-x^2\right)\sum_{n=0}^{\infty} a_n . n(n-1) x^{n-2} + \sum_{n=0}^{\infty} c_n x^n = 0$$

$\Rightarrow$ $\displaystyle\sum_{n=0}^{\infty} a_n . n(n-1) x^{n-2} - \sum_{n=0}^{\infty} a_n . n(n-1) x^n + 2\sum_{n=0}^{\infty} a_n x^n = 0$

$\Rightarrow$ $\displaystyle\sum_{n=0}^{\infty} a_n . n(n-1) x^{n-2} - \sum_{n=0}^{\infty} a\{_n n(n-1) - 2\} x^n = 0$

$\Rightarrow$ $\displaystyle\sum_{n=0}^{\infty} a_n n(n-1) x^{n-2} - \sum_{n=0}^{\infty} a_n (n-2)(n+1) x^n = 0$ [4]

Now, we equate to zero, the coefficient of x^{n-2} yields the recurrence relation: $a_n . n(n-1) - a_{n-2}(n-4)(n-1) = 0$

$\Rightarrow$ $a_n = \dfrac{n-4}{n} a_{n-2}$ [5]

Putting $n = 2, 4, 6, 8$, in turn [5] gives

$$a_n \cdot n(n-1) - a_{n-2}(n-4)(n-1) = 0$$

i.e., $a_2 = -a_0; \quad a_4 = 0; \quad a_6 = \left(\frac{2}{6}\right)a_4 = 0;$

$$a_8 = a_{10} = \dots = 0$$

Putting $n = 3, 5, 7, \dots$ in turn [5] gives

i.e., $a_3 = -\frac{a_1}{3}; \quad a_5 = \frac{a_3}{5};$

$$= -\frac{a_1}{15}, \quad a_7 = \frac{395}{7}$$

$$= -\frac{a_1}{35}$$

Putting these values in [2], we have

$$y = \left(a_0 + a_2 x^2 + a_4 x^4 + \dots\dots\right) + \left(a_1 x + a_3 x^3 + a_5 x^5 + \dots\dots\right)$$

$$y = (a_0 - a_0 x^2) + \left[a_1 x - \left(\frac{a_1}{3}\right)x^3 - \left(\frac{a_1}{15}\right)x^5 - \left(\frac{a_1}{35}\right)x^7 + \dots\right]$$

$$y = a_0(1 - x^2) + a_1\left(x - \frac{x^3}{3} - \frac{x^5}{15} - \frac{x^7}{35}\dots\right)$$

(a_0, a_1 being arbitrary constants).

14. Find the Power Series solution of $(1 - x^2)y'' - 2xy' + 2y = 0$ about $x = 0$.

Solution: Given $(1 - x^2)y'' - 2xy' + 2y = 0\dots$ [1]

Let $y = \displaystyle\sum_{k=0}^{\infty} a_k x^k = a_0 + a_1 x + a_2 x^2 + \dots + a_n x^n + \dots$ [2]

be the required solution.

Finding y', y'', we get

$$y' = \frac{dy}{dx} = \sum_{k=1}^{\infty} a_k \cdot k x^{k+1},$$

$$y'' = \sum_{k=2}^{\infty} a_k \cdot k(k-1)x^{k-2}$$

Now substitute for y, y', y''

From equation [3] into [1], we get

$$(1-x^2)\sum a_k . k(k-1)x^{k-2} - 2x\sum a_k \cdot kx^{k-1} + 2\sum a_k x^k = 0$$

$$\sum a_k \cdot k \cdot (k-1)x^{k-2} - \sum a_k k(k-1)x^k - 2\sum a_k \cdot kx^k + 2\sum a_k x^k = 0$$

$$\sum a_k \cdot k \cdot (k-1)x^{k-2} - \sum [k(k-1)+2k-2]a_k x^k = 0$$

$$\sum a_k \cdot k \cdot (k-1)x^{k-2} - \sum (k^2+k-2)a_k x^k = 0$$

where the limits for the summation in the first term, extends from $k = 2$ to ∞ and the second from $k = 0$ to ∞. Now we equate to zero the coefficient of x^k, we have $(k+2)(k+1)a_{k+2} - (k^2+k-2)a_k = 0$

$$a_{k+2} = \frac{k^2+k-2}{(k+2)(k+1)}a_k$$

or

$$= \frac{(k+2)(k-1)}{(k+2)(k+1)}a_k$$

$$a_{k+2} = \frac{k-1}{k+1}a_k$$

$$a_2 = -a_0, \ a_3 = 0, \ a_4 = \frac{a_2}{3} = -\frac{a_0}{3}; \ a_5 = \frac{2}{4}, \ a_3 = 0$$

$$a_6 = \frac{3}{5} \ a_4 = \frac{3}{5}\left(-\frac{a_0}{3}\right) = -\frac{a_0}{5};$$

$$a_7 = \frac{4}{5} \ a_5 = 0, \text{ and so on}$$

$$y = a_0 + a_1 x + a_2 x^2 + a_3 x^3 + a_4 x^4 + ...$$

$$y = a_0 + a_1 x - a_0 x^2 + 0 - \frac{a_0}{3}x^4 + 0 - \frac{a_0}{5}x^6 + 0 + ...$$

$$y = a_0\left[1 - x^2 - \frac{x^4}{3} - \frac{x^6}{5} + ...\right] + a_1 x$$

15. Obtain the series solution of: $x^2 y'' + xy' + (x-1)y = 0$

Solution: Here $x = 0$ is a regular point.

Let $\quad y = \sum_{r=0}^{\infty} a_r x^{m+r}$ be a solution. [1]

$\therefore \quad y' = \sum (m+r)\, a_r x^{m+r-1};$

$$y'' = \sum (m+r)(m+r-1)a_r x^{m+r-2}$$

Substituting y, y', y'' in the given equation, we get

$$\sum_{r=0}^{\infty}(m+r)(m+r-1)a_r x^{m+r} + \sum_{r=0}^{\infty}(m+r)a_r x^{m+r}$$

$$+ \sum_{r=0}^{\infty} a_r x^{m+r+2} - \sum_{r=0}^{\infty} a_r x^{m+r} = 0 \qquad [2]$$

The lowest power of x is x^m.

So, indicial equation yields $m(m-1)+m-1=0 \Rightarrow m^2 =1 \Rightarrow m = \pm 1$

Hence, the roots differ by an integer 2. Let us start with the smallest root $(m=-1)$

Now [2] can be written as:

$$\sum \Big[(m+r)^2 -1\Big]a_r x^{m+r} + \sum a_r x^{m+r=2} = 0$$

$$\sum \Big[\{m+r)^2 -1\}a_r + a_{r-2}\Big]x^{m+r} + (m^2 -1)a_0 x^m$$

$$+\Big[(m+1)^2 -1\Big]a_1 x^{m+1} = 0 \qquad [3]$$

$\therefore$ we obtain the following recurrence relation

$$a_r = -\frac{a_r - 2}{(m+r)^2 -1}, \; r \geq 2$$

and $a_0 \neq 0$; $a_1 = 0$ at $m = -1$

For $r = 2$, $a_2 = -\dfrac{a_0}{(m+2)^2 -1}$

But for $m = -1$, a_2 is undefined. Also the consequent terms depending on a_2 will be undefined.

Let $a_0 = b_0(m+1)$

$\therefore \quad a_2 = -\dfrac{b_0(m+1)}{(m+3)(m+1)} = -\dfrac{b_0}{(m+3)}$

for $r = 3$, $a_3 = -\dfrac{a_1}{(m+3)^2 -1} = 0$

Similarly $a_5 = a_7 = \ldots = 0$

for $r = 4$, $a_4 = \dfrac{a_2}{(m+4)^2 - 1} = \dfrac{b_0}{(m+3)^2 (m+5)}$

Hence one independent solution is

$$y_1(x) = b_0 x^m \left[m + 1 - \frac{1}{m+3} x^2 + \frac{1}{(m+3)^2 (m+5)} x^4 \right] \qquad [4]$$

For $m = -1$

$$y_1(x) = \frac{b_0}{x} \left[-\frac{1}{2} x^2 + \frac{1}{16} x^4 .... \right]$$

$$= -\frac{b_0}{2} \left[x - \frac{x^3}{8} + ... \right]$$

Now from [4]

$$\frac{\partial y}{\partial m} = b_0 x^m \log x \left[m + 1 - \frac{1}{m+3} x^2 + \frac{1}{(m+3)^2 \cdot (m+5)} x^4 + ... \right]$$

$$+ b_0 x^m \left[1 + \frac{1}{(m+3)^2} \cdot x^2 - \frac{(3m+13)}{(m+3)^3 (m+5)^2} \cdot x^4 + ... \right]$$

At $m = -1$ $\therefore$ $y_2 = \left(\dfrac{\partial y}{\partial m} \right) = b_0 \left[y_1 \log x + \dfrac{1}{x} \left(1 + \dfrac{1}{4} x^2 - \dfrac{10}{2^3 \cdot 4^2} x^4 .... \right) \right]$

Hence, the complete solution is

$$y = A \left[x - \frac{x^3}{8} + ... \right] + \left[\left(x - \frac{x^3}{8} + ... \right) \log x + \frac{1}{x} \left(1 + \frac{1}{4} x^2 - \frac{10}{2^3 \cdot 4^2} x^4 + ... \right) \right]$$

EXERCISES

Solve the following equations by Frobenius method.

1. $x^2 y'' + 2xy' - 2y = 0$ $\qquad \left[\textit{Ans. } y = a_0 x + \dfrac{a_1}{x^2} \right]$

2. $2x(1+x)y'' + (1+x)y' - 3y = 0$ $\qquad \left[\begin{array}{l} \textit{Ans. } y_0(x) = 1 + 3x + x^2 - \dfrac{x^3}{5} + ... \\[2mm] \qquad y_{1/2}(x) = x^{1/2}(1+x) \end{array} \right]$

3. $4x^2y'' + y = 0$

$$\left[Ans: y = \sqrt{x}\left(a_0 + a_1 \log \sqrt{x}\right) \right]$$

4. $2x^2y'' + x(x-1)y' + y = 0$

$$\left[Ans. \ \ y_1(x) = a_0 x\left(1 - \frac{x}{3} + \frac{x^2}{3\cdot5} + ...\right) \right.$$
$$\left. y_{1/2}(x) = a_0 x^{1/2} e^{-x/2} \right]$$

5. $9x(1-x)y'' - 12y' + 4y = 0$

$$\left[Ans: \ \ y = a\left(1 + \frac{1}{3}x + \frac{1\cdot4}{3\cdot6}x^2 + ...\right) \right.$$
$$\left. + b_{x_{1/3}}\left(1 + \frac{8}{10}x + \frac{8\cdot11}{10\cdot13}x^2 + ...\right) \right]$$

6. (a) $2x^2y'' - xy' + (1-x^2)y = 0$

(b) $2x^2\ y'' - xy' + (1-x^2)y = x^2$

$$\left[Ans. \ (a) \ \ y = bx^{1/2}\left(1 + \frac{x^2}{2\cdot3} + \frac{x^4}{2\cdot3\cdot4\cdot7} + ...\right) = bv, \text{say} \right]$$

$$\left[Ans. \ (b) \ \ y = x^k(A_0 + A_1x + A_2x^2 + ...) \right.$$
$$\left. \text{or} \quad y = au + br + f(x) \right]$$

Legendre's Equation and Polynomials

Legendre's Equation

The differential equation

$$(1-x^2)\frac{d^2y}{dx^2} - 2x\cdot\frac{dy}{dx} + n(n+1)y = 0 \qquad [1]$$

is known as Legendre's equation. The parameter n is a real number. In most applications only integral values of n are needed.

To obtain a solution of [1], assume

$$y = \sum_{m=0}^{\infty} a_m x^m \qquad [2]$$

Substitute [2] and its derivatives in [1], then

$$(1-x^2)\sum_{m=2}^{\infty} m(m-1)a_m x^{m-2} - 2x\sum_{m=1}^{\infty} ma_m x^{m-1} + k\sum_{m=0}^{\infty} a_m x^m = 0$$

where $k = n(n+1)$

Rewriting $\displaystyle\sum_{m=2}^{\infty} m(m-1)a_m x^{m-2} - \sum_{m=2}^{\infty} m(m-1)a_m x^m - 2\sum_{m=0}^{\infty} ma_m x^m + k\sum_{m=0}^{\infty} a_m x^m = 0$ [3]

[3] is an indicial equation. Since [2] is a solution of [1], So, we equate to zero, the sum of the coefficients of each power of x.

Now, coefficient of x^0 comes from the first and the fourth series in [3],

Thus $2a_2 + n(n+1)a_0 = 0$.... [4]

Coefficients of x^1 arise from the first, the third and the fourth series in [3]

so, $6a_3 + [-2 + n(n+1)]a_1 = 0$.... [5]

All the four series in [3] contribute coefficients of x^r for $r \geq 2$.

Thus $(r+2)(r+1)a_{r+2} + \left[-r(r-1) - 2r + n(n+1)\right]a_r = 0$ [6]

on solving equation [6], we get

$$a_{r+2} = -\frac{(n-r)(n+r+1)}{(r+2)(r+1)}a_r$$ [7]

for $r = 0, 1, 2,....$

Since
$$\left\{\begin{aligned}
&-r(r-1) - 2r + n(n+1) \\
&= -r^2 + r - 2r + n^2 + n \\
&= (n^2 - r^2 + n - r) \\
&= (n-r)(n+r+1)
\end{aligned}\right\}$$

[7] is known as a recurrence relation or recursion formula, which determines all coefficients in terms of a_1 or a_0.

Thus $a_2 = \dfrac{-(n)(n+1)}{2!}a_0; \; (r=0)$

$a_3 = \dfrac{-(n-1)(n+1)}{3!}a_1; \; (r=1)$

$a_4 = \dfrac{-(n-2)(n+3)}{4.3}a_2;$

$a_5 = \dfrac{-(n-3)(n+4)}{5.4}a_3;$

or $\quad a_4 = \dfrac{(n-2)n\,(n+1)(n+3)}{4!} a_0$;

$$a_5 = -\dfrac{(n-3)\,(n-1)(n+2)(n+4)}{5!} a_1$$;

In general, the coefficients with even subscripts are

$$a_{2m} = \dfrac{(n-2m+2)(n+2m-1)}{(2m)(2m-1)} a_{2m-2}$$

and coefficients with odd subscripts are

$$a_{2m+1} = \dfrac{-(n-2m+2)(n+2m)}{(2m)(2m+1)} a_{2m-1}$$

Substituting these coefficients in [2], we get

$$y = a_0 y_1 + a_1 y_2 \qquad\qquad\qquad [8]$$

Where $\quad y_1 = 1 - \dfrac{n(n+1)}{2!} x^2 + \dfrac{(n-2)n(n+1)(n+3)}{4!} x^4 \qquad [9]$

and $\quad y_2 = x - \dfrac{(n-1)(n+2)}{3!} x^3 + \dfrac{(n-3)(n-1)(n+2)(n+4)}{5!} x^5 \qquad [10]$

[9] and [10] converge for $|x| < 1$, y_1 and y_2 are linearly independent (i.e., $\dfrac{y_1}{y_2}$ is not a constant)

Thus $y = y\,(x)$ given by [8] is the general solution of Legendre's equation [1] and is valid for $-1 < x < 1$.

Legendre's Polynomials: $P_n(x)$

Legendre's equation and its solutions are of much importance, both in mathematical theory and in applications to practical problems. If n is not an integer, each of the series in [8] is an infinite series.

It is to be noted that if 'n' is a positive even integer, $y_1(x)$ becomes a polynomial of degree n. Similarly if n is an odd integer, $y_2(x)$ becomes a polynomial of degree n. Thus, if n is an integer (even or odd), the solution [8] always contains a polynomial and an infinite series.

If the value of the polynomials at $x = 1$ becomes one for properly chosen a_0 or a_1, then these polynomials are called Legendre ploynomials of degree n and is denoted by $P_n(x)$, whereas, the infinite series solution with properly chosen a_0 or a_1 is called Legendre's function of second kind and is denoted by $Q_n(x)$.

The Legendre polynomials $P_n(x)$ are defined as follows:

$$P_n(x) = \frac{(-1)^{\frac{1}{2}n} 1 \cdot 3 \cdot 5 \ldots (n-1)}{2 \cdot 4 \cdot 6 \ldots n} \left[1 - \frac{n(n+1)}{2!} + \frac{(n-2)n(n+1)(n+1)}{4!} x^4 \ldots \right] (n \text{ even}) \quad [1]$$

$$P_n(x) = (-1)^{\frac{1}{2}(n-1)} \frac{1 \cdot 3 \cdot 5, \ldots n}{2 \cdot 4 \cdot 6, \ldots (n-1)} \left[x - \frac{(n-1)(n-2)}{3!} x^3 + \ldots \right] (n \text{ odd}) \quad [2]$$

The above two expression for $P_n(x)$ may be replaced by a single expression as follows:

$$P_n(x) = \sum_{r=0}^{m} \frac{(-1)^r (2n-2r)! x^{n-2r}}{2^n r!(n-r)(n-2r)} \quad [3]$$

where the last value of r is $m = \dfrac{n}{2}$ when n is even and $m = \dfrac{n-1}{2}$ if n is odd. Hence [3] is the expression for the Legendre polynomial of order n.

By putting $n = 0, 1, 2, 3, 4, 5, 6$, etc. in [3], we get the following few Legendre polynomials:

$$P_0(x) = 1; \quad (\text{for } n = 0, m = 0)$$

$$P_1(x) = x; \quad (\text{for } n = 1, m = 0)$$

$$P_2(x) = \frac{1}{2}(3x^2 - 1); \quad \text{for } n = 2, m = 1, r = 0 \text{ to } 1$$

$$P_3(x) = \frac{1}{2}(5x^3 - 3x); \quad (\text{for } n = 3, m = 1, r = 0 \text{ to } 1)$$

$$P_4(x) = \frac{1}{8}(35x^4 - 30x^2 + 3); \quad (\text{for } n = 4, m = 2, r = 0 \text{ to } 2)$$

$$P_5(x) = \frac{1}{8}(63x^5 - 70x^3 + 15x); \quad (\text{for } n = 5, m = 2, r = 0 \text{ to } 2)$$

$$p_6(x) = \frac{1}{16}(231x^6 - 315x^4 + 105x^2 - 5); \quad (\text{for } n = 6, m = 3, r = 0 \text{ to } 3)$$

Note: (i) At $x = 1$, $P_n(x = 1) = P_n(1) = 1$

(ii) Any polynomial $f(x)$ of degree n can be expressed in terms of $P_n(x)$

as $f(x) = \sum_{m=0}^{n} c_m P_m(x)$

Fourier Legendre Expansion of $f(x)$

Let $f(x)$ be a function defined on $[-1, 1]$,

Suppose $f(x) = \sum_{n=0}^{\infty} c_n P_n(x)$ [1]

To find c_n we multiply both sides of [1] by $P_n(x)$ and integrate from -1 to 1, we get

$$\int_{-1}^{1} f(x) P_n(x) dx = c_n \int_{-1}^{1} P_n^2(x)) dx$$

$$\left[\because \int_{-1}^{1} P_n(x) P_m(x) dx = 0 \ \ if \ \ m \neq n \right]$$

$$= \frac{2c_n}{2n+1} \ \ \text{(by orthogonal property of Legendre's polynomial)}$$

$$\therefore c_n = \frac{2n+1}{2} \int_{-1}^{1} f(x) P_n(x) dx \hspace{2cm} [2]$$

The series of [1] whose coefficients c_n are given by [2] is called the **'Fourier Legendre Expansion** of $f(x)$.

Rodrigue's Formula

To prove that $P_n(x) = \dfrac{1}{2^n \cdot n!} \dfrac{d^n}{dx^n} (x^2 - 1)^n$

Proof: Let $y = (x^2 - 1)^n$

$\therefore \qquad \dfrac{dy}{dx} = n(x^2 - 1)^{n-1} 2x$

or, $\quad y_1 = 2nx \dfrac{(x^2 - 1)^n}{x^2 - 1}$

$\therefore \qquad (x^2 - 1) y_1 - 2nxy = 0$.

Applying Leibnitz's theorem and differentiating $(n + 1)$ times, we get

$$\left[(x^2 - 1) y_{n+2} + (n+1) y_{n+1} (2n) + \frac{n+1}{2} y_n(2) \right] - 2n \left[xy_{n+1} + (n+1) y_n \right] = 0$$

$\therefore \qquad (x^2 - 1) y_{n+2} + 2x \cdot y_{n+1} - n(n+1) y_n = 0 \hspace{2cm} [1]$

Put $\quad y_n = v; \quad \therefore \ y_{n+1} = \dfrac{dv}{dx} \ and \ y_{n+2} = \dfrac{d^2v}{dx^2}$

$\therefore$ [1] becomes $\left(x^2 - 1\right)\dfrac{d^2v}{dx^2} + 2x\dfrac{dv}{dx} - n(n+1)v = 0$

i.e., $\left(1 - x^2\right)\dfrac{d^2v}{dx^2} - 2x\dfrac{dv}{dx} + n(n+1)v = 0$

which is the Legendre's equation whose solution is $P_n(x)$.

Hence $P_n(x) = cy_n$ where c is a constant.

$$= c \cdot \frac{d^n}{dx^n}\left[\left(x^2 - 1\right)^n\right] \qquad [2]$$

putting $x = 1$, we get

$$P_n(1) = c\left[\frac{d^n}{dx^n}(x-1)^n(x+1)^n\right]_{x=1}$$

We have $P_n(1) = 1$

$\therefore \quad 1 = c\left[(x-1)^n\dfrac{d^n}{dx^n}(x+1)^n + n_{c_1}n(x-1)^{n-1}\dfrac{d^{n-1}}{dx^{n-1}}(x+1)^n + \ldots + (x+1)^n\dfrac{d^n}{dx^n}(x-1)^n\right]_{x=1}$

$$= \left[c(x+1)^n\frac{d^n}{dx^n}(x-1)^n\right]_{x=1}$$

$$= \left[c(x+1)^n\, n!\right]_{x=1}$$

$$= c \cdot 2^n$$

$\Rightarrow \quad c = \dfrac{1}{2^n \cdot n!}$ substituting this in [2], we get $P_n(x) = \dfrac{1}{2^n \cdot n!}\dfrac{d^n}{dx^n}\left[\left(x^2 - 1\right)^n\right]$

16. Express: $2 - 3x + 4x^2$ in terms of Legendre's Polynomials

Solution: $1 = P_0(x);\ x = P_1(x);\ \dfrac{\left(3x^2 - 1\right)}{2} = P_2(x);$

$\Rightarrow \quad x^2 = \dfrac{\left[2P_2(x) + 1\right]}{3} \qquad [1]$

Now, $2 - 3x + 4x^2 = 2P_0(x) - 3p_1(x) + \left(\dfrac{4}{3}\right)\left[2P_2(x) + 1\right]$, by [1]

$$= 2P_0(x) - 3P_1(x) + \left(\dfrac{8}{3}\right)P_2(x) + \dfrac{4}{3}P_0(x)$$

$$= \frac{10}{3}P_0(x) - 3P_1(x) + \frac{8}{3}P_2(x)$$

17. Express: $x^4 - 2x^3 + 3x^2 - 4x + 5$ in term of Legendre polynomials, deriving the values of $P_n(x)$, $n = 0, 1, 2, 3, 4$ by any known formula. [VTU, Aug., 2000]

Solution: We have the Rodrigues formula

$$P_n(x) = \frac{1}{2^n n!} \frac{d^n}{dx^n}(x^2 - 1)^n \qquad\qquad [1]$$

We put $n = 0, 1, 2, 3,$ and 4 in the formula [1]

$\therefore \qquad P_0(x) = \frac{1}{2^0 \cdot 0!} \frac{d^0}{dx^0}(x^2 - 1)^0 = 1$

$\Rightarrow \qquad P_0(x) = 1$

$P_1(x) = \frac{1}{2} \cdot \frac{d}{dx}(x^2 - 1) = \frac{1}{2}(2x) \Rightarrow P_1(x) = x$

$P_2(x) = \frac{1}{4 \times 2!} \cdot \frac{d^2}{dx^2}(x^2 - 1)^2 = \frac{1}{8}\frac{d^2}{dx^2}(x^4 + 1 - 2x^2)$

$\qquad = \frac{1}{8} \cdot \frac{d}{dx}(4x^3 - 4x)$

$\qquad = \frac{1}{2}(3x^2 - 1)$

$P_2(x) = \frac{1}{2}(3x^2 - 1)$

$\Rightarrow \qquad x^2 = \frac{1}{3}(2P_2(x) + 1) = \frac{1}{3}(2P_2(x) + P_0(x))$

$P_3(x) = \frac{1}{2^3 \cdot 3!} \frac{d^3}{dx^3}(x^2 - 1)^3 = \frac{1}{48} \cdot \frac{d^3}{dx^3}(x^6 - 3x^4 + 3x^2 - 1)$

$\qquad = \frac{1}{48}(120x^3 - 72x) = \frac{24}{48}(5x^3 - 3x)$

$P_3(x) = \frac{1}{2}(5x^3 - 3x) \Rightarrow x^3 = \frac{1}{5}(2P_3(x)3P_1(x))$

$P_4(x) = \frac{1}{2^4 \cdot 4!} \frac{d^4}{dx^4}(x^2 - 1)^4 = \frac{1}{8}(35x^4 - 30x^2 + 3)$

$\Rightarrow \qquad x^4 = \frac{8}{35}P_4(x) + \frac{4}{7}P_2(x)\frac{1}{5}P_0(x)$

$$f(x) = x^4 - 2x^3 + 3x^2 - 4x + 5$$

$$= \frac{8}{35} P_4(x) + \frac{4}{7} P_2(x) + \frac{1}{5} P_0(x) - \frac{4}{5} P_3(x) + 2P_2(x) + P_0(x) - 4P_1(x) + 5P_0(x)$$

$$f(x) = \frac{8}{35} P_4(x) - \frac{4}{5} P_3(x) + \frac{18}{7} P_2(x)$$

$$= \frac{26}{5} P_1(x) + \frac{31}{5} P_0(x)$$

18. Express: $x^4 + 3x^3 - x^2 + 5x - 2$ in terms of Legendre polynomials.

Solution: $f(x) = x^4 + 3x^3 - x^2 + 5x - 2$

we have $P_0(x) = 1, P_1(x) = x$

$$P_2(x) = \frac{1}{2}(3x^2 - 1) \Rightarrow x^2 = \frac{1}{3}\left[2P_2(x) + P_0(x)\right]$$

$$P_3(x) = \frac{1}{2}(5x^3 - 3x) \Rightarrow x^3 = \frac{1}{5}\left[2P_3(x) + 3P_1(x)\right]$$

$$P_4(x) = \frac{1}{8}(35x^4 - 30x^2 + 3)$$

$$\Rightarrow \quad x^4 = \frac{1}{35}(8P_4(x) + 30x^2 - 3)$$

$$= \frac{1}{35}\left[8P_4(x) + 20P_2(x) + 7P_0(x)\right]$$

$$f(x) = \frac{8}{35} P_4(x) + \frac{20}{35} P_2(x) + \frac{7}{35} P_0(x) + \frac{6}{5} P_3(x) + \frac{9}{5} P_1(x)$$

$$- \frac{2}{3} P_2(x) - \frac{1}{3} P_0(x) + 5P_1(x) - 2P_0(x)$$

$$f(x) = \frac{8}{35} P_4(x) + \frac{6}{5} P_3(x) - \frac{2}{21} P_2(x) + \frac{34}{5} P_1(x) - \frac{32}{15} P_0(x)$$

19. Show that: **(a)** $P_2(\cos\theta) = \frac{1}{4}(1 + 3\cos 2\theta)$ **(b)** $P_3(\cos\theta) = \frac{1}{8}(3\cos\theta + 5\cos\theta)$

Solution: **(a)** We have $p_2(x) = \frac{1}{2}(3x^2 - 1)$

$$\therefore \quad P_2(\cos\theta) = \frac{1}{2}(3\cos^2\theta - 1)$$

But $\cos^2\theta = \dfrac{1}{2}(1+\cos 2\theta)$

i.e., $P_2(\cos\ \theta) = \dfrac{1}{2}\left[\dfrac{3}{2}(1+\cos 2\theta)-1\right]$

$= \dfrac{1}{4}[3+3\cos 2\theta - 2]$

Thus $P_2(\cos\theta) = \dfrac{1}{4}(1+3\cos 2\theta)$

(b) We have $P_3(x) = \dfrac{1}{2}(5x^3 - 3x)$

$\therefore\qquad P_3(\cos\ \theta) = \dfrac{1}{2}(5\cos^3\theta - 3\cos\ \theta)$

$\left(\because \cos^3\theta = \dfrac{1}{4}(\cos\ 3\theta + 3\cos\theta)\right)$, then

$P_3(\cos\theta) = \dfrac{1}{2}\left[5.\dfrac{1}{4}(\cos 3\theta + 3\cos\theta)-3\cos\theta\right]$

$= \dfrac{1}{8}[5\cos 3\theta + 15\cos\theta - 12\cos\theta]$

$\therefore\qquad P_3(\cos\theta) = \dfrac{1}{8}(5\cos 3\theta + 3\cos\theta)$

20. Using the generating function for Legendre's polynomials, show that
    (a) $P_n(1) = 1$;
    (b) $P_n(-1) = (-1)^n$;
    (c) $P_n(-x) = (-1)^n \cdot P_n(x)$

Solution: By generating function, we have $(1-2xz+z^2)^{-\frac{1}{2}} = \displaystyle\sum_{n=0}^{\infty} P_n(x)z^n$

(a) put $x = 1$; $\quad\therefore\ (1-2xz+z^2)^{-\frac{1}{2}} = \displaystyle\sum_{n=0}^{\infty} P_n(1)z^n$

but L.H.S $= \left[(1-z)^2\right]^{-\frac{1}{2}} = (1-z)^{-1} = 1+z+z^2+... = \displaystyle\sum_{n=0}^{\infty} z^n$

Thus, $\displaystyle\sum_{n=0}^{\infty} P_n(1)z^n = \sum_{n=0}^{\infty} z^n$

$\Rightarrow$ $\quad P_n(1) = 1$, (on equating the coefficients of z^n both sides)

(b) Put $x = -1$ in the generating function

$\therefore \quad \left(1 + 2z + z^2\right)^{-\frac{1}{2}} = \displaystyle\sum_{n=0}^{\infty} P_n(-1)z^n$

i.e., $\quad \displaystyle\sum_{n=0}^{\infty} P_n(-1)z^2 = \left[(1+z)^2\right]^{-\frac{1}{2}} = (1+z)^{-1}$

$\qquad\qquad = 1 - z + z^2 - z^3 + \dots.$

$\qquad\qquad = \displaystyle\sum_{n=0}^{\infty} (-1)^n z^n$

Equating the coefficients of z^n, we get $P_n(-1) = (-1)^n$

(c) Changing x to $-x$ in the generating function, we get

$$\sum_{n=0}^{\infty} P_n(-x)z^n = \left(1 + 2xz + z^2\right)^{-\frac{1}{2}}$$

Now changing z to $-z$

$$\sum_{n=0}^{\infty} P_n(-x)\cdot(-z)^n = \left(1 - 2xz + z^2\right)^{-\frac{1}{2}}$$

But $\left(1 - 2xz + z^2\right)^{-\frac{1}{2}} = \displaystyle\sum_{n=0}^{\infty} P_n(x)\cdot z^n$

$$\sum_{n=0}^{\infty} P_n(-x)\cdot(-1)^n z^n = \sum_{n=0}^{\infty} P_n(x)z^n$$

Equating coefficients of z^n, we have

$P_n(-x)(-1)^n = P_n(x)$

Multiply by $(-1)^n$

$\therefore \quad P_n(-x)(-1)^{2n} = (-1)^n P_n(x)$

But $(-1)^{2n} = 1$

Hence $P_n(-x) = (-1)^n \cdot P_n(x)$

21. Show that: $P_n(0) = 0$ if n is odd, $(-1)^{\frac{n}{2}} \dfrac{1 \cdot 3 \cdot 5 \ldots n-1}{2 \cdot 4 \cdot 6 \ldots n}$ if n is even.

Solution: We know that

$$\sum_{n=0}^{\infty} P_n(x) z^n = \left(1 - 2xz + z^2\right)^{-\frac{1}{2}} \qquad \qquad [1]$$

(put $x = 0$) we get $\displaystyle\sum_{n=0}^{\infty} P_n(0) z^n = \left(1 + z^2\right)^{-\frac{1}{2}}$

$$= 1 + \left(-\frac{1}{2}\right)(z^2) + \frac{\left(-\frac{1}{2}\right)\left(-\frac{3}{2}\right)}{1 \cdot 2} \cdot (z^2)^2 + \frac{\left(-\frac{1}{2}\right)\left(-\frac{3}{2}\right)\left(-\frac{5}{2}\right)}{1 \cdot 2 \cdot 3} - (z^2)^3 + \ldots$$

We notice that the power of 'z' in the R.H.S. are even. This implies that the coefficients of odd powers must be zero.

$P_n(0) = 0$ if n is odd.

Let $n = 2k$

Then, $P_n(0) =$ coefficient of z^{2k} on R.H.S.

$$= \frac{\left(-\frac{1}{2}\right)\left(-\frac{3}{2}\right)\left(-\frac{5}{3}\right) \ldots \text{to } k \text{ terms}}{1 \cdot 2 \cdot 3 \ldots k} = (-1)^k \cdot \frac{1 \cdot 3 \cdot 5 \ldots (2k-1)}{2^k \cdot 1 \cdot 2 \cdot 3 \ldots k}$$

$$= (-1)^k \cdot \frac{1 \cdot 3 \cdot 5 \ldots (2k-1)}{2 \cdot 4 \cdot 6 \ldots 2k}$$

$2k = n$

Thus, $P_n(0) = (-1)^{\frac{n}{2}} \dfrac{1 \cdot 3 \cdot 5 \ldots (n-1)}{2 \cdot 4 \cdot 6 \ldots n}$, if n is even.

22. Prove that: **(a)** $\displaystyle\int_{-1}^{1} P_n(x)\, dx = 2$ if $n = 0$

(b) $\displaystyle\int_{-1}^{1} P_n(x)\, dx = 0$ if $n \geq 1$.

Solution: (a) When $n = 0$, $P_n(x) = P_0(x) = 1$

$\therefore \quad \displaystyle\int_{-1}^{1} P_n(x)\, dx = \int_{-1}^{1} dx = 2$

(b) Using Rodrigue's formula, we have

$$\int_{-1}^{1} P_n(x)\,dx = \frac{1}{2^n \cdot n!}\int_{-1}^{1} D^n\left(x^2-1\right)^n dx, \quad \text{where } D^n = \frac{d^n}{dx^n}$$

$$= \frac{1}{2^n \cdot n!}\left[D^{n-1}\left(x^2-1\right)^n\right]_{-1}^{1}$$

$$= \frac{1}{2^n \cdot n!}\left[D^{n-1}\left\{(x-1)^n(x+1)^n\right\}\right]_{-1}^{1}$$

$$= \frac{1}{2^n \cdot n!}\left[D^{n-1}(x-1)^n \cdot (x+1)^n + {}^{n-1}C_1 D^{n-2}(n-1)^n D(n+1)^n + \ldots \atop +(x-1)^n \cdot D^{n-1}(x+1)^n\right]_{-1}^{1}$$

$$\left[\because \text{ by Leibnitz's theorem, } D^n[uv] = D^n u \cdot v + {}^n C_1 D^{n-1} u \cdot Dr + \ldots\ldots + u \cdot D^n v\right]$$

$$= \frac{1}{2^n \cdot n!}\left[n!(n-1)(n+1)^n + \ldots\ldots + n!(x+1)(x-1)^n\right]_{-1}^{1} = 0$$

$$\because \quad D^n(ax+b)^m = a^n \frac{m!}{(m-n)!}(ax+b)^{m-n}$$

23. Show that: $\displaystyle\int_{-1}^{+1} x^m P_n(x)\,dx = 0$ if $m < n$ and hence deduce that

$$\int_{-1}^{+1} P_m(x) P_n(x)\,d_n = 0 \text{ if } m \neq n$$

Solution: Using Rodrigue's formula, we have

$$P_n(x) = \frac{1}{2^n \cdot n!}\frac{d^n}{dx^n}\left(x^2-1\right)^n$$

$$\therefore \quad \int_{-1}^{1} x^m P_n(x)\,dx = \frac{1}{2^n \cdot n!} \int_{-1}^{1} x^m D^n\left(x^2-1\right)^n dx \quad \left(D^n = \frac{d^n}{dx^n}\right)$$

$$= \frac{1}{2^n \cdot n!}\left[\left\{x^m D^{n-1}\left(x^2-1\right)^n\right\}_{-1}^{1} - m\int_{-1}^{1} x^{m-1} D^{n-1}\left(x^2-1\right)^n dx\right] \tag{1}$$

$$= \frac{(-1)!m}{2^n \cdot n!}\int_{-1}^{1} x^{m-1} D^{n-1}\left(x^2-1\right)^n dx$$

[∴ The first term in [1] vanishes on using Leibnitz's theorem, *see* previous Example 22]

$$= \frac{(1)^1 m}{2^n \cdot n!}\left[\left\{x^{m-1}D^{n-2}\left(x^2-1\right)^n\right\}_{-1}^{1} - (m-1)\int_{-1}^{1}x^{m-2}D^{n-2}\left(x^2-1\right)^n dx\right]$$

$$= \frac{(-1)^2 m(m-1)}{\left(2^n \cdot n!\right)}\int_{-1}^{1}x^{m-2}D^{n-2}\left(x^2-1\right)dx \qquad [2]$$

(the first term vanishes as before)

$$= \frac{(-1)^m m(m-1)\dots\dots3\cdot2\cdot1}{2^n \cdot n!} \times \int_{-1}^{1}x^{m-m}D^{n-m}\left(x^2-1\right)^n dx$$

(on continuing the similar steps $m-2$ times more and noting that $m < n$)

$$= \frac{(-1)^m m!}{2^n \cdot n!}\int_{-1}^{1}\frac{d}{dx}\left\{\frac{d^{n-m-1}}{dx^{n-m-1}}\left(x^2-1^n\right)\right\}dx$$

$$= \frac{(-1)^m \cdot m!}{2^n \cdot n!}\left[\frac{d^{n-m-1}}{dx^{n-m-1}}\left(x^2-1\right)^n\right]_{-1}^{1}$$

Hence $\int_{-1}^{1}x^m P_n(x)dx = \dfrac{(-1)^m \cdot m!}{2^n \cdot n!}\left[d^{n-m-1}\left\{(x-1)^n(x+1)^n\right\}\right]_{-1}^{1} = 0$

(by using Leibnitz's theorem and simplifying as before)

$$\int_{-1}^{1}x^m P_m(x)dx = 0 \text{ if } m < n \qquad [3]$$

Deduction: Since $P_m(x)$ is a polynomial of degree m, so we can take $P_m(x) = x^m$ in the above result.

Hence $\displaystyle\int_{-1}^{+1}P_m(x)P_n(x)dx = 0$ if $m < n$ \qquad [1]

Similarly, we can show that $\displaystyle\int_{-1}^{+1}P_n(x)P_m(x)dx = 0$ if $n < m$ $(i.e.\ m > n)$ \qquad [2]

Combining [1] and [2], we can write $\displaystyle\int_{-1}^{+1}P_m(x)P_n(x)dx = 0$ if $m \neq n$ \qquad [3]

24. Show that: $\displaystyle\int_{-1}^{+1}f(x)P_n(x)dx = \frac{(-1)^n}{2^n \cdot n!}\int_{-1}^{+1}f^{(n)}(x)\left[\left(x^2-1\right)^n\right]dx$

where $f^{(n)}(x) = \dfrac{d^n}{dx^n}\{f(x)\}$

Solution: Using Rodrigue's formula, we have

$$\int_{-1}^{+1}f(x)P_n(x)dx = \frac{1}{2^n \cdot n!}\int_{-1}^{+1}f(x)D^n\left(x^2-1\right)^n dx$$

$$= \frac{1}{2^n \cdot n!} \left[\left\{ f(x) D^{n-1} \left(x^2 - 1 \right)^n \right\}_{-1}^{1} - \int_{-1}^{1} f'(x) D^{n-1} \left(x^2 - 1 \right)^n dx \right] \qquad [1]$$

(by parts)

$$= \frac{(-1)^2}{2^n \cdot n!} \int_{-1}^{1} f'(x) D^{n-1} \left(x^2 - 1 \right)^n dx$$

(the first term in [1] vanishes on using Leibnitz's theorem as shown in the previous solved examples)

$$= \frac{(-1)^1}{2^n \cdot n!} \left[\left\{ f'(x) D^{n-2} \left(x^2 - 1 \right)^n \right\}_{-1}^{1} - \int_{-1}^{1} f''(x) D^{n-2} \left(x^2 - 1 \right)^n dx \right] \qquad \text{(by parts)}$$

$$= \frac{(-1)^2}{2^n \cdot n!} \int_{-1}^{+1} f''(x) D^{n-2} \left(x^2 - 1 \right)^n dx$$

($\therefore$ the first term in the previous step vanishes as explained in examples solved earlier)

$$= \frac{(-1)^n}{2^n \cdot n!} \int_{-1}^{1} f^{(n)}(x) D^{n-n} \left(x^2 - 1 \right)^n dx$$

(on continuing the similar steps $n-2$ times more)

$$= \frac{(-1)^n}{2^n \cdot n!} \int_{-1}^{1} \left(x^2 - 1 \right) f^{(n)}(x) dx$$

Thus $\displaystyle \int_{-1}^{+1} f(x) P_n(x) dx = \frac{(-1)^n}{2^n \cdot n!} \int_{-1}^{1} \left(x^2 - 1 \right)^n f^{(n)}(x) dx$

25. Show that: $\displaystyle \int_{-1}^{+1} \frac{P_n(x)}{\sqrt{1 - 2xz + z^2}} \, dx = \frac{2}{2n+1} z^n$

Solution: Using generating function, we have

$$\frac{1}{\sqrt{1 - 2xz + z^2}} = \sum_{m=0}^{\infty} P_m(x) z^m$$

$\therefore \qquad \displaystyle \frac{P_n(x)}{\sqrt{1 - 2xz + z^2}} = \sum_{m=0}^{\infty} P_n(x) . P_m(x) z^m$

Integrating w.r.t. x from -1 to 1,

$$\int_{-1}^{1} \frac{P_n(x)}{\sqrt{1-2xz+z^2}} dx = \sum_{m=0}^{\infty} \int_{-1}^{1} P_m(x) P_n(x) \cdot z^m dx$$

By orthogonal property, $\int_{-1}^{1} P_n(x) P_m(x) dx = 0$ if $n \ne m$.

Hence, R.H.S. $= \int_{-1}^{1} P_n(x) P_n(x) dx \, z^n$, (other terms vanish)

$$= \left(\int_{-1}^{1} \left[P_n(x) \right]^2 dx \right) \cdot z^n$$

$$= \frac{2}{2n+1} \cdot z^n$$

$$\int_{-1}^{1} \frac{P_n(x)}{\sqrt{1-2xz+z^2}} dx = \frac{2}{2n+1} \cdot z^n$$

26. Expand: $f(x)$ in the form $\sum_{r=0}^{\infty} c_r P_r(x)$, where

$$f(x) = \begin{cases} 0 & -1 < x < 0 \\ 1, & 0 < x < 1 \end{cases} \qquad\qquad [1]$$

Solution: We know that $f(x) = \sum_{r=1}^{\infty} c_r P_r(x)$ \qquad [2]

Where $c_r = \left(r + \frac{1}{2} \right) \int_{-1}^{1} f(x) P_r(x) dx$

$$= \frac{2r+1}{2} \left[\int_{-1}^{0} f(x) P_r(x) dx + \int_{0}^{1} f(x) P_r(x) dx \right]$$

$\therefore \qquad c_r = \frac{2r+1}{2} \int_{+1}^{1} P_r(x) dx, \text{ using } [1]$ \qquad [3]

Putting $r = 0$, 1, 2,... successively, in [3] we get

$$c_0 = \frac{1}{2} \int_{0}^{1} P_0(x) dx = \frac{1}{2} \int_{0}^{1} (1) dx = \frac{1}{2}$$

$$c_1 = \frac{3}{2} \int_{0}^{1} P_1(x) dx = \frac{3}{2} \int_{0}^{1} x \, dx = \frac{3}{4}$$

$$c_2 = \frac{5}{2} \int_{0}^{1} P_2(x) dx = \int_{0}^{1} \frac{3x^2 - 1}{2} dx = 0$$

$$c_3 = \frac{7}{2} \int_{0}^{1} P_3(x) dx = \frac{7}{2} \int_{0}^{1} \frac{5x^3 - 2x}{2} dx = -\frac{7}{16}$$

and so on. Using these values in [2], we get

$$f(x) = \left(\frac{1}{2}\right)P_0(x) + \left(\frac{3}{4}\right)P_1(x) - \left(\frac{7}{16}\right)P_3(x) + \ldots + c_r P_r(x) + \ldots$$

where, $c_r = \left(r + \frac{1}{2}\right)\int_{-1}^{1} P_r(x)\,dx$

27. Expand: the function $f(x) = \begin{cases} 0 & \text{in } -1 < x < 0 \\ x & \text{in } 0 < x < 1 \end{cases}$ in terms of Legendre polynomials.

Solution: The Fourier Legendre expansion of $f(x)$ is

$$f(x) = \sum_{n=0}^{\infty} c_n P_n(x)$$

Where, $c_n = \dfrac{2n+1}{2}\int_{-1}^{1} f(x) P_n(x)\,dx \quad = \dfrac{2n+1}{2}\int_{0}^{1} x P_n(x)\,dx$

$\therefore \quad c_0 = \dfrac{1}{2}\int_{0}^{1} x P_0(x)\,dx \quad = \dfrac{1}{2}\int_{-1}^{1} x\,dx = \dfrac{1}{2}\left[\dfrac{x^2}{2}\right]_0^1 = \dfrac{1}{4}$

$c_1 = \dfrac{3}{2}\int_{0}^{1} x P_1(x)\,dx = \dfrac{3}{2}\int_{0}^{1} x^2\,dx \quad = \dfrac{3}{2}\left[\dfrac{x^3}{3}\right]_0^1 = \dfrac{1}{2}$

$c_2 = \dfrac{5}{2}\int_{-1}^{1} x P_2(x)\,dx \quad = \dfrac{5}{2}\int_{0}^{1} x\left(\dfrac{3x^2-1}{2}\right)dx \quad = \dfrac{5}{4}\left[\dfrac{3x^4}{4} - \dfrac{x^2}{2}\right]_0^1 = \dfrac{5}{16}$

$c_3 = \dfrac{7}{2}\int_{0}^{1} x P_3(x)\,dx \quad = \dfrac{7}{4}\int_{0}^{1} x\left(\dfrac{5x^3-3x}{2}\right)dx \quad = \dfrac{7}{4}\left[x^5 - x^3\right]_0^1 = 0$

$c_4 = \dfrac{9}{2}\int_{0}^{1} x P_4(x)\,dx \quad = \dfrac{9}{2}\int_{0}^{1} x\left(\dfrac{35x^4 - 30x^2 + 3}{8}\right)dx$

$\quad = \dfrac{9}{16}\left[\dfrac{35x^6}{6} - \dfrac{30x^4}{4} + \dfrac{3x^2}{2}\right]_0^1 \quad = -\dfrac{3}{32}$

$\therefore \quad f(x) = \dfrac{1}{4}P_0 + \dfrac{1}{2}P_1 + \dfrac{5}{16}P_2 - \dfrac{3}{32}P_4 + \ldots$

EXERCISES

1. Express the following in terms of Legendre Polynomials:

a) $1 + x - x^2$

$$\left[Ans: \frac{2}{3}P_2(x) + P_1(x) + \frac{2}{3}P_0(x) \right]$$

b) $x^4 + x^3 + x^2 + x + 1$

$$\left[Ans: \frac{8}{35}P_4(x) + \frac{2}{5}P_3 + \frac{26}{25}P_2(x) + \frac{3}{5}P_1(x) + \frac{23}{15}P_0(x) \right]$$

c) $1 + 2x - 3x^3 + 4x^3$

$$\left[Ans: \frac{8}{5}P_3(x) - 2P_2(x) + \frac{22}{5}P_1(x) \right]$$

d) $x^3 + 1$

$$\left[Ans: \frac{2}{3}P_3(x)\frac{3}{5}P_1(x) + P_0(x) \right]$$

2. Show that:

a) $x^5 = \frac{8}{63}\left[P_5(x) + \frac{7}{2}P_3(x) + \frac{27}{8}P_1(x) \right]$ b) $x^3 = \frac{2}{5}P_3(x) + \frac{3}{5}P_1(x)$

3. Prove that $P_n(-x) = (-1)^n P_n(x)$

4. Show that $\int_{-1}^{+1} x P_n(x)dx = \frac{2n}{4n^2 - 1}$

5. $\int_{-1}^{+1}(1-x^2) \cdot P_m^1(x) P_n^1(x)dx \begin{cases} = 0 & \text{where } m \neq n \\ = \dfrac{2n(n+1)}{2n+1} & \text{when } m = n \end{cases}$

where $P_m(x)$ in the Legendre polynomial.

6. Prove that $\int_{-1}^{1} P_n(x)(1 - 2xt + t^2)^{-\frac{1}{2}} dx = \frac{2t^n}{2t+1}$

7. Show that $\dfrac{1 - t^2}{(1 - 2xt + t^2)^{\frac{3}{2}}} = \sum_{n=0}^{\infty}(2n+1)t^n P_n(x)$

8. Expand $4x^3 - 2x^2 - 3x + 8$ in terms of Legendre Polynomials in the interval $[-1, 1]$.

9. If $f(x) = \begin{cases} 0 & \text{in } -1 < x < 0 \\ 1 & \text{in } 0 < x < 1 \end{cases}$, Show that $f(x) = \frac{1}{2}P_0(x) + \frac{3}{4}P_1(x) - \frac{7}{16}P_3(x)$

Bessel's Equation and Bessel's Function of First Kind

Bessel's Equation

The differential equation of the form

$$x^2 y'' + xy' + \left(x^2 - n^2\right)y = 0 \qquad\qquad [1]$$

or $\qquad y'' + \left(\dfrac{1}{x}\right)y' + \left(1 - \dfrac{n^2}{x^2}\right)y = 0 \qquad\qquad [1]'$

is called Bessel's equation of order n, n being a non-negative constant. We now solve [1] in series by using the well-known method of Frobenius.

Let us assume a solution of [1] in the form

$$y = \sum_{r=0}^{\infty} a_r x^{k+r}$$

$$= a_0 x^k + a_1 x^{k+1} + a_2 x^{k+2} + \ldots$$

so that $\quad y' = \sum_{r=0}^{\infty} a_r (k+r) x^{k+r-1}$

and $\quad y'' = \sum_{r=0}^{\infty} a_r (k+r)(k+r-1) x^{k+r-2}$

Substituting these values in the equation, we have

$$x^2 \sum_{r=0}^{\infty} a_r (k+r)(k+r-1) x^{k+r-2} + x \sum_{r=0}^{\infty} a_r (k+r) x^{k+r-1} + \left(x^2 - n^2\right) \sum_{r=0}^{\infty} a_r x^{k+r} = 0$$

or $\quad \sum_{r=0}^{\infty} a_r (k+r)(k+r-1) x^{k+r} + \sum_{r=0}^{\infty} a_r (k+r) x^{k+r} + \sum a_r x^{k+r+2} - n^2 \sum_{r=0}^{\infty} a_r x^{k+r} = 0$

or $\quad \sum_{r=0}^{\infty} a_r \left[(k+r)(k+r-1) + (k+r) - n^2\right] x^{k+r} + \sum_{r=0}^{\infty} a_r x^{k+r+2} = 0$

or $\quad \sum_{r=0}^{\infty} a_r \left[(k+r) - n^2\right] x^{k+r} + \sum_{r=0}^{\infty} a_r x^{k+r+2} = 0$

Equate to zero, the coefficient of x^k, we get

$$a_0 \left[(k+0)^2 = n^2\right] \quad (r=0)$$

or $\quad k^2 = n^2$ or $k = n \quad a_0 \neq 0$

Again, equate to zero, the coefficient of x^{k+1}; $(r = 1)$

$$a_1\left[(k+1)^2 = n^2\right] = 0$$

i.e., $a_1 = 0$, since $(k+1)^2 - n^2 \neq 0$

To find a relation in successive coefficient, we equate to zero, the coefficient of x^{k+r+2}, we get

$$a_r + 2\left[(k+r+2)^2 - n^2\right] + a_r = 0$$

or $\qquad a_{r+2} = -\dfrac{1}{(k+r+2)^2 - n^2}.a_r$

$\therefore \qquad a_3 = a_5 = a_7 = ... = 0$ since $a_1 = 0$

If $\quad r = 0; \qquad a_2 = -\dfrac{1}{(k+2)^2 - n^2}a_0$

If $\quad r = 2, \qquad a_4 = -\dfrac{1}{(k+4)^2 - n^2}a_2$

$$= \dfrac{1}{\left[(k+2)^2 - n^2\right]\left[(k+4)^2 - n^2\right]}a_0 \quad \text{and so on.}$$

On putting down the values of the coefficient in [2], we have

$$y = a_0 x^k - \dfrac{a_0}{(k+2)^2 - n^2}x^{k+2} + \dfrac{a_0}{\left[(k+2)^2 - n^2\right]\left[(k+4)^2 - n^2\right]}x^{k+4} + ...$$

$$y = a_0 x^k\left[1 - \dfrac{1}{(k+2)^2 - n^2}x^2 + \dfrac{1}{\left[(k+2)^2 - n^2\right]\left[(k+4)^2 - n^2\right]}x^4 - ...\right]$$

For $\quad k = n$

$$y = a_0 x^n\left[1 - \dfrac{1}{2\cdot2(n+1)}x^2 + \dfrac{1}{2^2\cdot2^2\cdot2!(n+1)(n+2)}x^4 - ...\right] \qquad [3]$$

where a_0 is an arbitrary constant.

For $\quad k = -n$

$$y = a_0 x^{-n}\left[1 - \dfrac{1}{2\cdot2(1-n)}x^2 + \dfrac{1}{2^2\cdot2^2\cdot2!(1-n)(2-n)}x^4 - ...\right]$$

Bessel's function of first kind ($J_n(x)$)

The solution of Bessel's equation found above are called Bessel's functions. We know that the solution of Bessel's equation in ascending powers of x is given by [3]

$$y = a_0 x^n \left[1 - \frac{x^2}{2 \cdot 2 \cdot (n+1)} + \frac{x^4}{2 \cdot 4 \cdot 2^2 (n+1)(n+2)} - \cdots \right]$$

where a_0 is an arbitrary constant.

If a_0 is chosen to be equal to $\dfrac{1}{2^n \Gamma(n+1)}$, then

$$y = \frac{x^n}{2^n \Gamma(n+1)} \sum_0^\infty \frac{(-1)^r x^{2r}}{2^{2r} \cdot r! \cdot (n+1)(n+2)\ldots(n+r)} \qquad \text{from [3]}$$

But $\quad \Gamma(n+1) = n!$

$\therefore \quad \Gamma(n+1) \cdot (n+1)(n+2)\ldots(n+r)$

$\quad = n!(n+1)(n+2)\ldots(n+r)$

$\quad = (n+r)! = \Gamma(n+r+1)$

$$\therefore \quad y = \sum_0^\infty \frac{(-1)^r}{r!\,\Gamma(n+r+1)} \left(\frac{x}{2} \right)^{n+2r}$$

The R.H.S. of above is called $J_n(x)$. (Bessel's functions of first kind)

$$\therefore \quad J_n(x) = \sum_0^\infty \frac{(-1)^r}{r!\,\Gamma(n+r+1)} \left(\frac{x}{2} \right)^{n+2r}$$

Putting $-n$ for n we get the other solution of Bessel's equation as:

$$J_{-n}(x) = \sum_0^\infty \frac{(-1)^r}{r!\,\Gamma(-n+r+1)} \left(\frac{x}{2} \right)^{-n+2r}$$

The solution $J_n(x)$, $J_{-n}(x)$ are two solution of Bessel's Differential equation and its general solution is $y = AJ_n(x) + BJ_{-n}(x)$

Note: 1. Equation [1] is known as Bessel's function of first kind [i.e., $J_n(x)$].

2. If the independent variable x is changed to λx where λ is a constant, then Bessel's differential equation will be

$$x^2 \frac{d^2 y}{dx^2} - x \frac{dy}{dx} + (\lambda^2 x^2 - n^2) y = 0 \quad \text{and its general solution is}$$

$$y = AJ_n(\lambda x) + BJ_{-n}(\lambda x)$$

EXAMPLES

1. Determine the values of

(a) $J_{\frac{1}{2}}(x)$ (b) $J_{-\frac{1}{2}}(x)$ (c) $J_{\frac{3}{2}}(x)$ (d) $J_{-\frac{3}{2}}(x)$

Solution: (a) $J_{\frac{1}{2}}(x) = \sqrt{\left(\dfrac{2}{\pi n}\right)} \sin x$

We know that $J_n(x) = \dfrac{x^n}{2^n \Gamma(n+1)}\left[1 - \dfrac{-x^2}{2 \cdot 2(n+1)} + \dfrac{x^4}{2 \cdot 4 \cdot 2^2(n+1)(n+2)} + ...\right]$ [1]

Putting $n = \dfrac{1}{2}$, we get

$$J_{\frac{1}{2}}(x) = \dfrac{x^{\frac{1}{2}}}{2^{\frac{1}{2}}\Gamma\left(\dfrac{3}{2}\right)}\left[1 - \dfrac{x^2}{2 \cdot 3} + \dfrac{x^4}{2 \cdot 3 \cdot 4 \cdot 5} + ...\right]$$

$$= \dfrac{x^{\frac{1}{2}}}{2^{\frac{1}{2}}\dfrac{1}{2}\Gamma\left(\dfrac{1}{2}\right)} \cdot \dfrac{1}{x}\left[x - \dfrac{x^3}{3!} + \dfrac{x^5}{5!} - ...\right]$$

$$= \sqrt{\left(\dfrac{2}{\pi x}\right)} \sin x$$

(b) To prove that $J_{\frac{1}{2}}(x) = \sqrt{\left(\dfrac{2}{\pi x}\right)} \cos x$

Putting $n = -\dfrac{1}{2}$ in [1], we get

$$J_{\frac{1}{2}}(x) = \dfrac{x^{-\frac{1}{2}}}{2^{-\frac{1}{2}}\Gamma\dfrac{1}{2}}\left[1 - \dfrac{x^2}{2} + \dfrac{x^4}{2 \cdot 3 \cdot 4} + ...\right]$$

$$= \sqrt{\left(\dfrac{2}{\pi x}\right)}\left[1 - \dfrac{x^2}{2!} + \dfrac{x^4}{4!} + ...\right] = \sqrt{\left(\dfrac{2}{\pi x}\right)} \cdot \cos x$$

(c) To prove that $\quad J_{\frac{3}{2}}(x)=\sqrt{\left(\dfrac{2}{\pi x}\right)}\left[\dfrac{\sin x}{x}-\cos x\right]$

Solution: Put $\quad n=\dfrac{3}{2};\quad$ we get

$$J_n=\dfrac{x^2}{2^n\sqrt{n+1}}\left[1-\dfrac{x^2}{2\cdot 2(n+1)}+\dfrac{x^4}{2\cdot 4\cdot 2^2\cdot(n+1)(n+2)}+\ldots\right]$$

$$J_{\frac{3}{2}}(x)=\dfrac{x^{\frac{3}{2}}}{2^{\frac{3}{2}}\Gamma\dfrac{5}{2}}\left[1-\dfrac{x^2}{2\cdot 5}+\dfrac{x^4}{2\cdot 4\cdot 5\cdot 7}-\dfrac{x^6}{2\cdot 4\cdot 6\cdot 5\cdot 7\cdot 9}+\ldots\right]$$

$$=\dfrac{x^{-\frac{3}{2}}}{2\Gamma 2\cdot\dfrac{3}{2}\cdot\dfrac{1}{2}\Gamma\pi}\left[x^2-\dfrac{x^4}{2\cdot 5}+\dfrac{x^6}{2\cdot 4\cdot 5\cdot 7}-\dfrac{x^8}{2\cdot 4\cdot 6\cdot 5\cdot 7\cdot 9}+\ldots\right]$$

$$=\sqrt{\left(\dfrac{2}{x\pi}\right)}\left[\dfrac{x^2}{3}-\dfrac{x^4}{2\cdot 3\cdot 5}+\dfrac{x^6}{2\cdot 3\cdot 4\cdot 5\cdot 7}+\dfrac{x^8}{2\cdot 3\cdot 4\cdot 6\cdot 5\cdot 7\cdot 9}+\ldots\right]$$

$$=\sqrt{\left(\dfrac{2}{\pi x}\right)}\left[\dfrac{2x^2}{2\cdot 3}-\dfrac{4x^4}{5!}+\dfrac{6x^6}{7!}-\dfrac{8x^8}{9!}+\ldots\right]$$

$$=\sqrt{\left(\dfrac{2}{\pi x}\right)}\left[\dfrac{(3-1)}{3!}x^2-\dfrac{(5-1)}{5!}x^4+\dfrac{(7-1)}{7!}x^6-\dfrac{(9-1)}{9!}x^8+\ldots\right]$$

$$=\sqrt{\left(\dfrac{2}{\pi x}\right)}\left[\left\{\dfrac{x^2}{2!}-\dfrac{x^2}{3!}\right\}-\left\{\dfrac{x^4}{4!}-\dfrac{x^4}{5!}\right\}+\left\{\dfrac{x^6}{6!}-\dfrac{x^6}{7!}\right\}+\ldots\right]$$

$$=\sqrt{\left(\dfrac{2}{\pi x}\right)}\left[\left\{\dfrac{-x^2}{3!}+\dfrac{x^4}{5!}-\dfrac{x^6}{7!}+\ldots\right\}-\left\{-\dfrac{x^2}{2!}\right\}+\left\{\dfrac{x^4}{4!}+\dfrac{x^6}{7!}\right\}+\ldots\right]$$

$$=\sqrt{\left(\dfrac{2}{\pi x}\right)}\left[\dfrac{1}{x}\left\{x-\dfrac{x^3}{3!}+\dfrac{x^5}{5!}-\dfrac{x^7}{7!}+\ldots\right\}-\left\{1-\dfrac{x^2}{2!}\right\}+\left\{\dfrac{x^4}{4!}-\dfrac{x^6}{6!}\right\}+\ldots\right]$$

$$=\sqrt{\left(\dfrac{2}{\pi x}\right)}\left[\dfrac{\sin x}{x}-\cos x\right]$$

(d) $\quad J_{-\frac{3}{2}}(x) = \sqrt{\left(\dfrac{2}{\pi x}\right)}\left[-\dfrac{1}{x}\cos x - \sin x\right]$

$$J_n(x) = \dfrac{x^2}{2^n\Gamma(n+1)}\left[1 - \dfrac{x^2}{2\cdot 2(n+1)} + \dfrac{x^4}{2\cdot 4\cdot 2^2(n+1)(n+2)} + \cdots\right]$$

$(n+1)\cdot\Gamma(n+1) = \Gamma(n+2)$

Multiply above and below by $(n + 1)$

$\therefore\quad J_n(x) = \dfrac{x^n(n+1)}{2^n\Gamma(n+1)}\left[1 - \dfrac{x^2}{2\cdot 2(n+1)} + \dfrac{x^4}{2\cdot 4\cdot 2^2(n+1)(n+2)}\right]$

Now putting $n = -\dfrac{3}{2}$

$$J_{-\frac{3}{2}} = \dfrac{x^{-\frac{3}{2}}\left(-\dfrac{1}{2}\right)}{2^{-\frac{3}{2}}\sqrt{\dfrac{1}{2}}}\left[1 + \dfrac{x^2}{2} - \dfrac{x^4}{2\cdot 4\cdot 1}\right]$$

$$= -\sqrt{\left\{\dfrac{2}{\pi x}\right\}}\dfrac{1}{\pi}\left\{1 + x^2\left(1 - \dfrac{1}{2}\right) - x^4\left(\dfrac{1}{6} - \dfrac{1}{2x}\right)\cdots\right\}$$

$$= -\sqrt{\dfrac{2}{\pi x}}\left[\dfrac{1}{x}\right]\left\{1 - \dfrac{x^2}{2!} + \dfrac{x^4}{4!}\cdots\right\} + \dfrac{1}{x}\left\{x^2 - \dfrac{x^4}{3!}\cdots\right\}$$

$$= -\sqrt{\left\{\dfrac{2}{\pi x}\right\}}\left\{\dfrac{1}{x}\cos x + \left\{x - \dfrac{x^3}{3!} + \cdots\right\}\right\}$$

$$= -\sqrt{\left\{\dfrac{2}{\pi x}\right\}}\left[-\dfrac{1}{x}\cos x - \sin x\right]$$

where n is an integer,

2. Show that: $J_{-n}(x) = (-1)^n\cdot J_n(x)$

Solution: Method (1): By Definition,

$$J_n(x) = \sum_{r=0}^{\infty}\dfrac{(-1)^r}{r!\Gamma n+r+1}\left(\dfrac{x}{2}\right)^{n+2r}$$

$$J_{-n}(x) = \sum_{r=0}^{\infty} \frac{(-1)^r}{r!\,\Gamma(-n+r+1)}\left(\frac{x}{2}\right)^{-n+2r}$$

If $r = 0, 1, 2,\ldots n-1$, then $-n+r+1$ is a negative integer or zero.

$$\Gamma(-n+r+1) = \infty \quad \text{or} \quad \frac{1}{\Gamma(-n+r+1)} = 0$$

Therefore the corresponding terms do not appear in the summation

Hence, $\quad J_{-n}(x) = \sum_{r=n}^{\infty} \frac{(-1)^r}{r!\,\Gamma(-n+r+1)}\left(\frac{x}{2}\right)^{-n+2}$

write $r = n + s$, where $s = 0, 1, 2, 3,$

$$\therefore \quad J_{-n}(x) = \sum_{s=0}^{\infty} \frac{(-1)^{n+s}}{(n+s)!\,\Gamma(s+1)}\cdot\left(\frac{x}{2}\right)^{n+2s}$$

Since n and s are non-negative integers,

we have $\Gamma(s+1) = s!$

$(n+s)! = \Gamma(n+s+1)$

and $\quad J_{-n}(x) = \sum_{s=0}^{\infty} \frac{(-1)^n \cdot (-1)^s}{\Gamma(n+s+1)\cdot s!}\cdot\left(\frac{x}{2}\right)^{n+}$

$\quad = (-1)^n J_n(x)$ by definition.

Thus, $J_{-n}(x) = (-1)^n J_n(x)$, if '$n$' is any positive integer.

Method (2):

(1) When n is an integer show that $J_{-n}(x) = (-1)^n J_n(x)$

by definition, we have $J_{-n}(x) = \sum_{r=0}^{\infty} \frac{(-1)^r}{r!\,(r-n)!}$ \hfill [1]

because, in this case $\Gamma(-n+r+1) = (r-n)!$

(Here $r \geq n$ meaningful) $\quad (\because$ if $r < n)$

Setting $s = r - n$ in [1] we get $J_{-n}(x) = \sum_{r=0}^{\infty} \frac{(-1)^{n+s}}{s!\,(n+s)!}\frac{x^{n+2s}}{2}$

$$= (-1)^n \sum_{r=0}^{\infty} \frac{(-1)^s}{s!(n+s)!} \left(\frac{x}{2}\right)^{n+2s}$$

$$= (-1)^n . J_n(x)$$

$$\left[\because (n+s)! = \Gamma(n+s+1) \right]$$

$$\therefore \quad J_{-n}(x) = (-1)^n J_n(x)$$

Generating Function

The function $e^{\frac{x}{2}\left(t-\frac{1}{t}\right)} = \sum_{-\infty}^{\infty} J_n(x) t^n$ is called the generating function of Bessel's function.

Method (1): $\quad e^{\frac{x}{2}\left(t-\frac{1}{t}\right)} = e^{\left(\frac{xt}{2}\right)} . e^{\left(\frac{x}{2t}\right)}$

$$= \sum_{r=0}^{\infty} \frac{\left(\dfrac{xt}{2}\right)^r}{r!} . \sum_{k=0}^{\infty} \left(\frac{-\dfrac{x}{2t}}{k!}\right)^k$$

$$= \sum_{r=0}^{\infty} \sum_{k=0}^{\infty} \frac{(-1)^k \left(\dfrac{x}{2}\right)^{r+k}}{r!k!} t^{r-k}$$

Let $r - k = n$, so that n varies from $-\infty$ to $+\infty$,

then, $e^{\frac{x}{2}\left(t-\frac{1}{t}\right)}$

$$= \sum_{-\infty}^{\infty} \left\{ \sum_{k=0}^{\infty} \frac{(-1)^k}{(k+n)!k!} \left(\frac{x}{2}\right)^{n+2k} \right\} t^n$$

$$= \sum_{-\infty}^{\infty} J_n(x) t^n$$

$$\left(\because e^x = 1 + \frac{x}{1!} + \frac{x^2}{2!} + ... \infty \right)$$

Show that: $e^{\frac{x}{2}\left(t-\frac{1}{t}\right)} = \sum t^n J_n(x)$

Method (2): We can write $e^{\frac{x}{2}\left(t-\frac{1}{t}\right)} = e^{\left(\frac{x}{2}\right)t} \cdot e^{\left(-\frac{x}{2}\right)\frac{1}{t}}$

$$\left[\left\{1+\left(\frac{x}{2}\right)\frac{t}{1!}+\left(\frac{x}{2}\right)^2\frac{t^2}{2!}+...+\left(\frac{x}{2}\right)^n\frac{t^n}{n!}+\left(\frac{x}{2}\right)^{n+1}\cdot\frac{t^{n+1}}{(n+1)!}+...\right\}\right.$$

$$\left.\left\{1-\left(\frac{x}{2}\right)\cdot\frac{1}{t1!}+\left(\frac{x}{2}\right)^2\cdot\frac{1}{t^2 2!}-\left(\frac{x}{2}\right)^3\cdot\frac{1}{t^3}\cdot\frac{1}{3!}+...\right\}\right]$$

When we multiply terms of t^n, t^{n+1}, t^{n+2}...in the first bracket with $1, \dfrac{1}{t}, \dfrac{1}{t^2}...$ in the second bracket, we get the terms of t^n.

Thus, the coefficient of t^n in the product are:

$$=\left(\frac{x^n}{2}\right)^n\frac{t^n}{n!}(1)-\left(\frac{x}{2}\right)^{n+2}\frac{t^n}{(n+1)1!}+\left(\frac{x}{2}\right)^{n+4}\frac{t^n}{(n+2)!2!}+...$$

$$=t^n\left[\left(\frac{x}{2}\right)^n\cdot\frac{1}{n!}-\frac{\left(\frac{x}{2}\right)^{n+2}}{(n+1)!1!}+\frac{\left(\frac{x}{2}\right)^{n+4}}{(n+2)!2!}+...+\frac{(-1)^r\left(\frac{x}{2}\right)^{n+2r}}{(n+r)!r!}\right]$$

$$=t^n\sum_{r=0}^{\infty}\frac{(-1)^r}{(n+r)!r!}\left(\frac{x}{2}\right)^{n+2r}$$

$$=t^n\sum_{r=0}^{\infty}\frac{(-1)^r}{r!\Gamma(n+r+1)}\left(\frac{x}{2}\right)^{n+2r}=t^n\cdot J_n(x)$$

Hence, the coefficient of t^n in the expansion of $e^{\frac{x}{2}\left(t-\frac{1}{t}\right)}$ is $J_n(x)$

Similarly, the coefficient of (t^{-n}) in the expansion of $e^{\frac{x}{2}\left(t-\frac{1}{4}\right)}$ is $J_n(x)$

Since, $J_{-n}(x)=(-1)^n J_n(x)$ therefore

the coefficient of t^{-n} in the expansion of $(-1)^n J_n(x)$

Method (3): Find the value of $J_n(x)$ when $n=0$ i.e., $J_n(x)$

By definition, $\qquad J_n(x) = \sum_{r=0}^{\infty} \frac{(-1)^r}{r!(n+r)!} \left(\frac{x}{2}\right)^{n+2r}$

putting $n = 0$, we get $J_0(x) = \sum_{r=0}^{\infty} \frac{(-1)^r}{r!r!} \left(\frac{x}{2}\right)^{2r}$

or $J_0(x) = \sum_{r=0}^{\infty} \frac{(-1)^r}{(r!)^2} \left(\frac{x}{2}\right)^{2r}$ (This is Bessel's function of order zero).

Method (4): Prove that $e^{\frac{x}{2}\left(z-\frac{1}{z}\right)} = J_0(x) + \sum_{n=1}^{\infty} J_n(x) \left[z^n + \frac{(-1)^n}{z^n}\right]$

We know that $J_n(x)$ is the coefficient of z^n.

We have the coefficient of $z^0 = J_0(x)$

the coefficient of $z^1 = J_1(x)$

the coefficient of $z^n = J_n(x)$

Thus the coefficient of $z^{(-1)} = J_{-1}(x)$

the coefficient of $z^{(-2)} = J_{-2}(x)$

coefficient of $z^{(-n)} = J_{-n}(x)$

summing up all the terms, we have

$$\left(z^0 J_0(x) + z^1 J_1(x) + z^2 J_2(x) + ... + z^n J_n(x) + ...\right)$$
$$+ \left(z^- J_{-1}(x) + z^{-2} J_{-2}(x) + ... + z^{-n} J_{-n}(x)\right)$$

or $\quad \sum_{n=0}^{\infty} z^n J_n(x) + \sum_{n=1}^{\infty} z^{-n} J_{-n}(x)$

$$= J_0(x) + \sum_{n=1}^{\infty} z^n J_n(x) + \sum_{n=1}^{\infty} z^{-n} J_{-n}(x) \quad \text{Since} \quad \left[J_{-n}(x) = (-1)^n J_n(x)\right]$$

$$= J_0(x) + \sum_{n=1}^{\infty} \left[z^n + \frac{(-1)^n}{z^n}\right] J_n(x)$$

Trigonometric Expansion involving Bessel's Functions

We have $e^{\frac{x}{2}\left(z-\frac{1}{z}\right)}$

$$= J_0(x) + \left(z - \frac{1}{z}\right)J_1(x) + \left(z^2 + \frac{1}{z^2}\right)J_2(x) + ... + \left(z^3 - \frac{1}{z^3}\right)J_3(x) \quad [1]$$

put $\quad z = e^{i\theta} = \cos\theta + i\sin\theta$

$\therefore \quad \dfrac{1}{z} = e^{-i\theta} = \cos\theta - i\sin\theta$

$\therefore \quad z + \dfrac{1}{z} = 2\cos\theta \quad$ and $\quad z - \dfrac{1}{z} = 2\,i\,\sin\theta$

$\therefore \quad z^n + \dfrac{1}{z^n} = 2\cos\theta \quad$ and $\quad z^n - \dfrac{1}{z^n} = 2\,i\,\sin\theta$

$\because \quad e^{iy} = cox\ y + i\sin y$

$e^{-iy} = cox\ y - i\sin y$

Making the substitutions in [1], we get

$$e^{ix\sin\theta} = J_0 + 2i\sin\theta J_1 + 2\cos2\theta J_2 + 2i\sin3\theta J_3 + 2\cos4\theta J_4$$

or $\quad \cos(x\sin\theta) + i\sin(x\sin\theta)$

$$= \left[J_0 + (2\cos2\theta)J_2 + (2\cos4\theta)J_4 + ...\right] + i\left[(2\sin\theta)J_1 + (2\sin3\theta)J_3 + ...\right]$$

Equating R_e and I_m parts, we get (Jacobi Series)

$$\cos(x\sin\theta) = J_0 + 2J_2\cos2\theta + 2J_4\cos4\theta + ... \qquad [2]$$

$$\sin(x\sin\theta) = 2J_1\sin\theta + 2J_3\sin3\theta + 2J_5\sin5\theta + ... \qquad [3]$$

[2] and [3] are called Jacobi's series. On putting $\theta = \left(\dfrac{\pi}{2} - \alpha\right)$ in [2] and [3]

we get

$$\cos(x\cos\alpha) = J_0 - 2J_2\cos2\alpha + 2J_4\cos4\alpha - ....$$

$$\sin(x\cos\alpha) = 2J_1\cos\alpha - 2J_3\cos3\alpha + 2J_5\cos5\alpha - ....$$

EXAMPLES

1. Prove the following.

   (a) $\cos x = J_0(x) - 2J_2(x) + 2J_n(x)....$

   $$= J_0(x) + 2\sum_{n=1}^{\infty}(-1)^n \cdot J_2(x)$$

   (b) $\sin x = 2\sum_{n=0}^{\infty}(-1)^n J_{2n+1}(x)$

   $$= 2J_1 - 2J_3 + 2J_5 + ...$$

   We know that $e^{\frac{x}{2}\left[z-\frac{1}{z}\right]} = J_0(x) + \sum_{n=1}^{\infty} J_n(x)\left[z^n + \frac{(-1)^n}{z^n}\right]$ [1]

   For $z = i = \sqrt{-1}$, we have $e^{\left[\frac{x}{2}\left(z-\frac{1}{z}\right)\right]} = e^{\left[\frac{x}{2}\left(i-\frac{1}{i}\right)\right]} = e^{ix} = \cos x + i\sin x$

   and $\left[z^n + \frac{(-1)^n}{z^n}\right] = \left[z^n + (-1)^n i^{-n}\right]$

   We know that

   $$\cos(x\sin\theta) = J_0(x) + 2\cos 2\theta J_2(x) + 2\cos 4\theta J_4(x),....$$

   and $\sin(x\sin\theta) = 2\sin\theta J_1(x) + 2\sin 3\theta J_3(x) + ...$ [2]

   putting $\left(\theta = \frac{1}{2}\pi\right)$ we have,

   $$\cos x = J_0(x) - 2J_2(x) + 2J_4(x) + ...$$

   and $\sin x = 2J_1(x) - 2J_3(x) + 2J_5(x)....$ [3]

   $$\cos x = J_0(x) + 2\sum_{n=1}^{\infty}(-1)^n J_{2n}(x)$$

   $$\sin x = 2\sum_{n=0}^{\infty}(-1)^n J_{2n+1}(x)$$

2. Prove that: $\quad x\sin x = 2\sum_{n=1}^{\infty}(-1)^{n+1}(2n)^2 J_{2n}(x)$

Solution: By Jacobi's cosine series;

$$\cos(x\sin\theta) = J_0 + 2J_2\cos 2\theta + 2J_4\cos 4\theta + ...$$

Differentiating w.r.t θ

$$\sin(x\sin\theta)\cdot x\cos\theta$$

$$= -2J_2\sin 2\theta\cdot 2 - 2J_4\cdot\sin 4\theta.4 + ...$$

Differentiating again w.r.t. θ

$$\cos(x\sin\theta)\cdot x^2\cos^2\theta + \sin(x\sin\theta)\cdot x\sin\theta$$

$$= -2J_2\cos 2\theta\cdot 2^2 - 2J_4\cos 4\theta\cdot 4^2....$$

put $\quad\theta = \dfrac{\pi}{2}$, and use $\sin\dfrac{\pi}{2} = 1$, $\cos\dfrac{\pi}{2} = 0$ etc.

$$\cos\left[x\sin\frac{\pi}{2}\right]x^2\cos^2\frac{\pi}{2} + \sin\left(x\sin\frac{\pi}{2}\right)x\sin\frac{\pi}{2}$$

$$= 2\left\{-J_2\cos\pi\cdot 2^2 - J_4\cos 2\pi\cdot 4^2 - J_6\cos 3\pi\cdot 6^2 - ...\right\}$$

$$0 + \sin(x).x$$

$$= 2\left\{J_2\cdot 2^2 - J_4\cdot 4^2 + J_6\cdot 6^2 - + ...\right\}$$

or $\quad x\sin x = 2\left\{\sum_{n=1}^{\infty}(-1)^{n+1}(2n)^2 J_{2n}(x)\right\}$

Bessel's Integrals

1. To Prove that

(a) $\quad J_0(x) = \dfrac{1}{\pi}\displaystyle\int_0^{\pi}\cos(x\sin\theta)d\theta$

(b) $\quad J_n(x) = \dfrac{1}{\pi}\displaystyle\int_0^{\pi}\cos(n\theta - x\sin\theta)d\theta$

Proof: We know that

$$\cos(x\sin\theta) = J_0 + 2J_2\cos 2\theta + 2J_4\cos 4\theta + ...\qquad\qquad [1]$$

$$\sin(x\sin\theta) = 2J_1\sin\theta + 2J_3\sin 3\theta + ...\qquad\qquad [2]$$

(a) Integrating [1] between the limits 0 and π, we have

$$\int_0^\pi \cos(x\sin\theta)d\theta$$

$$= \int_0^\pi (J_0 + 2J_2 \cos 2\theta + 2J_4 \cos 4\theta + ...)$$

$$= J_0 \int_0^\pi d\theta + 2J_2 \int_0^\pi \cos 2\theta \, d\theta + 2J_4 \int_0^\pi \cos 4\theta \, d\theta + ...$$

$$= J_0 \pi + \theta + 0$$

$$J_0 = \frac{1}{\pi} \int_0^\pi \cos(x\sin\theta)d\theta.$$

(b) Multiplying [1] by $\cos n\theta$ and integrating between the limits 0 and π, we have

$$\int_0^\pi \cos(x\sin\theta)\cos n\theta \, d\theta$$

$$= \int_0^\pi [J_0 \cos n\theta + 2J_2 \cos 2\theta \cos n + 2J_4 \cos 4\theta \cos n\theta + ...]d\theta$$

$$= 2J_0 \int_0^\pi \cos n\theta \, d\theta + 2J_2 \int_0^\pi \cos 2\theta \cos\theta \, d\theta + ... = 0 \quad \text{if } n \text{ is odd. [3]}$$

$$= \pi J_n \quad \text{if } n \text{ is even.} \tag{4}$$

Again multiplying [2] by $\sin n\theta$ and integrating between the limits 0 and π, we have

$$\int_0^\pi \sin(x\sin\theta)\sin n\theta \, d\theta$$

$$= \int_0^\pi (2J_1 \sin\theta \sin n\theta + 2J_3 \sin 3\theta \sin n\theta + ...)d\theta$$

$$= 2J_1 \int_0^\pi \sin\theta \sin n\theta \, d\theta + 2J_3 \int_0^\pi \sin 3\theta \sin n\theta \, d\theta$$

$$= 0 \quad \text{if } n \text{ is even} \tag{5}$$

$$= \pi J_n \quad \text{if } n \text{ is odd} \tag{6}$$

Adding [3] and [6] or [4] and [5] we get,

$$\int_0^\pi [\cos(x\sin\theta)\cos n\theta + \sin(x\sin\theta)\sin n\theta]d\theta = \pi J_n$$

or, $\int_0^\pi \cos(n\theta - x\sin d\theta) \, d\theta = \pi J_n$

or $J_n = \frac{1}{\pi} \int_0^\pi \cos(n\theta - x\sin\theta)d\theta$

2. Prove that: $J_0^2 + 2J_1^2 + ... = 1$

Proof: $\cos(x\sin\theta) = J_0 + 2J_2\cos 2\theta + 2J_4\cos 4\theta + ...$ By Jacobi's Series [1]

$\sin(x\sin\theta) = 2J_1\sin\theta + 2J_3\sin 3\theta + ...$ [2]

Squaring, $\cos^2(x\sin\theta)$

$= (J_0 + 2J_2\cos 2\theta + ...)^2$

$= J_0^2 + 4J_2^2\cos^2 2\theta + 4J_4^2\cos^2 4\theta + ... + 4J_0 J_2\cos 2\theta + 4J_0 J_4\cos 4\theta + ...$

$+ 8J_2 J_4\cos 2\theta\cos 4\theta + ...$

Integrating w.r.t. θ from 0 to π, we get

$\int_0^\pi \cos^2(x\sin\theta)\,d\theta$

$= J_0^2\int_0^\pi d\theta + 4J_2^2\int_0^\pi \cos^2 2\pi d\theta + ... + 4J_0 J_2\int_0^\pi \cos 2\theta\,d\theta + ...8J_2 J_4\int_0^\pi \cos 2\theta\cos 4\theta d\theta + ...$

$= J_0^2[0]_0^\pi + 2^2(J_2^2 + J_4^2 + ...)\dfrac{\pi}{2} +$ all other integrals vanish

$$\begin{cases} \int_0^\pi 2\sin^2 n\theta\,d\theta = \pi \\[2mm] \int_0^\pi 2\cos^2 n\theta\,d\theta = \pi \\[2mm] \int_0^\pi \sin n\theta\sin m\theta\,d\theta = 0 \\[2mm] \int_0^\pi \cos\theta\cos m\theta\,d\theta = 0 \end{cases}$$

Hence, we have, $J_0^2\pi + 2J_2^2\pi + 2J_4^2\pi + ...$

$= \int_0^\pi \cos^2(x\sin\theta)\,d\theta$

Similarly, $\int_0^\pi \sin^2(x\sin\theta)\,d\theta$

$= 2^2\left[J_1^2 + J_3^2 + J_5^2 + ...\right]\dfrac{\pi}{2}$ all other integrals vanish   [3]

Adding [2] and [3] using

$\int_0^\pi \left[\cos^2(x\sin\theta) + \sin^2(x\sin\theta)\right]d\theta$

$= J_0^2\pi + 2\left[J_2^2 + J_4^2 + ...\right]\pi + 2\left[J_1^2 + J_3^2 + ...\right]\pi,$

or $\quad \int_0^\pi d\theta = \pi = \pi\left[J_0^2 + 2J_1^2 + 2J_2^2 + ...\right]$

or $\quad \boxed{J_0^2 + 2J_1^2 + 2J_2^2 + ... = 1}$

3. Prove that: $\dfrac{d}{dx}\left[J_n^2 + J_{n+1}^2\right] = 2\left(\dfrac{n}{x}J_n^2 - \dfrac{n+1}{x}J_{n+1}^2\right)$

Proof: We have the formula

$$xJ_n' = nJ_n - xJ_{n+1} \qquad\qquad [1]$$

$$xJ_n' = nJ_n + xJ_{n-1} \qquad\qquad [2]$$

putting $n + 1$ for 'n' in [2] we get

$$xJ_{n+1}' = -(n+1)J_{n+1} + xJ_n \qquad\qquad [3]$$

Now, $\dfrac{d}{dx}\left[J_n^2 + J_{n+1}^2\right]$

$$= 2J_nJ_n' + 2J_{n+1}J_{n+1}' \qquad\qquad [4]$$

Putting the values of J_n' and J_{n+1}' from [1], [2] and [3], we get [4],

$$\dfrac{d}{dx}\left[J_n^2 + J_{n+1}^2\right]$$

$$= \dfrac{2}{x}\left[J_n\left(nJ_n - xJ_{n+1}\right) + J_{n+1}\left\{-(n+1)J_{n+1} + nJ_n\right\}\right]$$

$$= 2\left[\dfrac{n}{x}J_n^2 - \dfrac{n+1}{x}J_{n+1}^2\right]$$

4. Prove that: $J_0^2 + 2\left[J_1^2 + J_2^2 + ...\right] = 1$

Proof: Deduce that $\left|J_0(x)\right| \le 1, \left|J_n(x)\right| \le 2^{-\frac{1}{2}}, (n \ge 1)$

We have (from Example 3), this $\dfrac{d}{dx}\left[J_n^2 + J_{n+1}^2\right] = 2\left(\dfrac{n}{x}J_n^2 - \dfrac{n+1}{x}J_{n+1}^2\right)$ putting

$n = 0, 1, 2, 3,....$ we have

$$\dfrac{d}{dx}\left(J_0^2 + J_1^2\right) = 2\left(0 - \dfrac{1}{x}J_1^2\right)$$

$$\frac{d}{dx}\left(J_1^2 + J_2^2\right) = 2\left(\frac{1}{x}J_1^2 - \frac{2}{x}J_2^2\right)$$

$$\frac{d}{dx}\left(J_2^2 + J_3^2\right) = 2\left(\frac{2}{x}J_2^2 - \frac{3}{x}J_3^2\right)$$

Adding, we have

$$\frac{d}{dx}\left[J_0^2 + 2\left(J_1^2 + J_2^2 + J_3^2 + ...\right)\right] = 0$$

Since $J_n \to \infty$, as $n \to \infty$.

Integrating, we have $J_0^2 + 2\left(J_1^2 + J_2^2 + ...\right) = c$ (constant)

Putting $x = 0$

$$\left(J_0^2\right)_{x=0} = c \ \ or \ \ 1 = c$$

$$\left(J_1\right)_{x=0} = 0$$

$$\left(J_2\right)_{x=0} = 0 \text{ etc.}$$

Hence $J_0^2 + 2\left(J_1^2 + J_2^2 + J_3^2 + ...\right) = 1$

Deduction: we have proved that $J_0^2 + 2\left(J_1^2 + J_2^2 + ... + J_n^2 + ...\right) = 1$

Since $J_1^2, J_2^2, J_3^2, ...$ are all positive or zero. $\therefore J_0^2 \leq 1$ here $|J_0| \leq 1$

$$|J_0(x)| \leq 1$$

Also, $|2J_n^2| \leq 1$

or $\quad |J_n| \leq \dfrac{1}{\sqrt{2}}$

Hence $|J_n| \leq 2^{-\frac{1}{2}}$ i.e., $|J_n(x)| \leq 2^{-\frac{1}{2}}$, (for $n \geq 1$)

5. $\dfrac{d}{dx}\left(xJ_n J_{n+1}\right) = x\left(J_n^2 - J_{n+1}^2\right)$

Solution: $\dfrac{d}{dx}\left(xJ_n J_{n+1}\right)$

$$= 1 \cdot J_n J_{n+1} x\left[J_n' J_{n+1} + J_n J_{n+1}'\right]$$

$$= J_n J_{n+1} + (xJ_n') J_{n+1} + J_n (xJ_{n+1}')$$ [1]

From recurring formula I and II,

$$= xJ_n' = nJ_n - xJ_{n+1}$$ [2]

$$xJ_n' = -nJ_n + xJ_{n-1}$$ [3]

Replacing n by $(n+1)$ in [3], we have

$$= xJ_{n+1}' = -(n+1)J_{n+1} + xJ_n$$ [4]

Substituting the values of xJ_n' and xJ_{n+1}' from [2] and [4], in [1], we have

$$\frac{d}{dx}(xJ_n J_{n+1})$$

$$= J_n J_{n+1} + (nJ_n - xJ_{n+1}) J_{n+1} + J_n \{-(n+1)J_{n+1} + xJ_n\}$$

$$= x(J_n^2 - J_{n+1}^2)$$

6. By using $J_{n+1}(x) + J_{n-1}(x) = \dfrac{2n}{x} J_n(x)$

Deduce that $J_4(x) = \dfrac{8}{x}\left[\dfrac{6}{x^2} - 1\right] J_1(x) + \left[1 - \dfrac{24}{x^2}\right] J_0(x)$

Solution: Given

$$J_{n+1}(x) + J_{n-1}(x) = \frac{2n}{x} J_n(x)$$ [1]

or $$J_{n+1}(x) = \frac{2n}{x} J_n(x) - J_{n-1}(x)$$

Putting $n = 3$, we obtain,

$$J_4(x) = \frac{6}{x} J_3(x) - J_2(x)$$ [2]

we have to again put, $n = 1, 2$ respectively in [1] to obtain $J_2(x)$ and $J_3(x)$

$$J_2(x) = \frac{2}{x} J_1(x) - J_0(x),$$

$$J_3(x) = \frac{4}{x} J_2(x) - J_1(x),$$

i.e., $$J_3(x) = \frac{4}{x}\left[\frac{2}{n} J_1(x) - J_0(x)\right] - J_1(x),$$

or $\quad J_3(x) = \dfrac{8}{x^2} J_1(x) - \dfrac{4}{x} J_0(x) - J_1(x)$

Use these in R.H.S. of [2] we obtain,

$$J_4(x) = \dfrac{6}{x}\left[\dfrac{8}{x^2} J_1(x) - \dfrac{4}{x} J_0(x) - J_1(x)\right] - \left[\dfrac{2}{x} J_1(x) - J_0(x)\right]$$

$$= J_1(x) = \left[\dfrac{48}{x^3} - \dfrac{6}{x} - \dfrac{2}{x}\right] + J_0(x)\left[1 - \dfrac{24}{x^2}\right]$$

i.e., $\quad J_4(x) = \dfrac{8}{x}\left(\dfrac{6}{x^2} - 1\right) J_1(x) + \left(1 - \dfrac{24}{x^2}\right) J_0(x)$

7. With the help of Jacobi's Series show that $\dfrac{x}{2} = J_1 + 3J_3 + 5J_5 + ...$

Solution: We have, by the Jacobi's Series

$$\cos(x\sin\theta) = J_0 + 2J_2\cos 2\theta + 2J_4\cos 4\theta + ... \qquad [1]$$

$$\sin(x\sin\theta) = 2J_1\sin\theta + 2J_3\sin 3\theta + 2J_5\sin 5\theta + ... \qquad [2]$$

Difference [2] w.r.t. θ, we have

$$\cos(x\sin\theta)x\cos\theta$$

$$= 2J_1\cos\theta + 2J_3\cdot 3\cos\theta + 2J_5\cdot 5\cos 5\theta + ...$$

Putting $\theta = 0$, in the above we obtain $x = 2(J_1 + 3J_3 + 5J_5 + ...)$

$$\dfrac{x}{2} = J_1 + 3J_3 + 5J_5 + ...$$

8. If $a > 0$, prove that $\displaystyle\int_0^\infty e^{-ax} J_0(bx)\,dx = \dfrac{1}{\sqrt{a^2 + b^2}}$

Solution: We know that $J_0(x) = \dfrac{1}{\pi}\displaystyle\int_0^\pi \cos(x\sin\phi)\,d\phi$

Hence, $\quad J_0(bx) = \dfrac{1}{\pi}\displaystyle\int_0^\pi \cos(bx\sin\phi)\,d\phi \qquad [1]$

Now, $\int_0^\infty e^{-ax} J_0(bx)\, dx$

$$= \int_0^\infty e^{-ax} \left\{ \frac{1}{\pi} \int_0^\pi \cos(bx\sin\phi)\, d\phi \right\} dx, \text{ using [1]}$$

$$= \frac{1}{\pi} \int_0^\infty \left\{ \int_0^\pi e^{-ax} \cos(bx\sin\phi)\, d\phi \right\} dx$$

$$= \frac{1}{\pi} \int_0^\pi \left\{ \int_0^\infty e^{-ax} \cos(bx\sin\phi)\, dx \right\} d\phi$$

(on interchanging the order of Integration)

$$= \frac{1}{\pi} \int_0^\pi \left\{ \int_0^\infty e^{-ax} \frac{e^{ibx\sin\phi} + e^{-ibx\sin\phi}}{2}\, dx \right\} d\phi$$

$$= \frac{1}{2\pi} \int_0^\pi \left\{ \int_0^\infty \left[e^{-(a-ib\sin\phi)x} + e^{-(a+ib\sin\phi)x} \right] dx \right\} d\phi$$

$$= \frac{1}{2\pi} \int_0^\pi \left[\frac{e^{-(a-ib\sin\phi)x}}{-(a-ib\sin\phi)} + \frac{e^{-(a+ib\sin\phi)x}}{-(a+ib\sin\phi)} \right]_0^\infty dx$$

$$= \frac{1}{2\pi} \int_0^\pi \left[\frac{1}{a-ib\sin\phi} + \frac{1}{a+ib\sin\phi} \right] d\phi$$

$$= \frac{a}{\pi} \int_0^\pi \frac{d\phi}{a^2 + b^2 \sin^2\phi}$$

$$= \frac{a}{\pi} \int_0^\pi \frac{\cosec^2\phi\, d\phi}{b^2 + a^2 \cosec^2\phi}$$

$$= \frac{a}{\pi} \int_0^\pi \frac{\cosec^2\phi\, d\phi}{b^2 + a^2 \left(1 + \cosec^2\phi\right)}$$

$$= \frac{2a}{\pi} \int_0^{\frac{\pi}{2}} \frac{\cosec^2\phi\, d\phi}{\left(a^2 + b^2\right) + a^2 \cosec^2\phi}$$

$$= \frac{2a}{\pi} \int_\infty^0 \frac{(-dt)}{\left(a^2 + b^2\right) + a^2 t^2} \quad \text{(Putting } \cot\phi = t \text{ so that } -\cosec^2\phi\, d\phi = dt\text{)}$$

$$= -\frac{2a}{\pi a^2} \int_\infty^0 \frac{dt}{t^2 + \left(a^2 + b^2\right)/a^2}$$

$$= +\frac{2}{a\pi} \int_0^\infty \frac{dt}{t^2 + \left[\sqrt{a^2 + b^2}/a^2\right]}$$

$$= \frac{2}{a\pi} \frac{1}{\left(\sqrt{a^2 + b^2}/a\right)} \left[\tan^{-1} \frac{t}{\sqrt{a^2 + b^2}/a}\right]_0^\infty$$

$$= \frac{2}{\pi\left(\sqrt{a^2 + b^2}\right)} \left(\frac{\pi}{2} - 0\right) = \frac{1}{\left(\sqrt{a^2 + b^2}\right)}$$

Orthogonality of Legendre Polynomials and Bessel's Function

(i) Orthogonality of Legendre's Polynomials

Theorem:

$$\int_{-1}^1 P_m(x) P_n(x) \, dx = \begin{cases} 0, & \text{if } m \neq n \\ \dfrac{2}{(2n+1)}, & \text{if } m = n \end{cases}$$

or $\quad \displaystyle\int_{-1}^{+1} P_m(x) P_n(x) \, dx = \frac{2}{2n+1} \delta_{mn}, \quad$ where $\delta_{mn} = \begin{cases} 0, & \text{if } m \neq n \\ 1, & \text{if } m = n \end{cases}$

Proof: Case (i) $m \neq n$

Let $u = P_m(x)$ and $v = P_n(x)$ are the solutions of the Legendre's equation.

$\therefore \quad \left(1 - x^2\right) u'' - 2xu' + m(m+1)u = 0 \qquad\qquad [1]$

$\left(1 - x^2\right) v'' - 2xv' + n(n+1)v = 0 \qquad\qquad [2]$

Applying [1].v–[2].u, yields,

$$\left(1 - x^2\right)(u''v - uv'') - 2x(u'v - v'u) + uv\left[m(m+1) - n(n+1)\right] = 0$$

$$\Rightarrow \quad \frac{d}{dx}\left[\left(1 - x^2\right)(u'v - v'u)\right] = -uv\left[\left(m^2 - n^2\right) + (m - n)\right]$$

$\Rightarrow \quad \dfrac{d}{dx}\Big[\big(1-x^2\big)\big(u'v-v'u\big)\Big] = -uv(m-n)+(m+n+1)$

$\Rightarrow \quad \dfrac{d}{dx}\Big[\big(1-x^2\big)\big(u'v-v'u\big)\Big] = uv\,(n-m)+(m+n+1)$

Integrating both sides with respect to x between the limits -1 to 1, we get

$$\Big[\big(1-x^2\big)\big(u'v-v'u\big)\Big]_{-1}^{1} = (n-m)(m+n+1)\int_{-1}^{1}uv\,dx.$$

$\therefore \quad 0 = (n-m)(n+m+1)\int_{-1}^{1}P_m(x)P_n(x)\,dx$

$\therefore \quad \int_{-1}^{1}P_m(x)P_n(x)\,dx = 0$

Case (ii) $m = n$. We know that $\big(1-2xt+t^2\big)^{-\frac{1}{2}} = \displaystyle\sum_{n=0}^{\infty}t^nP_n(x)$

Squaring both sides we get, $\big(1-2xt+t^2\big)^{-1} = \left[\displaystyle\sum_{n=0}^{\infty}t^nP_n(x)\right]^2$

$= \Big[P_0 + tP_1(x)+t^2P_2(x)+...+t^kP_k(x)+...\Big]\times\Big[P_0+tP_1(x)+t^2P_2(x)+t^lP_l(x)+...\Big]$

$\displaystyle\sum_{n=0}^{\infty}t^{2n}\Big[P_n(x)\Big]^2 + 2\sum_{n=0}^{\infty}t^{k+l}P_k(x)P_l(x)\Big]$ where $k \neq l$

Integrating both sides with respect to x between the limits -1 to 1, we get

$$\int_{-1}^{1}\frac{dx}{1-2xt+t^2} = \sum_{n=0}^{\infty}t^{2n}\int_{-1}^{1}\big[P_n(x)\big]^2\,dx + 2\sum_{n=0}^{\infty}t^{k+l}\int_{-1}^{1}P_k(x)P_l(x)\,dx$$

$\Rightarrow \quad -\dfrac{1}{2t}\Big[\log\big(1-2xt+t^2\big)\Big]_{-1}^{1} = \displaystyle\sum_{n=0}^{\infty}t^{2n}\int_{-1}^{1}\big[p_n(x)\big]^2\,dx.$

since $\int_{-1}^{1}P_k(x)P_l(x)\,dx = 0$ by case (i)

$\therefore \quad -\dfrac{1}{2t}\Big[\log(1-t)^2 - \log(1+t)^2\Big] = \displaystyle\sum_{n=0}^{\infty}t^{2n}\int_{-1}^{1}\big[P_n(x)\big]^2\,dx$

$\Rightarrow \quad \dfrac{1}{t}\Big[\log(1+t) - \log(1-t)\Big] = \displaystyle\sum_{n=0}^{\infty}t^{2n}\int_{-1}^{1}\big[P_n(x)\big]^2\,dx$

$\Rightarrow \quad \dfrac{1}{t}\left[\left(t - \dfrac{t^2}{2}+\dfrac{t^3}{3}-\dfrac{t^4}{4}+...\right)+\left(t+\dfrac{t^2}{2}+\dfrac{t^3}{3}+\dfrac{t^4}{4}+...\right)\right] = \displaystyle\sum_{n=0}^{\infty}t^{2n}\int_{-1}^{1}\big[P_n(x)\big]^2\,dx$

$$\therefore \quad 2\left[1+\frac{t^2}{3}+\frac{t^4}{5}+...+\frac{t^{2n}}{2n+1}+....\right]$$

$$=\sum_{n=0}^{\infty}t^{2n}\int_{-1}^{1}\left[P_n(x)\right]^2 dx$$

Equating the coefficient of t^{2n} we get

$$\int_{-1}^{1}\left[P_n(x)\right]^2 dx=\frac{2}{2n+1}, \text{ Hence the theorem.}$$

(ii) Orthogonality of Bessel's function

If α and β are the roots of $J_n(ax)=0$, then

$$\int_0^a xJ_n(\alpha x)J_n(\beta x)dx=\begin{cases}0, \text{ if }\alpha\neq\beta\\[2mm]\dfrac{a^2}{2}J_{n+1}^2(a\alpha), \text{ if }\alpha=\beta\end{cases}$$

Proof : Case (i) $\alpha\neq\beta$

Let $u=J_n(\alpha x)$ and $v=J_n(\beta x)$ respectively be the solutions of the equations;

$$\left.\begin{array}{l}\text{and } x^2u''+xu'+\left(\alpha^2x^2-n^2\right)u=0;\\[2mm]\qquad x^2v''+xv'+\left(\beta^2x^2-n^2\right)v=0;\end{array}\right\} \qquad\begin{array}{l}[1]\\[2mm][2]\end{array}$$

Applying $[1]\times\left(\dfrac{v}{x}\right)-[2]\times\left(\dfrac{u}{x}\right)$ yields

$$x\left(u''v-uv''\right)+\left(u'v-uv'\right)+\left(\alpha^2-\beta^2\right)xuv=0;$$

or $\quad \dfrac{d}{dx}\left\{x\left(u'v-uv'\right)\right\}=\left(\beta^2-\alpha^2\right)xuv$ \qquad [3]

Integrating both sides of [3] from $x=0$ to a

$$\left(\beta^2-\alpha^2\right)\int_0^a xuvdx=\left[x\left(u'v-uv'\right)\right]_0^a$$

$$=a\left[u'(a)v(a)-u(a)v'(a)\right] \qquad [4]$$

where [4] denotes differentiation w.r.t. x.

Now $\quad u'=\dfrac{d}{dx}u=\dfrac{d}{dx}J_n(\alpha x)=\alpha J_n'(\alpha x)$ \qquad [5]

Thirdly, $v' = \dfrac{dv}{dx} = \dfrac{d}{dx} J_n(\beta x) = \beta J_n'(\beta x)$ [6]

Substituting u' and v' from [5] and [6] in [4] we get

$$\int_0^a x J_n(\alpha x) J_n(\beta x)\, dx$$

$$= \frac{a}{\beta^2 - \alpha^2} \Big[\alpha J_n'(\alpha a) J_n(\beta a) - \beta J_n(\alpha a) J_n'(\beta a)\Big]$$ [7]

Since $J_n(\alpha x) = J_n(\beta x) = 0$

$\quad$ ($\because$ α and β are roots of $J_n(\alpha x) = 0$)

Thus for $\alpha \neq \beta$, $\int_0^a x J_n(\alpha x) J_n(\beta x)\, dx = 0$ [8]

[8] is known as the orthogonality relation for Bessel's functions.

Case (ii) $\beta = \alpha$

If $\beta = \alpha$, then R.H.S. of [4] is $\dfrac{0}{0}$ form.

Assuming α as a root of $J_n(ax) = 0$,
evaluate R.H.S. of [4] as $\beta \to \alpha$

$$\lim_{\beta \to \alpha} \int_0^a x J_n(\alpha x) J_n(\beta x)\, dx$$

$$= \lim_{\beta \to \alpha} \left(\frac{a}{\beta^2 - \alpha^2}\right) \Big[\alpha J_n'(a\alpha) J_n(a\beta) - 0\Big]$$

Since $J_n(a\alpha) = 0$,

Now applying L'Hospitals rule, (differentiating w.r.t. β) we get

$$= \lim_{\beta \to \alpha} \frac{a}{2\beta} \Big[\alpha J_n'(a\alpha) \cdot a J_n'(a\beta)\Big] = \frac{a^2}{2} \Big[J_n'(a\alpha)\Big]^2$$

but, from the recurrence relation;

$$J_{n+1}(x) = \frac{x}{x} J_n(x) - J_n'(x)$$

put $x = a\alpha$, then $J_{n+1}(a\alpha) = \dfrac{n}{a\alpha} J_n(a\alpha) - J_n'(a\alpha)$.

Since α is a root, $J_n(x\alpha) = 0$. Then $J_n'(a\alpha) = J_{n+1}(a\alpha)$

Thus for $\alpha \neq \beta$, $x J_n(\alpha x) J_n(\beta x)\, dx = \dfrac{a^2}{2}\Big[J_n'(a\alpha)\Big]^2 = \dfrac{a^2}{2}\Big[J_{n+1}(a\alpha)\Big]^2$

Note: By using the recurrence formula,

$$J_{n-1}(a\alpha) + J_{n+1}(a\alpha) = \frac{2n}{a\alpha} J_n(a\alpha), \text{ we have}$$

$$J_{n-1}(a\alpha) = -J_{n+1}(a\alpha) \text{ (since } J_n(a\alpha) = 0$$

Thus, $\int_0^a x J_n(\alpha x) J_n(\beta x) dx = \frac{a^2}{2} [J_{n-1}(a\alpha)]^2$

EXERCISES

1. Prove that $\cos x = J_0(x) + 2\sum_{n=1}^{\infty} (-1)^n J_{2n}(x)$

2. Show that:

(a) $J_0(x) = \frac{2}{\pi} \int_0^{\frac{\pi}{2}} \cos(x \sin \theta) d\theta$

(b) $\int_0^{\frac{\pi}{2}} J_1(x \cos \theta) d\theta = \frac{1 - \cos x}{x}$

(c) $\int_0^{\infty} e^{-ax} J_0(bx) dx = \frac{1}{\sqrt{a^2 + b^2}}$

(d) $\int_0^{\infty} J_0(x) dx = 1$

3. $\int_0^{\infty} e^{-x} J_0(x) dx = \frac{1}{\sqrt{2}}$

4. Prove that $x J_n'(x) = -n J_n(x) + x J_{n-1}(x)$

5. Express $J_4(x)$ in terms of $J_0(x)$ and $J_1(x)$ $J_1(x)$

6. Prove that $J_{n+3} + J_{n+5} = \frac{2}{x}(n+4)J_{n+4...}$

7. Show that $x^2 J_n''(x) = (n^2 - n - x^2) J_n(x) + x J_{n+1}(x)$

8. $\int_0^x x^{n+1} J_n(x) dx = x^{n+1} J_{n+1}(x)$

9. If $n > -1$, show that $\int_0^x x^{-n} J_{n+1}(x) dx = \frac{1}{2^n \Gamma(n+1)} - x^{-n} J_n(x)$

10. Obtain the solution of the following differential equation in terms of Bessel's functions;

(a) $y'' + \dfrac{y'}{x} + \left(1 - \dfrac{1}{9x^2}\right)y = 0$

(b) $xy'' + 2y' + \dfrac{1}{2}xy = 0$

(c) $4y'' + 9xy = 0$.

3

LAPLACE TRANSFORM

Introduction

Laplace transform is a very powerful technique that replaces operations of calculus by operations of algebra. The application of Laplace Transform lies in the solution of an initial value problem, consisting of an ordinary (or Partial) differential equation together with initial conditions. The integral defining the transform will converge for some useful engineering signals.

Consider a function $f(t)$, defined in the interval $a \le t \le b$. For a fixed s (real or complex) if the integral $\int_a^b f(t)K(s,t)dt$ exists finitely and is equal to, say, $\phi(s)$ (s is called the transform parameter), then $\phi(s)$ is called the integral transform of $f(t)$ w.r.t. t, with kernel $K(s, t)$ and the transformation of "$f(t)$ in the t domain" to $\phi(s)$ in the s domain" is called an integral transformation, because this transformation is effected by means of an integral.

Definition

If $f(t)$ is a function of t defined for all $t \ge 0$ and if the integral $\int_0^\infty e^{-st}f(t)dt$ exists, then it is certainly a function of the parameter s. This function of s, denoted as $\phi(s)$ is called the Laplace transform of $f(t)$ or $\phi(s)$.

Thus, $L[f(t)] = \int_0^\infty e^{-st}f(t)dt = \phi(s)$ when the integral exists. [1]

The function $f(t)$ is called the Inverse Laplace transform of $\phi(s)$ and is denoted by $L^{-1}\{\phi(s)\}$ or $L^{-1}[\phi(s)]$

Note: If $K(s,t) = e^{-st}$, $a = 0, b = \infty$, then the integral transform is called Laplace transform. Thus, if $f(t)$ is defined on the semi-infinite interval $t \ge 0$, the Laplace transform (L.T.) of $f(t)$ is defined by $L[f(t)] = \phi(s) = \int_0^\infty e^{-st}f(t)dt$ provided this integral is convergent, i.e. if it exists finitely for some of the values of s. In this case, we say that the L. T. of $f(t)$ exists for these values of s.

Thus, the process of multiplying $f(t)$ by e^{-st} and integrating the product between zero and infinity transforms the function $f(t)$ to a new function of the new variable "s". This operation (or process) is called the Laplace transformation of $f(t)$.

Existence conditions: Laplace Transform does not exist for all functions. The L.T. of $f(t)$ exists provided the improper integral in the R.H.S. of equation [1] converges (has a finite value).

If it exists, it is uniquely determined. The following conditions are to be satisfied:

(1) If $f(t)$ is piecewise continuous on every finite interval.

(2) $f(t)$ satisfies the following inequality $|f(t)| \le b \cdot e^{at}, \forall\, t \ge 0$ and for some constants a and b. Then $L[f(t)]$ exists. The function which satisfies the condition (2) is known as the function of **exponential order**.

Illustration

$$\cosh t < e^t \,\forall\, t > 0$$

$$t^n < n!\, e^t \ (n = 0, 1, 2 \dots)\ \forall\, t > 0$$

But $e^{t^2} > be^{at}$, whatever may be 'a' and 'b'.

so, $L\left[e^{t^2}\right]$ does not exist.

Similarly $\dfrac{1}{t}$ does not have L.T.

Note : Now, $t^{\frac{1}{2}}$ is not a continuous function at $t = 0$. But still $L[f(t)]$ exists.

This shows that continuity is a sufficient condition (but not necessary) for the existence of its L.T.

$$f(t) = \frac{1}{\sqrt{t}};$$

at $t = 0$, $f(t)$ becomes infinite and hence not piecewise continuous on $t > 0$ but still it has L.T.

Also L.T. may exist in certain instances where f is not of exponential order. (However, the L.T. integral does not exist finitely for $\dfrac{1}{t}$, which also becomes infinite at $t = 0$)

EXAMPLES

1. Consider $f(t) = t^2$

Since $\lim\limits_{t \to \infty} \dfrac{t^2}{e^{3t}} = \text{finite}$, $f(t) = t^2$ is of exponential order say 3.

2. Let $f(t) = t^n, n > 0$

For any real $s > 0$,

$$\lim_{t \to \infty} e^{-st} t^n = \lim_{t \to \infty} \frac{t^n}{e^{st}}$$

$\lim_{t \to \infty} \dfrac{n!}{s^n e^{st}} = 0$ by successive application of L' Hospital's rule.

In this case, $s = 0$ and hence the given function is of exponential order 0.

3. Let $f(t) = e^{at}$,

Since $\lim_{t \to \infty} e^{at} e^{-st} = \lim_{t \to \infty} e^{-(s-a)t} = 0$, when $s > a$.

$\therefore \quad e^{at}$ is of exponential order.

4. Let $f(t) = e^{t^2}$,

Since $\lim_{t \to \infty} e^{-st} e^{t^2} = \lim_{t \to \infty} e^{t(t-s)} = \infty = \text{not finite}$

Hence e^{t^2} cannot be of exponential order. This can also be seen from the fact that no matter how large we choose M and α,

$e^{t^2} > M e^{\alpha t}$ for all $t > t_0$ where t_0 is a sufficiently large number depending on M and α. It can be seen that e^{t^n} is not of exponential order for any $n > 1$.

5. Let $f(t) = \sin(t^2)$

We know that $\left| \sin(t^2) \right| \le 1, \forall\ t$ or, $\left| \sin(t^2) \right| \le 1e^t, \forall\ t$

Thus, with $M = 1$, $\alpha = 0$ this condition is called 'exponentially bounded'.

Hence $\sin(t^2)$ is of exponential order zero.

Note: A function $f(t)$ is said to be exponentially bounded if $\left[e^{-\alpha t} f(t) \right]$ is finite for all positive values of x.

Laplace Transform of Some Elementary Functions

EXAMPLES

1. Let $f(t) = a$, where a is constant and $t \ge 0$

Then, $L\{f(t)\} = L\{a\} = \int_0^\infty e^{-st} a\, dt = -\dfrac{a}{s} e^{-st} \Big]_0^\infty$

$$\therefore \quad L\{a\} = \frac{a}{s}, \text{ when } s > 0$$

Note: Laplace transform does not exist for $s \leq 0$

It follows for $a = 0$

$$L\{0\} = 0$$

for $a = 1$, $L\{1\} = \frac{1}{s}$, $s > 0$.

2. Let $f(t) = e^{at}$, $a > 0$

Then, $L\{e^{at}\} = \int_0^\infty e^{-st} e^{at} dt = \int_0^\infty e^{-(s-a)t} dt$

$$= \frac{e^{-(s-a)t}}{-(s-a)} \Bigg]_{t=0}^\infty = \frac{1}{(s-a)} \quad (s > a)$$

Thus $L\{e^{at}\} = \frac{1}{s-a}$ when $s > a$

Note: Laplace transform does not exist when $s \leq a$

3. Let $f(t) = \cos at$

$$\phi(s) = \int_0^\infty e^{-st} \cos at \, dt$$

$$= \frac{s}{s^2 + a^2}$$

4. Let $f(t) = \sin at$

$$\phi(s) = \int_0^\infty e^{-st} \sin at \, dt = \frac{a}{s^2 + a^2}$$

5. Let $f(t) = t^n$ where n is a positive integer.

$$L\{t^n\} = \int_0^\infty e^{-st} t^n dt$$

$$= \left[-\frac{t^n e^{-st}}{s} \right]_0^\infty - \int_0^\infty \left(-\frac{1}{s} \right) e^{-st} n t^{n-1} dt \quad \text{(on integration by parts)}$$

$$= -\frac{1}{s} \cdot \lim_{t \to 0} \frac{t^n}{e^{st}} + \frac{n}{s} \int_0^\infty e^{-st} t^{n-1} dt$$

If $s > 0$, by applying L'Hospital's rule successively,

it can be shown that as $t \to \infty$,

$$L\{t^n\} = \frac{n}{s} L\{t^{n-1}\}, = \frac{n}{s} \cdot \frac{n-1}{s} L[t^{n-2}], \quad s > 0.... \tag{1}$$

By a repeated application of equation,

$$L(1) = \frac{1}{s}, \quad s > 0, \text{ we have}$$

$$L(t^n) = \frac{n}{s} \cdot \frac{n-1}{s} \cdot \frac{n-2}{s} \cdots \frac{2}{s} \cdot \frac{1}{s} L(t^0)$$

but $L(t^0) = L(1) = \frac{1}{s}$;

$$\therefore \quad L[t^n] = \frac{n \cdot (n-1)...2 \cdot 1}{s^n} \cdot \frac{1}{s}$$

or $\quad L[t^n] = \frac{n!}{s^{n+1}}, \quad s > 0$

Remark: $L[t] = \left[\frac{1!}{s^2}\right], \quad L[t^2] = \left(\frac{2!}{s^3}\right)$

Properties

P_1: If $f(t)$ and $g(t)$ are functions for which Laplace transform exists, then

(i) $L[f(t) + g(t)] = L[f(t)] + L[g(t)]$

(ii) $L[cf(t)] = cL[f(t)]$ for any constant c.

(This is called as Linearity property)

Proof: (i) By the definition, we have

$$L[f(t) + g(t)] = \int_0^\infty e^{-st}[f(t) + g(t)] dt$$

$$= \int_0^\infty e^{-st} f(t) dt + \int_0^\infty e^{-st} g(t) dt$$

$$\therefore \quad L[f(t) + g(t)] = L[f(t)] + L[g(t)]$$

Also, **(ii)** $L[cf(t)] = \int_0^\infty e^{-st} cf(t) dt$

$$= c\int_0^\infty e^{-st} f(t)\, dt$$

$$\therefore \quad L\big[cf(t)\big] = cL\{f(t)\}$$

In view of properties (i) and (ii), the Laplace transformation operator L is a linear operator.

Note : $L\big[af(t)+bg(t)\big] = aL\big[f(t)\big]+bL\big[g(t)\big]$

for any constants a and b generalizing, we obtain;

$$L\left[\sum_{i=1}^{n} a_i f_i(t)\right] = \sum_{i=1}^{n} a_i L\big[f_i(t)\big] \qquad \text{[1] for any constants } a_1, a_2, ..., a_n$$

P_2: If $L\{f(t)\} = \phi(s)$, then

$$L\big[f(at)\big] = \frac{1}{a}\phi\left(\frac{s}{a}\right) \text{ and } L\left[f\left(\frac{t}{a}\right)\right] = a\phi(as)$$

Proof : $L\big[f(t)\big] = \int_0^\infty e^{-st} f(t)\, dt = \phi(s)$ [1]

$$\therefore \quad L\big[f(at)\big] = \int_0^\infty e^{-st} f(at)\, dt \qquad\qquad\qquad [2]$$

(Put $at = z$; $dt = \dfrac{dz}{a}$)

$$= \frac{1}{a}\int_0^\infty e^{-(s/a)z} f(z)\, dz \qquad\qquad\qquad [3]$$

$$= \frac{1}{a}\phi\left(\frac{s}{a}\right)$$

$$\therefore \quad L\big[f(at)\big] = \frac{1}{a}\phi\left(\frac{s}{a}\right) \qquad\qquad\qquad\qquad [4]$$

Changing a to $\dfrac{1}{a}$ in equation [4],

Hence, $L\left[f\left(\dfrac{t}{a}\right)\right] = a\phi(as)$ [5]

P_3: If $L\big[f(t)\big] = \phi(s)$, then

  (i) $L\big[e^{at} f(t)\big] = \phi(s-a)$ (ii) $L\big[e^{-at} f(t)\big] = \phi(s+a)$

Proof: By definition, we have

$$\phi(s-a) = \int_0^\infty e^{-(s-a)t} f(t) dt$$

$$= \int_0^\infty e^{-st} \left\{ f(t) e^{at} \right\} dt$$

$$= L\left\{ e^{at} f(t) \right\}$$

$$\therefore \quad L\left[e^{at} f(t) \right] = \phi(s-a), \text{ which proves (i)}$$

(ii) $\phi(s+a) = \int_0^\infty e^{-(s+a)t} f(t) dt$

$$= \int_0^\infty e^{-st} \left\{ e^{-at} f(t) \right\} dt$$

$$= L\left\{ e^{-at} f(t) \right\}.$$

Thus, $L\left\{ e^{-at} f(t) \right\} = \phi(s+a)$ which proves (ii)

P_4: (Change of scale with shifting)

It $L[f(t)] = \phi(s)$ then

$$L\left[e^{bt} f(at) \right] = \frac{1}{a} \phi\left(\frac{s-b}{a} \right)$$

Proof : $L\left[e^{bt} f(at) \right] = \int_0^\infty e^{-st} . e^{bt} . f(at) dt$

$$= \int_0^\infty e^{-(s-b)t} f(at) dt$$

put $at = z \Rightarrow dt = \dfrac{dz}{a}$

$$= \frac{1}{a} \int_0^\infty e^{-(s-b)\frac{z}{a}} f(z) dz$$

$$= \frac{1}{a} \phi\left(\frac{s-b}{a} \right)$$

Definition of Gamma Function

For positive values of n, the integral $\int_0^\infty e^{-x} x^{n-1} dx$ is called a Gamma function of order n. This is written as Gamma (n), or $\Gamma(n)$;

$$\therefore \quad \int_0^\infty e^{-x} x^{n-1} dx = \Gamma(n)$$

$$\int_0^\infty e^{-x}x^n dx = \overline{|n+1|};$$

$$\int_0^\infty e^{-x}x^{n-2}dx = \overline{|(n-1)|}$$

Properties

(i) The value of $\Gamma(1)$ is equal to 1.

$$\Gamma(n) = \int_0^\infty e^{-x}x^{n-1}dx; \quad \text{(Put } n = 1)$$

$$\therefore \quad \Gamma(1) = \int_0^\infty e^{-n}x^{1-1}dx = \int_0^\infty x^0 e^{-x}dx = \int_0^\infty e^{-x}dx$$

$$= \left[-e^{-x}\right]_0^\infty = (-)\left[e^{-\infty} - e^{-0}\right] = -(0-1) = 1$$

(ii) $\Gamma(n) = (n-1)\Gamma(n-1)$

$$\Gamma(n) = \int_0^\infty x^{n-1}e^{-x}dx$$

(Integrate by parts)

$$= \left[x^{n-1}\left(-e^{-x}\right)\right]_0^\infty - \int_0^\infty \left(-e^{-x}\right)(n-1)x^{n-2}dx$$

$$= -\left[\lim\left(x^{n-1}e^{-n}\right) - 0.e^0\right] + (n-1)\int_0^\infty e^{-x}x^{m-2}dx$$

$$= -(0-0) + (n-1)\int_0^\infty e^{-x}x^{(n-1)-1}dx$$

$$= (n-1)\Gamma(n-1)$$

$$\Gamma(n) = (n-1)\Gamma(n-1)$$

(iii) $\Gamma(n) = (n-1)!$

(if "n" is a positive integer)

By a repeated application of above, we get

$$\Gamma(n) = (n-1)\Gamma(n-1)$$

$$= (n-1)\left[(n-2)\Gamma(n-2)\right] = (n-1)(n-2)\left[(n-3)\Gamma(n-3)\right]$$

$$= (n-1)(n-2)(n-3)\Gamma[n-3]; \text{ and so on.}$$

Also $\Gamma(2) = 1 \cdot \Gamma(1)$

Since "n" is an integer, this reduction leads to (5, 4, 3, 2 and 1)

Hence, we get (if n is an integer)

$$\Gamma(n) = (n-1)(n-2)(n-3)\ldots 4, 3, 2, 1\, \Gamma(1)$$

$$= (n-1)! \left[\Gamma(1)\right] = (n-1)!\, 1 = (n-1)!$$

Thus, $\Gamma(n) = (n-1)!$

$$\Gamma(n+1) = n!$$

$$\Gamma(3) = 2!$$

(iv) $\int_0^\infty e^{-ax} x^{n-1} dx = \left[\dfrac{\Gamma(n)}{a^n}\right]$; '$a$' is positive

Put $ax = t$; $adx = dt$; $\left(\dfrac{1}{a}\right) dx = dt$

Also, when $x = 0$; $t = 0$; $x = \infty$ gives $t = \infty$

$$\therefore \quad \int_0^\infty e^{-ax} x^{n-1} dx = \int_0^\infty \left[e^{-t}\left(\dfrac{t}{a}\right)^{n-1}\right]\left(\dfrac{1}{a}\right) dt$$

$$= \left(\dfrac{1}{a^n}\right) \int_0^\infty e^{-t} t^{n-1} dt = \left(\dfrac{1}{a^n}\right) \Gamma(n).$$

Hence, when n is an integer, we have

$$\int_0^\infty e^{-st} t^{n-1} dt = \dfrac{\Gamma(n)}{s^n} = \dfrac{(n-1)!}{s^n};$$

$$\boxed{\int_0^\infty e^{-st} t^n dt = \dfrac{\Gamma(n+1)}{s^{n+1}} = \dfrac{n!}{s^{n+1}};}$$

(v) $\Gamma\left(\dfrac{1}{2}\right) = \sqrt{\pi}$; and putting $x^2 = t$;

$$\int_0^\infty e^{-x^2} dx = \dfrac{1}{2} \int_0^\infty e^{-t} t^{\frac{1}{2}-1} dt$$

$$= \dfrac{1}{2} \Gamma\left(\dfrac{1}{2}\right) = \dfrac{\sqrt{\pi}}{2}$$

$$\Rightarrow \quad \int_\infty^\infty e^{-x^2} dx = \left(\sqrt{\pi}\right)$$

Note: Let $f(t) = t^b$, where b is a non-negative real number, $b > 0$, then

$$L\left[t^b\right] = \int_0^\infty e^{-st} t^b dt \qquad\qquad \text{put } st = x$$

$$e^{-x}\left(\frac{x}{s}\right)^b \frac{dx}{s} = \frac{1}{s^{b+1}}\int_0^\infty e^{-x}x^b\,dx$$

$$L\left[t^b\right] = \frac{1}{s^{b+1}}\Gamma(b+1), \text{ where } s > 0, \text{ and } b+1 > 0$$

Here, the Gamma function is defined as $\Gamma(\alpha) = \int_0^\infty e^{-t}t^{\alpha-1}dt$ with $\alpha > 0$

Laplace Transforms of sinh (at) and cosh (at)

(i) $L[\sinh at] = L\left[\frac{1}{2}\left(e^{at} - e^{-at}\right)\right]$

$$= \frac{1}{2}\left[L\left(e^{at}\right) - L\left(e^{-at}\right)\right]$$

$$= \frac{1}{2}\left[\frac{1}{s-a} - \frac{1}{s+a}\right], \ s > a \text{ and } s > -a$$

$\therefore \quad L[\sinh at] = \frac{a}{s^2 - a^2} s > |a|$

$$L[\cosh at] = L\left[\frac{1}{2}\left(e^{at} + Le^{-at}\right)\right]$$

$$= \frac{1}{2}\left[L\left(e^{at}\right) + L\left(e^{-at}\right)\right]$$

$$= \frac{1}{2}\left[\frac{1}{s+a} - \frac{1}{s-a}\right], \ \therefore \ L[\cosh at] = \frac{s}{s^2 - a^2}, \ s > |a|$$

Laplace Transforms of sin (at) and cos (at)

$$L[\cos at + i\sin at] = L\left[e^{iat}\right] = \frac{1}{(s-ia)}$$

$\therefore \quad L[\cos at] + iL[\sin at]$

$$= \frac{1}{(s-ia)} = \frac{s+ia}{s^2+a^2}$$

Equate Re and Im parts, we have $L[\cos at] = \frac{s}{s^2+a^2}; \ L[\sin at] = \frac{a}{s^2+a^2}$

EXAMPLES

1. Find the Laplace transforms of the following functions;

(a) $e^{at} - e^{bt}$ (b) $\cos^2 at$ (c) $\left(5e^{2t} - 3\right)^2$

(d) $3t^4 - 2t^3 - 4e^{-3t} - 2\sin 5t - 3\cos 2t$ (e) $5t^3 + 3t^2 - 6t + 3e^{-5t}$

(f) $\cos^2 3t + \sin 5t + \sin 2t$ (g) $\cos^3 2t$ (h) $64\sin^5 t + \cos(2t+5)$

(i) $e^{2t}\sinh^2 at$ (j) $\left(t \pm \dfrac{1}{\sqrt{t}}\right)^3$

Solution:

(a) $L\{e^{at} - e^{bt}\} = L\left[e^{at}\right] - L\left[e^{bt}\right]$

$$= \frac{1}{(s-a)} - \frac{1}{(s-b)}$$

$$= \frac{a-b}{(s-a)(s-b)}$$

(b) $L\{\cos^2 at\} = L\left\{\dfrac{1+\cos 2at}{2}\right\}$

$$= \frac{1}{2}L\{1\} + \frac{1}{2}L\{\cos 2at\} = \frac{1}{2}\cdot\frac{1}{s} + \frac{1}{2}\cdot\frac{s}{s^2 + 4a^2}$$

(c) $L\left\{\left(5e^{2t} - 3e^t\right)^2\right\}$

$$= L\left\{25e^{4t} - 30e^{2t} + 9\right\}$$

$$= 25\cdot\frac{1}{s-4} - 30\cdot\frac{1}{s-2} + 9\cdot\frac{1}{s}$$

(d) $L\left\{3t^4 - 2t^3 + 4e^{-3t} - 2\sin 5t + 3\cos 2t\right\}$

$$= 3L\{t^4\} - 2\{t^3\} + 4L\{e^{-3t}\} - 2L\{\sin 5t\} + 3L\{\cos 2t\}$$

$$= 3\cdot\frac{4!}{t^5} - 2\frac{3!}{t^4} + 4\frac{1}{s+3} - 2\frac{5}{s^2 + 5^2} + 3\frac{s}{s^2 + 2^2}$$

(e) $L\left[5t^3 + 3t^2 - 6t + 3e^{-5t}\right]$

$$= 5L\left(t^3\right) + 3L\left(t^2\right) - 6L(t) + 3L\left(e^{-5t}\right)$$

$$= 5\cdot\frac{3!}{s^4} + 3\cdot\frac{2}{s^3} - 6\cdot\frac{1}{s^2} + 3\cdot\frac{1}{s+5}$$

$$= \frac{30}{s^4} + \frac{6}{s^3} - \frac{6}{s^2} + \frac{3}{s+5}$$

(f) $L\left[\cos^2 3t + \sin 5t \sin 2t\right]$

$$= L\left[\frac{1}{2}(1+\cos 6t) + \frac{1}{2}(\cos 3t - \cos 7t)\right]$$

$$= \frac{1}{2}\left[\frac{1}{s} + \frac{s}{s^2 + 36}\right] + \frac{1}{2}\left[\frac{s}{s^2 + 9} - \frac{s}{s^2 + 49}\right]$$

(g) $L\left[\cos^3(2t)\right]$

Since, $\cos 6t = 4\cos^3 2t - 3\cos 2t$

$\Rightarrow$ $\cos^3(2t) = \frac{1}{4}\left[\cos 6t + 3\cos 2t\right]$

$\therefore$ $L\left(\cos^3 2t\right) = \frac{1}{4}\left[\frac{s}{s^2 + 36} + 3 \cdot \frac{s}{s^2 + 4}\right]$

(h) $L\left[64\sin^5 t + \cos(2t + 5)\right]$

Since, $\sin^5 t = \frac{1}{2^4}\left[\sin 5t - {}^5C_1 \sin 3t + {}^5C_2 \sin t\right]$

$$= \frac{1}{16}\left[\sin 5t - 5\sin 3t + 10\sin t\right]$$

$\therefore$ $L\left[64\sin^5 t + \cos(2t + 5)\right]$

$$= L\left[4(\sin 5t - 5\sin 3t + 10\sin t)\right] + L\left[\cos(2t + 5)\right]$$

$$= 4\left[\frac{5}{s^2 + 25} - 5 \cdot \frac{3}{s^2 + 9} + 10 \cdot \frac{1}{s^2 + 1}\right] + L\left[\cos 2t \cos 5 - \sin 2t \sin 5\right]$$

$$= \frac{20}{s^2 + 25} - \frac{60}{s^2 + 9} + \frac{40}{s^2 + 1}\cos 5 \cdot \frac{s}{s^2 + 4} - \sin 5 \cdot \frac{2}{s^2 + 4}$$

(i) $L\left[e^{2t}\sinh^2 at\right]$

$$= L\left[e^{2t}\left(\frac{e^{at} - e^{-at}}{2}\right)^2\right]$$

$$= \frac{1}{4}L\left[e^{2t}\left(e^{2at} + e^{-2at} - 2\right)\right]$$

$$= \frac{1}{4} L\left[e^{2(a+1)t} + e^{-2(a-1)t} - 2e^{2t} \right]$$

$$\therefore \quad L\left[e^{2t} \sinh^2 at \right] = \frac{1}{4} \left\{ \frac{1}{s-2a-2} + \frac{1}{s-2a-2} - \frac{2}{s-2} \right\}$$

(j) $L\left(\sqrt{t} \pm \frac{1}{\sqrt{t}} \right)^3$

$$= L\left\{ \left(\sqrt{t}\right)^3 + 3\left(\sqrt{t}\right)^2 \left(\frac{1}{\sqrt{t}}\right) + 3\left(\sqrt{t}\right)\left(\frac{1}{\sqrt{t}}\right)^2 + \left(\frac{1}{\sqrt{t}}\right)^3 \right\}, \quad \text{(taking positive sign)}$$

$$= L\left\{ t^{\frac{3}{2}} + 3t^{\frac{1}{2}} + 3t^{-\frac{1}{2}} + t^{-\frac{3}{2}} \right\}$$

$$= L\left[t^{\frac{3}{2}} \right] + 3L\left[t^{\frac{1}{2}} \right] + 3L\left[t^{-\frac{1}{2}} \right] + L\left[t^{-\frac{3}{2}} \right]$$

$$= \frac{\left| \frac{3}{2} + 1 \right.}{s^{\frac{5}{2}}} \pm 3 \cdot \frac{\left| \frac{1}{2} + 1 \right.}{s^{\frac{3}{2}}} \pm 3 \cdot \frac{\left| -\frac{1}{2} + 1 \right.}{s^{-\frac{1}{2}+1}} \pm \frac{\left| -\frac{3}{2} + 1 \right.}{s^{-\frac{5}{2}+1}}$$

$$= \frac{\sqrt{\pi}}{4} \left[\frac{3}{s^{\frac{5}{2}}} \pm \frac{6}{s^{\frac{3}{2}}} \pm \frac{12}{s^{\frac{1}{2}}} + \frac{8}{5^{\frac{1}{2}}} \right]$$

2. Find: $L\{f(t)\}$ where $f(t) = \begin{cases} 0, & 0 < t < 1 \\ t, & 1 < t < 4 \\ 0, & t > 4 \end{cases}$

Solution:

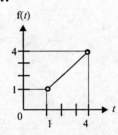

$$L\{f(t)\} = \int_0^\infty e^{-st} f(t)\, dt$$

$$= \int_0^1 0 \cdot e^{-st} dt + \int_1^4 t \cdot e^{-st} dt + \int_4^\infty 0 \cdot e^{-st} dt$$

Integrating by parts,

$$= -\frac{t}{s} e^{-st} - \frac{e^{-st}}{s^2} \Bigg]_1^4$$

$$= e^{-s} \left(\frac{1}{s} + \frac{1}{s^2} \right) - e^{-4s} \left(\frac{4}{s} + \frac{1}{s^2} \right)$$

3. Find: $L[f(t)]$ where $f(t) = \begin{cases} e^t, & 0 < t < 1 \\ 0, & t > 1 \end{cases}$

Solution:

$$L[f(t)] = \int_0^\infty e^{-st} f(t) dt$$

$$= \int_0^1 e^{-st} f(t) dt + \int_1^\infty e^{-st} f(t)$$

$$= \int_0^1 e^{-st} e^t dt + \int_1^\infty e^{-st} (0) dt$$

$$= \int_0^1 e^{(1-s)t} \cdot dt + 0$$

$$= \left[\frac{e^{(1-s)t}}{1-s} \right]_0^1 = \frac{1}{(1-s)} \left[e^{(1-s)} - 1 \right]$$

4. Find: $L[f(t)]$ where $f(t) = \begin{cases} \sin 2t, & 0 < t < \pi \\ 0, & t > \pi \end{cases}$

Solution:

$$= \int_0^\pi e^{-st} f(t) dt + \int_\pi^\infty e^{-st} 0 \, dt, \quad \text{(by data)}$$

$$= \left[e^{-st} \frac{(-s \cdot \sin 2t - 2\cos 2t)}{(-s)^2 + 2^2} \right]_0^\pi$$

$$= \frac{-2}{(s^2 + 4)} \left[e^{-st} \cos 2t \right]_0^\pi$$

$\because \qquad \sin 2\pi = 0 = \sin 0$

$$L[f(t)] = \frac{-2}{s^2+4}\left[e^{-st}\cos 2\pi - e^0 \cos 0\right] = -\frac{2}{s^2+4}\left[e^{-\pi s}-1\right].$$

Thus $L[f(t)] = \frac{-2}{s^2+4}\left[e^{-st}\cos 2\pi - e^0 \cos 0\right] = -\frac{2}{s^2+4}\left[e^{-\pi s}-1\right]$

5. Find: (i) $L\left[\sin\sqrt{t}\right]$ (ii) $L\left[\cos\sqrt{t}\right]$

Solution: We know that $\sin\theta = \theta - \dfrac{\theta^3}{3!} + \dfrac{\theta^5}{5!} - \ldots$ to ∞

Hence $\sin\left(\sqrt{t}\right) = t^{\frac{1}{2}} - \dfrac{t^{\frac{3}{2}}}{3!} + \dfrac{t^{\frac{5}{2}}}{5!} \ldots$ to ∞

(i) $L\left[\sin\left(\sqrt{t}\right)\right] = L\left(t^{\frac{1}{2}}\right) - \dfrac{1}{3!}L\left(t^{\frac{3}{2}}\right) - \dfrac{1}{5!}L\left(t^{\frac{5}{2}}\right) \ldots$ to ∞

$$= \frac{\Gamma\left(\frac{3}{2}\right)}{s^{\frac{3}{2}}} - \frac{1}{3!}\frac{\Gamma\left(\frac{5}{2}\right)}{s^{\frac{5}{2}}} + \frac{1}{5!}\frac{\Gamma\left(\frac{7}{2}\right)}{s^{\frac{7}{2}}} - \ldots$$

$$\left\{L(t^n) = \frac{\Gamma(n+1)}{s^{n+1}}\right\}$$

Now $\Gamma(n+1) = n\Gamma(n)$ and $\Gamma\left(\dfrac{1}{2}\right) = \sqrt{\pi}$

$\therefore$ $L\left[\sin\sqrt{t}\right] = \dfrac{\sqrt{\pi}}{s^{\frac{3}{2}}}\left[\dfrac{1}{2} - \dfrac{1}{3!}\cdot\dfrac{3\cdot1\cdot1}{2\cdot2}\cdot\dfrac{1}{s} + \dfrac{1}{s^2 5!}\dfrac{5\cdot3\cdot1}{2\cdot2\cdot2}\ldots\right]$

$$= \frac{1}{2s}\left(\frac{\pi}{s}\right)^{\frac{1}{2}}\left[1 - \frac{1}{2^2 s} + \frac{1}{\left(2^2 s\right)^2 2!} - \frac{1}{\left(2^2 s\right)^3 3!} + \ldots\right]$$

$$= \frac{1}{2s}\left(\frac{\pi}{s}\right)^{\frac{1}{2}}\left[e^{-\frac{1}{2^2 s}}\right] = \frac{1}{2s}\left(\frac{\pi}{s}\right)^{\frac{1}{2}} e^{-\left(\frac{1}{4s}\right)}$$

(ii) $L\left(\cos\sqrt{t}\right)$

We know that $\cos\theta = 1 - \dfrac{\theta^2}{2!} + \dfrac{\theta^4}{4!} - \dfrac{\theta^6}{6!} + \ldots$

Hence $\cos\left(\sqrt{t}\right) = \sum_{n=0}^{\infty} \dfrac{(-1)^n \left(t^{\frac{1}{2}}\right)^{2n}}{(2n)!}$

$\qquad = \sum \dfrac{(-1)^n}{(2n)!} t^n$

$\therefore \qquad L\left[\cos\left(\sqrt{t}\right)\right] = L\left\{\sum \dfrac{(-1)^n}{(2n)} t^n\right\}$

$\qquad = \sum_{n=0}^{\infty} L\left\{\dfrac{(-1)^n}{(2n)!} t^n\right\}$

(by Linearity property)

$\qquad = \sum_{n=0}^{\infty} \dfrac{(-1)^n}{(2n)!} L\{t^n\}$

$\qquad = \sum_{n=0}^{\infty} \dfrac{(-1)^n}{(2n)!} \dfrac{n!}{s^{n+1}}$

6. Find: (i) $L\left[\sin^2(at)\right]$ (ii) $L\left[\sin^3(at)\right]$ (iii) $L\left[\sin^4(at)\right]$

Solution:

(i) $L\left[\sin^2(at)\right] = L\left\{\dfrac{1}{2}(1 - \cos 2at)\right\}$

$\qquad = \dfrac{1}{2}\left\{L(1) - L(\cos 2at)\right\}$

$\qquad = \dfrac{1}{2}\left[\dfrac{1}{s} - \dfrac{s}{s^2 + 4a^2}\right]$

$\qquad = \dfrac{2a^2}{s\left(s^2 + 4a^2\right)}$

$\therefore \qquad L\left[\sin^2(at)\right] = \dfrac{2a^2}{s\left(s^2 + 4a^2\right)}$

(ii) We know that

$\sin^3\theta = \dfrac{3}{4}\sin\theta - \dfrac{1}{4}\sin^3\theta$

$\therefore \qquad L\left[\sin^3(at)\right] = \frac{3}{4}L\left[\sin(at)\right] - \frac{1}{4}L\left[\sin 3at\right]$

$= \frac{3}{4} \cdot \frac{a}{s^2+a^2} - \frac{1}{4} \cdot \frac{3a}{\left(s^2+9a^2\right)}$

$= \frac{3}{4}\left[\frac{as^2+9a^2-as^2-a^3}{\left(s^2+a^2\right)\left(s^2+9a^2\right)}\right]$

$= \frac{3}{4}\left[\frac{8a^3}{\left(s^2+a^2\right)\left(s^2+9a^2\right)}\right]$

$= \frac{6a^3}{\left(s^2+a^2\right)\left(s^2+9a^2\right)}$

(iii) $L\left[\sin^4(at)\right] = L\left[\left\{\sin^2(at)\right\}^2\right]$

$= L\left[\left\{\frac{1-\cos 2at}{2}\right\}^2\right]$

$= \frac{1}{4}L\left[\left(1-\cos 2at\right)^2\right]$

$= \frac{1}{4}L\left[1-2\cos(at)+\cos^2(2at)\right]$

$= \frac{1}{4}L\left[1-2\cos(at)+\frac{1+\cos(4at)}{2}\right]$

$= \frac{1}{8}\left\{L(3)-4L(\cos 2at)+L(\cosh at)\right\}$

$= \frac{1}{8}\left\{\frac{3}{5}-\frac{4s}{s^2+4a^2}+\frac{s}{s^2+16a^2}\right\}$

7. Find: (i) $L\left[\cos^2(at)\right]$ (ii) $L\left[\cos^3(at)\right]$ (iii) $L\left[\cos^4(at)\right]$

Solution:

(i) $L\left[\cos^2(at)\right] = L\left[\frac{1+\cos 2at}{2}\right]$

$= \frac{1}{2}\left[L(1+\cos 2at)\right]$

$$= \frac{1}{2}\Big[L\{1\} + L(\cos 2at)\Big]$$

$$= \frac{1}{2}\Bigg[\frac{1}{s} + \frac{s}{s^2 + 4a^2}\Bigg]$$

$$= \Bigg[\frac{1}{2s} + \frac{s}{2(s^2 + 4a^2)}\Bigg]$$

(ii) $L\Big[\cos^3(at)\Big]$

We know that $\cos^3\theta = \dfrac{3}{4}\cos\theta + \dfrac{1}{4}\cos 3\theta$

$$L\Big[\cos^3(at)\Big] = L\Bigg[\frac{3}{4}\cos(at) + \frac{1}{4}\cos 3at\Bigg]$$

$$= \frac{3}{4}L\Big[\cos(at)\Big] + \frac{1}{4}L\Big[\cos(3at)\Big]$$

$$= \frac{3}{4}\cdot\frac{s}{s^2 + a^2} + \frac{1}{4}\cdot\frac{s}{s^2 + 9a^2}$$

$$= \frac{3s}{4(s^2 + a^2)} + \frac{2}{4(s^2 + 9a^2)}$$

(iii) $\quad L\Big[\cos^4(at)\Big] = L\Big[\big\{\cos^2(at)\big\}^2\Big]$

$$= L\Bigg[\frac{1 + \cos(2at)}{2}\Bigg]^2$$

$$= L\Bigg[\frac{1}{4}\big(1 + 2\cos(2at) + \cos^2(2at)\big)\Bigg]$$

$$= \frac{1}{4}L\Bigg[1 + 2\cos(2at) + \Bigg(\frac{1 + \cos 4at}{2}\Bigg)\Bigg]$$

$$= \frac{1}{8}L\big[3 + 4\cos 2at + \cos 4at\big]$$

$$= \Bigg(\frac{1}{8}\Bigg)\Big[L(3) + L(4\cos 2at) + L(\cos 4at)\Big]$$

$$= \Bigg(\frac{1}{8}\Bigg)\Bigg[\frac{3}{s} + \frac{4s}{s^2 + 4a^2} + \frac{s}{s^2 + 16a^2}\Bigg]$$

$$= \left(\frac{3}{8s}\right) + \frac{s}{2\left(s^2 + 4a^2\right)} + \frac{s}{8\left(s^2 + 16a^2\right)}$$

8. Find: (i) $L\left[\sin(at)\sin(2at)\right]$ (ii) $L\left[\sin(at)\sin(2at)\sin(3at)\right]$

Solution: We know that $2\sin A \sin B = \cos(A-B) - \cos(A+B)$

(i) $L\left[\sin(at)\sin(2at)\right]$

$$= L\left[\frac{1}{2}\{\cos(at) - \cos(3at)\}\right]$$

$$= \frac{1}{2} \cdot L(\cos at) - \frac{1}{2} L\cos(3at)$$

$$= \frac{1}{2} \cdot \frac{s}{s^2 + a^2} - \frac{1}{2} \cdot \frac{s}{s^2 + 9a^2}$$

$$= \frac{1}{2}\left[\frac{8a^2 s}{\left(s^2 + a^2\right)\left(s^2 + 9a^2\right)}\right]$$

$$= \frac{4a^2 s}{\left(s^2 + a^2\right)\left(s^2 + 9a^2\right)}$$

(ii) We know that $2\sin A \sin B = \cos(A-B) - \cos(A+B)$

$\therefore \qquad L\left[\sin(at) \cdot \sin(2at) \cdot \sin(3at)\right]$

$$= L\left[\sin(at) \cdot \sin(3at) \cdot \sin(2at)\right]$$

$$= \frac{1}{2} L\left[\sin at \left(\cos(at) - \cos(5at)\right)\right]$$

$$= \frac{1}{2}\sin(at)\cos(at) - \frac{1}{2}\cos(5at)\sin(at)$$

$$= \frac{1}{2}\sin(2at) - \frac{1}{4}(\sin 6at - \sin 4at)$$

$$= \frac{1}{4}\left[\sin(2at) - \sin(6at) + \sin 4at\right]$$

$\therefore \qquad L\left[\sin(at) \cdot \sin(2at) \cdot \sin(3at)\right]$

$$= \frac{1}{4}\left\{ L\left[\sin(2at)\right] - L\left[\sin(6at)\right] + L\left[\sin(4at)\right]\right\}$$

$$= \frac{1}{4} \cdot \frac{2a}{s^2 + 4a^2} - \frac{1}{4} \cdot \frac{6a}{s^2 + 36a^2} + \frac{4a}{4\left(s^2 + 16a^2\right)}$$

$$= \left[\frac{a}{2\left(s^2 + 4a^2\right)} - \frac{3a}{2\left(s^2 + 36a^2\right)} + \frac{a}{s^2 + 16a^2}\right]$$

9. Find: (i) $L\left[\cos(at)\cos(2at)\right]$ (ii) $L\left[\cos(at)\cdot\cos(2at)\cdot\cos(3at)\right]$

   Solution: We know that $2C_A C_B = C_{A+B} + C_{A-B}$ [1]

   (i) $\cos(at)\cos(2at) = \dfrac{1}{2}\left[2\cos(2at)\cos(at)\right]$

$$= \frac{1}{2}\left[\cos(3at) + \cos(at)\right] \quad \text{using [1]}$$

   $\therefore$ $L\left[\cos(at).\cos(2at)\right] = \dfrac{1}{2}\left[L(\cos(3at))\right] + L\left[\cos(at)\right]$

$$= \frac{1}{2} \cdot \frac{s}{s^2 + (3a)^2} + \frac{1}{2} \cdot \frac{s}{s^2 + (a^2)}$$

$$= \frac{1}{2}\left[\frac{s^3 + a^2 s + s^3 + 9a^2 5}{\left(s^2 + 9a^2\right)\left(s^2 + a^2\right)}\right]$$

$$= \frac{\left(s^3 + 5a^2 s\right)}{\left(s^2 + a^2\right)\left(s^2 + 9a^2\right)}$$

   (ii) $L\left[\cos(at)\cos(2at)\cos(3at)\right]$

$$= L\left[\frac{1}{2}\left(2\cos(3at)\cos(at)\right)\cos(2at)\right]$$

$$= L\left\{\frac{1}{2}\left[\cos(4at) + \cos(2at)\right].\cos(2at)\right\}$$

$$= L\left\{\frac{1}{4}\left[2\cos(4at)\cos(2at)\right] + 2\cos^2(2at)\right\}$$

$$= \frac{1}{4}L\left\{\cos(6at) + \cos(2at) + 1 + \cos(4at)\right\}$$

$$= \frac{1}{4}\Big[L(1) + L\cos(2at) + L\cos(4at) + L\cos(6at)\Big]$$

$$= \frac{1}{4}\left[\frac{1}{s} + \frac{s}{s^2 + 4a^2} + \frac{s}{s^2 + 16a^2} + \frac{s}{s^2 + 36a^2}\right]$$

10. If $L[f(t)] = \dfrac{e^{-\frac{1}{s}}}{s}$ find $L\big[e^{-t} f(3t)\big]$

Solution: We know that from change of scale property that

$$L[f(at)] = \frac{1}{a}\phi\left(\frac{s}{a}\right) \tag{1}$$

Here $a = 3$, replace s by $\dfrac{s}{3}$

$$\therefore \quad L[f(3t)] = \frac{1}{3} \cdot \frac{e^{-\frac{3}{5}}}{\frac{s}{3}} = \frac{e^{-\frac{3}{5}}}{s}$$

Again, by shift theorem,

i.e., $\quad L\big[e^{-at} f(t)\big] = \phi(s + a) \tag{2}$

Here $a = 1$, $\therefore L\big[e^{-t} f(3t)\big] = \dfrac{e^{-\frac{3}{(s+1)}}}{s+1}$

(on replacing s by $(s - a) = (s - (-1)) = s + 1$).

11. Find L.T. of the following functions:

   (i) $e^{at} \sin bt$ (ii) $e^{at} \cos bt$ (iii) $e^{at} \sinh bt$ (iv) $e^{at} \cosh bt$ (v) $e^{at} t^n$

Solution: We know that

   (i) $L[\sin bt] = \dfrac{b}{s^s + b^2}$, Then

$$L[\sin bt] = \left[\frac{b}{s^2 + b^2}\right]_{s \to (s-a)}$$

$$\therefore \quad L\big[e^{at} \sin bt\big] = \frac{b}{(s-a)^2 + b^2}$$

(ii) $L[\cos bt] = \dfrac{s}{s^2 + b^2}$ then

$$L[e^{at} \cos bt] = \left[\dfrac{s}{s^2 + b^2}\right]_{s \to (s-a)}$$

(iii) $L[\sin bt] = \dfrac{b}{s^2 - b^2}$

$\therefore$ $\quad L[e^{at} \sin bt] = \dfrac{b}{s^2 - b^2}\Bigg]_{s \to (s-a)} = \dfrac{b}{(s-a)^2 - b^2}$

(iv) $L[\cosh bt] = \dfrac{s}{(s^2 - b^2)}$

$\therefore$ $\quad L[e^{at} \cosh bt] = \dfrac{s}{s^2 - b^2}\Bigg]_{s \to (s-a)}$

$$= \dfrac{(s-a)}{(s-a)^2 - b^2}$$

$\therefore$ $\quad L[e^{at} \cosh bt] = \dfrac{(s-a)}{(s-a)^2 - b^2}$

(v) $L[e^{at} t^n] = \dfrac{n!}{s^{n+1}}\Bigg]_{s \to (s-a)}$

$$= \dfrac{n!}{(s-a)^{n+1}}$$

12. Evaluate: (i) $L\left[t^{\frac{7}{2}} e^{3t}\right]$ (ii) $L\left[3t^5 - 2t^4 + 4e^{-5t} - 3\sin 6t + 4\cos 4t\right]e^{2t}$

(iii) $L[\cosh at . \cos bt]$

Solution:

(i) $L\left[t^{\frac{7}{2}}\right] = \dfrac{\Gamma\left(\dfrac{7}{2}+1\right)}{s^{\frac{7}{2}+1}} = \dfrac{\dfrac{7}{2} \cdot \dfrac{5}{2} \cdot \dfrac{3}{2} \cdot \dfrac{1}{2}\sqrt{\left(\dfrac{1}{2}\right)}}{s^{\frac{9}{2}}} = \dfrac{105\sqrt{\pi}}{16s^{\frac{9}{2}}}$

By first shift theorem,

$$L\left[e^{3t},t^{\frac{7}{2}}\right]=\frac{105\sqrt{\pi}}{16s^{\frac{9}{2}}}\Bigg]_{s\to(s-3)}=\frac{105\sqrt{\pi}}{16(s-3)^{\frac{9}{2}}}$$

(ii) $L\left[3t^{5}-2t^{4}+4e^{-5t}-3\sin 6t+4\cos 4t\right]$

$$=3L\left[t^{5}\right]-2L\left[t^{4}\right]+4L\left[e^{-5t}\right]-3L\left[\sin 6t\right]+4L\left[\cos 4t\right]$$

$$=3\cdot\frac{5!}{s^{6}}-2\cdot\frac{4!}{s^{5}}+\frac{1}{s+5}-3\cdot\frac{6}{s^{2}+36}+4\cdot\frac{s}{s^{2}+16}$$

By first shift theorem,

$$L\left\{\left[3t^{5}-2t^{4}+4e^{-5t}-3\sin 6t+4\cos 4t\right]e^{2t}\right\}$$

$$=\frac{360}{s^{6}}-\frac{48}{s^{5}}+\frac{4}{s+5}-\frac{1.8}{s^{2}+36}+\frac{4s}{s^{2}+16}$$

with s replaced by $(s-2)$

$$=\frac{360}{(s-2)^{6}}-\frac{48}{(s-2)^{5}}+\frac{4}{s+3}-\frac{8}{(s-2)^{2}+36}+\frac{4(s-2)}{(s-2)^{2}+16}$$

(iii) $L\left[\cosh at\cdot\cos bt\right]$

$$=L\left[\frac{1}{2}\left(e^{at}+e^{-at}\right)\cdot\cos bt\right]$$

$$=\frac{1}{2}L\left[e^{at}\cos bt\right]+\frac{1}{2}\left[e^{at}\cos bt\right]$$

By shift theorem,

$$=\frac{1}{2}\cdot\frac{s}{s^{2}+b^{2}}\Bigg]_{s\to(s-a)}+\frac{1}{2}\cdot\frac{s}{s^{2}+b^{2}}\Bigg]_{s\to(s+a)}$$

$$=\frac{1}{2}\cdot\frac{(s-a)}{(s-a)^{2}+b^{2}}+\frac{1}{2}\cdot\frac{s+a}{(s+a)^{2}+b^{2}}$$

13. Find the L.T. of $f(t)$ given by;

(i) $(t+2)^{2}e^{t}$ (ii) $e^{-4t}\cosh 2t$ (iii) $\sinh at\sin at$

Solution:

(i) $L\left[(t+2)^2 e^t\right]$

$$= L\left[t^2 e^t + 4te^t + 4e^t\right]$$

$$= L\left[t^2 e^t\right] + 4L\left[te^t\right] + 4L\left[e^t\right]$$

$$= \left[\frac{2!}{s^3}\right]_{s\to(s-1)} + 4\left[\frac{1}{s^2}\right]_{s\to(s-1)} + 4.\frac{1}{(s-1)}$$

$$= \frac{2!}{(s-1)^3} + 4.\frac{1}{(s-1)^2} + 4.\frac{1}{(s-1)}$$

$$= \frac{2 + 4(s-1) + 4(s-1)^2}{(s-1)^3}$$

$$= \frac{4s^2 - 8s + 4 + 2 + 4s - 4}{(s-1)^3}$$

$$= \frac{\left(4s^2 - 4s + 2\right)}{(s-1)^3}$$

(ii) $L\left[e^{-4t} \cosh 2t\right]$

Now, $L[\cosh 2t] = L\left(\dfrac{e^{2t} + e^{2t}}{2}\right)$

$$= \frac{1}{2}\left[\frac{1}{(s-2)} + \frac{1}{s+2}\right]$$

$\therefore$ $L\left[e^{-4t} \cdot \cos 2t\right]$

$$= \frac{1}{2}\left[\frac{1}{s-2}\right]_{s\to s+4} + \frac{1}{2}\left[\frac{1}{s+2}\right]_{s\to s+4}$$

$$= \frac{1}{2}.\frac{1}{(s+2)} + \frac{1}{2}\frac{1}{(s+6)}$$

$$= \frac{1}{2}\left[\frac{(s+6) + s + 2}{(s+2)(s+6)}\right]$$

$$= \frac{1}{2}\left[\frac{2s+8}{\left(s^2 + 8s + 12\right)}\right]$$

$$= \frac{(s+4)}{(s^2+8s+12)}$$

(iii) $L[\sinh at \cdot \sin at]$

$L[\sinh at \cdot \sin at]$

$$L[\sinh at] = \frac{a}{s^2-a^2} = \phi(s) \qquad\qquad [1]$$

$\therefore$ $\left[e^{iat} \sinh at\right] = \phi(s-ia)$ $\qquad$ by First shifting theorem

$$= \frac{a}{(s-ia)^2 - a^2}$$

$$= \frac{a}{(s^2-2a^2)-2ias} \cdot \frac{\left[(s^2-2a^2)+2ias\right]}{\left[(s^2-2a^2)+2ias\right]}$$

$$= \frac{a(s^2-2a^2)+2ia^2 s}{(s^2-2a^2)+4a^2 s^2}$$

$\Rightarrow$ $\quad L[\sinh at \cos at] + iL[\sinh at \sin at]$

$$= \frac{a(s^2-2a^2)}{s^4+4a^4} + i\frac{2a^2 s}{s^4+4a^4}$$

Equating *Re* and *Im* parts, we get

(a) $L[\sinh at \cos at] = \dfrac{a(s^2-2a^2)}{s^4+4a^4}$ and

(b) $L[\sinh at.\sin at] = \dfrac{2a^2 s}{s^4+4a^4}$

Transforms of Derivatives

(a) Multiplication by *s*:

If $f(t), f'(t), f''(t)...$ are all function of the exponential order, (defined in $t \ge 0$), then

(i) $\ L\{f'(t)\} = s\phi(s) - f(0)$

(ii) $\ L\{f''(t)\} = s^2\phi(s) - sf(0) - f'(0)$

(iii) $L\{f'''(t)\} = s^3\phi(s) - s^2 f(0) - sf'(0) - f''(0)$

Similarly, for L.T. of derivatives of order n.

$$L\{f^{(n)}(t)\} = s^n \phi(s) - s^{n-1} f(0) - s^{n-2} f'(0)...f^{(n-1)}(0)$$

We know that a function $f(t)$ is said to be of the exponential order, if as $t \to \infty$, the value of $(e^{-st} f(t)) \to 0$. Here, $f(t)$, $f'(t)$, $f''(t)...$ are all of exponential order.

Hence we have

$$\lim_{t \to \infty} e^{-st} f(t) = 0; \ \lim_{t \to \infty} e^{-st} f'(t) = 0;$$

$$\lim_{t \to \infty} e^{-st} f''(t) = 0$$

(i) $\phi(s) = L\{f(t)\} = \int_0^\infty e^{-st} f(t) dt$ [1]

(ii) $L[f'(t)] = \int_0^\infty e^{-st} f'(t) dt$ [by parts]

$$= \left[e^{-st} f(t) \right]_0^\infty - \int_0^\infty f(t) \left[\left(\frac{d}{dt} \right) (e^{-st}) \right] dt$$

$$= \lim_{t \to \infty} e^{-st} f(t) - \lim_{t \to \infty} \left[e^{-st} f(t) \right] - \int_0^\infty f(t)(-s) e^{-st} dt$$

$$= \left[0 - e^{-0} f(0) \right] + s \int_0^\infty e^{-st} f(t) dt$$

$$= 0 - f(0) + s.\phi(s)$$

$\therefore \quad L[f'(t)] = s\phi(s) - f(0)$ [2]

(iii) $L\{f''(t)\} = \int_0^\infty e^{-st} f''(t) dt$ [by parts]

$$= \left[e^{-st} f(t) \right]_0^\infty - \int_0^\infty f'(t)(-s) e^{-st} dt$$

$$= \left[\lim_{t \to \infty} \left[e^{-st} f'(t) \right] - e^{-0} f'(0) + s \int_0^\infty e^{-st} f'(t) dt \right]$$

$$= 0 - f'(0) + sLf'(t)$$

$$= -f'(0) + s \left[s\phi(s) - f(0) \right]$$

$$= -f'(0) + s^2 \phi(s) - sf(0)$$

$\therefore \quad L\{f''(t)\} = \left[s^2 \phi(s) - sf(0) - f'(0) \right]$ [3]

(iv) $L\{f'''(t)\} = \int_0^\infty e^{-st} f'''(t) dt$

$\qquad = \left[e^{-st} f''(t) \right]_0^\infty - \int_0^\infty e^{-st} (-s) \cdot f''(t) dt$

$\qquad = \left[0 - 1 \cdot f''(0) + s \int_0^\infty e^{-st} f''(t) dt \right]$

$\qquad = -f''(0) + s \left[Lf''(t) \right]$

$\qquad = -f''(0) + s \left[s^2 \phi(s) - sf(0) - f'(0) \right]$

$\therefore \quad L\{f'''(t)\} = \left[s^3 \phi(s) - s^2 f(0) - sf'(0) - f''(0) \right]$ [4]

14. Given that $L[t \sin at] = \left[\dfrac{(2as)}{\left(s^2 + a^2\right)^2} \right]$ find $L[at \cos at + \sin at]$

Solution: $L[at \cos at + \sin at]$

$\qquad = L\left[\dfrac{d}{dt} (t \sin at) \right]$

$\qquad = sL[t \sin at] - [t \sin at]$

$\qquad = s \cdot \dfrac{2as}{\left(s^2 + a^2\right)^2}$

$\therefore \quad L[at \cos at + \sin at] = \dfrac{2as^2}{\left(s^2 + a^2\right)^2}$

15. Using the results: $L[f'(t)] = sL[f(t)] - f(0)$

and $L[f''(t)] = s^2 L[f(t)] - sf(o) - f'(0)$.

Find $L[t^2], L[e^{at}], L[\sin at]$ and $L[\cos at]$

Solution: Given $f(t) = t^2$

$\qquad f(0) = 0, f'(0) = 0, f''(t) = 2$

By theorem, $L[f''(t)] = s^2 \phi(s) - sf(0) - f'(0)$

$$L[2] = s^2\phi(s) - s.0 - 0$$

$$\therefore \quad L(t^2) = \frac{1}{s^2}L[2] = \frac{2}{s^2}L[1]$$

$$= \frac{2}{s^2} \cdot \frac{1}{s} = \frac{2}{s^3} = \frac{2!}{s^3}$$

Given, $f(t) = e^{at}$

$$f(0) = e^0 = 1, \quad f'(0) = a \cdot e^0 = a$$

Since $L[f'(t)] = sL\{f(t)\} - f(0)$

Then, $L[e^{at}] = sL\{e^{at}\} - 1$

$\Rightarrow \quad aL\{e^{at}\} - sL\{e^{at}\} = -1$

$\Rightarrow \quad L\{e^{at}\} = \dfrac{1}{(s-a)}$

Given, $f(t) = \sin at$

$$L[f''(t)] = s^2[f(t)] - sf(0) - f'(0)$$

$\Rightarrow \quad L[-a^2 \cdot \sin at] = s^2 L[\sin at] - s(0) - a[1]$

$\Rightarrow \quad -a^2 L(\sin at) - s^2 L(\sin at) = -a$

$$\therefore \quad L(\sin at) = \frac{a}{(s^2 + a^2)}$$

Given $f(t) = \cos at$

$\therefore \quad L[f''(t)] = s^2[Lf(t)] - sf(0) - f'(0),$ we get

$$L[-a^2 \cos at] = s^2 L[\cos at] - s(1) - 0$$

i.e., $-a^2[L(\cos at) - s^2 L(\cos at)] = -s$

$\Rightarrow \quad L(\cos at) = \dfrac{s}{s^2 + a^2}$

Given $L\{\sin\sqrt{t}\} = \dfrac{\sqrt{\pi}}{2s^{\frac{3}{2}}} e^{-\frac{1}{4s}}$

Prove that $L\left[\dfrac{\cos\sqrt{t}}{\sqrt{t}}\right]=\left(\dfrac{\pi}{s}\right)^{\frac{1}{2}}e^{-\frac{1}{4s}}$

Let $\quad f(t)=\dfrac{\cos\sqrt{t}}{\sqrt{t}}$

Since $\dfrac{\cos\sqrt{t}}{2\sqrt{t}}$ is the derivative of $\sin\sqrt{t}$,

We take $g(t)=\sin\sqrt{t}$;

$\Rightarrow \quad g'(t)=\dfrac{\cos\sqrt{t}}{2\sqrt{t}}$; and $g(0)=0$.

$\therefore \quad L\{g'(t)\}=sL\{g(t)\}-g(0)$

$\qquad L\left[\dfrac{\cos\sqrt{t}}{2\sqrt{t}}\right]=s\cdot L\{\sin\sqrt{t}\}-0$

$\qquad \dfrac{1}{2}L\left\{\dfrac{\cos\sqrt{t}}{\sqrt{t}}\right\}=s\cdot\sqrt{\pi}\cdot\dfrac{e^{-\frac{1}{4s}}}{2s^{\frac{3}{2}}}$

$\qquad L\left[\dfrac{\cos\sqrt{t}}{\sqrt{t}}\right]=\sqrt{\dfrac{\pi}{s}}\cdot e^{-\frac{1}{4s}}$

Given $f(t)=t\cdot\cos at$

Show that $L[t\cos at]=\dfrac{\left(s^2-a^2\right)}{\left(s^2-a^2\right)^2}$

Given $f(t)=t\cdot\cos at$

$\qquad f'(t)=at\cdot\sin at+\cos at$

$\qquad f''(t)=-a[at\cos at+\sin at]-a\sin at$

$\qquad f''(t)=-a^2t\cos at-2a\sin at$

$\qquad f(0)=0;\ f'(0)=1$

Using $L[f''(t)]=s^2\phi(s)-s\cdot f(0)-f'(0)$

$\Rightarrow \quad \left(s^2+a^2\right)L[t\cos at]=1-2aL[\sin at]$

$$= 1 - 2a \cdot \frac{a}{s^2 + a^2}$$

$$= \frac{\left(s^2 - a^2\right)}{\left(s^2 + a^2\right)}$$

$$\therefore \quad L[t \cos at] = \frac{\left(s^2 - a^2\right)}{\left(s^2 + a^2\right)^2}$$

Transform of Integrals

If $f(t)$ is of exponential order as $t \to \infty$ and piecewise continuous in the interval $0 \le t \le T$ for any finite T, then

$$L\left[\int_0^t f(u)\,du\right] = \frac{1}{s} L[f(t)], \; s > 0$$

Proof: Let $g(t) = \int_0^t f(u)\,du$

Then $g'(t) = f(t)$ and $g(0) = 0$

by derivative theorem,

$$\phi(s) = L\{f(t)\} = L\{g'(t)\} = sL\{g(t)\} - g(0)$$

$$= s \cdot L\big[g(t)\big]$$

$$\therefore \quad L\big[g(t)\big] = \frac{\phi(s)}{s}$$

or $\quad L\left[\int_0^t f(u)\,du\right] = \frac{\phi(s)}{s} = \frac{L[f(t)]}{s}$

Note: (i) If $f(t)$ is of the exponential order, and $f(t) = \int_0^t f(t)\,dt$. This is a function of the upper limit t, [and 't' in $f(t)$ under the integral sign is the dummy variable].

By the Fundamental theorem,

$$F'(t) = f(t); \text{ also } \lim_{t \to \infty}\left[e^{-st} f(t)\right] = 0 \text{ as } t \to \infty$$

$$L\big[F(t)\big] = \int_0^\infty e^{-st} F(t)\,dt$$

$$= \int_0^\infty F(t) e^{-st}\,dt \;\; \text{(by parts)}$$

$$= \left[\frac{F(t)e^{-st}}{-s} \right]_0^\infty - \int_0^\infty \frac{e^{-st}}{-s} F'(t) dt$$

$$= \left(-\frac{1}{s} \right) \left[\lim e^{-st} F(t) - e^0 F(0) \right] + \left(\frac{1}{s} \right) \int_0^\infty e^{-st} f'(t) dt$$

$$= \left(-\frac{1}{s} \right) \left[0 - F(0) \right] + \left(\frac{1}{s} \right) \int_0^\infty e^{-st} f(t) dt$$

$$= \left(\frac{1}{s} \right) F(0) + \left(\frac{1}{s} \right) L\{f(t)\}$$

$$\therefore \quad L \left[\int_0^t f(t) dt \right] = \frac{1}{s} \int_0^\infty f(t) dt = \frac{1}{s} \phi(s)$$

Note: (ii) If $F(t) = \int_0^t f(t) dt$; put $t = 0$

$$F(0) = \int_0^t f(t) dt = \int_0^0 f(t) dt = 0$$

Putting $t = 0$, in the above, we get,

$$\therefore \quad L \left[\int_0^t f(t) dt \right] = 0 + \frac{1}{2} \phi(s) = \frac{1}{s} L[f(t)]$$

To Prove that $L \left\{ \int_0^t \int_0^t {}_{n\ times} \cdots \int_0^t f(t) dt \right\} = \dfrac{\phi(s)}{s^n}$

If $L[f(t)] = \phi(s)$, then

$$L \left\{ \int_0^t dt_1 \int_0^h f(u) du \right\} = \frac{\phi(s)}{s^2}$$

The definite integral can be written as $\int_0^t \int_0^t f(t) dt^2$

Generalization for nth integral

$$L \left\{ \int_0^t \int_0^t {}_{ntimes} \cdots \int_0^t f(t) dt \right\} = \frac{\phi(s)}{s^n}$$

---

16. $L \left[\int_0^t \int_0^t \int_0^t \cos au \, du \, du \, du \right]$

Solution: Let $f(t) = \cos at$

$$L[f(t)] = L[\cos at] = \frac{s}{s^2 + a^2}$$

Using the theorem on L.T. of integral,

$$L\left[\int_0^t \cos(au)du\right] = \frac{1}{s}\frac{s}{s^2+a^2} = \frac{1}{s^2+a^2}$$

Applying repeatedly $L\left[\int_0^t\int_0^t \cos au\,du\,du\right] = \frac{1}{s}\cdot\frac{1}{s^2+a^2}$

$\therefore \quad L\left\{\int_0^t\int_0^t\int_0^t \cos au\,du\,du\,du\right\} = \frac{1}{s^2}\cdot\frac{1}{s^2+a^2}$

17. Show that $\displaystyle\int_{t=0}^{\infty}\int_{u=0}^{\infty}\frac{e^{-t}\sin u}{u}du\,dt = \frac{\pi}{4}$

Solution:

The definite integral on the L.H.S is the L.T. of $\displaystyle\int_0^t\frac{\sin u}{u}du$ with $s=1$

We know that $\displaystyle L\left[\int_0^t\frac{\sin u}{u}du\right] = \int_{t=0}^{\infty}\int_{u=0}^{t}\frac{e^{-st}\sin u}{u}du\,dt$

$$= \frac{1}{s}\cdot\tan^{-1}\frac{1}{s}\bigg|_{s=1} = \tan^{-1}(1) = \frac{\pi}{4}$$

18. Find $\displaystyle L\left\{\int_0^t\frac{1-e^{-u}}{u}du\right\}$

Solution: Here $f(t) = \dfrac{\left(1-e^{-t}\right)}{t}$

$$L[f(t)] = L\left[\frac{1-e^{-t}}{t}\right] = \phi(s) = \log\left(1+\frac{1}{s}\right)$$

Using the theorem L.T. of Integral

$$L\left[\int_0^t\frac{1-e^{-u}}{u}du\right] = \frac{1}{s}\log\left(1+\frac{1}{s}\right)$$

19. Find $\displaystyle L\left[\int_0^t e^{at}\sin bt\,dt\right]$

Solution: Let $f(t) = e^{at}\sin bt$

and $\quad L[\sin bt] = \dfrac{b}{s^2+b^2}$

by first shifting theorem, $L\left[e^{at}\sin bt\right]=\dfrac{b}{(s-a)^{2}+b^{2}}$

$$L\left[\int_{0}^{t}e^{at}\sin bt\,dt\right]=\frac{1}{s}\cdot\frac{b}{(s-a)^{2}+b^{2}}=\frac{b}{s\left[(s-a)^{2}+b^{2}\right]}$$

20. Find $L\left[\int_{0}^{t}t^{2}e^{3t}\,dt\right]$

Solution: Let $f(t)=t^{2}$

$\therefore\quad L(t^{2})=\dfrac{2!}{s^{3}}=\dfrac{2}{s^{3}}$

$\therefore$ by first shifting theorem, $L\left[e^{3t}t^{2}\right]=\dfrac{2}{(s-3)^{3}}$

$\therefore\quad L\left[\int_{0}^{t}t^{2}e^{3t}\,dt\right]=\dfrac{1}{s}\cdot\dfrac{2}{(s-3)^{3}}=\dfrac{2}{s(s-3)^{3}}$

21. Find $L\left[\int_{0}^{t}\left(at^{2}+bt+c\right)dt\right]$

Solution: L.H.S. $=\left[\dfrac{at^{3}}{3}+\dfrac{bt^{2}}{2}+ct\right]$

$=\dfrac{a}{3}\cdot\dfrac{3!}{s^{4}}+\dfrac{b}{2}\cdot\dfrac{2!}{s^{3}}+c\cdot\dfrac{1}{s^{2}}$

$=\dfrac{2a}{s^{4}}+\dfrac{b}{s^{3}}+\dfrac{1}{s^{2}}$ [1]

R.H.S. $=\dfrac{1}{s}\left[aL(t^{2})+bL(t)+cL(1)\right]$

$=\dfrac{1}{s}\left[a\cdot\dfrac{2!}{s^{3}}+b\cdot\dfrac{1}{s^{2}}+c\cdot\dfrac{1}{s}\right]$

$=\dfrac{2a}{s^{4}}+\dfrac{b}{s^{3}}+\dfrac{c}{s^{2}}$ [2]. From [1] and [2], the result follows.

(b) Multiplication by powers of t

If $L[f(t)] = \phi(s)$ then

$$L[t^n f(t)] = (-1)^n \frac{d^n}{ds^n}[\phi(s)]$$

$$L[t^n f(t)] = (-1)^n \phi(s)$$

Proof: Given, $L[f(t)] = \phi(s)$

$\therefore$ $\phi(s) = L[f(t)] = \int_0^\infty e^{-st} f(t)\, dt$ [1]

$\therefore$ $\dfrac{d}{ds}[\phi(s)] = \phi'(s) = \dfrac{d}{ds}\left[\int_0^\infty e^{-st} f(t)\, dt\right]$

$$= \int_0^\infty \frac{\partial}{\partial s}\{e^{-st}\} f(t)\, dt$$

(by Leibnitz's rule on differentiation under the integral sign)

$$= \int_0^\infty -t e^{-st} f(t)\, dt$$

$$= -\int_0^\infty e^{-st}[t(t)]\, dt$$

$$= -L[tf(t)]$$

Hence $L[tf(t)] = -\dfrac{d}{ds}[\phi(s)] = -\phi'(s)$ [2]

On differentiating equation [2] twice w.r.t. s we get

$$\frac{d^2\phi}{ds^2} = \frac{d^2}{ds^2}\left[\int_0^\infty e^{-st} f(t)\, dt\right]$$

$$= \int_0^\infty \frac{\partial^2}{\partial s^2}[e^{-st}] f(t)\, dt$$

$$= \int_0^\infty f(t)(-t)^2 e^{-st}\, dt$$

$$= (-1)^2 \int_0^\infty e^{-st}[t^2 f(t)]\, dt$$

$$= (-1)^2 L[t^2 f(t)] \quad \text{[by definition]}$$

$$\frac{d^n}{ds^n}[\phi(s)] = \frac{d^n}{ds^n}\left[\int_0^\infty e^{-st} f(t)\, dt\right]$$

$$= \int_0^\infty \frac{\partial}{\partial s^n} \left[e^{-st} \right] f(t)\, dt$$

$$= \int_0^\infty f(t) \cdot (-t)^n e^{-st}\, dt$$

$$= (-1)^n \int_0^\infty e^{-st} \left[t^n f(t) \right] dt$$

$$= (-1)^n L \left[t^n f(t) \right]$$

$$\Rightarrow \quad L \left[t^n f(t) \right] = (-1)^n \frac{d^n}{ds^n} \left[\phi(s) \right]$$

$$= (-1)^n \phi^{(n)}(s)$$

$$L \left[t^n f(t) \right] = (-1)^n \phi^{(n)}(s)$$

or $\quad L \left[t^n f(t) \right] = (-1)^n \dfrac{d^n}{ds^n} \left[\phi(s) \right]$

22. Find the L.T. of the following functions

(a) $t \sin at$ 　　　(b) $t \cdot e^{-2t} \sin t$ 　　　(c) $\left[t^2 - 3t + 2 \right] \sin 3t$

(d) Show that $\displaystyle \int_0^\infty t^2 e^{-4t} \sin 2t\, dt = \frac{11}{500}$

Solution:

(a) $L[\sin at] = \dfrac{a}{s^2 + a^2}$.

$\therefore \quad L[t \sin at] = -\dfrac{d}{ds} \left[\dfrac{a}{s^2 + a^2} \right] = \dfrac{2as}{\left(s^2 + a^2 \right)^2} \quad (n=1)$

(b) $L[\sin t] = \dfrac{1}{s^2 + 1}$

$L \left[e^{-2t} \cdot \sin t \right] = \dfrac{1}{\left(s+2 \right)^2 + 1} = \dfrac{1}{s^2 + 4s + 5}$

By first shifting theorem and by multiplication by t, we get

$$L \left[t \cdot \left(e^{-2t} \sin t \right) \right] = -\dfrac{d}{ds} \left[\dfrac{1}{s^2 + 4s + 5} \right]$$

$$= \dfrac{2s + 4}{\left(s^2 + 4s + 5 \right)^2}$$

(c) $L[\sin 3t] = \dfrac{3}{s^2 + 3^2} = \dfrac{3}{s^2 + 9}$

$$L\left[\left(t^2 - 3t + 2\right)\sin 3t\right] = L\left[t^2 \sin 3t\right] - 3L\left[t \sin 3t\right] + 2L\left[\sin 3t\right]$$

$$= (-1)^2 \frac{d^2}{ds^2}\left[\frac{3}{s^2 + 9}\right] - 3(-1)\frac{d}{ds}\left[\frac{3}{s^2 + 9}\right] + 2\frac{3}{s^2 + 9}$$

$$= \frac{\left(-6 + 24s^2\right)}{\left(s^2 + 9\right)^3} + 3\frac{\left(-6s\right)}{\left(s^2 + 9\right)^2} + \frac{6}{s^2 + 9}$$

$$= \frac{6s^4 - 18s^3 + 126s^2 - 162s + 432}{\left(s^2 + 9\right)^3}$$

(d) $\displaystyle\int_0^\infty e^{-4t}\left[t^2 \sin 2t\right]dt$

$\Rightarrow$ $L\left[t^2 \sin 2t\right]$ with $s = 4$ but $L[\sin 2t] = \dfrac{2}{s^2 + 2^2} = \dfrac{2}{s^2 + 4}$

$\therefore$ $L\left[t^2 \sin 2t\right] = (-1)^2 \dfrac{d^2}{ds^2}\left[\dfrac{2}{s^2 + 4}\right] = \dfrac{d}{ds}\left[\dfrac{-4s}{\left(s^2 + 4\right)^2}\right]$

$$= -4 \cdot \left.\frac{\left(f - 3s^2\right)}{\left(s^2 + 4\right)^3}\right|_{s=4} = \frac{11}{500}$$

23. Obtain the L.T. of each of the following functions :

(a) $t \sinh at$;

(b) $t \cosh at$;

(c) te^{2t}

(d) $t^2 e^{2t}$

(e) $t^2(\sin at)$

(f) $t^3 \sin t$

(g) $te^t \sinh t$

(h) $te^{-2t}\cos 2t$

(i) $\dfrac{t^4}{\sqrt{t}}$

(j) $\displaystyle\int_0^\infty e^{-st}t^3 \cos t\, dt$

(k) $\displaystyle\int_0^\infty e^{-3t}t \cdot \sin t\, dt$

Solution:

(a) $L[t \sinh at] = -\dfrac{d}{ds}L(\sinh at)$

$$= -\frac{d}{ds}\left[\frac{a}{s^2 - a^2}\right]$$

$$= \frac{2as}{\left(s^2 - a^2\right)^2}$$

(b) $L[t \cosh at] = -\dfrac{d}{ds} L(\cosh at)$

$$= -\frac{d}{ds}\left[\frac{s}{s^2 - a^2}\right]$$

$$= -\frac{\left(s^2 + a^2\right)}{\left(s^2 - a^2\right)^2}$$

(c) $L\left[te^{2t}\right] = -\dfrac{d}{ds}\dfrac{1}{(s-2)} = \dfrac{1}{(s-2)^2}$

(d) $L\left[t^2 e^{2t}\right] = -\dfrac{d^2}{ds^2}\left(\dfrac{1}{(s-2)}\right) = \dfrac{2}{(s-2)^3}$

(e) $L\left[t^2 (\sin at)\right] = \dfrac{d^2}{ds^2}\left[\dfrac{a}{s^2 + a^2}\right]$

$$= \frac{6as^2 - 2a^3}{\left(s^2 + a^2\right)^3}$$

(f) $L\left[t^3 \sin t\right] = (-1)^3 \dfrac{d^3}{ds^3}\left[\dfrac{1}{s^2 + 1}\right] = \dfrac{24s\left(s^2 - 1\right)}{\left(s^2 + 1\right)^4}$

e^t amounts to shifting, we shall first find $L[t \sinh t]$

$$L[t \sinh t] = -\frac{d}{ds} L[\sinh t]$$

$$= -\frac{d}{ds}\left[\frac{1}{s^2 - 1}\right]$$

$$= -\frac{2s}{\left(s^2 - 1\right)^2}$$

$$L\left[e^t t \sinh t\right] = \frac{2(s-1)}{\left[(s-1)^2 - 1\right]^2} = \frac{2(s-1)}{s^2(s-2)^2}$$

(g) $L\left[te^{-2t}\cos 2t\right]$

$$L[t\cos 2t]=\frac{s^2-4}{\left(s^2+4\right)^2}$$

$\therefore$ $\quad L\left[e^{-2t}t\cos 2t\right]=\dfrac{\left(s^2+2\right)^2-4}{\left[\left(s^2+2\right)^2+4\right]^2}$

$\qquad\qquad\qquad =\dfrac{s(s+4)}{\left(s^2+4s+8\right)^2}$

(h) $L\left[\dfrac{t^4}{\sqrt{t}}\right]$

Let $\quad f(t)=\dfrac{1}{\sqrt{t}};$

$\therefore$ $\quad L[f(t)]=L\left[\dfrac{1}{\sqrt{t}}\right]=\sqrt{\pi}s^{-\frac{1}{2}}$

$\therefore$ $\quad L\left[\dfrac{t^4}{\sqrt{t}}\right]=(-1)^4\dfrac{d^4}{ds^4}\left(\sqrt{\pi}.s^{-\frac{1}{2}}\right)$

$\qquad\qquad =\left(-\dfrac{1}{2}\right)\left(\dfrac{-3}{2}\right)\left(\dfrac{-5}{2}\right)\left(\dfrac{-7}{2}\right)\sqrt{\pi}\cdot s^{-\frac{9}{2}}$

$\qquad\qquad =\dfrac{105}{16}\sqrt{\pi}s^{-\frac{9}{2}}$

(i) Given, $\displaystyle\int_0^\infty e^{-st}t^3\cos t\,dt=L\left[t^3\cos t\right]$

Thus $L[\cos t]=\dfrac{s}{s^2+1}$

$\therefore$ $\quad L\left[t^3\cos t\right]=(-1)^3\dfrac{d^3}{ds^3}\left[\dfrac{s}{s^2+1}\right]=\dfrac{6\left(s^4-6s^2+1\right)}{\left(s^2+1\right)^4}$

$\therefore$ $\quad \displaystyle\int_0^\infty e^{-st}t^3\cos t\,dt=\dfrac{6\left(s^4-6s^2+1\right)}{\left(s^2+1\right)^4}$

(j) Given, $\int_0^\infty e^{-3t} t \cdot \sin t \, dt$

$\qquad = L[t \sin t] = \phi(s)$

Now $\phi(s) = L(t \sin t)$

$\qquad = -\dfrac{d}{ds}[\sin t]$

$\qquad = -\dfrac{d}{ds}\left[\dfrac{1}{s^2+1}\right]$

$\qquad = \dfrac{2s}{\left(s^2+1\right)^2}$; [taking $s = 3$]

$\therefore \quad \int_0^\infty e^{-3t} t \sin t \, dt = \phi(3)$

$\qquad = \dfrac{2 \cdot 3}{\left(3^2+1\right)^2} = \dfrac{6}{100} = \dfrac{3}{50}$

(k) Given, $\int_0^\infty e^{-3t} \left(t \cos 2t\right) dt$

$\qquad = L[t \cos 2t]$

$\qquad = -\dfrac{d}{ds}[L(\cos 2t)]$

$\qquad = -\dfrac{d}{ds}\left[\dfrac{s}{s^2+4}\right]$

$\qquad = -\dfrac{\left(s^2+4\right)-2s^2}{\left(s^2+4\right)^2}$

$\qquad = -\dfrac{s^2-4}{\left(s^2+4\right)^2}$

or $\quad \int_0^\infty e^{-st} \left(t \cos 2t\right) dt = \dfrac{\left(s^2-4\right)}{\left(s^2-4\right)^2}$

Put $s = 3$ we get

$\qquad \int_0^\infty e^{-3t} t \cos 2t \, dt = \dfrac{5}{\left(3^2-4\right)^2} = \dfrac{5}{169}$

EXERCISES

Find L.T. of the following functions;

1. $e^{-2t} \sin 3t + e^t t \cos t$

$$\left[Ans. \quad \frac{3}{s^2 + 4s + 13} + \frac{s^2 - 2s}{\left(s^2 - 2s + 2\right)^2} \right]$$

2. $t \cdot (3\sin 2t - 2\cos 2t)$

$$\left[Ans. \quad \frac{8 + 12s - 2s^2}{\left(s^2 + 4\right)^2} \right]$$

3. $t^2 \sin 2t$

$$\left[Ans. \quad \frac{16 - 12s^2}{\left(s^2 + 4\right)^3} \right]$$

4. $t^2 e^{-3t} \cos t$

$$\left[Ans. \quad \frac{(25 + 6)\left(s^2 + 6s + 6\right)}{\left(s^2 + 6s + 10\right)^3} \right]$$

5. $t \sin^3 t$

$$\left[Ans. \quad \frac{24s\left(s^2 + 5\right)}{\left(s^2 + 1\right)^2 \left(s^2 + 9\right)^2} \right]$$

6. $t \cos^3 t$

$$\left[Ans. \quad \frac{1}{4}\left[\frac{s^2 - 9}{\left(s^2 + 9\right)^2} + \frac{3\left(s^2 - 1\right)}{\left(s^2 + 1\right)^2} \right] \right]$$

7. $\left(t^2 + 4\right)\cos 2t$

$$\left[Ans. \quad \frac{2s\left(s^2 - 12\right)}{\left(s^2 + 4\right)^3} + \frac{4s}{s^2 + 4} \right]$$

8. Prove that $\displaystyle\int_0^\infty t e^{-2t} \sin 3t \, dt = \frac{12}{169}$

Division by '*t*'

If $L[f(t)] = \phi(s)$, **then**

$$L\left[\frac{f(t)}{t}\right] = \int_s^\infty \phi(s)\, ds$$

Provided $\lim_{t\to 0}\dfrac{f(t)}{t}$ **exists**

Proof: Given, $\phi(s) = L[f(t)]$ [1]

Integrating both sides w.r.t. '*s*' from *s* to ∞, we get

$$\int_s^\infty \phi(s)\, ds = \int_0^\infty \left[\int_0^\infty e^{-st} f(t)\, dt\right] ds$$

$$= \int_0^\infty f(t)\left[\int_0^\infty e^{-st}\, ds\right] dt$$

Interchanging the order of integration w.r.t. '*s*' and '*t*'

$$= \int_0^\infty f(t)\left[\frac{e^{-st}}{-t}\right]_s^\infty dt$$

$$= \int_0^\infty f(t)\left[0 + \frac{e^{-st}}{t}\right] dt$$

$$= \int_0^\infty e^{-st}\frac{f(t)}{t}\, dt = L\left[\frac{f(t)}{t}\right]$$

Hence, $L\left[\dfrac{f(t)}{t}\right] = \int_s^\infty \phi(s)\, ds$ [2]

Note: By a repeated application of [2] we can obtain

$$L\left[\frac{f(t)}{t^2}\right] = L\left[\frac{1}{t}\cdot\frac{f(t)}{t}\right] = \int_s^\infty L\left[\frac{f(t)}{t}\right] ds$$

$$= \int_s^\infty \int_s^\infty \phi(s)\, ds\, ds$$

Similarly, $L\left[\dfrac{f(t)}{t^n}\right] = \underbrace{\int_s^\infty \int_s^\infty \ldots\ldots \int_s^\infty}_{n\ integrals} \phi(s)\,\underbrace{ds.ds \ldots ds}_{n\ times}$

EXAMPLES

1. Find the Laplace transform of

(a) $\dfrac{\left[e^{-bt} - e^{-at} \right]}{t}$, $(a \neq b)$ (b) $\dfrac{\left[1 - e^{-at} \right]}{t}$ (c) $\dfrac{\left[\cos at - \cos bt \right]}{t}$, $(a \neq b)$

(d) $\left[\dfrac{\sin wt}{t} \right]$

Solution:

(a) $L\left[\dfrac{e^{-bt} - e^{-at}}{t} \right]$

$= \displaystyle\int_s^\infty L\left(e^{-bt} - e^{-at} \right) ds$

$= \displaystyle\int_s^\infty L\left[\dfrac{1}{s+b} - \dfrac{1}{s+a} \right] ds \, 1$

$= \left[\log(s+b) - \log(s+a) \right]_{s=s}^{s=\infty}$

$= \left[\log \dfrac{s+b}{s+a} \right]_s^\infty$

$= \lim_{s \to \infty} \, \log \dfrac{s+b}{s+a} - \log \dfrac{s+b}{s+a}$

Now, $\lim_{s \to \infty} \log\left(\dfrac{s+b}{s+a} \right) = \lim_{s \to \infty} \log\left(\dfrac{1 + \dfrac{b}{s}}{1 + \dfrac{a}{s}} \right) = \log 1 = 0$

$\therefore \quad L\left[\dfrac{e^{-bt} - e^{-at}}{t} \right] = \log \dfrac{s+a}{s+b}$

(b) $L\left[\dfrac{1 - e^{-at}}{t} \right] = \displaystyle\int_s^\infty L\left(1 - e^{-at} \right) ds$

$= \displaystyle\int_s^\infty \left[\dfrac{1}{s} - \dfrac{1}{s+a} \right] ds$

$= \left[\log s - \log(s+a) \right]_{s=s}^{s=\infty}$

$= \left[\log \dfrac{s}{s+a} \right]_{s=s}^{s=\infty}$

$$= \lim_{s \to \infty} \log \frac{s}{s+a} - \log \frac{s}{s+a}$$

$$= \lim_{s \to \infty} \log \frac{1}{1+\left(\dfrac{a}{s}\right)} + \log \frac{s+a}{s}$$

$$= 0 + \log \frac{s+a}{s} = \log \frac{s+a}{s}$$

(c) $L\left[\dfrac{\cos at - \cos bt}{t}\right]$

$$= \int_s^\infty (\cos at - \cos bt)\, ds$$

$$= \int_s^\infty \left(\frac{s}{s^2+a^2} - \frac{s}{s^2+b^2}\right) ds$$

$$= \left[\frac{1}{2}\log\left(s^2+a^2\right) - \frac{1}{2}\log\left(s^2+b^2\right)\right]_s^\infty$$

$$= \left[\frac{1}{2}\log\frac{\left(s^2+a^2\right)}{\left(s^2+b^2\right)}\right]_s^\infty$$

$$= \frac{1}{2}\lim_{s \to \infty}\log\frac{\left(s^2+a^2\right)}{\left(s^2+b^2\right)} - \frac{1}{2}\log\frac{\left(s^2+b^2\right)}{\left(s^2+a^2\right)}$$

$$= \frac{1}{2}\log\left[\frac{1+\left[\dfrac{a^2}{b^2}\right]}{1+\left[\dfrac{b^2}{s^2}\right]}\right] + \frac{1}{2}\log\frac{\left(s^2+b^2\right)}{\left(s^2+a^2\right)}$$

$$= \frac{1}{2}\log 1 + \frac{1}{2}\log\frac{s^2+b^2}{s^2+a^2}$$

$\therefore \quad L\left[\dfrac{\cos at - \cos bt}{t}\right] = \dfrac{1}{2}\log\dfrac{s^2+b^2}{s^2+a^2}$

(d) $L\left[\dfrac{\sin wt}{t}\right] = \int_s^\infty L(\sin wt)\, ds$

$$= \int_s^\infty \frac{w}{s^2+w^2}\, ds$$

$$= \left[\tan^{-1}(\infty) - \tan^{-1}\left(\frac{s}{w}\right)\right]$$

$$= \frac{\pi}{2} - \tan^{-1}\left(\frac{s}{w}\right)$$

$$\therefore \quad L\left[\frac{\sin wt}{t}\right] = \cot^{-1}\left(\frac{s}{w}\right)$$

or $\quad \tan^{-1}\left(\frac{w}{s}\right)$

[Using, $\tan^{-1} x + \cot^{-1} x = \left(\frac{\pi}{2}\right)$ and $\tan^{-1} x = \cot^{-1}\left(\frac{1}{x}\right)$]

2. (a) Obtain the L.T. of the following functions

(i) $\dfrac{\cos 2t}{t}$ (ii) $\dfrac{1 - \cos 2t}{t}$ (iii) $\dfrac{e^{3t}}{t}$ (iv) $\dfrac{e^{-t}\sin t}{t}$

(b) Given, $L\left[2\sqrt{\dfrac{t}{n}}\right] = \dfrac{1}{s^{\frac{3}{2}}}$,   prove that $\dfrac{1}{\sqrt{s}} = L\left[\dfrac{1}{\sqrt{\pi t}}\right]$

Solution: (a) (i) $L[\cos 2t] = \dfrac{s}{s^2 + 4}$

Hence, $L\left[\dfrac{\cos 2t}{t}\right] = \int_s^\infty L(\cos 2t)\,ds = \int_s^\infty \dfrac{s}{s^2 + 4}\,ds$

$$= \frac{1}{2}\Big[\log(s^2 + 4)\Big]_s^\infty = -\frac{1}{2}\log(s^2 + 4)$$

$\Rightarrow \quad \dfrac{\cos 2t}{t}$ does not have Laplace transform

(ii) $L\left[\dfrac{1 - \cos 2t}{t}\right]$

$L[1 - \cos 2t]$

$= L(1) - L[\cos 2t]$

$= \left(\dfrac{1}{s} - \dfrac{s}{s^2 + 4}\right) = \varphi(s)$

$$\therefore \quad L\left[\frac{f(t)}{t}\right] = \int_s^\infty \varphi(s)\,ds$$

$$\Rightarrow \quad L\left[\frac{1-\cos 2t}{t}\right] = \int_s^\infty \left(\frac{1}{s} - \frac{s}{s^2+4}\right)ds$$

$$= \left[\log s - \frac{1}{2}\log\left(s^2+4\right)\right]_s^\infty$$

$$= \left[\log\frac{s}{\sqrt{s^2+4}}\right]_s^\infty$$

$$= \left[\log(1) - \log\frac{1}{\sqrt{1+\dfrac{4}{s^2}}}\right] = \log\left(\frac{\sqrt{s^2+4}}{s}\right)$$

(iii) $L\left[\dfrac{e^{3t}}{t}\right]$

Let, $\quad f(t) = e^{3t}$

$$\therefore \quad L[f(t)] = \frac{1}{(s-3)} \quad (s>3)$$

Hence, $\quad L\left[\dfrac{f(t)}{t}\right] = \int_s^\infty \left(\dfrac{1}{s-3}\right)ds$

$$= \left[\log(s-3)\right]_s^\infty$$

$$= \infty - \log(s-3)$$

$\because \ \log 1 = 0; \ \log 0 = -\infty; \ \log\infty = \infty$

Then $L\left[\dfrac{e^{3t}}{t}\right]$ does not exist.

(iv) $L\left[\dfrac{e^{-t}\sin t}{t}\right] = \int_s^\infty L\left[e^{-t}\sin t\right]ds$

but $\quad L\left(e^{-t}\sin t\right) = \left[L(\sin t)\right]_{s\to(s+1)} = \dfrac{1}{(s+1)^2+1}$

$$\therefore \quad L\left[\frac{e^{-t}\sin t}{t}\right] = \int_s^\infty \frac{1}{(s+1)^2 + 1}\,ds$$

$$= \int_{u=s+1}^\infty \frac{du}{u^2 + 1} \quad (u = s+1)$$

$$= \left[\tan^{-1}(u)\right]_{u=s+1}^\infty$$

$$= \frac{\pi}{2} - \tan^{-1}(s+1)$$

$$= \cot^{-1}(s+1)$$

(b) We have $\dfrac{1}{t}\left[2\sqrt{\dfrac{t}{n}}\right] = \dfrac{2}{\sqrt{\pi t}}$

Hence $L\left[\dfrac{2}{\sqrt{\pi t}}\right] = L\left[\dfrac{2\sqrt{\dfrac{t}{\pi}}}{t}\right] = \displaystyle\int_s^\infty L\left[s\dfrac{\sqrt{t}}{\pi}\right]ds$

$$= \int_s^\infty \frac{1}{s^{3/2}}\,ds = \frac{2}{\sqrt{s}}; \quad \text{Hence } L\left[\frac{1}{\sqrt{\pi t}}\right] = \frac{1}{2}L\left[\frac{2}{\sqrt{\pi t}}\right] = \frac{1}{2}\cdot\frac{2}{\sqrt{s}} = \frac{1}{\sqrt{s}}$$

3. Evaluate $L\left[\dfrac{1-\cos t}{t^2}\right]$

Solution: $L\left[\dfrac{1-\cos t}{t^2}\right] = L\left[\dfrac{1}{t}\left(\dfrac{1-\cos t}{t}\right)\right]$ [1]

Consider $L\left[\dfrac{1-\cos t}{t}\right] = \displaystyle\int_s^\infty L(1-\cos t)\,ds$

$$= \int_s^\infty \left[\frac{1}{s} - \frac{s}{s^2+1}\right]ds = \left[\log s - \frac{1}{2}\log(s^2+1)\right]_s^\infty$$

$$= \log\frac{s}{\sqrt{s^2+1}}\Bigg]_s^\infty = \log\frac{1}{\sqrt{1+\dfrac{1}{s^2}}}\Bigg]_s^\infty$$

$$\therefore \quad L\left[\frac{1-\cos t}{t}\right] = \log(1) - \log\frac{s}{\sqrt{s^2+1}} = \log\frac{\sqrt{s^2+1}}{s}$$

Now, considering [1] we have

$$L\left[\frac{1}{t}\left\{\frac{1-\cos t}{t}\right\}\right] = \int_s^\infty L\left[\frac{1-\cos t}{t}\right]ds$$

$$= \int_s^\infty \log\frac{\sqrt{s^2+1}}{s}ds$$

$$= -\frac{1}{2}\int_s^\infty \log\frac{s^2}{s^2+1}ds \quad \text{(by parts)}$$

$$= \left(-\frac{1}{2}\right)\left[s\log\frac{s^2}{s^2+1}\right]_s^\infty - \int_s^\infty \frac{(s^2+1)}{s^2}\cdot\frac{(s^2+1)(2s)-2s^3 s\,ds}{(s^2+1)^2}$$

$$= \left(-\frac{1}{2}\right)\left[s\cdot\log\frac{s^2}{s^2+1} - 2\int\frac{ds}{(s^2+1)}\right]_s^\infty$$

$$= \left(-\frac{1}{2}\right)\left[s\log\frac{s^2}{s^2+1} - 2\tan^{-1}(s)\right]_s^\infty$$

$$= \left(-\frac{1}{2}\right)\left[0 - s\log\frac{s^2}{s^2+1} - 2\frac{\pi}{2} + 2\tan^{-1}(s)\right]$$

$$L\left(\frac{1-\cos t}{t^2}\right) = \frac{\pi}{2} - \tan^{-1}(s) + \frac{s}{2}\log\frac{s^2}{s^2+1}$$

or $\quad L\left(\frac{1-\cos t}{t^2}\right) = \cot^{-1}(s) + s\log\frac{s}{\sqrt{s^2+1}}$

4. Prove that $\displaystyle\int_0^\infty \frac{e^{-3t}-e^{-6t}}{t}dt = \log 2$

Solution: Let $f(t) = e^{-3t} - e^{-6t}$

$\therefore \quad L[f(t)] = \left(\frac{1}{s+3} - \frac{1}{s+6}\right) = \varphi(s)$

$\therefore \quad L\left[\frac{f(t)}{t}\right] = \int_s^\infty \left[\frac{1}{s+3} - \frac{1}{s+6}\right]ds$

$$= \log \frac{s+3}{s+6} \Big\}_s^{\infty} = \log \frac{1+\left(\dfrac{a}{s}\right)}{1+\left(\dfrac{b}{s}\right)} \Bigg)_0^{\infty}$$

$$= \log 1 - \log \frac{1+\left(\dfrac{a}{s}\right)}{1+\left(\dfrac{b}{s}\right)} = 0 - \log \frac{(s+a)}{(s+b)} = \log \frac{(s+b)}{(s+a)}$$

where $a = 3$; $b = 6$

we get $\displaystyle\int_0^{\infty} e^{-st} \left[\frac{e^{-3t}-e^{-6t}}{t}\right] dt = \log \frac{(s+6)}{(s+3)}$

$\therefore \quad \displaystyle\lim_{s \to 0^+} \int_0^{\infty} \frac{e^{-3t}-e^{-6t}}{t} \, dt = \log 2$

5. Find $L\left[\dfrac{2\sin 5t \cos 3t}{t}\right]$

Solution: We have $2\sin A \sin B = \sin(A+B) - \sin(A-B)$

Let $f(t) = 2\sin 5t \cos 3t = \sin 8t - \sin 2t$

If we take $a = 8$, $b = 2$ in the previously solved examples, we get

$\therefore \quad L\left[\dfrac{2\sin 5t \cos 3t}{t}\right] = \left(\tan^{-1}\left(\dfrac{s}{2}\right) - \tan^{-1}\left(\dfrac{s}{8}\right)\right)$

EXERCISES

1. Show that $L\left[e^{2t}(\cos 4t + 3\sin 4t)\right] = \dfrac{s+10}{s^2 - 4s + 20}$

2. Show that $L\left[te^{at} \sin at\right] = \dfrac{2a(s-a)}{\left(s^2 - 2as + 2a^2\right)^2}$

3. Find $L\left[te^{-t} \sin^2 t\right]$

$$\left[\textit{Ans.} \; \frac{1}{2}\left[\frac{1}{(s+1)^2} + \frac{d}{ds}\left[\frac{s+1}{(s+1)^2+a} \right] \right] \right]$$

4. Prove that $L\left[\dfrac{e^{-at} - e^{-bt}}{t} \right] = \log\left(\dfrac{s+b}{s+a} \right)$

Heaviside's unit step function

The unit step function is defined as

$$H(t-a) = 0 \; \text{if} \; t < a$$
$$= 1 \; \text{if} \; t > a$$

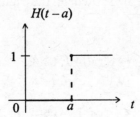

$H(t-a)$ is also denoted by $U_a(t)$. In particular, when $a = 0$

$$H(t) = 0 \qquad \text{if} \; t < 0$$
$$= 1 \qquad \text{if} \; t > 0$$

If $f(t)$ is multiplied by unit step function $H(t-a)$, ("engineering function"), several effects can be produced as shown:

(switching off and on, shifted to the right by 3 units)

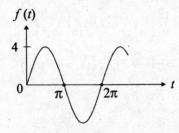

$$f(t) = 4\sin t \; \text{(given function)}$$

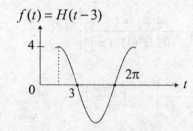

$$f(t) = H(t-3) \quad \text{(Switching off and on)}$$

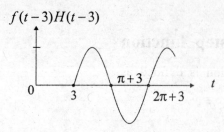

$f(t-3)H(t-3)$ Shifted to the right by 3 units

Theorem: If $f(t-a)H(t-a) \begin{cases} f(t-a), & \text{if } t > a \\ 0, & \text{if } t < a \end{cases}$

$$L[f(t-a)H(t-a)] = e^{-as}\varphi(s) \quad \text{where} \quad L(f(t)) = \varphi(s)$$

Proof: $L[f(t-a)H(t-a)] = \int_0^\infty [f(t-a)H(t-a)e^{-st}dt]$

$$= \int_0^a e^{-st}\left[f(t-a)H(t-a)dt + \int_a^\infty f(t-a)H(t-a)\right]e^{-st}dt$$

$$= 0 + \int_a^\infty e^{-st}f(t-a)dt$$

Put $t-a = u; \ dt = du$ then

$$L[f(t-a)H(t-a)] = \int_0^\infty e^{-s(u+a)}f(u)\,du = e^{-as}\int_0^\infty e^{-su}f(u)\,du$$

$\therefore \quad L[f(t-a)H(t-a)] = e^{-as}L[f(t)] = e^{-as}\varphi(s)$

Note: If $f(t) = 1$, then

$$L[H(t-a)] = \frac{e^{-as}}{s}$$

EXAMPLES

1. Show that $f(t) = f_1(t), \quad 0 < t < a$

$$= f_2(t), \quad t > a$$

can be written as $f(t) = f_1(t) + \{f_2(t) - f_1(t)\} H(t-a)$

> **Proof:** Since $H(t-a) = 0$, when $t < a$
>
> so that $f(t) = f_1(t)$, for $t < a$
>
> when $t > a$, $H(t-a) = 1$ so that
>
> In general,
>
> $\quad f(t) = f_1(t)$, for $0 < t < a_1$
>
> $\quad\quad = f_2(t)$, for $a_1 < t < a_2$
>
> $\quad\quad = \dots$
>
> $\quad\quad = f_{n-1}(t)$ for $a_{n-2} < t < a_{n-1}$
>
> $\quad\quad = f_n(t)$ for $t > a_{n-1}$
>
> then, $f(t) = f_1(t) + \{f_2(t) - f_1(t)\} H(t-a_1) + \dots + \{f_n(t) - f_{n-1}(t)\} H(t-a_{n-1})$

2. Express in terms of Heaviside's unit step function

$$f(t) = \sin t, \; 0 < t < \pi$$

$$= \sin 2t, \; \pi < t < 2\pi$$

$$= \sin 3t, \; t > 2\pi$$

> **Solution:** Let $f_1(t) = \sin t; \; f_2(t) = \sin 2t; \; f_3(t) = \sin 3t$
>
> so that $f(t) = f_1(t) + (f_2 - f_1) H(t-\pi) + (f_3 - f_2) H(t-2\pi)$
>
> $\quad\quad = \sin t + (\sin 2t - \sin t) H(t-\pi) + (\sin 3t - \sin 2t) H(t-2\pi)$

3. Express in terms of Heaviside's unit step function

$$f(t) = e^{-t}, \; 0 < t < 3$$

$$= 0, \; t > 3$$

> **Solution:** Let $f_1(t) = e^{-t}; \; f_2(t) = 0$ then

$f(t)$ can be written as

$$f(t) = f_1(t) + \{f_2(t) - f_1(t)\} H(t-3)$$

$$= e^{-t} + (0 - e^{-t}) H(t-3)$$

$$= e^{-t} (1 - H(t-3))$$

$$L[f(t)] = L(e^{-t} - e^{-t} H(t-3))$$

$$= L[e^{-t}] - L(e^{-t} H(t-3))$$

$$= \frac{1}{s+1} - \frac{e^{-3(s+1)}}{s+1}$$

Since $L[H(t-3)] = \dfrac{e^{-3s}}{s}$ and

$$L[e^{-t} H(t-3)] = \frac{e^{-3(s+1)}}{(s+1)}$$

4. Express in terms of Heaviside's unit step function

$$g(t) = 0, \ 0 < t < \pi/2$$

$$= \sin t, \ t > \pi/2$$

Solution: Express $\sin t$ in terms of $\left(t - \dfrac{\pi}{2}\right)$

by observing that $\sin t = \cos\left(t - \dfrac{\pi}{2}\right)$

Hence, $g(t) = H\left(t - \dfrac{\pi}{2}\right)\left(t - \dfrac{\pi}{2}\right) = \begin{cases} 0, & 0 < t < \dfrac{\pi}{2} \\ \cos\left(t - \dfrac{\pi}{2}\right), & t > \dfrac{\pi}{2} \end{cases}$

where $f(t) = \cos t, \ t > 0$

$$L(g(t)) = L\left[H\left(t - \frac{\pi}{2}\right) f\left(t - \frac{\pi}{2}\right)\right] = e^{-\frac{\pi}{2}s} \cdot \varphi(s)$$

where $\varphi(s) = L[f(t)] = L(\cos t) = \dfrac{s}{s^2+1}$

$$\therefore \quad L[g(t)] = \frac{se^{-\frac{\pi}{2}s}}{s^2+1}$$

5. $4\sin(t-3)H(t-3)$

Solution: By applying the *t*-shift theorem,

we have $L[4\sin t] = \varphi(s) = \dfrac{4}{s^2+1}$

and $L[4\sin(t-3)H(t-3)] = e^{-3s}\varphi(s) = e^{-3s}\dfrac{4}{s^2+1}$

EXERCISES

Find L.T. by expressing $f(t)$ in unit step functions

1. $f(t) = \begin{cases} t^2, & 0 < t \le 2 \\ 0, & t > 2 \end{cases}$
$\left[\textit{Ans.} \quad t^2\left[H(t)-H(t-2)\right]\dfrac{2\left(1-e^{-2s}\right)}{s^3} - \dfrac{4e^{-2s}(1+s)}{s^2} \right]$

2. $f(t) = \begin{cases} 2, & 0 < t < \pi \\ 0, & \pi < t < 2\pi \\ \sin t, & t > 2\pi \end{cases}$
$\left[\begin{array}{l} \textit{Ans.} \quad f(t) = 2H(t) - 2H(t-\pi) + H(t-2\pi)\sin t \\ \qquad\qquad \varphi(s) = \dfrac{2}{s} - \dfrac{2e^{-\pi s}}{s} + \dfrac{e^{-2\pi s}}{s^2+1} \end{array} \right]$

3. Staircase function

$f(t) = 1; \ 0 < t < 1$

$\quad = 2, \ 1 < t < 2$

$\quad = 3, \ 2 < t < 3$
$\left[\textit{Ans.} \quad \dfrac{1}{s(1-e^{-s})} \right]$

Dirac's Delta Function

Paul Dirac (1902 -1984) English physicist, Nobel prize winner.

When a very large force acts for a short interval of time, then the product of the force and the time is called impulse in applied mechanics, e.g. forces like earthquake that produce large effects on a system when applied for a very short time interval can be represented by an impulse function.

The unit impulse function is the limiting function

i.e., $f(t)$ in the interval $(a, a+\varepsilon)$

$$= \int_a^{a+\varepsilon} f(t)\,dt$$

Now define the function

$$\delta_\varepsilon(t-a) = \begin{cases} 0 & \text{for } t < a \\ \dfrac{1}{\varepsilon} & \text{for } a \le t \le a+\varepsilon \\ 0 & \text{for } t > a \end{cases}$$

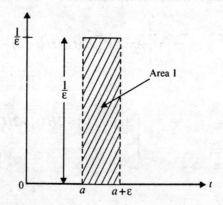

Area 1

It can also be represented in terms of two unit step functions as follows

$$\delta_\varepsilon(t-a) = \frac{1}{\varepsilon}\Big[H(t-a) - H\big(t-(a+\varepsilon)\big)\Big]$$

Note that

$$\int_0^\infty \delta_\varepsilon(t-a)\,dt = \int_0^a 0 + \int_a^{a+\varepsilon} \frac{1}{\varepsilon}\,dt + \int_{a+\varepsilon}^\infty 0 = 1$$

Thus the impulse I_ε is 1

$$\therefore \quad L[\delta_\varepsilon(t-a)] = \frac{1}{\varepsilon}L[H(t-a) - H(t-(a+\varepsilon))] = \frac{1}{\varepsilon s}\Big[e^{-as} - e^{-(a+\varepsilon)s}\Big] = e^{-as}\frac{(1-e^{-\varepsilon s})}{\varepsilon s}$$

Definition: The unit impulse function denoted by $\delta(t-a)$ is defined as follows:

$$\delta(t-a) = \lim_{\varepsilon \to 0}\delta_\varepsilon(t-a)$$

$$= \begin{cases} \infty & \text{when } t = a \\ 0 & \text{otherwise} \end{cases}$$

EXAMPLES

1. Find $L[\delta_\varepsilon(t-a)]$

Solution: $L[\delta_\varepsilon(t-a)] = \int_0^\infty e^{-st}\delta_\varepsilon(t-a)\,dt$

$$= \frac{1}{\varepsilon}\int_a^{a+\varepsilon} e^{-st}\,dt$$

$$= \int_0^a e^{-st}(0)\,dt + \int_a^{a+\varepsilon} e^{-st}\frac{1}{\varepsilon}\,dt + \int_{a+\varepsilon}^\infty e^{-st}(0)\,dt$$

$$= \frac{1}{\varepsilon}\cdot\frac{e^{-st}}{-s}\Bigg\}_a^{a+\varepsilon}$$

$$= -\frac{1}{\varepsilon s}\Big[e^{-s(a+\varepsilon)} - e^{-as}\Big]$$

$$= e^{-as}\left[\frac{1-e^{-\varepsilon s}}{\varepsilon s}\right]$$

Proceeding to the limits as $\varepsilon \to 0$ on both sides

We get

$$\lim_{\varepsilon \to 0}L[\delta_\varepsilon(t-a)] = e^{-as}\lim_{\varepsilon \to 0}\left[\frac{1-e^{-\varepsilon s}}{\varepsilon s}\right]$$

$$\Rightarrow \quad L[\delta(t-a)] = e^{-as} \qquad\qquad [1]$$

If $a = 0$, then

$$L[\delta(t)] = 1 \qquad\qquad [2]$$

Properties

P_1: To prove that

$$\int_{-\infty}^{\infty} f(t)\delta(t-a)\,dt = f(a)$$

(provided $f(t)$ is continuous)

Proof:

$$\int_{-\infty}^{\infty} f(t)\delta(t-a)\,dt = \int_{-\infty}^{a} f(t)\delta(t-a)\,dt + \int_{a}^{a+\varepsilon} f(t)\delta(t-a)\,dt + \int_{a+\varepsilon}^{\infty} f(t)\delta(t-a)\,dt$$

$$= \lim_{\varepsilon\to 0}\int_{a}^{a+\varepsilon} f(t)\frac{1}{\varepsilon}\,dt = \lim_{\varepsilon\to 0}\frac{1}{\varepsilon}\int_{a}^{a+\varepsilon} f(t)\,dt = \lim_{\varepsilon\to 0}\frac{1}{\varepsilon}\big[(a+\varepsilon)-a\big]f(\xi) \quad \text{[By the mean}$$

value theorem for integrals] $(a<\xi<a+\varepsilon)$

If $f(t)$ is continuous in $(a<t<b);(a<\xi<b)$

then $\int_{a}^{b} f(t)\,dt = (b-a)f(\xi) = \lim_{\varepsilon\to 0} f(\xi) = f(a)$

$\therefore \qquad \int_{-\infty}^{\infty} f(t)\delta(t-a)\,dt = f(a)$ [3]

P_2: $L\big[f(t)\delta(t-a)\big] = \int_{0}^{\infty} e^{-st} f(t)\delta(t-a)\,dt$

$$= \int_{0}^{\infty} g(t)\delta(t-a)\,dt = g(a)$$

where $\big[g(t) = e^{-st} f(t)\big]$; using [3]

$$= e^{-as} f(a)$$

Hence $L\big[f(t)\delta(t-a)\big] = e^{-as} f(a)$ [4]

If $a = 0$, in [4] we get

$$L\big[f(t)\delta(t)\big] = f(0)$$

2. Find L.T. of the functions

(a) $t^n\delta(t-a)$ (b) $e^{at}\delta(t-b)$ (c) $\sin 2t\,\delta(t-2)$

Solution: We know that $L\big[f(t)\delta(t-a)\big] = e^{-as} f(a)$

(a) Let $f(t) = t^n$

Here $a = a$

$$\therefore \quad L\left[t^n\delta(t-a)\right]=e^{-as}f(a)=e^{-as}a^n=a^n e^{-as}$$

(b) Let $f(t)=e^{at}$

and $a=b$;

$$\therefore \quad L\left[e^{at}\delta(t-b)\right]=e^{-as}f(a)=e^{-bs}f(b)=e^{-bs}f(b)=e^{-b(s-a)}=e^{-(s-a)b}$$

(c) Let $f(t)=\sin 2t$

and $a=2$

$$\therefore \quad L\left[\sin 2t\delta(t-2)\right]=e^{-as}f(a)=e^{-2s}f(2)=e^{-2s}\sin 2(2)=e^{-2s}\sin 4$$

3. Find L.T. of the function

   (a) $\sin 2t\ \delta\left(t-\dfrac{\pi}{4}\right)-t^2\delta(t-u)$ (b) $\dfrac{1}{t}\delta(t-a)$

   Solution:

   (a) $f(t)=\sin 2t;\ a=\dfrac{\pi}{4}$

   $$\therefore \quad L\left[\sin 2t\delta\left(t-\dfrac{\pi}{4}\right)\right]=e^{-\left(\frac{\pi}{4}\right)s}f\left(\dfrac{\pi}{4}\right)=e^{-\left(\frac{\pi}{4}\right)s}\sin 2\left(\dfrac{\pi}{4}\right)$$

   $$=e^{-\left(\frac{\pi}{4}\right)s}=e^{-\left(\frac{\pi s}{4}\right)}$$

   taking $f(t)=t^2$, $a=4$

   $$\therefore \quad L\left[t^2\delta(t-u)\right]=e^{-as}f(a)=e^{-4s}f(u)=e^{-4s}4^2=16e^{-4s}=3^{-\left(\frac{\pi s}{4}\right)}-16e^{-4s}$$

   (b) $f(t)=\dfrac{1}{t};\ a=a$

   $$\therefore \quad L\left[\dfrac{1}{t}\delta(t-a)\right]=e^{-as}f(a)=e^{-as}\dfrac{1}{a}=\left(\dfrac{e^{-as}}{a}\right)$$

Laplace Transforms of periodic functions

Periodic function: A function $f(t)$ is said to be periodic with period $T>0$, if
$f(t+T)=f(t)$ or $f(t)=f(t+T)=f(t+2T)=...=f(t+nT)$, $n=1,2,3....$

Laplace Transforms of periodic functions

If $f(t)$ is periodic function with period $T > 0$

then $L[f(t)] = \dfrac{\int_0^T e^{-st} f(t)\, dt}{(1 - e^{-sT})}$

Proof: We know that

$$L[f(t)] = \int_0^\infty e^{-st} f(t)\, dt \qquad [1]$$

$$= \int_0^T e^{-st} f(t)\, dt + \int_T^{2T} e^{-st} f(t)\, dt + \dots \qquad [2]$$

Now, $\displaystyle \int_0^T e^{-st} f(t)\, dt = \int_0^T e^{-st} f(t)\, dt$

Consider $\displaystyle \int_T^{2T} e^{-st} f(t)\, dt$

$$\left\{ \begin{array}{l} \text{put } t = T + u; \ dt = du \\ \text{when } t = T; \ u = 0 \\ \text{when } t = 2T; \ u = T \end{array} \right\}$$

$$\therefore \quad \int_T^{2T} e^{-st} f(t)\, dt = \int_0^T e^{-s(T+u)} f(u + T)\, du$$

$$= \int_0^T e^{-sT} e^{-su} f(u)\, du \qquad \left(\because f(u+T) = f(u) \right)$$

$$= e^{-sT} \int_0^T e^{-su} f(u)\, du$$

$$= e^{-sT} \int_0^T e^{-st} f(t)\, dt$$

$$\left(\because \int_a^b f(u)\, du = \int_a^b f(t)\, dt \right)$$

Similarly, $\displaystyle \int_{2T}^{3T} e^{-st} f(t)\, dt = e^{-2sT} \int_0^T e^{-st} f(t)\, dt$ and so on

$\therefore$ [2] reduces to

$$L[f(t)] = \int_0^T e^{-sT} f(t)\, dt + e^{-sT} \int_0^T e^{-sT} f(t)\, dt + \dots$$

$$= \left[1 + e^{-sT} + \left(e^{-sT} \right)^2 + \dots \right] \int_0^T e^{-st} f(t)\, dt$$

$$\left(\because f(u+T) = f(u+2T) = f(u+3T) = \dots f(u) \right)$$

$$= \frac{1}{1-e^{-sT}} \int_0^T e^{-st} f(t)\, dt;$$

$$\left(\because 1+r+r^2+...\infty = \frac{1}{1-r} \text{ and } |r|=|e^{-sT}|<1 \right)$$

Hence $L[f(t)] = \dfrac{1}{1-e^{-sT}} \displaystyle\int_0^T e^{-st} f(t)\, dt$

EXAMPLES

1. A periodic function $f(t)$ with period 2 is defined by

$$f(t) = \begin{cases} t, & 0<t<1 \\ 2-t, & 1<t<2 \end{cases}$$

Find $L[f(t)]$

Solution:

$$L[f(t)] = \frac{1}{1-e^{-2s}} \int_0^2 e^{-st} f(t)\, dt$$

$$= \frac{1}{(1-e^{-2s})} \left[\int_0^1 e^{-st} f(t)\, dt + \int_1^2 e^{-st} (2-t)\, dt \right]$$

$$= \frac{1}{1-e^{-2s}} \left[t \cdot \frac{e^{-st}}{-s} - \frac{e^{-st}}{(-s)^2} \right]_0^1 + \left[(2-t)\frac{e^{-st}}{-s} - \frac{(-1)e^{-st}}{(-s)^2} \right]_1^2$$

$$= \frac{1}{(1-e^{-2s})} \cdot \frac{1}{s^2} \left(1-e^{-s}\right)^2$$

$$= \frac{1}{s^2} \left[\frac{1-e^{-s}}{1+e^{-s}} \right] = \frac{1}{s^2} \left[\frac{e^{\frac{s}{2}}-e^{-\frac{s}{2}}}{e^{\frac{s}{2}}+e^{-\frac{s}{2}}} \right] = \frac{1}{s^2} \tanh\left(\frac{s}{2}\right)$$

2. Find the L.T. of the wave from

$$f(t) = \left[\frac{2t}{3}\right]; \ (0 \le t \le 3)$$

Solution: We know that $L[f(t)] = \dfrac{1}{1-e^{-sT}} \int_0^T e^{-st} f(t) dt$ [1]

$\therefore$ we have $L\left[\dfrac{2t}{3}\right] = \dfrac{\int_0^3 e^{-st}\left(\dfrac{2}{3}t\right) dt}{1-e^{-3s}}$

$$= \frac{1}{1-e^{-3s}}\left[\frac{te^{-st}}{-s} - (1)\frac{e^{-st}}{s^2}\right]_0^3$$

$$= \frac{2}{3}\cdot\frac{1}{1-e^{-3s}}\left[\frac{3e^{-3s}}{-s} - \frac{e^{-3s}}{s^2} + \frac{1}{s^2}\right]$$

$$= \frac{2}{3}\frac{1}{(1-e^{-3s})}\left[\frac{3e^{-3s}}{-s} + \frac{1-e^{-3s}}{s^2}\right]$$

$$= \frac{2e^{-3s}}{-s(1-e^{-3s})} + \frac{2}{3s^2}$$

3. If $f(t) = \begin{cases} 3t, & 0 < t < 2 \\ 6, & 2 < t < 4 \end{cases}$ and $f(t+4) = f(t)$

Solution: Given, $f(t)$ is periodic with period = 4

$\therefore$ $L[f(t)] = \dfrac{1}{1-e^{-4s}} \int_0^4 e^{-st} f(t) dt$ [1]

$$= \frac{1}{(1-e^{-4s})}\left[\int_0^2 e^{-st}(3t) dt + \int_2^4 e^{-st}(6) dt\right]$$

$$= \frac{1}{(1-e^{-4s})}\left\{\left[3\left\{t\frac{e^{-st}}{-s}\right\} - (1)\frac{e^{-2s}}{(-s)^2}\right]_0^2 + 6\left[\frac{e^{-st}}{-s}\right]_2^4\right\}$$

$$= \frac{1}{(1-e^{-4s})}\left\{3\left(-2\frac{e^{-2s}}{-s} - \frac{e^{-2s}}{s^2}\right) - 3\left(0 - \frac{1}{s^2}\right) - \frac{6}{s}\left(e^{-4s} - e^{-2s}\right)\right\}$$

$$= \frac{1}{\left(1-e^{-4s}\right)} \left\{ \frac{3}{s^2} - \frac{3e^{-2s}}{s^2} - \frac{6e^{-4s}}{s} \right\}$$

$$= 3\frac{\left(1-e^{+2s} - 2se^{-4s}\right)}{s^2\left(1-e^{-4s}\right)}$$

4. Find the L.T. of:

$$f(t) = \begin{cases} E\sin wt, & \text{if } 0 < t < \dfrac{\pi}{w} \\ 0, & \text{if } y\dfrac{\pi}{w} < t \le \dfrac{2\pi}{w} \end{cases} \qquad \begin{cases} \text{given that} \\ f\left(t + \dfrac{2\pi}{w}\right) = f(t) \end{cases}$$

Solution: Since $f(t)$ is periodic with period $\dfrac{2\pi}{w}$

$$\therefore \qquad L[f(t)] = \frac{1}{1-e^{-sT}} \int_0^T e^{-st} f(t)\,dt \qquad\qquad [1]$$

$$\therefore \qquad L[f(t)] = \frac{1}{1-e^{-s\left(\frac{2\pi}{w}\right)}} \int_0^{\left(\frac{2\pi}{w}\right)} e^{-st} f(t)\,dt \ ; \ \left(T = \frac{2\pi}{w} \right)$$

$$= \frac{1}{1-e^{-\left(\frac{2\pi s}{w}\right)}} \int_0^{\frac{\pi}{w}} E \cdot e^{-st} \sin wt\,dt$$

$$= \frac{1}{1-e^{-(2\pi s/w)}} \left[e^{-st} \frac{-s\sin wt - w\cos wt}{s^2 + w^2} \right]_0^{\frac{\pi}{w}}$$

$$= \frac{E}{1-e^{-\frac{(2\pi s)}{w}}} \cdot \frac{w\left(e^{-s\pi/w} + 1\right)}{\left(s^2 + w^2\right)}$$

$$= \frac{Ew\left(e^{-s\pi/w} + 1\right)}{\left(1-e^{-s\pi/w}\right)\left(1+e^{-\pi s/w}\right)\left(s^2 + w^2\right)}$$

$$L[f(t)] = \frac{Ew}{\left(1-e^{-\pi s/w}\right)\left(s^2 + w^2\right)}$$

5. Find $L[f(t)]$

where $f(t) = 1, \quad 0 \le t < 2$

$\qquad = -1, \quad 2 \le t < 4$

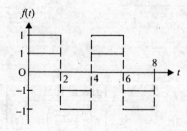

Solution: Here $T = 4$; Applying theorem,

$$L[f(t)] = \frac{1}{1 - e^{-s(4)}} \int_0^4 e^{-st} f(t) \, dt$$

$$= \frac{1}{1 - e^{-4s}} \left[\int_0^2 e^{-st} \cdot 1 \, dt + \int_2^4 e^{-st} (-1) \, dt \right]$$

$$= \frac{1}{1 - e^{-4s}} \left[\frac{e^{-st}}{s} \Big\}_0^2 + \frac{e^{-st}}{s} \Big\}_2^4 \right]$$

$$= \frac{1}{1 - e^{-4s}} \left(\frac{1}{s} \right) \left[-e^{-2s} + 1 + e^{-4s} - e^{-2s} \right]$$

$$= \frac{1 - e^{-2s}}{s \left(1 + e^{-2s} \right)}$$

6. Find the L.T. of saw-tooth wave

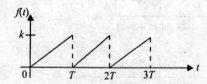

$$f(t) = \frac{k}{T} t, \ 0 < t < T \ \text{ and } \ f(t + T) = f(t)$$

Solution: $L[f(t)] = \dfrac{1}{1 - e^{-sT}} \displaystyle\int_0^T e^{-sT} \left(\dfrac{k}{T} t \right) dt \qquad$ (by parts)

$$\int_0^T te^{-st} dt = \left\{ -\frac{t}{s} e^{-st} \right\}_0^T + \frac{1}{s} \int_0^T e^{-st} dt$$

$$= -\frac{t}{s} e^{-st} \Big|_0^T - \frac{1}{s^2} \left(e^{-sT} - 1 \right)$$

$$= -\frac{T}{s} e^{-sT} - \frac{1}{s^2} \left(e^{-sT} - 1 \right)$$

$$L[f(t)] = \frac{1}{\left(1 - e^{-sT}\right)} \frac{k}{T} \left[-\frac{T}{s} e^{-sT} - \frac{1}{s^2} \left(e^{-sT} - 1 \right) \right]$$

$$= \frac{k}{Ts^2} - \frac{ke^{-sT}}{s\left(1 - e^{-Ts}\right)}, \ s > 0$$

EXERCISES

Find the L.T. of the following periodic functions.

1. $f(t) = t, \ 0 < t < a$

$= -t + 2a, \ a < t < 2a$

$\left[Ans. \ \dfrac{1}{s^2} \tanh \dfrac{as}{2} \right]$

2. $f(t) = 1, \ 0 < t < 1$

$= 0, 1 < t < 2$ with period 3

$= -1, \ 2 < t < 3$

$\left[Ans. \ \dfrac{1}{s} \left(\dfrac{3}{\left(1 - e^{-3s}\right)} - \dfrac{1}{\left(1 - e^{-s}\right)} - 1 \right) \right]$

3. $f(t) = \begin{cases} a, & \text{for } 0 \le t \le a \\ -a, & \text{for } a < t \le 2a \end{cases}$

$\left[Ans. \ \dfrac{a}{s} \tanh \left(\dfrac{as}{2} \right) \right]$

4. $f(t) = \begin{cases} \cos t, & 0 < t \le \pi \\ -1, & \pi \le t < 2\pi \end{cases}$

$\left[Ans. \ \dfrac{s}{\left(1 + s^2\right)\left(1 - e^{-\pi s}\right)} - \dfrac{e^{-s\pi}}{s\left(1 + e^{-\pi s}\right)} \right]$

Inverse Transforms

If $L[f(t)] = \varphi(s)$ then $f(t)$ is known as the inverse Laplace Transform (I.L.T) or inverse transform of $\varphi(s)$ and is denoted by $L^{-1}[\varphi(s)]$

Thus, $f(t) = L^{-1}(\varphi(s))$ [1]

L^{-1} is known as the inverse Laplace transform operator and is such that $LL^{-1} = L^{-1}L = I$

Note: I.L.T of $\varphi(s)$ need not exist for all $\varphi(s)$

EXAMPLES

1. Find $f(t)$, where $\varphi(s) = \dfrac{a}{s}$, is a constant

    ***Solution*:** We know that $L[a] = \dfrac{a}{s}$

$\Rightarrow \quad a = L^{-1}\left[\dfrac{a}{s}\right]$

That $f(t) = a = L^{-1}\left[\dfrac{a}{s}\right] = L^{-1}\{\varphi(s)\}$

Similarly, $L\{e^{at}\} = \dfrac{1}{s-a}$

$\Rightarrow \quad L^{-1}\left\{\dfrac{1}{s-a}\right\} = e^{at}$

and $\quad L\{\cos at\} = \dfrac{s}{s^2 + a^2}$

$\Rightarrow \quad L^{-1}\left[\dfrac{s}{s^2 + a^2}\right] = \cos at$

Properties

P_1: $L[f(t)] = \varphi_1(s)$ and $L[g(t)] = \varphi_2(s)$

then $L^{-1}[c_1\varphi_1(s) + c_2\varphi_2(s)] = c_1 L^{-1}\{\varphi_1(s)\} + c_2 L^{-1}\{\varphi_2(s)\} = c_1 f(t) + c_2 g(t)$

Proof: We know that

$$L[c_1 f(t) + c_2 g(t)] = c_1 L[f(t)] + c_2 L[g(t)] = c_1\varphi_1(s) + c_2\varphi_2(s)$$

$\Rightarrow \quad c_1 f(t) + c_2 g(t) = L^{-1} \left[c_1 \phi_1(s) + c_2 \phi_2(s) \right]$

Since $f(t) = L^{-1} \left[\phi_1(s) \right]$ and $g(t) = L^{-1} \left[\phi_2(s) \right]$

We have

$$c_1 L^{-1} \left\{ \phi_1(s) \right\} + c_2 L^{-1} \left\{ \phi_2(s) \right\} = L^{-1} \left[\left\{ c_1 \phi_1(s) \right\} + \left\{ c_2 \phi_2(s) \right\} \right] = L^{-1} \left[c_1 \phi_1(s) + c_2 \phi_2(s) \right]$$

$\Rightarrow \quad L^{-1}$ is a linear operator

This result can readily be generalized to a finite number of functions.

P_2 : (*shift theorem*)

If $\quad L^{-1} \left\{ \phi(s) \right\} = f(t)$, then

$\qquad L^{-1} \left[\phi(s-a) \right] = e^{at} f(t) = e^{at} L^{-1} \left[\phi(s) \right]$

Proof: We know that

$$L \left[e^{at} f(t) \right] = \phi(s-a)$$

$\Rightarrow \quad e^{at} f(t) = L^{-1} \left[\phi(s-a) \right]$

$\Rightarrow$ If s is replaced by $(s-a)$ in $\phi(s)$ then $f(t)$ is multiplied by e^{at}

P_3 : *change of scale property*

i.e., $\quad L^{-1} \left\{ \phi(as) \right\} = \dfrac{1}{a} f\left(\dfrac{t}{a} \right)$

Proof: We know that

$$L \left[f(at) \right] = \frac{1}{a} \phi\left(\frac{s}{a} \right)$$

(replace a by $\dfrac{1}{a}$)

$$L \left[f\left(\frac{t}{a} \right) \right] = a \phi(as)$$

or, $\quad f\left(\dfrac{t}{a} \right) = L^{-1} \left[a \phi(as) \right]$ Thus $L^{-1} \left[\phi(as) \right] = \dfrac{1}{a} f\left(\dfrac{t}{a} \right)$

List of important results on inverse transforms

$$L^{-1}[\varphi(s+a)] \quad = \quad e^{-at}L^{-1}[\varphi(s)]$$

$$L^{-1}[\phi(s-a)] \quad = \quad e^{at}L^{-1}[\varphi(s)]$$

$$L^{-1}[s\varphi(s)] \quad = \quad \frac{d}{dt}L^{-1}[\varphi(s)] \text{ provided } L^{-1}[\varphi(s)] \text{ vanishes for } t=0$$

$$L^{-1}\left[\frac{1}{s}\varphi(s)\right] \quad = \quad \int_0^t L^{-1}[\varphi(s)]dt$$

$$L^{-1}\left[\frac{1}{s^2}\varphi(s)\right] \quad = \quad \int_0^t\int_0^t L^{-1}[\varphi(s)](dt)^2$$

$$L^{-1}[\varphi(s)] \quad = \quad -\frac{1}{t}L^{-1}[\varphi'(s)]$$

$$L^{-1}[\varphi(s)] \quad = \quad tL^{-1}\left[\int_0^t \varphi(s)\,ds\right]$$

$$L^{-1}[\varphi_1(s).\varphi_2(s)] \quad = \quad L^{-1}[\varphi_1(s)] * L^{-1}[\varphi_2(s)]$$

$$= \int_0^t f(u)g(t-u)\,du = \int_0^t g(u)f(t-u)\,du$$

If $L^{-1}[\varphi_1(s)] = f(t)$ and $L^{-1}[\varphi_2(s)] = g(t)$

If $L^{-1}[\varphi(s)] = f(t)$ then $L^{-1}\left[\int_s^\infty \varphi(s)\,ds\right] = \dfrac{f(t)}{t}$

2. Find the inverse Laplace transform of the following functions.

(a) $\dfrac{3}{s+4}$ (b) $\dfrac{5}{s+3}$ (c) $\dfrac{1}{2s-3}$ (d) $\dfrac{4}{3s-1}$ (e) $\dfrac{8s}{s^2+16}$ (f) $\dfrac{2s+1}{s(s+1)}$

(g) $\dfrac{1}{4s+5}$

Solution:

(a) Let $\varphi(s) = \dfrac{3}{s+4}$

$\Rightarrow L^{-1}[\varphi(s)] = 3L^{-1}\left[\dfrac{1}{s+4}\right] = 3 \cdot e^{-4t}$

(b) Let $\varphi(s) = \dfrac{5}{s+3}$

$\therefore L^{-1}[\varphi(s)] = 5L^{-1}\left[\dfrac{1}{s+3}\right] = 5e^{-3t}$

(c) $\quad L^{-1}\left[\dfrac{1}{2s-3}\right]=\dfrac{1}{2}L^{-1}\left[\dfrac{1}{s-\dfrac{3}{2}}\right]=\dfrac{1}{2}e^{\frac{3}{2}t}$

(d) $\quad L^{-1}\left[\dfrac{4}{3s-1}\right]=\dfrac{4}{3}L^{-1}\left[\dfrac{1}{s-\dfrac{1}{3}}\right]=\dfrac{4}{3}e^{\frac{1}{3}t}$

(e) $\quad L^{-1}\left[\dfrac{8s}{s^2+16}\right]=8L^{-1}\left[\dfrac{s}{s^2+u^2}\right]=8\cos 4t$

(f) Let $\phi(s)=\dfrac{2s+1}{s(s+1)}$

$\therefore \quad L^{-1}\left[\dfrac{2s+1}{s(s+1)}\right]=\left[L^{-1}\left\{\dfrac{s+1+s}{s(s+1)}\right\}\right]$

$=L^{-1}\left\{\dfrac{1}{s}+\dfrac{1}{s+1}\right\}$

$=L^{-1}\left[\dfrac{1}{s}\right]+L^{-1}\left[\dfrac{1}{s+1}\right]$

$=1+e^{-t}$

(g) Let $\phi(s)=\dfrac{1}{4s+5}$

3. Evaluate:

(a) $L^{-1}\left[\dfrac{2}{s^2+16}\right]$ (b) $L^{-1}\left[\dfrac{4s}{s^2-16}\right]$ (c) $L^{-1}\left[\dfrac{1}{s^2+9}\right]$ (d) $L^{-1}\left[\dfrac{1}{9s^2+4}\right]$

(e) $L^{-1}\left[\dfrac{2s-5}{4s^2+25}\right]$ (f) $L^{-1}\left[\dfrac{3s-12}{s^2+8}\right]$ (g) $L^{-1}\left[\dfrac{s-4}{s^2-4}\right]$ (h) $L^{-1}\left[\dfrac{s\cos\alpha+w\sin\alpha}{s^2-w^2}\right]$

(i) $L^{-1}\left[\dfrac{2s+1}{s^2-4}\right]$

Solution:

(a) $\quad L^{-1}\left[\dfrac{2}{s^2+16}\right]=2L^{-1}\left[\dfrac{1}{s^2+16}\right]=2L^{-1}\left[\dfrac{1}{s^2+4^2}\right]$

$$= 2\left[\frac{\sin 4t}{4}\right] = \frac{\sin 4t}{2}$$

$$\left[\because L^{-1}\left[\frac{1}{s^2 + a^2}\right] = \frac{\sin at}{a}\right]$$

(b) $\quad L^{-1}\left[\frac{4s}{s^2 - 16}\right] = 4\, L^{-1}\left[\frac{s}{s^2 - 16}\right]$

$$= 4\cosh 4t$$

$$\left[\because L^{-1}\left(\frac{s}{s^2 - 9^2}\right) = \cosh at\right]$$

(c) $\quad L^{-1}\left[\frac{1}{s^2 + 9}\right] = L^{-1}\left[\frac{1}{s^2 + 3^2}\right] = \frac{1}{3}\sin 3t$

(d) $\quad L^{-1}\left[\frac{s}{9s^2 + 4}\right]$

$$= \frac{1}{9} L^{-1}\left[\frac{s}{s^2 + \left(\frac{2}{3}\right)^2}\right]$$

$$= \frac{1}{9}\cos\left(\frac{2}{3}t\right)$$

(e) $\quad L^{-1}\left[\frac{2s - 5}{4s^2 + 25}\right]$

$$= \frac{1}{4} L^{-1}\left[\frac{2s - 5}{s^2 + \frac{25}{4}}\right] = \frac{1}{4} L^{-1}\left[\frac{2s - 5}{s^2 + \left(\frac{5}{2}\right)^2}\right]$$

$$= \frac{1}{2} L^{-1}\left[\frac{s}{s^2 + \left(\frac{5}{2}\right)^2}\right] - \frac{5}{4} L^{-1}\left[\frac{1}{s^2 + \left(\frac{5}{2}\right)^2}\right]$$

$$= \frac{1}{2}\cos\frac{5}{2}t - \frac{5}{4}\cdot\frac{2}{5}\sin\frac{5}{2}t$$

$$= \frac{1}{2}\left[\cos\frac{5t}{2} - \sin\frac{5}{2}t\right]$$

(f) $L^{-1}\left[\dfrac{s}{s^2+8}\right] - 12L^{-1}\left[\dfrac{1}{s^2+8}\right]$

$$= 3L^{-1}\left[\frac{s}{s^2+\left(\dfrac{2}{2}\right)^2}\right] - 12L^{-1}\left[\frac{1}{s^2+\left(\dfrac{2}{2}\right)^2}\right]$$

$$= 3\cos(2\sqrt{2})t - 3\sqrt{2}\sin(2\sqrt{2})t$$

(g) $L^{-1}\left[\dfrac{s-4}{s^2-4}\right] = L^{-1}\left[\dfrac{s}{s^2-4}\right] - 4L^{-1}\left[\dfrac{1}{s^2-4}\right]$

$$= \cosh 2t - 4\left[\frac{\sinh t}{2}\right]$$

$$= \cosh 2t - 2\sinh 2t$$

(h) $L^{-1}\left[\dfrac{\cos w + w\sin\alpha}{s^2+w^2}\right]$

$\therefore \qquad = (\cos\alpha)L^{-1}\left[\dfrac{s}{s^2+w^2}\right] + (\sin\alpha)L^{-1}\left[\dfrac{w}{s^2+w^2}\right]$

$$= \cos\alpha\cos wt + \sin\alpha\cos wt$$

$$= \cos(wt - \alpha)$$

(i) $L^{-1}\left[\dfrac{2s+1}{s^2-4}\right]$

$$= \cos L^{-1}\left[\frac{2s+1}{s^2-4}\right] = L^{-1}\left[\frac{2s}{s^2-4}\right] + L^{-1}\left[\frac{1}{s^2-4}\right]$$

$$= 2\cdot\cosh 2t + \frac{1}{2}\sinh 2t$$

4. Find $L^{-1}\left[\dfrac{1}{s}e^{-\frac{1}{\sqrt{s}}}\right]$

Solution:

$$e^{-\frac{1}{\sqrt{s}}} = \sum_{n=0}^{\infty}\left(-\frac{1}{\sqrt{s}}\right)^{n}\frac{1}{n!} = \sum_{n=0}^{\infty}\frac{(-1)n}{n!}\cdot\frac{1}{s^{\frac{n}{2}}}$$

$$\frac{1}{s}e^{-\frac{1}{\sqrt{s}}} = \sum_{n=0}^{\infty}\frac{(-1)^{n}}{n!}\frac{1}{s^{\frac{n}{2}+1}}$$

$$L^{-1}\left[\frac{1}{s}e^{-\frac{1}{\sqrt{s}}}\right] = L^{-1}\left\{\sum_{n=0}^{\infty}\frac{(-1)^{n}}{n!}\frac{1}{s^{\frac{n}{2}+1}}\right\}$$

$$= \sum_{n=0}^{\infty}\frac{(-1)^{n}}{n!}L^{-1}\left\{\frac{1}{s^{\frac{n}{2}+1}}\right\}$$

$$= \sum_{n=0}^{\infty}\frac{(-1)^{n}}{n!}\cdot\frac{t^{\frac{n}{2}}}{\Gamma\left(\frac{n}{2}+1\right)}$$

5. Evaluate: $L^{-1}\left[\dfrac{3(s^{2}-2)^{2}}{2s^{5}}\right]$

Solution:

$$L^{-1}\left[\frac{3(s^{4}-4s^{2}+4)}{2s^{5}}\right]$$

$$= L^{-1}\left[\frac{3}{2}\cdot\frac{1}{s} - 6\cdot\frac{1}{s^{3}} + 6\cdot\frac{1}{s^{5}}\right]$$

$$= \frac{3}{2} - 3t^{2} + \frac{1}{4}t^{4}$$

6. Find $L^{-1}\left[\dfrac{64}{81s^{4}-256}\right]$

Solution: Let $\phi(s) = \dfrac{64}{81s^4 - 256}$

Now, $L^{-1}\left[\dfrac{a^3}{s^4 - a^4}\right] = \dfrac{1}{2}L^{-1}\left[\dfrac{a}{s^2 - a^2} - \dfrac{a}{s^2 + a^2}\right]$

$$= \dfrac{1}{2}(\sinh at - \sin at)$$

Rewriting $L^{-1}\left[\dfrac{64}{81s^4 - 256}\right]$

$$= L^{-1}\left[\dfrac{4^3}{(3s)^4 - 4^4}\right]$$

$$= L^{-1}[\phi(3s)] \quad \text{with } a = 4$$

where $\phi(s) = \dfrac{a^3}{s^4 - a^4}$ and

$$f(t) = \dfrac{1}{2}(\sinh at - \sin at)$$

By change of scale property with ($a = 3$), we have

$$L^{-1}[\phi(3s)] = \dfrac{1}{3}f\left(\dfrac{t}{3}\right) = \dfrac{1}{3}\left[\dfrac{1}{2}\sinh h\dfrac{4t}{3} - \sin\dfrac{4t}{3}\right]$$

7. **Evaluate:** $L^{-1}\left[\dfrac{1}{(s+a)^{n+1}}\right]$

$$L^{-1}\left[\dfrac{1}{(s+a)^{n+1}}\right] \quad n \geq 0;$$

$$= e^{-at}L^{-1}\left[\dfrac{1}{s^{n+1}}\right] = e^{-at}\dfrac{t^n}{n!} \quad \text{by shift theorem}$$

8. **Evaluate the Inverse Laplace Transform of the following.**

(a) $L^{-1}\left(\dfrac{s}{(s+a)^2 + b^2}\right)$ (b) $L^{-1}\left(\dfrac{3s}{s^2 - 25}\right)$ (c) $L^{-1}\dfrac{1}{\left(s^{\frac{3}{2}}\right)}$ (d) $L^{-1}\left[\dfrac{3s+1}{(s+1)^4}\right]$

(e) $L^{-1}\left[\dfrac{s+1}{s^2 - 6s + 25}\right]$ (f) $L^{-1}\left[\dfrac{1}{\sqrt{2s+3}}\right]$ (g) $L^{-1}[\phi(as+b)]$

Solution:

(a) $\phi(s) = \dfrac{s}{(s+a)^2 + b^2}$

$$L^{-1}[\phi(s) = L^{-1}\left[\dfrac{s}{(s+a)^2 + b^2}\right] = e^{-at}L^{-1}\left[\dfrac{s-a}{s^2+b^2}\right]$$

$$= e^{-at}\left[L^{-1}\left[\dfrac{s}{s^2+b^2}\right] - \dfrac{+a}{b}L^{-1}\left[\dfrac{b}{s^2+b^2}\right]\right]$$

$$= e^{-at}\left\{\cos bt - \dfrac{a}{b}\sin bt\right\}$$

(b) Let $\phi(s) = \dfrac{3s}{s^2 - 25}$

$$L^{-1}[\phi(s)] = L^{-1}\left[\dfrac{3s}{s^2 - 25}\right]$$

$$= 3L^{-1}\left[\dfrac{s}{s^2 - s^2}\right] = 3\cosh 5t$$

(c) Let $\phi(s) = \dfrac{1}{s^{\frac{3}{2}}}$

$$L^{-1}[\phi(s)] = L^{-1}\left[\dfrac{1}{s^{\frac{3}{2}}}\right] = \dfrac{t^{\frac{1}{2}}}{\sqrt{\dfrac{3}{2}}} = \dfrac{t^{\frac{1}{2}}}{\dfrac{1}{2}\sqrt{\left(\dfrac{1}{2}\right)}} = 2\sqrt{\dfrac{t}{\pi}}$$

(d) Let $\phi(s) = \dfrac{3s+1}{(s+1)^4}$

$$L^{-1}[\phi(s)] = L^{-1}\left[\dfrac{3s+1}{(s+1)^4}\right]$$

$$= e^{-t}L^{-1}\left[\dfrac{3(s-1)+1}{s^4}\right]$$

$$= e^{-t}\left\{3L^{-1}\left(\dfrac{1}{s^3} - 2L^{-1}\left(\dfrac{1}{s^4}\right)\right)\right\}$$

$$= e^{-t}\left[3\cdot\frac{t^2}{2!}-2\cdot\frac{t^3}{3!}\right]$$

$$= e^{-t}\left\{\frac{3}{2}t^2-\frac{1}{3}t^3\right\}$$

(e) Let $\phi(s)=\dfrac{s+1}{s^2-6s+25}$

$$L^{-1}[\phi(s)]=L^{-1}\left[\frac{s+1}{(s+3)^2+16}\right]$$

by First shifting theorem

$$= e^{-3t}L^{-1}\left(\frac{(s-3)+1}{s^2+16}\right)$$

$$= e^{-3t}\left\{L^{-1}\left\{\frac{s-2}{s^2+16}\right\}\right\}$$

$$= e^{-3t}\left\{\cos 4t-\frac{1}{2}\sin 4t\right\}$$

(f) Let $\phi(s)=\dfrac{1}{\sqrt{2s+4}}$

$$L^{-1}\left\{\frac{1}{\sqrt{2s+3}}\right\}=\frac{1}{\sqrt{2}}L^{-1}\left\{\frac{1}{\left(s+\frac{3}{2}\right)^{\frac{1}{2}}}\right\}$$

By First shifting theorem,

$$= \frac{1}{\sqrt{2}}e^{\frac{-3t}{2}}\cdot L^{-1}\left\{\frac{1}{s^{\frac{1}{2}}}\right\}$$

$$= \frac{1}{\sqrt{2}}e^{-\frac{2t}{2}}\cdot\frac{t^{-\frac{1}{2}}}{\Gamma(\frac{1}{2})}=\frac{1}{\sqrt{2\pi}}t^{-\frac{1}{2}}e^{-\frac{3t}{2}}$$

(g) $\phi(as+b)=\displaystyle\int_0^\infty e^{-(as+b)t}\cdot f(t)dt$

$$= \int_0^\infty e^{-ast}\cdot e^{-bt}\cdot f(t)dt$$

$$\left(\text{Put } at = u; \quad dt = \frac{du}{a} \right)$$

$$\phi(as+b) = \int_0^\infty e^{-\frac{b}{a}u} \cdot f\left(\frac{u}{a}\right) \cdot \frac{1}{a} \cdot du$$

$$= \frac{1}{a} \int_0^\infty e^{-su} \left\{ e^{-\frac{a}{b}u} \cdot f\left(\frac{u}{a}\right) \right\} du$$

$$\phi(as+b) = \frac{1}{a} L\left\{ e^{\frac{bu}{a}} \cdot f\left(\frac{u}{a}\right) \right\}$$

$$\Rightarrow L^{-1}[\phi(as+b)] = \frac{1}{a} e^{-\frac{bt}{a}} \cdot f\left(\frac{t}{a}\right)$$

$$\boxed{\begin{array}{c} L^{-1}\left\{ \phi^{(n)}(s) \right\} = (-1)^n \cdot t^n f(t), \\ n = 1,2,3,.... \end{array}}$$

9. Find the I.L.T of the following functions.

(a) $\dfrac{s+1}{(s^2+2s+2)^2}$ (b) $\dfrac{1}{(s-a)^3}$ (c) $\dfrac{1}{2}\log\dfrac{s^2+b^2}{s^2+a^2}$ (d) $\cot^{-1}\left(\dfrac{s+a}{b}\right)$

Solution:

(a) Let $\phi(s) = \dfrac{s+1}{(s^2+2s+2)^2}$

$$L^{-1}\left[\phi^{(s)}\right] = L^{-1}\left[\frac{s+1}{(s^2+2s+2)^2} \right]$$

$$= L^{-1}\left[\frac{s+1}{\left((s+1)^2+1\right)^2} \right] = e^{-t} \cdot L^{-1}\left[\frac{s}{(s^2+1)^2} \right]$$

We know that $\dfrac{d}{ds}\left[\dfrac{1}{s^2+1} \right] = \dfrac{-2s}{(s^2+1)^2}$

so that

$$\frac{s}{(s^2+1)^2} = \frac{1}{2}\frac{-d}{ds}\left[\frac{1}{(s^2+1)}\right]$$

but $\quad L^{-1}\left[\dfrac{1}{s^2+1}\right] = \sin t$

$\therefore \quad L^{-1}\left\{\dfrac{s+1}{(s^2+2s+2)^2}\right\} = e^{-t}L^{-1}\left\{\dfrac{s}{(s^2+1)^2}\right\}$

$$= e^{-t}\left(-\frac{1}{2}\right)L^{-1}\left\{\frac{d}{ds}\left(\frac{1}{(s^2+1)}\right)\right\}$$

$$= -\frac{1}{2}e^{-t}\cdot(-1)^1\cdot t^1\cdot L^{-1}\left[\frac{1}{s^2+1}\right]$$

$$= \frac{1}{2}e^{-t}\cdot t\cdot\sin t$$

(b) Let $\quad \phi(s) = \dfrac{1}{(s-a)^3}$

$$L^{-1}[\phi(s)] = L^{-1}\left[\frac{1}{(s-a)^3}\right] = e^{at}$$

$\Rightarrow \quad f(t) = L^{-1}[\phi(s)] = e^{at}$

$\therefore \quad \phi'(s) = \dfrac{-1}{(s-a)^2}$

$$\phi''(s) = \frac{(-1)(-2)}{(s-a)^3} = \frac{2}{(s-a)^3}$$

By inverse L.T. of derivative, with $n = 2$

$$L^{-1}\left[\frac{1}{(s-a)^3}\right] = \frac{1}{2}L^{-1}\{\phi''(s)\} = \frac{(-1)^2}{2}t^2 f(t)$$

$$= 1\cdot\frac{t^2\cdot e^{at}}{2} = \frac{t^2\cdot e^{at}}{2}$$

(c) Let $\phi(s) = \dfrac{1}{2}\log\dfrac{\left(s^2+b^2\right)}{\left(s^2+a^2\right)} = \dfrac{1}{2}\left[\log\left(s^2+b^2\right)-\log\left(s^2+b^2\right)\right]$

$\therefore \qquad \phi'(s) = \dfrac{1}{2}\cdot\dfrac{2s}{s^2+b^2} - \dfrac{1}{2}\cdot\dfrac{2s}{s^2+a^2}$

$$= \dfrac{s}{s^2+b^2} - \dfrac{s}{s^2+a^2}$$

$\therefore \qquad L^{-1}[\phi'(s)] = L^{-1}\left[\dfrac{s}{s^2+b^2} - \dfrac{s}{s^2+a^2}\right]$

$$= L^{-1}\left[\dfrac{s}{s^2+b^2}\right] - L^{-1}\left[\dfrac{s}{s^2+a^2}\right]$$

$$= \cos bt - \cos at$$

Using I.L.T, of derivatives property, we have

$$-tf(t) = L^{-1}[\phi'(s)] = \cos bt - \cos at$$

$\Rightarrow \qquad f(t) = \dfrac{-(\cos bt - \cos at)}{t}$

(d) Let $\phi(s) = \cot^{-1}\left(\dfrac{s+a}{b}\right)$

$\therefore \qquad \phi'(s) = \dfrac{1}{b}\left(\dfrac{-b^2}{(s+a)^2+b^2}\right)$

$$L^{-1}[\phi'(s)] = -L^{-1}\left\{\dfrac{b}{(s^2+a^2)+b^2}\right\}$$

$$= -e^{-at}\cdot\sin bt$$

$\Rightarrow \qquad -tf(t) = L^{-1}\{\phi'(s)\}$

$$= -e^{-at}\cdot\sin bt$$

$\Rightarrow \qquad f(t) = \dfrac{e^{-at}}{t}\sin bt$

EXAMPLES

$$\boxed{\begin{array}{l} \text{If } L^{-1}[\phi(s)] = f(t), then \\ L^{-1}\left\{ \int_s^\infty \phi(s)ds \right\} = \dfrac{f(t)}{t} \end{array}}$$

1. Find the inverse transform of the following.

(a) $\dfrac{s+1}{(s^2+2s+2)^2}$ (b) $\dfrac{s+2}{(s^2+4s+5)^2}$

Solution:

(a) Let $\phi(s) = \dfrac{s+1}{(s^2+2s+2)^2}$

$\therefore$ $L^{-1}[\phi(s)] = L^{-1}\left[\dfrac{s+1}{(s^2+2s+2)} \right] = f(t)$

$\therefore$ $L^{-1}\left\{ \int_0^\infty \dfrac{s+1}{(s^2+2s+2)^2} ds \right\} = \dfrac{f(t)}{t}$

$\Rightarrow$ $L^{-1}\left[-\dfrac{1}{(s^2+2s+2)^2} \right]_s^\infty = \dfrac{f(t)}{t}$

$\Rightarrow$ $L^{-1}\left[\dfrac{1}{2} \cdot \dfrac{1}{(s^2+2s+2)^2} \right] = \dfrac{f(t)}{t}$

$\Rightarrow$ $\dfrac{1}{2} e^{-t} L^{-1}\left[\dfrac{1}{s^2+1} \right] = \dfrac{f(t)}{t}$

$\Rightarrow$ $e^{-t} \sin t = \dfrac{f(t)}{t}$

$\therefore$ $L^{-1}\left[\dfrac{s+1}{(s^2+2s+2)^2} \right] = \dfrac{1}{2} t e^{-t} \sin t$

(b) Let $\phi(s) = \dfrac{(s+2)}{(s^2+4s+5)^2}$

$\therefore \qquad L^{-1}[\phi(s)]L^{-1}\left[\dfrac{s+2}{(s^2+4s+5)^2}\right] = f(t)$

$\Rightarrow \qquad L^{-1}\left[\displaystyle\int_s^\infty \dfrac{s+2}{(s^2+4s+5)^2}\,ds\right] = \dfrac{f(t)}{t}$

$\Rightarrow \qquad \dfrac{1}{2}L^{-1}\left[\dfrac{-1}{s^2+4s+5} = \dfrac{f(t)}{t}\right] = \dfrac{f(t)}{t}$

$\Rightarrow \qquad \dfrac{1}{2}L^{-1}\left[\dfrac{1}{s^2+4s+5} = \dfrac{f(t)}{t}\right] = \dfrac{f(t)}{t}$

or $\qquad \dfrac{1}{2}L^{-1}\left[\dfrac{1}{(s+2)^2+1}\right] = \dfrac{f(t)}{t}$

$\Rightarrow \qquad \dfrac{1}{2}e^{-2t}L^{-1}\left[\dfrac{1}{s^2+1}\right] = \dfrac{f(t)}{t}$

$\therefore \qquad \dfrac{1}{2}e^{-2t}(\sin t) = \dfrac{f(t)}{t}$

$\Rightarrow \qquad L^{-1}\left[\dfrac{s+2}{(s^2+4s+5)^2}\right] = f(t) = \dfrac{1}{2}te^{-2t}\sin t$

2. Evaluate $L^{-1}\left[\displaystyle\int_s^\infty \left(\dfrac{s}{s^2+a^2} - \dfrac{s}{s^2+b^2}\right)ds\right]$

Solution: Let $\phi(s) = \dfrac{s}{s^2+a^2} - \dfrac{s}{s^2+b^2}$

$\qquad\qquad = \cos at - \cos bt$

by I.L.T, of integral

$\qquad L^{-1}\left[\displaystyle\int_s^\infty \phi(s)ds\right]$

$\qquad\qquad = L^{-1}\left\{\displaystyle\int_s^\infty \left(\dfrac{s}{s^2+a^2} - \dfrac{s}{s^2+b^2}\right)ds\right\} = \dfrac{f(t)}{t}$

$\qquad\qquad = \dfrac{\cos at - \cos bt}{t}$

3. Find the inverse L.T. of

$$\frac{1}{2}\log\left(\frac{s+1}{s-1}\right)$$

Solution: Let $\phi(s)=\frac{1}{2}\log\left(\frac{s+s}{s-1}\right)$

$$=\frac{1}{2}[\log(s+1)-\log(s-1)]$$

$$=\frac{1}{2}\int_s^\infty\left(\frac{-ds}{s+1}-\frac{ds}{s-1}\right)$$

but we know that

$$\frac{1}{2}L^{-1}\left[\frac{1}{(s-1)}-\frac{1}{s+1}\right]=\frac{e^t-e^{-t}}{2}=\sinh t$$

Hence, $L^{-1}\left\{\frac{1}{2}\log\left(\frac{s+1}{s-1}\right)\right\}$

$$=L^{-1}\left\{\int_s^\infty\frac{1}{2}\left(\frac{ds}{s-1}-\frac{ds}{s+1}\right)=\frac{f(t)}{t}\right\}$$

$$=\frac{\sinh t}{t}$$

4. If $L^{-1}[\phi(s)]=f(t)$ and $f(0)=0$

then $L^{-1}[s\phi(s)]=\dfrac{df}{dt}$

(Multiplication by s^n)

Proof: Since $L[f'(t)]=s\phi(s)-f(0)=s\phi(s)$

Then $f'(t)=L^{-1}[s\phi(s)]$

$\Rightarrow$ Multiplication by s amounts to differentiating $f(t)$ w.r.t t once.

Example: Let $\phi(s)=\dfrac{s}{(s^2-a^2)}$

$$\frac{1}{a}L^{-1}\left\{\frac{a}{s^2-a^2}\right\}=\frac{\sinh at}{a}, \text{ and } \sinh 0=0$$

where $f(t)=\sinh at$

$$L^{-1}\left\{s\cdot\frac{1}{s^2-a^2}\right\}=\frac{d}{dt}\frac{\sinh at}{a}=\frac{a\cosh at}{a}$$

$$L^{-1}\left[\frac{s}{s^2-a^2}\right]=\cosh at.$$

5. Find $L^{-1}\left[\dfrac{s}{s^2+4}\right]$ given that $L^{-1}\left[\dfrac{1}{s^2+4}\right]=\dfrac{\sin 2t}{2}$

Solution: Given, $L^{-1}\left[\dfrac{1}{s^2+4}\right]=\dfrac{\sin 2t}{2}$

$$\Rightarrow \quad L^{-1}\left[s\cdot\frac{1}{s^2+4}\right]=\frac{d}{dt}\left(\frac{\sin 2t}{2}\right)$$

$$=\frac{2\cos 2t}{2}; \quad (\because \sin(0)=0)$$

$$=\cos 2t$$

$$\Rightarrow \quad L^{-1}\left[\frac{s}{s^2+4}\right]=\cos 2t$$

Division by powers of s

Prove that $L^{-1}\left\{\dfrac{\phi(s)}{s}\right\}=\displaystyle\int_0^t f(u)du$

Proof: Let $g(t)=\displaystyle\int_0^t f(u)du.$

Then $g'(t)=f(t); \ g(0)=0$

$\therefore \qquad L[g'(t)] = sL[g(t)] - g(0)$

$$= sL[g(t)],$$

but $\quad g'(t) = f(t)$

$$\phi(s) = L[f(t)] = L\{g'(t)\} = sL[g(t)]$$

$\therefore \qquad L[g(t)] = \dfrac{\phi(s)}{s}$

$\therefore \qquad L^{-1}\left\{\dfrac{\phi(s)}{s}\right\} = g(t) = \displaystyle\int_0^t f(u)\,du$

Similarly, $\quad L^{-1}\left[\dfrac{\phi(s)}{s^2}\right] = \displaystyle\int_0^t \int_0^v f(u)\,du\,dv$

In general, $\quad L^{-1}\left[\dfrac{\phi(s)}{s^n}\right] = \displaystyle\int_0^t \int_0^t \cdots \int_0^t f(t)(dt)^n$

EXAMPLES

1. Find $L^{-1}\left[\dfrac{1}{s(s^2+1)}\right]$

Solution: Comparing with $\dfrac{1}{s} \cdot \phi(s)$.

Let $\quad \phi(s) = \dfrac{1}{(s^2+1)}$

$$f(t) = L^{-1}[\phi(s)] = \sin t$$

Now, $\quad L^{-1}\left[\dfrac{\phi(s)}{s}\right] = \displaystyle\int_0^t f(u)\,du$

$$= \int_0^t \sin u \, du$$

$$= (-\cos u)_0^t$$

$$= (1 - \cos t)$$

$$\therefore \quad L^{-1}\left[\frac{1}{s(s^2+1)}\right] = (1-\cos t)$$

2. Find $L^{-1}\left[\dfrac{1}{s^2(s^2+1)}\right]$

Solution: Comparing with $\dfrac{\phi(s)}{s}$

Let $\quad \phi(s) = \dfrac{1}{s(s^2+1)}$

$$\therefore \quad f(t) = L^{-1}[\phi(s)]$$

$$= L^{-1}\left[\frac{1}{s(s^2+1)}\right]$$

$$= (1-\cos t)$$

$$\therefore \quad L^{-1}\left[\frac{\phi(s)}{s}\right] = L^{-1}\left[\frac{1}{s^2(s^2+1)}\right]$$

$$= \int_0^t (1-\cos u)\,du$$

$$= (u-\sin u)_{u=0}^{u=t}$$

$$= (t-\sin t)$$

3. Prove that the inverse L.T. of $\dfrac{1}{s^3(s^2+1)}$ is $\dfrac{t^2}{2}+\cos t-1$

Solution: Now $L^{-1}\left\{\dfrac{\dfrac{1}{(s^2+1)}}{s}\right\} = \int_0^t \sin u\,du$

$$= (-\cos u)_0^t = (1-\cos t)$$

$$\therefore \qquad L^{-1}\left\{\frac{\dfrac{1}{s(s^2+1)}}{s}\right\} = \int_0^t (1-\cos u)\,du$$

$$= (u - \sin u)_0^t$$

$$= (t - \sin t)$$

$$\therefore \qquad L^{-1}\left\{\frac{\dfrac{1}{s^2(s^2+1)}}{s}\right\} = \int_0^t (u - \sin u)\,du$$

$$= \left(\frac{u^2}{2} + \cos u\right)_0^t$$

$$= \frac{t^2}{2} + \cos t - 1$$

or $\qquad L^{-1}\left[\dfrac{1}{s^3(s^2+1)}\right] = \dfrac{t^2}{2} + \cos t - 1$

4. Find $L^{-1}\left[\dfrac{1}{s^3(s+1)}\right]$

Solution: $L^{-1}\left[\dfrac{1}{s+1}\right] = e^{-t} \quad L^{-1}\left[\dfrac{1}{s}\right] = e^{-t}$

Applying I.L.T of integrals, we get

$$L^{-1}\left[\frac{1}{s} \cdot \frac{1}{s+1}\right] = \int_0^t e^{-u}\,du = \left.\frac{e^{-u}}{-1}\right]_0^t = 1 - e^{-t}$$

Now consider

$$L^{-1}\left[\frac{1}{s} \cdot \frac{1}{s(s+1)}\right] = \int_0^t (1 - e^{-u})\,du$$

$$= u - \frac{e^{-u}}{-1} \Bigg]_0^t$$

$$= t + e^{-t} - 1$$

Finally,

$$L^{-1}\left[\frac{1}{s} \cdot \frac{1}{s^2(s+1)}\right] = \int_0^t (u + e^{-u} - 1)du$$

$$= -4 + \frac{u^2}{2} + \frac{e^{-4}}{-1}\Bigg]_0^t$$

$$= -t + \frac{t^2}{2} - e^{-t} + 1$$

$$= 1 - t + \frac{1}{2}t^2 - e^{-t}$$

5. Find $L^{-1}\left[\dfrac{1}{(s^2+1)^2}\right]$

Solution: Let $\phi(s) = \dfrac{1}{s^2+1}$

$\therefore$ $\dfrac{d}{ds}[\phi(s)] = \dfrac{-2s}{(s^2+1)^2}$

$$L^{-1}\left\{\frac{1}{s^2+1}\right\} = \sin t$$

$$L^{-1}\left\{\frac{-2s}{(s^2+1)^2}\right\} = L^{-1}\left[\frac{d}{ds}\left(\frac{1}{s^2+1}\right)\right]$$

$$= (-1)^1 \cdot t^1 \cdot \sin t$$

$$= -t \cdot \sin t$$

or $L^{-1}\left[\dfrac{s}{(s^2+1)^2}\right] = \dfrac{t}{2}\sin t$

Now by the result,

$$L^{-1}\left[\frac{\phi(s)}{s}\right] = \int_0^t f(u)\,du$$

we have, $L^{-1}\left[\dfrac{s}{s(s^2+1)^2}\right] = \int_0^t \dfrac{u}{2}\cdot\sin u\cdot du$

or $L^{-1}\left[\dfrac{1}{(s^2+1)^2}\right] = \dfrac{1}{2}[-u\cos u + \sin u]_0^t$

$$= \frac{1}{2}[-t\cos t + \sin t]$$

6. Find $L^{-1}\left[\dfrac{1}{s^2(s+1)^2}\right]$

Solution: Let $\dfrac{1}{(s+1)} = \phi(s)$

$$L^{-1}[\phi(s)] = L^{-1}\left[\frac{1}{s+1}\right] = e^{-t}$$

or $L^{-1}\left\{\dfrac{d}{ds}\left(\dfrac{1}{s+1}\right)\right\} = (-1)^1\cdot t^1\cdot e^{-t}$

$$= -te^{-t}$$

or $L^{-1}\left[\dfrac{1}{(s+1)^2}\right] = te^{-t}$

or $L^{-1}\left[\dfrac{1}{s(s+1)^2}\right] = \int_0^t xe^{-x}\,dx$

$$\left(\because L^{-1}\left[\frac{\phi(s)}{s}\right] = \int_0^t f(u)\,du\right)$$

$$= \left[-xe^{-x} + \int e^{-x}\,dx\right]_0^t$$

$$= [-e^{-x}(x+1)]_0^t = 1 - e^{-t}(t+1) \qquad [1]$$

or $\quad L^{-1}\left[\dfrac{s}{(s^2+1)^2}\right] = \dfrac{t}{2}\sin t$

Now, by the result,

$$L^{-1}\left[\dfrac{\phi(s)}{s}\right] = \int_0^t f(u)\,du$$

we have, $\quad L^{-1}\left[\dfrac{s}{s(s^2+1)^2}\right] = \int_0^t \dfrac{u}{2}\cdot\sin u\cdot du$

or $\quad L^{-1}\left[\dfrac{1}{(s^2+1)^2}\right] = \dfrac{1}{2}[-u\cos u + \sin u]_0^t$

$$= \dfrac{1}{2}[-t\cos t + \sin t]$$

7. Find $L^{-1}\left[\dfrac{1}{s^2(s+1)^2}\right]$

Solution: Let $\quad \dfrac{1}{(s+1)} = \phi(s)$

$$L^{-1}[\phi(s)] = L^{-1}\left[\dfrac{1}{s+1}\right] = e^{-t}$$

or $\quad L^{-1}\left\{\dfrac{d}{ds}\left(\dfrac{1}{s+1}\right)\right\} = (-1)^1\cdot t^1\cdot e^{-t}$

$$= -te^{-t}$$

or $\quad L^{-1}\left[\dfrac{1}{(s+1)^2}\right] = te^{-t}$

or $\quad L^{-1}\left[\dfrac{1}{s(s+1)^2}\right] = \int_0^t xe^{-x}\,dx$

$$\left(\therefore L^{-1}\left[\frac{\phi(s)}{s}\right] = \int_0^t f(u)du \right)$$

$$= \left[-xe^{-x} + \int e^{-x}dx\right]_0^t$$

$$= [-e^{-x}(x+1)]_0^t = 1 - e^{-t}(t+1) \qquad [1]$$

or $\quad L^{-1}\left[\dfrac{1}{s^2(s+1)^2}\right] = \int_0^t [1 - e^{-x}(x+1)]dx$

$$= [x + e^{-x}(x+1) + e^{-x}]_0^t$$

$$= t + e^{-t} + e^{-t}(t+1) - (1+1)$$

$$= te^{-t} + 2e^{-t} + t - 2$$

8. Find $\dfrac{s+2}{s^2(s+3)}$

Solution: $L^{-1}\left[\dfrac{s+2}{s^2(s+3)}\right] = L^{-1}\left[\dfrac{1}{s(s+3)}\right] + L^{-1}\left[\dfrac{2}{s^2(s+3)}\right] = R_1 + R_2$

We know that

$$L^{-1}\left[\frac{1}{s+3}\right] = e^{-3t} \cdot L^{-1}\left[\frac{1}{s}\right] = e^{-3t}$$

$$R_1 = L^{-1}\left[\frac{1}{s} \cdot \frac{1}{s+3}\right]$$

$$= \int_0^t e^{-3u} \cdot du \quad \text{(by I.L.T of integrals)}$$

$$= \frac{e^{-3u}}{-3}\bigg|_0^t = \frac{1}{3}(1 - e^{-3t})$$

$$R_2 = 2L^{-1}\left[\frac{1}{s^2} \cdot \frac{1}{s+3}\right] = 2L^{-1}\left[\frac{1}{3} \cdot \frac{1}{s(s+3)}\right]$$

$$= 2\int_0^t \frac{1}{3}(1-e^{-3u})du$$

$$= \frac{2}{3}\left[4-\frac{e^{-3u}}{-3}\right]_0^t = \frac{2}{3}\left[t+\frac{e^{-3t}}{3}\frac{1}{3}\right]$$

$$\therefore \quad L^{-1}\left[\frac{s+2}{s^2(s+3)}\right] = \frac{1}{3}-\frac{1}{3}e^{-3t}+\frac{2}{3}t+\frac{2}{9}e^{-3t}-\frac{2}{3}$$

$$= \frac{1}{9}+\frac{2}{3}t-\frac{1}{9}e^{-3t}.$$

Second shifting theorem

> If $L[f(t)] = \phi(s)$, then
> $L[f(t-a)\,H\,(t-a)] = e^{-as}\phi(s)$
> $\therefore f(t-a)H(t-a) = L^{-1}[e^{-as}\phi(s)]$

EXAMPLES

1. Find $L^{-1}\left[\dfrac{e^{-s}}{\sqrt{s+1}}\right]$

Solution: Let $\phi(s) = \dfrac{1}{\sqrt{s+1}}$ so that

$$f(t) = L^{-1}[\phi(s)] = L^{-1}\left[\frac{1}{(s+1)^{\frac{1}{2}}}\right]$$

$$= e^{-t}L^{-1}\left[\frac{1}{s^{\frac{1}{2}}}\right] = e^{-t}\cdot\frac{t^{-\frac{1}{2}}}{\sqrt{\pi}}$$

Using t – shift,

$$L^{-1}\left[\frac{e^{-s}}{\sqrt{s+1}}\right] = L^{-1}e^{-s}\cdot\phi(s)]$$

$$= f(t-1)\cdot H(t-1)$$

$$= \left[e^{-(t-1)}\cdot\frac{(t-1)^{\frac{-1}{2}}}{\sqrt{\pi}}\right]H(t-1)$$

$$= \begin{cases} e^{-(t-1)}\cdot\dfrac{(t-1)^{\frac{-1}{2}}}{\sqrt{\pi}}, & t>1 \\ 0, & 0<t<1 \end{cases}$$

2. Find $L^{-1}\left[\dfrac{1}{s^2-e^{-as}}\right]$

Solution: $\dfrac{1}{s^2-e^{-as}} = \dfrac{1}{s^2}\left[1-\dfrac{e^{-as}}{s^2}\right]^{-1}$

$$= \frac{1}{s^2}\sum_{n=0}^{\infty}\left(\frac{e^{-as}}{s^2}\right)^n = \sum_{n=0}^{\infty}\frac{e^{-ans}}{s^{2n+2}}$$

or, $$= \sum_{n=0}^{\infty}\frac{e^{-ans}}{s^{(2n+1)+1}}$$

Since, $L^{-1}\left[\dfrac{1}{s^{(2n+1)+1}}\right] = \dfrac{t^{2n+1}}{(2n+1)!}$

$\therefore \quad L^{-1}\dfrac{1}{s^2-e^{-as}} = L^{-1}\left[\displaystyle\sum_{n=0}^{\infty}\frac{e^{-ans}}{s^{2n+2}}\right]$

$$= \sum_{n=0}^{\infty}L^{-1}\left[\frac{e^{-ans}}{s^{2n+2}}\right]$$

$$= \sum_{n=0}^{\infty}\frac{(t-an)^{2n+1}}{(2n+1)!}H(t-an)$$

Convolution

The convolution of two functions $f(x)$ and $g(x)$ denoted by $(f*g)(t)$ is defined as

$$h(t) = (f*g)(t) = \int_0^t f(u)g(t-u)du$$

$(f*g)$ is called the convolution or *faltung* (German for folding) of f and g and can be regarded as a "generalised product" of these functions.

Note: To find the inverse transform of product of transforms $\phi(s) = \phi_1(s)\phi_2(s)$, calculate $[h(t) = f*g]$ which is the convolution of f and g.

Convolution Theorem

We prove that $L\{h(t) = L\{f*g\} = \phi(s) = \phi_1(s)\cdot\phi_2(s)$

or $L^{-1}\{\phi_1(s)\cdot\phi_2(s)\} = h(t) = f*g = L^{-1}[\phi_1(s)]*L^{-1}[\phi_2(s)]$

where $\phi_1(s)$ and $\phi_2(s)$ is the L.T. of $f(t)$ and $g(t)$ respectively.

Proof: From the definition of Laplace transforms,

$$L[f*g] = \int_0^\infty e^{-st}[f*g]dt$$

$$= \int_0^\infty e^{-st}\left[\int_0^t f(u)g(t-u)du\right]dt$$

$$= \int_0^\infty \left[\int_0^t e^{-st}f(u)g(t-u)du\right]dt$$

Since e^{-st} is independent of u, the variable of integration in the inner

integral $= \int_0^\infty\int_0^t e^{-st}f(u)g(t-u)dudt$ [1]

$$= \int\int_A e^{-st}f(u)g(t-u)dudt$$ [2]

Where A is the region of the (t, u) plane lying between the lines $u = 0$, $u = t$ and in the positive quadrant as shown below.

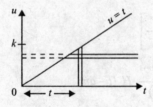

Evaluating the double integrals in [2] with the order of integration changed from the order of double integral in [1] we have

$$L[f * g] = \int_{u=0}^{u=\infty} \left[\int_{t=t}^{t=\infty} e^{-st} f(u)g(t-u)dt \right] du \qquad [3]$$

In the inner integral in [3], put $t = u + x$

then $dt = dx$. Also, the limits for x becomes 0 and u becomes ∞.

∴ the inner integral in [3] becomes

$$\int_0^\infty e^{-s(u+x)} f(u)g(x)dx$$

$$= f(u)e^{-su} \int_0^\infty e^{-sx} g(x)dx$$

$$= e^{-su} f(u)\phi_2(s)$$

when $\phi_2(s)$ is the L.T. of $g(x)$

substituting in [3], we get

$$L[f * g] = \int_{u=0}^\infty e^{-su} f(u)\phi_2(s)du$$

$$= \phi_2(s) \int_{u=0}^\infty e^{-su} f(u)du$$

$$= \phi_2(s) \cdot L[f(u)]$$

$$= \phi_2(s) \cdot \phi_1(s)$$

∴ $\quad L[f(t) * g(t)] = \phi_1(s)\phi_2(s)$

⇒ $\quad L^{-1}[\phi_1(s)\phi_2(s)] = f(t) * g(t)$

or $\quad L^{-1}[\phi_1(s)\phi_2(s)] = L^{-1}[\phi_1(s)] * L^{-1}[\phi_2(s)]$

Important and Valid Properties

P_1: $(f * g)(t) = (g * t)(t)$

Proof: Since $(f(t) * g(t)) = \int_0^t f(u)g(t-u)du$

$$= \int_t^0 f(t-z)g(z)(-dz)$$

(When $z, = (t-u); \quad (u = t-z)$)

$$= \int_t^0 g(z)f(t-z)dz$$

$$= \int_0^t g(z)f(t-z)dz$$

$$= g(t) * f(t)$$

$$\Rightarrow \boxed{f * g = g * f}$$

$P_2:$ $f*(g_1+g_2) = f*g_1 + f*g_2$

Solution: $f(t)*[g_1(t)+g_2(t)]$

$$= \int_0^t f(u)[g_1(t-u)+g_2(t-u)]du$$

$$= \int_0^t f(u)g_1(t-u)du + \int_0^t f(u)g_2(t-u)du$$

$$= f(t)*g_1(t) + f(t)*g_2(t)$$

thus, $f(t)*[g_1(t)+g_2(t)] = f(t)*g_1(t)+f(t)*g_2(t)$

$$\Rightarrow \boxed{f*(g_1+g_2) = f*g_1 + f*g_2}$$

EXAMPLES

1. Use Convolution theorem to find the inverse of the following.

(a) $\dfrac{1}{s^2(s^2+1)}$; (b) $\dfrac{16}{(s-2)(s+2)^2}$; (c) $\dfrac{1}{s(s+1)(s+2)}$; (d) $\dfrac{1}{(s^2+a^2)^2}$;

(e) $\dfrac{1}{(s-1)^5(s+2)}$; (f) $\dfrac{1}{s^2+4s+4}$; (g) $\dfrac{1}{s^2+4s+4}$; (h) $\dfrac{1}{s^2(s+a)^2}$;

(i) $\dfrac{s}{(s^2+1)}$; (j) $\dfrac{s}{(s+1)^2(s^2+1)}$; (k) $\dfrac{s}{(s^2+a^2)^2}$; (l) $\dfrac{s}{(s^2+4)^3}$;

(m) $\dfrac{s^2}{(s^2+a^2)^2}$; (n) $\dfrac{s^2}{(s^2+a^2)(s^2+b^2)}$; (o) $\left\{\dfrac{s+2}{(s^2+4s+5)^2}\right\}$

Solution:

(a) Given, $\phi(s) = \dfrac{1}{s^2(s^2+1)}$ [1]

so that $f(t) = L^{-1}[\phi_1(s)] = L^{-1}\left[\dfrac{1}{s^2}\right] = t$

$$g(t) = L^{-1}[\phi_2(s)] = L^{-1}\left[\dfrac{1}{s^2+1}\right] = \sin t$$

∴ By convolution theorem,

$$L^{-1}\left\{\dfrac{1}{s^2(s^2+1)}\right\} = f*g = \int_0^t (t-u)\cdot\sin u \, du \qquad \text{(by parts)}$$

$$= -t\cos t + t + t\cot - \sin t$$

$$= t - \sin t$$

(b) Given, $\phi(s) = \dfrac{16}{(s-2)(s+2)^2}$

Now, $\dfrac{1}{(s-2)} \cdot \dfrac{1}{(s+2)^2} = \phi_1(s)\cdot\phi_2(s)$

and $\quad f(t) = L^{-1}[\phi_1(s)] = L^{-1}\left[\dfrac{1}{(s-2)}\right] = e^{2t}$

$$g(t) = L^{-1}[\phi_2(s)] = L^{-1}\left[\dfrac{1}{(s+2)^2}\right]$$

$$= e^{-2t}\cdot L^{-1}\left\{\dfrac{1}{s^2}\right\} = te^{-2t}$$

Applying convolution theorem,

$$L^{-1}\left[\dfrac{16}{(s-2)(s+2)^2}\right]$$

$$= g*f = 16\int_0^t ue^{-2u}\cdot e^{2(t-u)}du$$

$$= 16e^{2t}\cdot\int_0^t ue^{-4u}du$$

$$= 16e^{2t}\left[\dfrac{ue^{-4u}}{-4} - 1\cdot\dfrac{e^{-4u}}{16}\right]_{u=0}^{t}$$

$$= e^{2t} - e^{-2t} - 4te^{-2t}$$

(c) Given, $\phi(s) = \dfrac{1}{s(s+1)(s+2)}$

$$\frac{1}{s(s+1)(s+2)} = \frac{1}{s(s+1)} \cdot \frac{1}{(s+2)}$$

where $\dfrac{1}{s(s+1)} = \dfrac{1}{s} \cdot \dfrac{1}{(s+1)}$

so that $f(t) = 1;\ g(t) = e^{-t}$

$$L^{-1}\left[\frac{1}{s} \cdot \frac{1}{s+1}\right] = f * g = \int_0^t 1 \cdot e^{-u}\, du$$

$$= 1 - e^{-t} = h(t)$$

$\therefore\quad L^{-1}\left[\dfrac{1}{s+2}\right] = J(t) = e^{-2t}$

$\therefore\quad L^{-1}\left[\dfrac{1}{s(s+1)} \cdot \dfrac{1}{(s+2)}\right] = h * J$

$$= \int_0^t e^{-2(t-u)} \cdot (1 - e^u)\, du$$

$$= e^{-2t} \int_0^t (e^{2u} - e^u)\, du$$

$$= e^{-2t}\left[\left\{\frac{e^{2u}}{2}\right\}_0^t - \left\{e^u\right\}_0^t\right]$$

$$= e^{-2t}\left[\frac{e^{2t}}{2} - \frac{1}{2} - (e^t - 1)\right]$$

$$= \frac{1}{2} + \frac{1}{2}e^{-2t} - e^{-t}.$$

(d) Given, $\phi(s) = \dfrac{1}{(s^2 + a^2)^2}$

Now, $\dfrac{1}{(s^2 + a^2)^2} = \left(\dfrac{1}{s^2 + a^2}\right)\left(\dfrac{1}{s^2 + a^2}\right)$

Hence, $f(t) = L^{-1}\left(\dfrac{1}{s^2 + a^2}\right) = \dfrac{1}{a}\sin at$

and $\quad g(t) = L^{-1}\left(\dfrac{1}{s^2 + a^2}\right) = \dfrac{1}{a}\sin at$

$\therefore \quad L^{-1}\left\{\dfrac{1}{(s^2 + a^2)^2}\right\} = f * g$

$$= \int_0^t \dfrac{\sin au}{a} \cdot \dfrac{\sin a(t - u)}{a}\,du$$

$$= \dfrac{1}{2a^2}\int_0^t [\cos a(2u - t) - \cos at]\,du$$

$$\left(\because \sin A \cdot \sin B = \dfrac{\cos(A - B) - \cos(A + B)}{2}\right)$$

$$= \dfrac{1}{2a^2}\left[\dfrac{\sin a(2u - t)}{2a} - \cos at \cdot u\right]_{u=0}^{a}$$

$$= \dfrac{1}{2a^2}\left[\dfrac{\sin at}{2a} - t\cos at - \dfrac{\sin(-at)}{2a}\right]$$

$$= \dfrac{1}{2a^3}[\sin at - at\cos\ at].$$

(e) Given, $\phi(s) = \dfrac{1}{(s - 1)^5 (s + 2)}$

Now, $\dfrac{1}{(s - 1)^5(s + 2)} = \left(\dfrac{1}{(s - 1)^2}\right)\left(\dfrac{1}{s + 1 - 1}\right)$

Here, $f(t) = L^{-1}\left[\dfrac{1}{(s - 1)^5}\right] = e^t L^{-1}\left[\dfrac{1}{s + 1 - 1}\right]^5$

$$= e^t L^{-1}\left[\dfrac{1}{s^5}\right] = \dfrac{e^t}{4!}t^4 = \dfrac{e^t t^4}{24}$$

$$g(t) = L^{-1}\left[\dfrac{1}{s + 2}\right] = e^{-2t}$$

$\therefore \quad L^{-1}\left[\dfrac{1}{(s - 1)^5(s + 2)}\right] = \int_0^t f(u)g(t - u)\,du = f * g$

$$= \dfrac{1}{24}\int_0^t e^u \cdot e^{-2(t-u)} \cdot u^4\,du$$

$$= \frac{1}{24} \int_0^t e^{-2t} \cdot e^{3u} \cdot u^4 du$$

$$= \frac{e^{-2t}}{24} \int_0^t u^4 e^{3u} du$$

$$= \frac{e^{-2t}}{24} \left\{ (u^4)\left(\frac{e^{3u}}{3}\right) - (4u^3)\left(\frac{e^{3u}}{9}\right) + (12u^2)\left(\frac{e^{3u}}{3}\right) - (24u)\left(\frac{e^{3u}}{81}\right) + (24)\left[\frac{e^{3u}}{243}\right] \right\}_{u=0}^t$$

$$\left(\begin{array}{l} \because \int uvds = uv_1 - u'u_2 + u''v_3 - u'''v_4... \\ \text{where } u' = \dfrac{du}{dx}; \ v_1 = \int vdx \text{ and so on} \end{array} \right)$$

$$= \frac{e^{-2t}}{24} \left[\frac{t^4 e^{3t}}{3} - \frac{4}{9}t^3 e^{3t} + \frac{4}{9}t^2 e^{3t} - \frac{8}{27}te^{3t} + \frac{8}{81}e^{3t} - \frac{8}{81} \right]$$

$$= \frac{e^t}{24} \left[\frac{t^4}{3} - \frac{4}{9}t^3 + \frac{u}{9}t^2 - \frac{8}{27}t + \frac{8}{81} \right] - \frac{e^{2t}}{243}$$

(f) $\dfrac{1}{s^2 + 4s + 4} = \dfrac{1}{(s+2)^2}$

$$= \frac{1}{(s+2)} \cdot \frac{1}{(s+2)}$$

$$= \phi_1(s)\phi_2(s)$$

$$f(t) = g(t) = e^{-2t}$$

$$L^{-1}[\phi_1(s)\phi_2(s)] = f(t) * g(t)$$

$$= \int_0^t f(t-u)g(u)du$$

$$= \int_0^t e^{-2(t-u)} e^{-2u} du$$

$$= \int_0^t e^{-2t} du$$

$$= e^{-2t} \int_0^t du = e^{-2t} \cdot t$$

(g) Let $\phi(s) = \dfrac{1}{(s+1)(s^2+9)} = \dfrac{1}{(s+1)} \cdot \dfrac{1}{(s^2+9)} = \phi_1(s)\phi_2(s)$

$$\phi_1(s) = \frac{1}{(s+1)}; \quad f(t) = L^{-1}[\phi_1(s)] = L^{-1}\left[\frac{1}{s+1}\right] = e^{-t}$$

$$\phi_2(s) = \frac{1}{s^2 + 3^2} = \frac{1}{3}\left(\frac{1}{s^2 + 3^2}\right)$$

$$g(t) = L^{-1}\left[\phi_2(s)\right] = L^{-1}\left[\frac{1}{3} \cdot \frac{3}{s^2 + 3^2}\right] = \frac{1}{3}$$

$$= \frac{1}{3}\sin 3t$$

By convolution theorem

$$L^{-1}[\phi_1(s)\phi_2(s)]$$

$$= f(t) * g(t) = (e^{-t}) * \left(\frac{1}{3}\sin 3t\right)$$

$$= \frac{1}{3}\int_0^t e^{-(t-u)} \cdot \sin 3u \, du$$

$$= \frac{1}{3}\int_0^t e^{-u} \cdot \sin 3(t-u) du$$

Let us evaluate

$$\int_0^t e^{-(t-u)} \cdot \sin 3u \, du$$

$$\int_0^t e^{-(t-u)} \sin 3u \, du = e^{-t}\int_0^t e^u \sin 3u \, du$$

$$= e^{-t}\left\{\frac{e^u}{10}(\sin 3u - 3\cos 3u)\right\}_{u=0}^t$$

$$= \frac{e^{-t}}{10}\left\{e^t(\sin 3t - 3\cos 3t) - (-3)\right\}$$

$$= \frac{1}{10}\left[\sin 3t - 3\cos 3t + 3e^{-t}\right]$$

(h) Let $\phi_1(s) = \frac{1}{s^2}$,

$$\phi_2(s) = \frac{1}{(s+a)^2}$$

$$\therefore \quad L^{-1}[\phi_1(s)] = t;$$

$$L^{-1}[\phi_2(s)] = e^{-at} \cdot t$$

∴ by convolution theorem,

$$L^{-1}\left[\frac{1}{s^2(s+a)^2}\right]$$

$$= \int_0^t (t-u)e^{-au}u\,du$$

$$= \int_0^t e^{-au}(ut-u^2)du$$

$$= \left[(ut-u^2)\frac{e^{au}}{-a}\right]_{u=0}^t - \int_0^t (t-2u)\left(\frac{e^{-au}}{(-a)}\right)du$$

$$= \frac{1}{a}\left\{\left[(t-2u)\left(\frac{e^{-au}}{-a}\right)\right]_0^t - \int_0^t (-2)\frac{e^{-au}}{(-a)}du\right\}$$

$$= \frac{1}{a^2}\left\{t(e^{-at}+1)+\frac{2}{a}(e^{-at}-1)\right\}$$

(i) Let $\phi(s) = \frac{s}{(s^2+1)}\cdot\frac{1}{(s^2+1)} = \phi_1(s)\phi_2(s)$

$$\phi_1(s) = \frac{s}{s^2+1}; \quad f(t) = L^{-1}[\phi_2(s)] = L^{-1}\left[\frac{s}{s^2+1}\right] = \cos t$$

$$\phi_2(s) = \frac{1}{s^2+1};$$

$$g(t) = L^{-1}[\phi_2(s)]$$

$$= L^{-1}\left[\frac{1}{s^2+1}\right]$$

$$= \sin t$$

$$L^{-1}[\phi_1(s)\phi_2(s)] = f(t)*g(t)$$

$$= \int_0^t f(u)g(t-u)du$$

$$= \int_0^t \cos u \sin(t-u)du$$

$$= \frac{1}{2}\int_0^t [\sin t + \sin(t-2u)]du$$

$$= \frac{1}{2}\left[u\sin t - \frac{1}{-2}\cos(t-2u) \right]_0^t$$

$$= \frac{1}{2}t \cdot \sin t.$$

(j) Let $\phi(s) = \dfrac{s}{(s+1)^2(s^2+1)}$;

Let $\phi(s) = \phi_1(s)\phi_2(s)$

$$= \frac{s}{(s+1)^2(s^2+1)} = \frac{s}{(s^2+1)} \cdot \frac{1}{(s+1)^2}; \text{ where}$$

$\phi_1(s) = \dfrac{s}{(s^2+1)}$; $\phi_2(s) = \dfrac{1}{(s+1)^2}$

Now, $L^{-1}[\phi_1(s)] = L^{-1}\left[\dfrac{s}{(s^2+1)} \right] = \cos t = f(t)$

$L^{-1}[\phi_2(s)] = L^{-1}\left[\dfrac{1}{(s+1)^2} \right] = te^{-t} = g(t)$

Hence by convolution theorem,

$$L^{-1}\left[\frac{s}{(s^2+1)(s+1)^2} \right]$$

$$= \int_0^t \cos u (t-u)e^{-(t-u)}du$$

$$= e^{-t}\int_0^t (t-u)\cos u \, e^u du$$

$$\left(\text{since } \int e^u \cos u \, du = \frac{e^u}{2}(\cos u + \sin u) \right) \qquad \text{(by parts)}$$

$$= e^{-t}\left[(t-u)\frac{e^u}{2}(\sin u + \cos u) \right]_0^t - \int_0^t \frac{e^u}{2}(\sin u + \cos u)(-1)du \right]$$

$$= e^{-t}\left[0 - \frac{1}{2}t + \frac{1}{2}\int_0^t e^u(\sin u + \cos u)du \right]$$

$$= e^{-t}\left[-\frac{1}{2}t + \frac{1}{2}e^{u}\sin u\right]_{0}^{t}$$

$$= e^{-t}\left[-\frac{1}{2}t + \frac{1}{2}e^{t}\sin t\right]$$

$$= -\frac{1}{2}(te^{-t} + \sin t)$$

(k) Let $\phi(s) = \dfrac{s}{(s^2 + a^2)^2} = \dfrac{s}{(s^2 + a^2)} \cdot \dfrac{1}{(s^2 + a^2)} = \phi_1(s) \cdot \phi_2(s)$

$\therefore \quad L^{-1}\left[\phi_1(s) \cdot \phi_2(s)\right] = L^{-1}\left[\dfrac{s}{(s^2 + a^2)} \cdot \dfrac{1}{(s^2 + a^2)}\right]$

$$= \cos at * \frac{\sin at}{a}$$

$$= \int_0^t \cos au \cdot \frac{\sin a(t-u)}{a} \, du$$

$$= \frac{1}{2a}\int_0^t \left[\sin at - \sin(2au - at)\right] du$$

$$= \frac{1}{2a}\left[u\sin at + \frac{\cos(2au - at)}{2a}\right]_0^t$$

$$= \frac{1}{2a}\left[t\sin at + \frac{\cos at}{2a} - \frac{\cos(-at)}{2a}\right]$$

$\therefore \quad L^{-1}\left[\dfrac{s}{(s^2 + a^2)^2}\right] = \dfrac{t\sin at}{2a}$

(l) Let $\phi(s) = \dfrac{s}{(s^2 + 4)^3} = \phi_1(s)\phi_2(s)$

where $\phi_1(s) = \dfrac{1}{(s^2 + 4)}; \quad \phi_2 = \dfrac{s}{(s^2 + 4)^2}$

Now, $L^{-1}[\phi_1(s)] = L^{-1}\left[\dfrac{1}{s^2 + 4}\right] = \dfrac{1}{2}\sin 2t$

$$\therefore \quad L^{-1}\left[\frac{-2s}{(s^2+4)^2}\right] = -t\frac{1}{2}\sin 2t$$

Since, $L^{-1}\left[\phi_1'(s)\right] = -tf(t)$

or, $\quad L^{-1}\left[\frac{s}{(s^2+4^2)^2}\right] = \frac{1}{4}t\sin 2t$

$\Rightarrow \quad L^{-1}\left[\phi_2(s)\right] = \frac{1}{4}t\sin 2t$

$\Rightarrow \quad L^{-1}\left[\phi_2(s)\right] = \frac{1}{4}t\sin 2t = g(t)$

$\therefore$ Using convolution theorem,

$$L^{-1}\left[\phi_1(s)\phi_2(s)\right] = \int_0^t f(t-u)g(u)du$$

$$L^{-1}\left[\frac{s}{(s^2+4)^3}\right] = \int_0^t \frac{1}{2}\sin 2(t-u)\cdot\frac{1}{4}u\sin 2u\,du$$

$$= \frac{1}{8}\int_0^t u\sin(2t-24)\sin 2u\,du$$

$$= \frac{1}{16}\left[\int_0^t u[\cos(2t-4u)du - \cos 2t\int_0^t u\,du\right]$$

$$= \frac{1}{64}[t\sin 2t - 2t^2\cos 2t].$$

(m) Let $\phi(s) = \dfrac{s^2}{(s^2+a^2)^2} = \phi_1(s)\phi_1(s)$

Where $\phi_1(s) = \dfrac{s}{(s^2+a^2)^2};$

Hence, by convolution theorem,

$$f(t) = g(t) * g(t)$$

Where $g(t) = L^{-1}[\phi_1(s)] = \cos at$

$$= \int_0^t g(u)\,g(t-u)\,du$$

$$= \int_0^t \cos au\cos a(t-u)du$$

$$= \frac{1}{2} \int_0^t [\cos(at) + \cos(2au - at)] du$$

$$= \frac{1}{2} \left[\cos at \int_0^t du + \int_0^t \cos(2au - at) du \right]$$

$$= \frac{1}{2} t \cos at + \left[\frac{\sin(2au - at)}{4a} \right]_0^t$$

$$= \frac{1}{2} t \cos at + \frac{1}{4a} [\sin at + \sin at]$$

$$= \frac{1}{2} t \cos at + \frac{1}{2a} \sin at$$

(n) Let $\phi(s) = \dfrac{s^2}{(s^2 + a^2)(s^2 + b^2)} = \phi_1(s) \cdot \phi_2(s)$

where $\phi_1(s) = \dfrac{s}{(s^2 + a^2)}; \; \phi_2(s) = \dfrac{s}{(s^2 + b^2)}$

Then, $L^{-1}[\phi_1(s)] = L^{-1} \left[\dfrac{s}{s^2 + a^2} \right] = \cos at = f(t)$

$$L^{-1}[\phi_2(s)] = L^{-1} \left[\frac{s}{(s^2 + b^2)} \right] = \cos bt = g(t)$$

∴ Using convolution theorem, we get

$$L^{-1}[\phi_1(s)\phi_2(s)] = \int_0^t f(u)g(t - u) du$$

∴ $L^{-1} \left[\dfrac{s}{(s^2 + a^2)(s^2 + b^2)} \right]$

$$= \int_0^t \cos au \cos b(t - u) du$$

$$= \frac{1}{2} \int_0^t [\cos[(a - b)u + bt] + \cos[(a + b)u - bt]] du$$

$$= \frac{1}{2} \left\{ \frac{\sin[(a - b)u + bt]}{a - b} + \sin \frac{\sin[a + b)u - bt]}{a + b} \right\}_0^t$$

$$= \frac{a \sin at - b \sin bt}{a^2 - b^2}, \quad a \neq b$$

(o) Let $\phi(s) = \dfrac{s+2}{(s^2+4s+5)^2} = \phi_1(s) \cdot \phi_2(s)$

where $\phi_1(s) = \dfrac{s+2}{(s^2+4s+5)}$

$\phi_2(s) = \dfrac{1}{s^2+4s+5}$

$\Rightarrow \quad f(t) = L^{-1}\left[\dfrac{s+2}{(s+2)^2+1}\right]$

$g(t) = L^{-1}\left[\dfrac{1}{(s+2)^2+1}\right]$

$f(t) = e^{-2t}L^{-1}\left[\dfrac{s}{s^2+1}\right]$

$\qquad = e^{-2t} \cdot \cos t$

$g(t) = e^{-2t}L^{-1}\left[\dfrac{1}{s^2+1}\right] = e^{-2t}\sin t$

$\therefore$ by convolution theorem,

$L^{-1}\left[\dfrac{s+2}{(s^2+4s+5)^2}\right] = \displaystyle\int_0^t e^{-2u}\cos u e^{-2(t-u)} \cdot \sin(t-u)\,du$

$\qquad = e^{-2t}\displaystyle\int_0^t \sin(t-u)\cos u\,du$

$\qquad = \dfrac{e^{-2t}}{2}\displaystyle\int_0^t [\sin(t-u+u) + \sin(t-u-u)]\,du$

$\qquad = \dfrac{e^{-2t}}{2}\displaystyle\int_0^t [\sin t + \sin(t-2u)]\,du$

$\qquad = \dfrac{e^{-2t}}{2}\left\{\sin t[u]_0^t + \dfrac{\cos(t-2u)}{2}\Big|_{u=0}^{t}\right\}$

$\qquad = \dfrac{e^{-2t}}{2}\left\{t\sin t + \dfrac{1}{2}(\cos t - \cos t)\right\}$

$\qquad = \dfrac{e^{-2t} \cdot t \cdot \sin t}{2}$

EXERCISES

Use convolution theorem to find inverse transforms of the following functions.

(1) $\dfrac{1}{s(s+2)(s-2)}$; $\qquad\qquad\left[Ans.\ \dfrac{1}{4}(\cosh 2t - 1) \right]$

(2) $\dfrac{1}{s(s^2+4)}$; $\qquad\qquad\left[Ans.\ \dfrac{1}{4}(1-\cos 2t) \right]$

(3) $\dfrac{1}{s^2(s^2+a^2)}$; $\qquad\qquad\left[Ans.\ \dfrac{1}{a^2}\left(t - \dfrac{\sin at}{a} \right) \right]$

(4) $\dfrac{s}{(s+1)(s+7)}$; $\qquad\qquad\left[Ans.\ \dfrac{1}{5}\left(7e^{-7t} - 2e^{-2t} \right) \right]$

(5) $\dfrac{s}{(2s+3)(3s+5)}$; $\qquad\qquad\left[Ans.\ \dfrac{5}{3}e^{[-(5\frac{1}{2})t]} - \dfrac{3}{2}e^{[+(-3\frac{1}{2})t]} \right]$

(6) $\dfrac{1}{[s^2(s+1)]^3}$; $\qquad\qquad\left[Ans.\ \dfrac{e^{-t}}{2}(t^2 + 4t + 6) + t - 3] \right]$

(7) $\dfrac{s^2+s}{(s^2+1)(s^2+2s+2)}$; $\quad\left[Ans.\ \dfrac{3}{5}\cos t + \dfrac{1}{5}\sin t + \dfrac{1}{5}e^{-t}(\sin t - 3\cos t) \right]$

(8) $\dfrac{1}{s^3(s+a)}$; $\qquad\qquad\left[Ans.\ \dfrac{1}{2a^3}\left(a^2t^2 - 2at + 2 - 2e^{-at} \right) \right]$

(9) $\dfrac{1}{s^3(s^2+a^2)}$; $\qquad\qquad\left[Ans.\ \dfrac{1}{a^4}(\cos at - 1) + \dfrac{t^2}{2a^2} \right]$

(10) $\dfrac{1}{(s^4+4)}$; $\qquad\qquad\left[Ans.\ \dfrac{1}{4}[\sin t \cosh t - \cos t \sinh t] \right]$

$$\left(\begin{array}{l} Hint:\ \dfrac{1}{s^4+4} = \dfrac{1}{s^2-25+2} \cdot \dfrac{1}{s^2+2s+2} \\ \therefore \quad evaluate\ (e^t \sin t) * (e^{-t} \sin t) \end{array} \right)$$

Partial Fractions

Let the given function be $\varphi(s) = \dfrac{P(s)}{Q(s)}$ where $P(s)$ and $Q(s)$ are polynomials in s. When the degree of $P(s) \le$ degree of $Q(s)$, then $\dfrac{P(s)}{Q(s)}$ can be written as the sum of simpler fractions, called partial fractions, depending on the nature of factors of the denominator as shown below.

	Factor in Denominator	Corresponding Partial Fractions
1.	Non-repeated linear factor $(a_0 s + a_1)$	$\dfrac{A}{a_0 s + a_1};\ A \ne 0$
2.	Repeated linear factor $(a_0 s + a_1)^r$ (r times repeated)	$\dfrac{A_1}{a_0 s + a_1} + \dfrac{A_2}{(a_0 s + a_1)^2} + ... + \dfrac{A_r}{(a_0 s + a_1)^r};\ A_r \ne 0$
3.	Non-repeated quadratic factor $(as^2 + bs + c)$	$\dfrac{As + B}{as^2 + bs + c}$ with at least one of A, B non-zero
4.	Repeated quadratic factor $(as^2 + bs + c)^r$ (r times repeated)	$\dfrac{A_1 s + B_1}{as^2 + bs + c} + \dfrac{A_2 s + B_2}{(as^2 + bs + c)^2} + ... + \dfrac{A_r s + B_r}{(as^2 + bs + c)^r}$ with at least one of A_r, B_r non-zero.

Hence $L^{-1}[\varphi(s)] = L^{-1}\left[\dfrac{P(s)}{Q(s)}\right]$

EXAMPLES

1. Evaluate the following inverse transforms

(a) $L^{-1}\left[\dfrac{1}{(s-1)}\right]$ (b) $L^{-1}\left[\dfrac{1}{(s+2)}\right]$ (c) $L^{-1}\left[\dfrac{1}{3s-5}\right]$

(d) $L^{-1}\left[\dfrac{1}{s(s+9)}\right]$ (e) $L^{-1}\left[\dfrac{1}{as+b}\right]$

Solution:

(a) Let $\varphi(s) = \dfrac{1}{(s-1)}$

$\therefore \quad f(t) = L^{-1}\left[\dfrac{1}{(s-1)}\right] = e^{t}$

(b) Let $\varphi(s) = \dfrac{1}{(s+2)}$

$\therefore \quad f(t) = L^{-1}\left[\dfrac{1}{(s+2)}\right] = e^{-2t}$

(c) Let $\varphi(s) = \dfrac{1}{(3s-5)}$

$\therefore \quad f(t) = L^{-1}\left[\dfrac{1}{(3s-5)}\right] = L^{-1}\left[\dfrac{1}{3\left(s-\dfrac{5}{3}\right)}\right]$

$\qquad = \dfrac{1}{3}L^{-1}\left[\dfrac{1}{\left(s-\dfrac{5}{3}\right)}\right] = \dfrac{1}{3}L^{-1}\left[\dfrac{1}{\left(s-\dfrac{5}{3}\right)}\right] = \dfrac{1}{3}\cdot e^{\left(\frac{5}{3}\right)t}$

(d) $\dfrac{1}{s(s+a)} = \dfrac{1}{a}\left[\dfrac{1}{s} - \dfrac{1}{s+a}\right]$

$\therefore \quad L^{-1}\left[\dfrac{1}{s(s+a)}\right] = \dfrac{1}{a}\left[1 - e^{-at}\right]$

(e) Let $\varphi(s) = \dfrac{1}{(as+b)} = \dfrac{1}{a\left[s+\dfrac{b}{a}\right]}$

$\therefore \quad f(t) = \dfrac{1}{a}L^{-1}\left[\dfrac{1}{\left(s+\dfrac{b}{a}\right)}\right] = \dfrac{1}{a}e^{-\left(\frac{b}{a}\right)t}$

2. Evaluate

(a) $L^{-1}\dfrac{3s+7}{s^2-2s-3}$ (b) $L^{-1}\dfrac{s^3+6s^2+14s}{(s+2)^4}$

Solution:

(a) Let $\dfrac{3s+7}{s^2-2s-3}=\dfrac{3s+7}{(s-3)(s+1)}=\dfrac{A}{(s-3)}+\dfrac{B}{(s+1)}$

$\Rightarrow \quad 3s+7=A(s+1)+B(s-3)$

$\qquad\qquad =(A+B)s+A-3B$

Equate the corresponding coefficients on both sides, we get

$\quad A+B=3; \ A-3B=7$

$\Rightarrow \quad A=4; \ B=-1$

Hence, $\dfrac{3s+7}{(s-3)(s+1)}=\dfrac{4}{(s-3)}-\dfrac{1}{s+1}$

$\therefore \quad L^{-1}\left[\dfrac{3s+7}{(s-3)(s+1)}\right]=4L^{-1}\left[\dfrac{1}{s-3}\right]-L^{-1}\left[\dfrac{1}{s+1}\right]=\left(4e^{3t}-e^{-t}\right)$

(b) We can express the given fraction as

$$\dfrac{s^3+6s^2+14s}{(s+2)^4}=\dfrac{A}{(s+2)^4}+\dfrac{B}{(s+2)^3}+\dfrac{C}{(s+2)^2}+\dfrac{D}{(s+2)}$$

$\Rightarrow \quad s^3+6s^2+14s=A+B(s+2)+C(s+2)^2+D(s+2)^3$

$\qquad\qquad = Ds^3+(6D+C)s^2+(12D+4C+B)S$

$\qquad\qquad +(8D+4C+2B+A)$

Equate the coefficients of 's'

$\quad A=-12; \ B=2; \ C=0; \ D=1$

$L^{-1}\left[\dfrac{s^3+6s^2+14s}{(s+2)^4}\right]=-12L^{-1}\left[\dfrac{1}{(s+2)^4}\right]+2L^{-1}\left[\dfrac{1}{(s+2)^3}\right]+L^{-1}\left[\dfrac{1}{s+2}\right]$

$\qquad\qquad =-12e^{2t}L^{-1}\left[\dfrac{1}{s^4}\right]+2e^{-2t}L^{-1}\left[\dfrac{1}{s^3}\right]+e^{-2t}$

$$= -2e^{-2t}t^3 + e^{-2t}t^2 + e^{-2t}$$

$$= e^{-2t}\{1 + t^2 - 2t^3\}$$

3. Find $L^{-1}\left[\dfrac{s}{(s+2)^2(2s-3)}\right]$

Solution: $\dfrac{s}{(s+2)^2(2s-3)} = \dfrac{A}{(s+2)} + \dfrac{B}{(s+2)^2} + \dfrac{C}{(2s-3)}$

By cover up rule,

$$B = \left[\dfrac{s}{2s-3}\right]_{s=-2} = \dfrac{2}{7}$$

$$C = \left[\dfrac{s}{(s+2)^2}\right]_{s=\frac{3}{2}} = \dfrac{6}{49}$$

$$\Rightarrow \dfrac{s}{(s+2)^2(2s-3)} = \dfrac{A(s+2)(2s-3) + \dfrac{2}{7}(2s-3) + \dfrac{6}{49}(s+2)^2}{(s+2)^2(2s-3)}$$

$$s = A(s+2)(2s-3) + \dfrac{2}{7}(2s-3) + \dfrac{6}{49}(s+2)^2$$

Put $s = 0$, to get A

$$\therefore \quad 0 = -6A - \dfrac{6}{7} + \dfrac{24}{49}$$

$$\Rightarrow \quad A = \dfrac{-3}{49}$$

$$\varphi(s) = \dfrac{-3}{49} \cdot \dfrac{1}{s+2} + \dfrac{2}{7} \cdot \dfrac{1}{(s+2)^2} + \dfrac{3}{49}\dfrac{1}{\left(s - \dfrac{3}{2}\right)}$$

$$\therefore \quad L^{-1}[\phi(s)] = \dfrac{-3}{49}L^{-1}\left[\dfrac{1}{s+2}\right] + \dfrac{2}{7}L^{-1}\left[\dfrac{1}{(s+2)^2}\right] + \dfrac{3}{49}L^{-1}\left[\dfrac{1}{s - \dfrac{3}{2}}\right]$$

$$\therefore \quad f(t) = \dfrac{-3}{49}e^{-2t}t + \dfrac{2}{7} \cdot e^{-2t} \cdot t + \dfrac{3}{49}e^{\frac{3t}{2}}$$

4. Find the inverse L.T of $\dfrac{1+2s}{(s+2)^2(s-1)^2}$

Solution: Let $\dfrac{1+2s}{(s+2)^2(s-1)^2} = \dfrac{A}{(s+2)} + \dfrac{B}{(s+2)^2} + \dfrac{C}{(s-1)} + \dfrac{D}{(s-1)^2}$

then $B = \left[\dfrac{1+2(-2)}{(-2-1)^2}\right] = \dfrac{-3}{3\times 3} = -\dfrac{1}{3}$

$D = \left[\dfrac{1+(2)(1)}{(1+2)^2}\right] = \dfrac{1}{3}$

$\therefore \quad \dfrac{1+2s}{(s+2)^2(s-1)^2} = \dfrac{A}{s+2} - \dfrac{1}{3(s+2)^2} + \dfrac{C}{(s-1)} + \dfrac{1}{3(s-1)^2}$ [1]

$\Rightarrow \quad 1+2s = A(s+2)(s-1)^2 - \dfrac{1}{3}(s-1)^2 + C(s-1)(s+2)^2 + \dfrac{1}{3}(s+2)^2$

Put $s=0; \ 1 = 2A - \dfrac{1}{3} - 4C + \dfrac{4}{3}$

or $0 = 2A - 4C \Rightarrow A = 2C$ [2]

Equate the coefficient of s^3 on both sides,

     $0 = A + C$

     $A = -C$ [3]

[2] and [3] $\Rightarrow \ 2C = -C$

     $C = 0$

$\therefore \quad A = 0$

$\therefore$ [1] becomes

$$\dfrac{1+2s}{(s+2)^2(s-1)^2} = \dfrac{1}{3}\left[\dfrac{1}{(s-1)^2} - \dfrac{1}{(s+2)^2}\right]$$

$\therefore \quad L^{-1}\left[\dfrac{1+2s}{(s+2)^2(s-1)^2}\right] = \dfrac{1}{3}L^{-1}\left[\dfrac{1}{(s-1)^2} - \dfrac{1}{(s+2)^2}\right]$

Now we know that

$$L^{-1}\left[\varphi^{(n)}(s)\right]=(-1)^{n}\,t^{n}f(t)$$

if $\quad L\left[f(t)\right]=\varphi(s)$

$$\therefore \quad L^{-1}\left[\frac{1}{(s-1)^{2}}\right]=-L^{-1}\left\{\frac{d}{ds}\left(\frac{1}{s-1}\right)\right\}=-(-1)^{1}\,t^{1}e^{t}=te^{t}$$

Similarly, $\quad L^{-1}\left[\frac{1}{(s+2)^{2}}\right]=te^{-2t}$

$$\therefore \quad L^{-1}\left[\frac{1+2s}{(s+2)^{2}(s-1)^{2}}\right]=\frac{t}{3}\left[-e^{-2t}+e^{t}\right]$$

5. Obtain the inverse L.T of the following functions

(a) $\dfrac{1}{s^{2}\left(s^{2}+1\right)}$ (b) $\dfrac{1}{s^{2}\left(s^{2}+1\right)\left(s^{2}+4\right)}$ (c) $\dfrac{1}{\left(s^{4}-a^{4}\right)}$

Solution:

(a) Let $\dfrac{1}{s^{2}\left(s^{2}+1\right)}=\dfrac{A}{s}+\dfrac{B}{s^{2}}+\dfrac{(Cs+D)}{\left(s^{2}+1\right)}$ [1]

(Here the parameter 's' occurs in even power only i.e., (s^{2}), there can be no odd power terms at all in the fraction).

$\therefore$ we have $A=0$ and $C=0$

$$\therefore \quad \frac{1}{s^{2}\left(s^{2}+1\right)}=\frac{0}{s}+\frac{B}{s^{2}}+\frac{0s+D}{s^{2}+7}$$

$$=\frac{B}{s^{2}}+\frac{D}{s^{2}+1}$$

$\Rightarrow \quad 1=B\left(s^{2}+1\right)+Ds^{2}$

($\therefore B=1;\ D=-1$, on equating the coefficients of like terms)

or $\quad f(t)=BL^{-1}\left[\dfrac{1}{s^{2}}\right]+DL^{-1}\left[\dfrac{1}{s^{2}+1}\right]$

$f(t)=(t-\sin t)$

(b) $\dfrac{1}{s^2\left(s^2+1\right)\left(s^2+4\right)} = \dfrac{A}{s^2} + \dfrac{B}{s^2+1} + \dfrac{C}{s^2+4}$ [1]

(Since 's' occurs in even powers only ∴ put $s^2 = p$ for purposes of Partial Fraction only)

We obtain from [1], that

$$A = \frac{1}{4}; \quad B = \left(-\frac{1}{4}\right); \quad C = \frac{1}{2}$$

∴ $\quad f(t) = L^{-1}\left(\dfrac{1}{s^2\left(s^2+1\right)\left(s^2+4\right)}\right) = \left(\dfrac{t}{4} - \dfrac{1}{3}\sin t + \dfrac{1}{4}\sin 4t\right)$

(c) Let $\dfrac{1}{s^4 - a^4} = \dfrac{1}{\left(s^2 - a^2\right)\left(s^2 + a^2\right)} = \varphi(s)$

$$= \left[\frac{1}{2a^2} \cdot \frac{1}{\left(s^2 - a^2\right)} - \frac{1}{2a^2} \cdot \frac{1}{\left(s^2 + a^2\right)}\right]$$

∴ $\quad f(t) = L^{-1}\left[\varphi(s)\right] = L^{-1}\left[\dfrac{1}{\left(s^2 - a^2\right)\left(s^2 + a^2\right)}\right]$

$$= \left(\frac{1}{2a^3}\right)\sinh at - \left(\frac{1}{2a^3}\right)\sin at$$

$$= \left(\frac{1}{2a^3}\right)\left[\sinh at - \sin at\right]$$

6. Evaluate $L^{-1}\left[\dfrac{2s+1}{s^2 + 3s + 1}\right]$

Solution: Here denominator $= \left(s^2 + 3s + 1\right)$ is not nicely factorisable, so we add and subtract

$$\left(\frac{1}{2}\text{coefficient } s\right)^2$$

∴ $\quad s^2 + 3s + 1 = s^2 + 3s + \left(\dfrac{3}{2}\right)^2 + 1 = \left(s + \dfrac{3}{2}\right)^2 - \dfrac{5}{4}$

Thus denominator has now become a function of $\left(s+\dfrac{3}{2}\right)$

We shall write numerator also in terms of $\left(s+\dfrac{3}{2}\right)$

as $\quad 2s+1=2\left(s+\dfrac{3}{2}\right)-2$

Now, $L^{-1}\left[\dfrac{2s+1}{s^2+3s+1}\right]=L^{-1}\left[\dfrac{2\left(s+\dfrac{3}{2}\right)-2}{\left(s+\dfrac{3}{2}\right)^2-\dfrac{5}{4}}\right]=e^{-\frac{1}{2}t}\cdot L^{-1}\left[\dfrac{2s-2}{s^2-\dfrac{5}{4}}\right]$

$$e^{-\frac{3}{2}t}\left\{2L^{-1}\left[\dfrac{s}{s^2-\left(\dfrac{\sqrt{5}}{2}\right)^2}\right]-2L^{-1}\left[\dfrac{1}{s^2-\left(\dfrac{\sqrt{5}}{2}\right)^2}\right]\right\}$$

$$=e^{-\frac{3}{2}t}\left\{2\cosh\dfrac{\sqrt{5}}{2}t-2\cdot\dfrac{2}{\sqrt{5}}\sinh\dfrac{\sqrt{5}}{2}t\right\}$$

$\therefore\quad L^{-1}\left[\dfrac{2s+1}{s^2+3s+1}\right]=e^{-\frac{3}{2}t}\left\{2\cosh\left(\dfrac{\sqrt{5}}{2}\right)t-\dfrac{4}{\sqrt{5}}\sinh\left(\dfrac{\sqrt{5}}{2}\right)t\right\}$

7. Evaluate $L^{-1}\left[\dfrac{5s-2}{3s^2+4s+8}\right]$

Solution: Denominator $=3s^2+4s+8$

Here $b^2-4ac=16-96<0$ and not a perfect square. Hence Denominator is not nicely factorisable.

Now, $\quad 3s^2+4s+8=3\left[s^2+\dfrac{4}{3}s+\dfrac{8}{3}\right]=3\left[\left(s+\dfrac{2}{3}\right)^2+\dfrac{20}{9}\right]$

Let $\quad \varphi(s) = \dfrac{5s-2}{3\left[\left(s+\dfrac{2}{3}\right)^2 + \dfrac{20}{9}\right]}$

$\varphi\left(s-\dfrac{2}{3}\right) = \dfrac{5\left(s-\dfrac{2}{3}\right)-2}{3\left(s^2+\dfrac{20}{9}\right)}$

$= \dfrac{15s-16}{9\left(s^2+\dfrac{20}{9}\right)}$

$= \dfrac{5}{3} \cdot \dfrac{s}{s^2+\left(\dfrac{\sqrt{20}}{3}\right)^2} - \dfrac{16}{9} \times \dfrac{3}{\sqrt{20}} \cdot \dfrac{\dfrac{\sqrt{20}}{3}}{s^2+\left(\dfrac{\sqrt{20}}{3}\right)^2}$

$\therefore \quad L^{-1}\left[\varphi\left(s-\dfrac{2}{3}\right)\right] = \dfrac{5}{3}\cos\left(\dfrac{t\sqrt{20}}{3}\right) - \dfrac{8}{3\sqrt{5}}\sin\left(\dfrac{t\sqrt{20}}{3}\right)$

or $\quad f(t) = e^{\frac{2}{3}t} L^{-1}\left\{\varphi\left(s-\dfrac{2}{3}\right)\right\} = \dfrac{e^{-\frac{2}{3}t}}{3}\left\{5\cos\left(\dfrac{t\sqrt{20}}{3}\right) - \dfrac{8}{\sqrt{5}}\sin\left(\dfrac{t\sqrt{20}}{3}\right)\right\}$

8. Find $L^{-1}\left[\dfrac{s+1}{2s^2+4s+7}\right]$

Solution: Denominator $= 2s^2+4s+7$;

$$16-4\cdot2\cdot7 = 16-56 < 0 \qquad\qquad [1]$$

and not a perfect square. Hence denominator is not nicely factorisable.

$\left(2s^2+4s+7\right) = 2\left(s^2+2s\right)+7$

$= 2\left[s^2+2s+1\right]+(7-2)$

$= 2(s+1)^2+5$

$L^{-1}\left[\varphi(s)\right] = L^{-1}\left[\dfrac{s+1}{2(s+1)^2+5}\right]$

$$= L^{-1}\left[\frac{1}{2} \cdot \frac{s+1}{(s+1)^2 + \dfrac{5}{2}}\right]$$

$$= \frac{1}{2} L^{-1}\left[\frac{s+1}{(s+1)^2 + \left(\dfrac{\sqrt{5}}{2}\right)^2}\right]$$

$$= \frac{1}{2} \cdot e^{-t} \cos\left(\frac{\sqrt{5}}{2}\right)t$$

9. Find $L^{-1}\left[\dfrac{2s-1}{s^2+4s+25}\right]$

Solution: Let $\varphi(s) = \dfrac{2s-1}{\left(s^2+4s+25\right)}$

Here denominator $= \left(s^2+4s+25\right)$

and $b^2 - 4ac = 16 - 100 = -84 < 0$

and not a square of a real number.

Hence denominator is not nicely factorisable.

$$s^2 + 4s + 25 = \left(s^2 + 4s\right) + 25$$

$$= \left[(s+2)^2 - 4\right] + 25$$

$$= (s+2)^2 + 21$$

$$= (s+2)^2 + \left(\sqrt{21}\right)^2$$

$$\therefore \qquad \varphi(s) = \frac{2s-1}{(s+2)^2 + \left(\sqrt{21}\right)^2}$$

$$\therefore \qquad \varphi(s-2) = \frac{2s-5}{s^2 + \left(\sqrt{21}\right)^2}$$

$$= 2 \cdot \frac{s}{s^2 + \left(\sqrt{21}\right)^2} - \frac{5}{21} \cdot \frac{\sqrt{21}}{s^2 + \left(\sqrt{21}\right)^2}$$

$$\therefore \quad f(t) = L^{-1}\varphi(s-2)$$

$$= e^{-2t}\left[2L^{-1}\frac{s}{s^2 + \left(\sqrt{21}\right)^2} - \frac{5}{\sqrt{21}}L^{-1}\frac{\sqrt{21}}{s^2 + \left(\sqrt{21}\right)^2}\right]$$

$$= e^{-2t}\left[2\cos\sqrt{21}t - \frac{5}{\sqrt{21}}\sin\sqrt{21}t\right]$$

10. Find $L^{-1}\left[\dfrac{s^2}{s^4 + 4a^4}\right]$

Solution: $s^4 + 4a^4 = \left(s^2\right)^2 + \left(2a^2\right)^2$

$$= \left(s^2 + 2a^2\right)^2 - \left(4a^2s^2\right)$$

$$= \left(s^2 + 2a^2\right)^2 - \left(2as\right)^2$$

$$= \left(s^2 + 2as + 2a^2\right)\left(s^2 - 2as + 2a^2\right)$$

Resolve $\dfrac{s^2}{s^4 + 4a^4}$ into Partial Fraction.

$$\frac{s^2}{s^4 + 4a^4} = \frac{As + B}{s^2 + 2as + 2a^2} + \frac{Cs + D}{s^2 - 2as + 2a^2}$$

Put $s^2 = p = \left(2as - 2a^2\right)$

$$\left(2as - 2a^2\right) = (Cs + D)(4as)$$

$$= 4aCs^2 + 4aDs$$

$$= 4aCP + 4aDS$$

$$= 4aC\left(2as - 2a^2\right) + 4aDs$$

$$= \left(8a^2C + 4aD\right)S - 8a^3C$$

$$\Rightarrow \quad C = \frac{1}{4a}; \ D = 0$$

Put $\quad s^2 = p = -2as - 2a^2$

$$-2as - 2a^2 = (As + B)(-4as)$$

$$= -4aAs^2 - 4aBs$$

$$= -4aA(-2aS - 2a^2) - 4aBS$$

$$= (8a^2 A - 4aB)s + 8a^3 A$$

$\Rightarrow \qquad A = -\dfrac{1}{4a}; \ B = 0 \ .$

$\therefore \qquad \dfrac{s^2}{s^4 + 4a^4} = \dfrac{1}{4a}\left[\dfrac{s}{s^2 - 2as + 2a^2} - \dfrac{s}{s^2 + 2as + 2a^2} \right]$

$$= \dfrac{1}{4a}\left[\dfrac{s}{(s-a)^2 + a^2} - \dfrac{s}{(s+a)^2 + a^2} \right]$$

$$f(t) = \dfrac{1}{4a}\left[e^{at} L^{-1}\left\{ \dfrac{s+a}{(s^2 + a^2)} \right\} - e^{-at} L^{-1}\left\{ \dfrac{s-a}{s^2 + a^2} \right\} \right]$$

$$= \dfrac{1}{4a}\left(e^{at}\{\cos at + \sin at\} - e^{-at}\{\cos at - \sin at\} \right)$$

$$= \dfrac{1}{2a}\left\{ \cos at\left[\dfrac{e^{at} - e^{-at}}{2} \right] + \sin at\left[\dfrac{e^{at} + e^{-at}}{2} \right] \right\}$$

$$= \dfrac{1}{2a}\left[\cos at.\sinh at + \sin at.\cosh at \right]$$

11. Find $L^{-1}\left[\dfrac{1}{(s-1)^5 (s+2)} \right]$

Solution:

$$L^{-1}\left[\dfrac{1}{(s-1)^5 (s+2)} \right] = e^t L^{-1}\left[\dfrac{1}{(s+1-1)^5 (s+1+2)} \right] = e^t L^{-1}\left[\dfrac{1}{s^5 (s+3)} \right] \quad [1]$$

To split $\dfrac{1}{s^5 (s+3)}$ into Partial Fraction by actual division, we have

$$3+s \overline{)\begin{array}{l} \dfrac{1}{3}-\dfrac{s}{9}+\dfrac{s^2}{27}-\dfrac{s^3}{81}+\dfrac{s^4}{243} \\[2mm] 1 \end{array}}$$

$$\dfrac{-\left(1+\dfrac{s}{3}\right)}{-\dfrac{s}{3}}$$

$$\dfrac{-\left(-\dfrac{s}{3}+\dfrac{s^2}{9}\right)}{\dfrac{s^2}{9}}$$

$$\dfrac{-\left(\dfrac{s^2}{9}-\dfrac{s^3}{27}\right)}{\dfrac{s^3}{27}}$$

$$\dfrac{-\left(\dfrac{s^3}{27}-\dfrac{s^4}{81}\right)}{\dfrac{s^5}{27}}$$

$$\dfrac{-\left(\dfrac{s^3}{27}-\dfrac{s^4}{81}\right)}{\dfrac{s^4}{81}}$$

$$\dfrac{-\left(\dfrac{s^4}{81}+\dfrac{s^5}{242}\right)}{-\dfrac{s^5}{243}}$$

$\dfrac{1}{s^5(s+3)}$ in [1] will become

$$\dfrac{1}{s^5}\left[\dfrac{1}{3}-\dfrac{s}{9}+\dfrac{s^2}{27}-\dfrac{s^3}{81}+\dfrac{s^4}{243}-\dfrac{s^5}{243(s+3)}\right]$$

$\therefore \quad L^{-1}\left[\dfrac{1}{s^5(s+3)}\right]$

$$=\dfrac{1}{3}\cdot\dfrac{t^4}{4!}-\dfrac{1}{9}\dfrac{t^3}{3!}+\dfrac{1}{27}\dfrac{t^2}{2!}-\dfrac{1}{81}\dfrac{t}{1!}+\dfrac{1}{243}\cdot\dfrac{t^0}{0!}-\dfrac{1}{243}e^{-3t}$$

$$\therefore \quad L^{-1}\left[\frac{1}{(s-1)^5(s+2)}\right]$$

$$= \frac{e^t}{72}\left[t^4 - \frac{4}{3}t^3 + \frac{5}{3}t^2 - \frac{8}{9}t + \frac{8}{27}\right] - \frac{e^{-2t}}{243}$$

EXERCISES

1. Find the inverse Laplace Transforms

(a) $\dfrac{1}{(s-2)^2+9}$ $\qquad\left[Ans.\ \dfrac{1}{3}e^{2t}\sin 3t\right]$

(b) $\dfrac{s}{(s+1)^2+4}$ $\qquad\left[Ans.\ e^{-t}\left(\cos 2t - \dfrac{\sin 2t}{2}\right)\right]$

(c) $\dfrac{s-3}{(s-1)^2+9}$ $\qquad\left[Ans.\ e^t\left(\cos 3t - \dfrac{2}{3}\sin 3t\right)\right]$

(d) $\dfrac{2s-5}{s^2+s-6}$ $\qquad\left[Ans.\ \dfrac{1}{5}\left(11e^{-3t} - e^{2t}\right)\right]$

(e) $\dfrac{3s+4}{s^2-3s-4}$ $\qquad\left[Ans.\ \dfrac{1}{5}\left(16e^{4t} - e^{-t}\right)\right]$

(f) $\dfrac{s-9}{(s-2)(s^2-5s+6)}$ $\qquad\left[Ans.\ -\dfrac{9}{20}e^{-2t} + \dfrac{5}{4}e^{2t} - \dfrac{4}{5}e^{3t}\right]$

4   LINEAR ALGEBRA: VECTORS

Addition of Vectors

Consider the vectors $\mathbf{u} = (u_1, u_2, ..., u_n)$ and $\mathbf{v} = (v_1, v_2, ..., v_n)$ in R^n. Then the sum, $\mathbf{u} + \mathbf{v}$ is the vector, given by

$$\mathbf{u} + \mathbf{v} = (u_1 + v_1, u_2 + v_2, ..., u_n + v_n)....$$ [1]

Physically, the sum $\mathbf{u} + \mathbf{v}$ represents the diagonal of the parallelogram formed by vectors $\mathbf{u}$ and $\mathbf{v}$ as shown below:

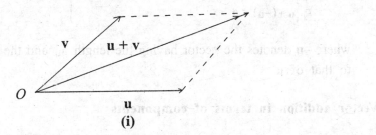

(i)

Let O be the origin of a coordinate system (of R^n), (a,b) and (c,d) be the end points of $\mathbf{u}$ and $\mathbf{v}$ respectively, then, we can prove geometrically that $(a + c, b + d)$ will be the end point of $\mathbf{u} + \mathbf{v}$, or equivalently

$$(a,b) + (c,d) = (a + c, b + d)$$

The two definitions of addition give the same result.

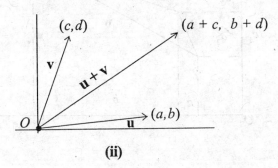

(ii)

Definition (vector addition): Given two vectors **u** and **v**, put the initial point of **v** at the terminal point of **u**; then the sum of **u** and **v** is defined as the vector **w** drawn from the initial point of **u** to the terminal point of **v** (Fig (iii)) and we write **w** = **u** + **v**.

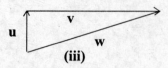

(iii)

Note: (i) If $\mathbf{u} = (a_1, a_2, a_3)$;

$\mathbf{v} = (b_1, b_2, b_3)$, then

$\mathbf{w} = \mathbf{u} + \mathbf{v} = (c_1, c_2, c_3)$

where $c_1 = a_1 + b_1$; $c_2 = a_2 + b_2$; $c_3 = a_3 + b_3$ [1]

From [1] we see that the vector addition has the following properties :

$$\left. \begin{array}{l} P_1 : \mathbf{u} + \mathbf{v} = \mathbf{v} + \mathbf{u} \ ; \ \text{(Commutativity)} \\ P_2 : (\mathbf{u} + \mathbf{v}) + \mathbf{w} = \mathbf{u} + (\mathbf{v} + \mathbf{w}) \ \text{(Associativity)} \\ P_3 : \mathbf{u} + \mathbf{0} = \mathbf{0} + \mathbf{u} = \mathbf{u} \\ P_4 : \mathbf{u} + (-\mathbf{u}) = \mathbf{0} \end{array} \right\} \qquad [2]$$

where −**u** denotes the vector having the length |**u**| and the direction opposite to that of **u**.

Vector addition in terms of components

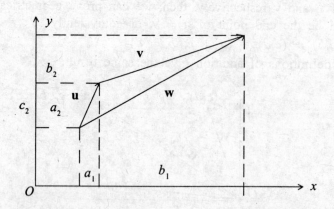

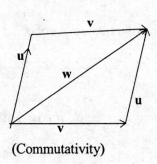

(Commutativity)

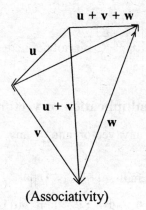

(Associativity)

EXAMPLES

1. Find: (i) $(3, -4, 5, -6) + (1, 1, -2, 4)$

        (ii) $(1, 2, -3) + (4, -5)$

Solution:

(i) $(3, -4, 5, -6) + (1, 1, -2, 4)$

    $= (3 + 1, -4 + 1, 5 - 2, -6 + 4)$

    $= (4, -3, 3, -2)$

(on adding the corresponding components)

(ii) $(1, 2, -3) + (4, -5)$ is not defined as the vectors have different number of components.

2. Find: (i) $\begin{bmatrix} 7 \\ -4 \\ 2 \end{bmatrix} + \begin{bmatrix} -3 \\ -1 \\ 5 \end{bmatrix}$

    (ii) $\begin{bmatrix} 1 \\ 3 \\ 5 \end{bmatrix} + \begin{bmatrix} -2 \\ 4 \end{bmatrix}$

Solution:

(i) $\begin{bmatrix} 7 \\ -4 \\ 2 \end{bmatrix} + \begin{bmatrix} -3 \\ -1 \\ 5 \end{bmatrix} = \begin{bmatrix} 7-3 \\ -4-1 \\ 2+5 \end{bmatrix} = \begin{bmatrix} 4 \\ -5 \\ 7 \end{bmatrix}$

(ii) $\begin{bmatrix} 1 \\ 3 \\ 5 \end{bmatrix} + \begin{bmatrix} -2 \\ 4 \end{bmatrix}$ is not defined as the vectors have different number of components.

Scalar multiplication of vectors

Let **u** be any vector and p any real number. Then the vector $p\mathbf{u}$ is defined as follows:

The length of $p\mathbf{u}$ is $|p||\mathbf{u}|$

If $\mathbf{u} \neq 0$ and $p > 0$, then $p\mathbf{u}$ has the direction of **u**.

If $\mathbf{u} \neq 0$ and $p < 0$, then $p\mathbf{u}$ has the direction opposite to **u**.

If $\mathbf{u} = 0$ or $p = 0$ (or both), then $p\mathbf{u} = 0$.

EXAMPLE

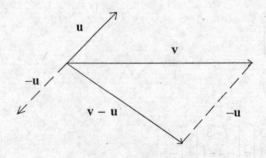

If $\mathbf{u} = (a_1, a_2, a_3)$, then

$p\mathbf{u} = (pa_1, pa_2, pa_3)$ and also for any vectors and real numbers.

(i) $p(\mathbf{u} + \mathbf{v}) = p\mathbf{u} + p\mathbf{v}$

(ii) $(c + k)\mathbf{u} = c\mathbf{u} + k\mathbf{u}$

(iii) $c(k\mathbf{u}) = (ck)\mathbf{u}$ (written $ck\mathbf{u}$)

(iv) $1\mathbf{u} = \mathbf{u}$

Note: (i) $0\mathbf{u} = 0$

(ii) $(-1)\mathbf{u} = -\mathbf{u}$

Instead of $\mathbf{v} + (-\mathbf{u})$ we simply write $\mathbf{v} - \mathbf{u}$ (*see* figure below):

Difference of two vectors

Component form of representation of vectors : $u = u_1 i + u_2 j + u_3 k$

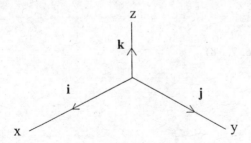

i,j,k are the unit vectors when the origin is chosen as their common initial point.

Definition

Let $\mathbf{u} = (u_1, u_2, ..., u_n)$ be any vector in R^n and let p be any scalar (real number) in R. Then the (scalar) product $p\mathbf{u}$ is the vector.

$$pu = (pu_1, pu_2, ...pu_n)$$

Physically, this product of a real number p and a vector **u**, say that reference point O, to be the vector whose magnitude is equal to the magnitude of **u** multiplied by $|p|$ and whose direction is that of **u** if $p \geq 0$, but is opposite to **u** if $p < 0$, as shown in Fig(i) below.

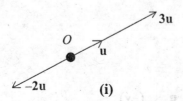

(i)

Let O be chosen as the origin of a coordinate system (of R^2) and suppose (a,b) is the end point of **u,** as shown in figure below. We can prove geometrically that the end point of $p\mathbf{u}$ is (pa, pb).

On the other hand, our definition yields $p(a,b) = (pa, pb)$, the same result.

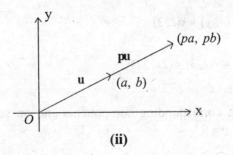

(ii)

EXAMPLES

Evaluate the following :

1. (a) $-3(4, -5, -6)$; $-(6, 7, -8)$

(b) $5\begin{bmatrix} -2 \\ 3 \\ 4 \end{bmatrix}$; $-2\begin{bmatrix} 7 \\ -5 \end{bmatrix}$

(c) $\mathbf{u} - \mathbf{v}$; where $\mathbf{u}$ and $\mathbf{v}$ are in R^n

(d) $(3, -5, 6, 8) - (4, 1, -7, 9)$; $\begin{bmatrix} 6 \\ -3 \end{bmatrix} - \begin{bmatrix} 2 \\ -5 \end{bmatrix}$

Solution:

(a) Here, $-3(4, -5, -6) = (-12, 15, 18)$ and for $-(6, 7, -8)$ we can either multiply each component by -1 or take the negative of each component; either way we obtain $(6, -7, 8)$

(b) $5\begin{bmatrix} -2 \\ 3 \\ 4 \end{bmatrix} = \begin{bmatrix} -10 \\ 15 \\ 20 \end{bmatrix}$

and $-2\begin{bmatrix} 7 \\ 5 \end{bmatrix} = \begin{bmatrix} -14 \\ 10 \end{bmatrix}$

(c) Since $\mathbf{u} - \mathbf{v} = \mathbf{u} + (-\mathbf{v})$

(d) $(3, -5, 6, 8) - (4, 1, -7, 9) = (3, -5, 6, 8) + (-4, -1, 7, -9)$

$= (-1, -6, 13, -1)$ and $\begin{bmatrix} 6 \\ -3 \end{bmatrix} - \begin{bmatrix} 2 \\ -5 \end{bmatrix} = \begin{bmatrix} 6 \\ -3 \end{bmatrix} + \begin{bmatrix} -2 \\ 5 \end{bmatrix} = \begin{bmatrix} 4 \\ 2 \end{bmatrix}$

2. Find x and y if $(4, y) = x(2, 3)$

Solution: $(4, y) = x(2, 3) = (2x, 3x)$

or $\quad 4 = 2x$; $y = 3x$

On equating the corresponding components and on solving for x and y, we get $x = 2$ and $y = 6$.

3. Given $\mathbf{u} = (2, -7, 1)$ $\mathbf{v} = (-3, 0, 4)$, $\mathbf{w} = (0, 5, -8)$

Find (i) $3\mathbf{u} - 4\mathbf{v}$ (ii) $2\mathbf{u} + 3\mathbf{v} - 5\mathbf{w}$

Solution:

$$\left\{ \begin{array}{l} \text{(i)}\ 3\mathbf{u} - 4\mathbf{v} = 3(2, -7, 1) - 4(-3, 0, 4) \\ \quad = (6, -21, 3) + (12, 0, -16) \\ \quad = (18, -21, -13) \end{array} \right\}$$

$$\left\{ \begin{array}{l} \text{(ii)}\ 2\mathbf{u} + 3\mathbf{v} - 5\mathbf{w} = 2(2, -7, 1) + 3(-3, 0, 4) - 5(0, 5, -8) \\ \quad = (4, -14, 2) + (-9, 0, 12) + (0, -25, 40) \\ \quad = (4 - 9 + 0, -14 + 0 - 25, 2 + 12 + 40) \\ \quad = (-5, -39, 54) \end{array} \right\}$$

Properties of vectors

P_1: $\boxed{(\mathbf{u} + \mathbf{v}) + \mathbf{w} = \mathbf{u} + (\mathbf{v} + \mathbf{w})}$, $\mathbf{u}, \mathbf{v}, \mathbf{w} \in R^n$

Proof: Let $u_i + v_i$ be the ith component of $\mathbf{u} + \mathbf{v}$

$\therefore$ $(u_i + v_i) + w_i$ is the ith component of $(\mathbf{u} + \mathbf{v}) + \mathbf{w}$. On the other hand, $v_i + w_i$ is the ith component of $\mathbf{v} + \mathbf{w}$ and so $u_i + (v_i + w_i)$ is the ith component of $\mathbf{u} + (\mathbf{v} + \mathbf{w})$. But $u_i, v_i,$ and w_i are real numbers and belong to R for which the associative law holds; i.e.,

$$(u_i + v_i) + w_i = u_i + (v_i + w_i), \quad \boxed{(i = 1, \dots, n)}$$

Hence, $\boxed{(\mathbf{u} + \mathbf{v}) + \mathbf{w} = \mathbf{u} + (\mathbf{v} + \mathbf{w}) \quad \text{Associativity}}$

P_2: $\boxed{\mathbf{u} + \mathbf{0} = \mathbf{u}}$

Proof: $\mathbf{u} + \mathbf{0} = (u_1, u_2, \dots, u_n) + (0, 0, \dots, 0)$

$$= (u_1 + 0, u_2 + 0, \dots, u_n + 0)$$

$$= (u_1, u_2, \dots, u_n) = \mathbf{u}$$

P_3: $\boxed{\mathbf{u} + (-\mathbf{u}) = 0}$

Proof: $\mathbf{u} + (-\mathbf{u}) = \left(u_1, u_2, ..., u_n\right) + \left(-u_1, -u_2, ... -u_n\right)$

$$= \left(u_1 - u_1, u_2 - u_2, ..., u_n - u_n\right)$$

$$= (0, 0, ..., 0) = 0$$

P_4: $\boxed{\mathbf{u} + \mathbf{v} = \mathbf{v} + \mathbf{u}}$

Proof: Since $u_i + v_i$ is the component of $\mathbf{u} + \mathbf{v}$ and $u_i + v_i$ is the ith component of $\mathbf{v} + \mathbf{u}$. But u_i and v_i are real numbers for which commutative law holds, i.e., $u_i + v_i = v_i + u_i$, $(i = 1,2...n)$, therefore $\mathbf{u} + \mathbf{v} = \mathbf{v} + \mathbf{u}$.

P_5: $\boxed{p(\mathbf{u} + \mathbf{v}) = p\mathbf{u} + p\mathbf{v}}$

Proof : By definition, $u_i + v_i$ is the ith component of $\mathbf{u} + \mathbf{v}$, $p(u_i + v_i)$ is the ith component of $p\mathbf{u} + p\mathbf{v}$. But p, u_i and v_i are real numbers; hence

$$p(u_i + v_i) = pu_i + pv_i \qquad (i = 1, 2, ...n)$$

Hence $\boxed{p(\mathbf{u} + \mathbf{v}) = p\mathbf{u} + p\mathbf{v}}$

P_6: $\boxed{(p + p')\mathbf{u} = p\mathbf{u} + p'\mathbf{u}}$

Proof : Since $(p + p')u_i$ is the ith component of the vector $(p + p')\mathbf{u}$. Also pu_i and $p'u_i$ are the ith components of $p\mathbf{u}$ and $p'u_i$ respectively. $pu_i + p'u_i$ is the ith component of $p\mathbf{u} + p'\mathbf{u}$. But p, p' and u_i are real numbers; hence

$$(p + p')u_i = pu_i + p'u_i \qquad (i = 1, 2, ...n)$$

$\Rightarrow$ $\boxed{(p + p')\mathbf{u} = p\mathbf{u} + p'\mathbf{u}}$

P_7: $\boxed{(pp')\mathbf{u} = p(p'\mathbf{u})}$

Proof: $p'u_i$ is the ith component of $p'\mathbf{u}$, $p(p'u_i)$ is the ith component of $p(p'\mathbf{u})$. But $(pp')u_i$ is the ith component of $(pp')\mathbf{u}$ and since p, p' and u_i are real numbers

$$(pp')u_i = p(p'u_i) \qquad (i = 1, 2, ...n)$$

$$\Rightarrow (pp')\mathbf{u} = p(p'\mathbf{u})$$

P_8: Prove that $\boxed{1 \cdot \mathbf{u} = \mathbf{u}}$

   Proof: $1.\mathbf{u} = 1\left(u_1, u_2, \ldots u_n\right)$

   $= \left(1u_1, 1u_2, \ldots, 1u_n\right)$

   $= \left(u_1, u_2, \ldots u_n\right) = \mathbf{u}$

   $\Rightarrow \quad \boxed{1 \cdot \mathbf{u} = \mathbf{u}}$

P_9: Prove that $0\mathbf{u} = \mathbf{0}$ for any vector $\mathbf{u}$
   Proof: Method (1):

   $0\mathbf{u} = 0\left(u_1, u_2, \ldots u_n\right)$

   $= \left(0u_1, 0u_2, \ldots 0u_n\right)$

   $= (0, 0, \ldots, 0) = \mathbf{0}$

   Method (2): We know that

   $\left(p + p'\right)\mathbf{u} = p\mathbf{u} + p'\mathbf{u},$

   $0\mathbf{u} = (0 + 0)\mathbf{u} = 0\mathbf{u} + 0\mathbf{u}$

   Adding $-(0\mathbf{u})$ to both sides gives

   $0\mathbf{u} + (-(0\mathbf{u})) = (0\mathbf{u} + 0\mathbf{u}) + (-(0\mathbf{u}))$

   $\mathbf{0} = 0\mathbf{u} + \left(0\mathbf{u} + (-(0\mathbf{u}))\right)$

   $\mathbf{0} = 0\mathbf{u} + \mathbf{0}$

   $\mathbf{0} = 0\mathbf{u}$

   (This method does not explicitly use coordinates.)

P_{10}: Show that $\boxed{p\mathbf{0} = \mathbf{0}}$ for any scalar p

   Solution: Method (1):

   $p\mathbf{0} = p(0, 0, \ldots, 0)$

   $= \left(p \cdot 0, p \cdot 0, \ldots, p.0\right)$

   $= (0, 0, \ldots 0)$

   $= \mathbf{0}$

Method (2): We know that $0u = 0$

$$0 + 0 = 0$$

and also by P_9

$$p0 = p(0+0) = p0 + p0$$

Adding $-(p0)$ to both sides leads to the required result, as in P_9

P_{11}: Show that $\boxed{(-1)u = -u}$

We know that $u + (-u) = 0$

$$u + (-u) = 0 = 0u = (1 + (-1)u) = u + (-1)u$$

and the result follows from adding $-u$ to both sides.

Field of vectors (F)

A field F is a set of elements where two operations say '+' and '×' i.e., addition and multiplication are consistently defined under the following rules :

If e_i and e_j are two elements of F,

then $(A_1): e_i + e_j = e_j + e_i$ (Commutative law)

$(A_2): e_i + (e_j + e_k) = (e_i + e_j) + e_k$ (Associativity)

$(A_3):$ for every e_i and $e_j \in F$ $\exists$ one e_k such that

$$e_i + e_k = e_j$$

Note that $(A_3) \Rightarrow \exists$ one $e_o \ni e_i + e_o = e_i$ for all i

and e_o is unique and is a kind of null element of the system

$(M_1): e_i e_j = e_j e_i$ (Commutative law of multiplication)

$(M_2): e_i (e_j e_k) = (e_i e_j) e_k$ (Associativity for multiplication)

$(M_3): e_i (e_j + e_k) = e_i e_j + e_i e_k$ (Distributive law)

$(M_4): \forall e_i$ and $e_j \in F, \exists$ an $e_k \in F$

$$e_i e_k = e_j \quad (e_i, e_j \neq e_o)$$

Note (i): (M_4) implies the existence of one e_i

such that $e_j e_i = e_j$

i.e., e_i is a kind of unit element of system.

Note (ii): (M_4) implies the existence of an inverse of a non-null element.

If we drop(A_1), (M_1) and (M_4) we get a system called a ring.

Further, if we drop only the condition (M_4), we get what is known as a commutative ring.

Field is an algebraic system, where

$$a, b \in F \Rightarrow a + b \in F, \ a - b \in F$$

$$a \times b \in F \text{ and } a \div b \in F \ (b \neq 0) \text{ holds good. (Closure condition)}$$

Summation symbol

Let us define a sum S_n as

$$S_n = \sum_{\alpha=1}^{n} f(\alpha) .... \qquad \qquad [1]$$

where $f(\alpha)$ is an algebraic expression involving an integer variable α, $n \geq 1$.

(Here 1 is the lower limit, n is the upper limit, and the Greek letter sigma functions as the summation symbol.)

In [1], $S_n = f(1) + f(2) + ... + f(n-1) + f(n)$

From this it is obvious that, for $n \geq 2$

$$\boxed{S_n = S_{n-1} + f(n)} \qquad \qquad [2]$$

EXAMPLES

1. If n_1 and n_2 are any integers such that $n_1 \leq n_2$

Define $\displaystyle\sum_{c=n_1}^{n_2} f(c)$

Solution: $\displaystyle\sum_{c=n_1}^{n_2} f(c) = f(n_1) + f(n_1+1) + f(n_1+2) + ... + f(n_2)$

For $n_2 < n_1$, the summation is usually defined to be zero.

2. Evaluate the following :

(a) $\displaystyle\sum_{c=1}^{4} c^3$ (b) $\displaystyle\sum_{j=2}^{5} j^2$ (c) $\displaystyle\sum_{c=1}^{5} x_c$ (d) $\displaystyle\sum_{i=1}^{n} a_i b_i$ (e) $\displaystyle\sum_{i=0}^{n} a_i x^i$ (f) $\displaystyle\sum_{c=1}^{p} a_{ic} b_{cj}$

Solution:

(a) $\displaystyle\sum_{c=1}^{4} c^3 = 1^3 + 2^3 + 3^3 + 4^3 = 1 + 8 + 27 + 64 = 100$

(b) $\displaystyle\sum_{j=2}^{5} j^2 = 2^2 + 3^2 + 4^2 + 5^2 = 4 + 9 + 16 + 25 = 54$

(c) $\displaystyle\sum_{c=1}^{5} x_c = x_1 + x_2 + x_3 + x_4 + x_5$

(d) $\displaystyle\sum_{i=1}^{n} a_i b_i = a_1 b_1 + a_2 b_2 + \dots + a_n b_n$

(e) $\displaystyle\sum_{i=0}^{n} a_i x^i = a_0 + a_1 x + a_2 x^2 + \dots + a_n x^n$

(f) $\displaystyle\sum_{c=1}^{p} a_{ic} b_{cj} = a_{i1} b_{1j} + a_{i2} b_{2j} + \dots + a_{ip} b_{pi}$

Multiplication of vectors

So far we have defined and studied addition of vectors and multiplication of vectors by scalars. We shall now introduce multiplication of vectors by vectors which has many applications in science and engineering.

Definition (scalar product) The scalar product of two vectors **u** and **v** is defined as the product of their magnitudes and the cosine of the angle between them. It is denoted by **u·v**.

Thus $\boxed{\mathbf{u} \cdot \mathbf{v} = |\mathbf{u}||\mathbf{v}|\cos\theta}$ [1]

where θ is the angle between the vectors **u** and **v**. It is also called the dot product.

The scalar product of two vectors is a scalar quantity.

We see that $\mathbf{u} \cdot \mathbf{v} = \mathbf{u}\big(|\mathbf{v}|\cos\theta\big) = (mag. \text{ of } \mathbf{u}) \times (\text{projection of } \mathbf{v} \text{ on } \mathbf{u})$

A physical example:

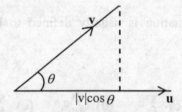

Physically, the scalar product is **F·x**, the work done by a constant force **F** when its point of application undergoes a displacement **x**.

Definition (cross product or vector product). The vector product of two vectors **u** and **v** is denoted by **u** × **v**, is a vector normal to **u** and **v** of magnitude $uv \sin \theta$, where θ is the angle between **u** and **v**. Its sense is such that **u**, **v** and **u**×**v** form a right handed system.

Thus $\mathbf{u} \times \mathbf{v} = (uv \sin \theta)\, \hat{\mathbf{n}}$ [1]

where $\hat{\mathbf{n}}$ is a unit vector normal to u and v such that $\mathbf{u}, \mathbf{v}, \hat{\mathbf{n}}$ form a right handed system.

Note: (i) The cross product or vector product is defined only for vectors in R^3.

(ii) **u** × **v** represents a vector area.

Illustration

Let $\mathbf{u} = (a_1, a_2, a_3); \mathbf{v} = (b_1, b_2, b_3)$ be vectors in R^3.

then the cross product is **u** × **v**

where $\mathbf{u} \times \mathbf{v} = (a_2 b_3 - a_3 b_2, a_3 b_1 - a_1 b_3, a_1 b_2 - a_2 b_1)$

we express the components as determinants as:

put the vector $\mathbf{v} = (b_1, b_2, b_3)$ under the vector $\mathbf{u} = (a_1, a_2, a_3)$

i.e., $\begin{bmatrix} a_1 & a_2 & a_3 \\ b_1 & b_2 & b_3 \end{bmatrix}$

then $u \times v = \left(\begin{vmatrix} \boxed{a_1} & a_2 & a_3 \\ \boxed{b_1} & b_2 & b_3 \end{vmatrix}, \begin{vmatrix} a_1 & \boxed{a_2} & a_3 \\ b_1 & \boxed{b_2} & b_3 \end{vmatrix}, \begin{vmatrix} a_1 & a_2 & \boxed{a_3} \\ b_1 & b_2 & \boxed{b_3} \end{vmatrix} \right)$

Explanation: Cover the first column and take the determinant to obtain the first component of **u** × **v**.

Cover the second column and take the determinant backward to obtain the second component.

Cover the third component and take the determinant to obtain the third component.

EXAMPLES

1. If **u** = (7, 3, 1) and **v** = (1,1,1), then

$$\mathbf{u} \times \mathbf{v} = \left(\begin{vmatrix} \boxed{7} & 3 & 1 \\ \boxed{1} & 1 & 1 \end{vmatrix} - \begin{vmatrix} 7 & \boxed{3} & 1 \\ 1 & \boxed{1} & 1 \end{vmatrix}, \begin{vmatrix} 7 & 3 & \boxed{1} \\ 1 & 1 & \boxed{1} \end{vmatrix} \right) = (3-1, 1-7, 7-3) = (2, -6, 4)$$

2. If $\mathbf{u} = (-4, 12, 2)$; $\mathbf{v} = (6, -18, -3)$, then to find $\mathbf{u} \times \mathbf{v}$

$$\mathbf{u} \times \mathbf{v} = \left(\begin{vmatrix} \boxed{-4} & 12 & 2 \\ \boxed{6} & -18 & -3 \end{vmatrix}, \begin{vmatrix} -4 & \boxed{12} & 2 \\ 6 & \boxed{-18} & -3 \end{vmatrix}, \begin{vmatrix} -4 & 12 & \boxed{2} \\ 6 & -18 & \boxed{-3} \end{vmatrix} \right)$$

$$= \left(-36 - (-36), 12 - 12, 72 - 72 \right) = (0, 0, 0) = \mathbf{0}$$

3. Show that $\mathbf{u} \times \mathbf{v}$ is orthogonal to both $\mathbf{u}$ and $\mathbf{v}$

Solution: $\mathbf{u} \cdot (\mathbf{u} \times \mathbf{v}) = a_1 (a_2 b_3 - a_3 b_2) + a_2 (a_3 b_1 - a_1 b_3) + a_3 (a_1 b_2 - a_2 b_1)$

$$= a_1 a_2 b_3 - a_1 a_3 b_2 + a_2 a_3 b_1 - a_1 a_2 b_3 + a_1 a_3 b_2 - a_2 a_3 b_1$$

$$= 0$$

Thus $\mathbf{u} \times \mathbf{v}$ is orthogonal to $\mathbf{u}$.

Similarly, $\mathbf{u} \times \mathbf{v}$ is orthogonal to $\mathbf{v}$.

Properties

Let $\mathbf{u} = (a_1, a_2, a_3)$; $\mathbf{v} = (b_1, b_2, b_3)$

(1) $\boxed{\mathbf{u} \times \mathbf{v} = -(\mathbf{v} \times \mathbf{u})}$

Proof: $\mathbf{u} \times \mathbf{v} = (a_2 b_3 - a_3 b_2, a_3 b_1 - a_1 b_3, a_1 b_2 - a_2 b_1)$

and $\quad -(\mathbf{v} \times \mathbf{u}) = -(b_2 a_3 - b_3 a_2, b_3 a_1 - b_1 a_3, b_1 a_2 - b_2 a_1)$

$$= (b_3 a_2 - b_2 a_3, b_1 a_3 - b_3 a_1, b_2 a_1 - b_1 a_2) = \mathbf{u} \times \mathbf{v}$$

$\Rightarrow \quad \boxed{\mathbf{u} \times \mathbf{v} = -(\mathbf{v} \times \mathbf{u})}$

$\Rightarrow \quad \mathbf{u} \times \mathbf{v} \neq \mathbf{v} \times \mathbf{u}$ (commutative law does not hold)

(2) $(k\mathbf{u}) \times \mathbf{v} = k(\mathbf{u} \times \mathbf{v}) = \mathbf{u} \times (k\mathbf{v})$

Proof: $k\mathbf{u} = (ka_1, ka_2, ka_3)$; hence

$$(k\mathbf{u}) \times \mathbf{v} = (ka_1 b_2 - ka_2 b_1, ka_3 b_1 - ka_1 b_3, ka_1 b_1 - ka_2 b_1)$$

$$= k(a_1 b_2 - a_2 b_1, a_3 b_1 - a_1 b_3, a_1 b_2 - a_2 b_1) = k(\mathbf{u} \times \mathbf{v})$$

Similarly, $\boxed{\mathbf{u} \times (k\mathbf{v}) = k(\mathbf{u} \times \mathbf{v})}$

(3) $(\mathbf{v}+\mathbf{w})\times\mathbf{u}=(\mathbf{v}\times\mathbf{u})+(\mathbf{w}\times\mathbf{u})$

Proof: $(\mathbf{v}+\mathbf{w})\times\mathbf{u}=-[\mathbf{u}\times(\mathbf{v}+\mathbf{w})]$

$$=-[\mathbf{u}\times\mathbf{v}+(\mathbf{u}\times\mathbf{w})]$$

$$=-(\mathbf{u}\times\mathbf{v})-(\mathbf{u}\times\mathbf{w})$$

$$=(\mathbf{v}\times\mathbf{u})+(\mathbf{w}\times\mathbf{u})$$

(4) (a) Vector product is associative w.r.t. a scalar i.e., $(m\mathbf{u})\times\mathbf{v}=m(\mathbf{u}\times\mathbf{v})=\mathbf{u}\times(m\mathbf{v})$

Proof: When $m>0$

There, $(m\mathbf{u})\times\mathbf{v}=m|\mathbf{u}||\mathbf{v}|\sin\theta\hat{\mathbf{n}}$

$$=m(|\mathbf{u}||\mathbf{v}|\sin\theta\hat{\mathbf{n}})$$

$$=m(\mathbf{u}\times\mathbf{v}) \tag{1}$$

$$=\mathbf{u}\times(m\mathbf{v}) \tag{2}$$

[1] and [2] prove the result similarly $m<0$

(b) Vector product is not associative w.r.t a vector i.e., $\mathbf{u}\times(\mathbf{v}\times\mathbf{w})\neq(\mathbf{u}\times\mathbf{v})\times\mathbf{w}$,

Verification: When $\mathbf{u}=\mathbf{v}$,

L.H.S. $=(\mathbf{u}\times\mathbf{v})\times\mathbf{w}\neq0$

R.H.S. $=(\mathbf{u}\times\mathbf{v})\times\mathbf{w}\neq0$

Hence, L.H.S. $\neq$ R.H.S.

(5) When $\mathbf{u}$ and $\mathbf{v}$ are parallel

Here $\theta=0°$, $\therefore\sin\theta=0$

$\therefore$ $\mathbf{u}\times\mathbf{v}=0$

In particular, $\mathbf{u}\times\mathbf{u}=0$, $\mathbf{v}\times\mathbf{v}=0$

Corollary: when $\mathbf{u}\times\mathbf{v}=0$

then either $\mathbf{u}=0$ or $\mathbf{v}=0$ or $\mathbf{u}$ and $\mathbf{v}$ are

parallel vectors.

(6) When $\mathbf{u}$ and $\mathbf{v}$ are perpendicular

Here $\theta=90°$, $\therefore\sin\theta=1$

$\therefore$ $\mathbf{u}\times\mathbf{v}=|\mathbf{u}||\mathbf{v}|(1)\hat{\mathbf{n}}$

(7) (a) When **u** and **v** are unit vectors

Here $\mathbf{u} \times \mathbf{v} = (1)\sin\theta\,\hat{\mathbf{n}}$

$\therefore \qquad |\mathbf{u} \times \mathbf{v}| = \sin\theta$

(b) When **u** and **v** are not unit vectors

Here $\mathbf{u} \times \mathbf{v} = |\mathbf{u}||\mathbf{v}|\sin\theta\,\hat{\mathbf{n}}$

$\therefore \qquad |\mathbf{u} \times \mathbf{v}| = |\mathbf{u}||\mathbf{v}|\sin\theta$

$\Rightarrow \qquad \sin\theta = \dfrac{|\mathbf{u} \times \mathbf{v}|}{|\mathbf{u}||\mathbf{v}|}$

(8) Vector product of unit vectors **i, j, k**

We know that **i, j, k** form a right handed system of mutually perpendicular vectors.

$\therefore \qquad$ **i** × **j** is a vector having modulus unity and direction parallel to **k**.

$\therefore \qquad \mathbf{i} \times \mathbf{j} = \mathbf{k} = -\mathbf{j} \times \mathbf{i}$

Similarly, $\mathbf{j} \times \mathbf{k} = \mathbf{i} = -\mathbf{k} \times \mathbf{j}$

and $\mathbf{k} \times \mathbf{j} = \mathbf{j} = -\mathbf{i} \times \mathbf{k}$

Also $\mathbf{i} \times \mathbf{i} = \mathbf{j} \times \mathbf{j} = \mathbf{k} \times \mathbf{k} = 0$

×	**i**	**j**	**k**
i	0	**k**	**−j**
j	**−k**	0	**−i**
k	**j**	**−i**	0

EXAMPLES

1. Prove Lagrange's identity

$$\|\mathbf{u} \times \mathbf{v}\|^2 = (\mathbf{u} \cdot \mathbf{u})(\mathbf{v} \cdot \mathbf{v}) - (\mathbf{u} \cdot \mathbf{v})^2$$

Proof: If $\mathbf{u} = (a_1, a_2, a_3)$ and $\mathbf{v} = (b_1, b_2, b_3)$, then

$$\|\mathbf{u} \times \mathbf{v}\|^2 = (a_2 b_3 - a_3 b_2)^2 + (a_3 b_1 - a_1 b_3)^2 + (a_1 b_2 - a_2 b_1)^2 \qquad [1]$$

$$(\mathbf{u} \cdot \mathbf{u})(\mathbf{v} \cdot \mathbf{v}) - (\mathbf{u} \cdot \mathbf{v})^2 = (a_1^2 + a_2^2 + a_3^2)(b_1^2 + b_2^2 + b_3^2) - (a_1 b_1 + a_2 b_2 + a_3 b_3)^2 \qquad [2]$$

From [1] and [2], the result follows.

2. Show that $\| \mathbf{u} \times \mathbf{v} \| = \| \mathbf{u} \| \, \| \mathbf{v} \| \sin \theta$

(where θ is the angle between $\mathbf{u}$ and $\mathbf{v}$)

Solution: Since $\mathbf{u} \cdot \mathbf{v} = \| \mathbf{u} \| \, \| \mathbf{v} \| \cos \theta$

and by using Lagrange's identity we have

$$\| \mathbf{u} \times \mathbf{v} \|^2 = (\mathbf{u} \cdot \mathbf{u})(\mathbf{v} \cdot \mathbf{v}) - (\mathbf{u} \cdot \mathbf{v})^2$$
$$= \| \mathbf{u} \|^2 \| \mathbf{v} \|^2 - \| \mathbf{u} \|^2 \| \mathbf{v} \|^2 \cos^2 \theta$$
$$= \| \mathbf{u} \|^2 \| \mathbf{v} \|^2 (1 - \cos^2 \theta)$$
$$= \| \mathbf{u} \|^2 \| \mathbf{v} \|^2 \sin^2 \theta$$

$\Rightarrow \quad \boxed{\| \mathbf{u} \times \mathbf{v} \| = \| \mathbf{u} \| \, \| \mathbf{v} \| \sin \theta}$

3. Find a unit vector $\mathbf{u}$ orthogonal to $\mathbf{v} = (1,3,4)$ and $\mathbf{w} = (2,-6, 5)$

Solution: Now the array $\begin{bmatrix} 1 & 3 & 4 \\ 2 & -6 & 5 \end{bmatrix}$ yields

$$\mathbf{v} \times \mathbf{w} = (-15 + 24, 8 + 5, -6 - 6) = (9, 13, -12)$$

Normalizing $\mathbf{v} \times \mathbf{w}$ to get

$$\mathbf{u} = \left(\frac{9}{\sqrt{39}}, \frac{13}{\sqrt{39}}, \frac{-12}{\sqrt{39}} \right)$$

4. Find a vector $\mathbf{w}$ normal to the plane H containing the points P_1, P_2 and P_3

Solution: H contains the vectors $\mathbf{u}$ and $\mathbf{v}$ $\begin{cases} \mathbf{u} = P_2 - P_1 \\ \mathbf{v} = P_3 - P_1 \end{cases}$

Hence $\mathbf{u} \times \mathbf{v}$ is normal to H.

The array $\begin{bmatrix} 1 & 3 & -4 \\ 4 & 1 & -2 \end{bmatrix}$ yields

$$\mathbf{w} = \mathbf{u} \times \mathbf{v} = (-6, +4, -16 + 2, 1 - 12) = (-2, -14, 11)$$

Vectors in C^n

5. If $\mathbf{u} = (-2i, 4i, 1 + 6i)$

$\mathbf{v} = (5 + i, 2 - 3i, 5)$ be vectors is C^3,

then $\mathbf{u} + \mathbf{v} = (8 - i, 2 + i, 6 + 6i)$

and $4i\mathbf{u} = (8 + 12i, -16, -24 + 4i)$

The dot product in C^n is defined as

$$\mathbf{u} \cdot \mathbf{v} = \sum_{k=1}^{n} z_k \overline{w_k} \qquad [1]$$

where $\mathbf{u} = (z_1, z_2, .., z_n)$
and $\mathbf{v} = (w_1, w_2, .., w_n)$
w_k is real iff $\overline{w_k} = w_k$,
Hence, when all z_k and w_k are real,

$$\mathbf{u} \cdot \mathbf{v} = \sum_{k=1}^{n} z_k w_k$$

which is the same real number.

The norm or length of **u**, is defined by

$$\|\mathbf{u}\| = \sqrt{\mathbf{u} \cdot \mathbf{u}}$$

$$= \sqrt{z_1 \overline{z_1} + z_2 \overline{z_2} + ... + z_n \overline{z_n}}$$

which is real and non-negative.

6. If $\mathbf{u} = (1 - 2i, 3 + i)$
    and $\mathbf{v} = (4 + 2i, 5 - 6i)$ are vectors in C^2

   $\mathbf{u}.\mathbf{v} = (1 - 2i) \ \overline{(4 + 2i)} + (3 + i)\overline{(5 - 6i)}$

   $= (1 - 2i) (4 - 2i) + (3 + i) (5 + 6i)$

   $= -10i + 9 + 13i$

   $\mathbf{v}.\mathbf{u} = (4 + 2i) (4 - 2i) + (3 + i) (5 + 6i)$

   $= 10i + 9 - 23i = 9 - 13i$

   $(\mathbf{u}.\mathbf{v} = \overline{\mathbf{u} \cdot \mathbf{v}})$

7. Find

   (i) $\|\mathbf{u}\|$ for $\mathbf{u} = (3 + 4i, 5 - 2i, 1 - 3i) \in C^3$

   (ii) $\|\mathbf{u}\|$ for $\mathbf{u} = (4 - i, 2i, 3 + 2i, 1 - 5i) \in C^4$

Solution:

   (i) $\|\mathbf{u}\|^2 = u \cdot u = z_1 \overline{z_1} + z_2 \overline{z_2} + z_3 \overline{z_3}$

$$= [(3)^2 + (4)^2] + [(5)^2 + (-2)^2] + [(1)^2 + (-3)^2] = 64;$$

so $\|\mathbf{u}\| = 8$

(ii) $\|\mathbf{u}\|^2 = [4^2 + (-1)^2] + [2^2] + [3^2 + 2^2] + [1^2 + (-5)^2] = 60$

or $\|\mathbf{u}\| = \sqrt{60} = 2\sqrt{15}.$

8. Prove that $\mathbf{u} \cdot \mathbf{v} = \overline{\mathbf{v} \cdot \mathbf{u}}$

for arbitrary, $\mathbf{u}$, $\mathbf{v}$ in C^n.

$$\mathbf{u} \cdot \mathbf{v} = \sum z_k \overline{w_k} = \overline{\sum w_k \overline{z_k}} = \overline{\mathbf{v} \cdot \mathbf{u}}$$

Interchanging $\mathbf{u}$ and $\mathbf{v}$ (or take conjugates of both sides)

$$\overline{\mathbf{v} \cdot \mathbf{u}} = \mathbf{u} \cdot \mathbf{v}$$

or $\mathbf{u} \cdot \mathbf{v} = \overline{\mathbf{v} \cdot \mathbf{u}}$

9. Prove that

(i) $(z\mathbf{u}) \cdot \mathbf{v} = z\,(\mathbf{u} \cdot \mathbf{v})$

(ii) $\mathbf{u} \cdot (z\mathbf{v}) = \overline{z}\,(\mathbf{u} \cdot \mathbf{v})$

Solution (i) $z\mathbf{u} = (zz_1, zz_2,..., zz_n),$

$$(z\mathbf{u}) \cdot \mathbf{v} = zz_1 \overline{w_1} + zz_2 \overline{w_2} + ... + zz_n \overline{w_n}$$
$$= z(z_1 \overline{w_1} + z_2 \overline{w_2} + ... + z_n \overline{w_n})$$
$$= z(\mathbf{u} \cdot \mathbf{v})$$

(ii) $\mathbf{u} \cdot (z\mathbf{v}) = \overline{(z\mathbf{v}) \cdot \mathbf{u}} = \overline{z(\mathbf{v} \cdot \mathbf{u})} = \overline{z}\ \overline{(\mathbf{v} \cdot \mathbf{u})} = \overline{z}(\mathbf{u} \cdot \mathbf{v}).$

Vector Space

Definition: A non-empty set V is called a vector space over a field F, if for any a, $b \in F$ and $\alpha, \beta \in V$, the following conditions are satisfied:

(i) V is an abelian additive group of vectors.

(ii) $a \in F, \alpha \in V \Rightarrow a\alpha \in V$ i.e., V is closed for the scalar multiplication, and the following four laws of scalar multiplication are satisfied:

$(V_1): a(\alpha + \beta) = a\alpha + a\beta$

$(V_2): (a+b)\alpha = a\alpha + b\alpha$

$$(V_3): a \cdot (b\alpha) = (ab) \cdot \alpha$$

and $(V_4): 1 \cdot \alpha = \alpha,$

where 1 is the unity of F.

A vector space V over a field F is denoted by $V(F)$. But sometimes we write it only as V, if it is clear as to which field is being considered.

Some Important Theorems

Theorem 1: Let $V(F)$ be a vector space over a field F.

Then (a) $c \cdot 0 = 0$ when and $c \in F$ and $0 \in V$

(b) $0 \cdot \alpha = 0$ where $0 \in F$ and $\alpha \in V$

(c) $(-c)\alpha = -(c\alpha) = c(-\alpha) \ \forall c \in F$ and $\alpha \in V$

(d) $c(\alpha - \beta) = (c\alpha - c\beta)$ $[\forall c \in F$ and $\alpha, \beta \in V]$.

Proof: (a) Let $c \cdot \alpha + c \cdot 0 = c \cdot (\alpha + 0) = c \cdot \alpha = c \cdot \alpha + 0$

$\therefore$ $c \cdot \alpha + c \cdot 0 = c \cdot \alpha + 0$

$\Rightarrow$ $c \cdot 0 = 0$ (by Left cancellation law)

(b) Let $c \cdot \alpha + 0 \cdot \alpha = (c + 0) \cdot \alpha = c \cdot \alpha + 0 \cdot \alpha$

$$= c \cdot \alpha + 0; \ [\text{from}(a)]$$

$\therefore$ $c \cdot \alpha + 0 \cdot \alpha = c \cdot \alpha + 0$ (by Left cancellation Law)

$0 \cdot \alpha = 0$

(c) Let $c \cdot \alpha + (-c) \cdot \alpha = [c + (-c)]\alpha$

$$= 0 \cdot \alpha = 0 \quad [\text{from}(b)]$$

and $(-c)\alpha + c\alpha = (-c + c)\alpha$

$$= 0 \cdot \alpha = 0; \ [\text{from (b)}]$$

$\therefore$ $c\alpha + (-c)\alpha = (-c)\alpha + c\alpha = 0$

i.e., $(-c)\alpha = $ is the inverse of $c \cdot \alpha$

i.e., $(-c)\alpha = -(c\alpha)$

Similarly, $c(-\alpha) = -(c\alpha)$

$\therefore$ $(-c)\alpha = -(c\alpha) = c(-\alpha)$

(d) Let $c(\alpha - \beta) = c(\alpha + (-\beta))]$

$$= c\alpha + c(-\beta)$$
$$= c\alpha + (-c)\beta$$
$$= c\alpha - c\beta.$$

Theorem 2: If V (F) is a vector space over a field F, then (i) $(-1)\ \alpha = -\alpha$

(ii) $\beta + (\alpha - \beta) = \alpha$

(iii) If $a\alpha = 0$ then either $a = 0$ or $\alpha = 0$.

Proof: (i) We have $(-c)\alpha = -(c\alpha)$

Take $c = 1$ $\therefore$ $(-1)\alpha = -(1 \cdot \alpha)$

i.e., $(-1)\alpha = -\alpha$

(ii) $\beta + (\alpha - \beta) = \beta + [\alpha + (-\beta)]$

$$= \beta + [-\beta + \alpha] \quad (\because V, +) \text{ is commutative}$$
$$= \beta + (-\beta)] + \alpha$$
$$= 0 + \alpha = \alpha$$

(iii) $a\alpha = 0$ (given)

Let $a \neq 0$, then we shall show that $\alpha = 0$.

Since $a \in$ the field F and $a \neq 0$.

There exists $a^{-1} \in F \ni a^{-1}a = a \cdot a^{-1} = 1$

Now $\alpha = 1 \cdot \alpha = (a^{-1}a)\alpha = a^{-1}(a\alpha) = a^{-1}(0) = 0$.

Again, if $a\alpha = 0$ and $\alpha \neq 0$ then we have $a = 0$

$\because$ otherwise, i.e., if $a \neq 0$ then as we have proved above

$\alpha = 0$ which contradicts the assumption that $\alpha \neq 0$.

$a\alpha = 0 \Rightarrow a = 0$ or $\alpha = 0$

Theorem 3: If $V(F)$ is a vector space then the cancellation laws hold.

(i) $a\alpha = b\alpha \Rightarrow a = b; a \neq 0, a, b \in F$

(ii) $a\alpha = a\beta \Rightarrow; \alpha = \beta; \alpha, \beta \in V$

Proof: (i) $a\alpha = b\alpha \Rightarrow a + (-b)\alpha = b\alpha + (-b)\alpha$

$\Rightarrow \quad [a + (-b)]\alpha = [b + (-b)]\alpha$

$\Rightarrow \quad [a + (-b)]\alpha = 0\alpha$

$\Rightarrow \quad [a + (-b)]\alpha = 0$

$\Rightarrow \quad a + (-b) = 0 \ (\because \alpha \neq 0 \text{ given})$

$\Rightarrow \quad a = b$

(ii) Since $a \neq 0$ therefore a^{-1} exists in $F \ni aa^{-1} = a^{-1}a = 1$

$\therefore \quad a\alpha = a\beta \Rightarrow a^{-1}(a\alpha) = a^{-1}(a\beta)$

$\Rightarrow \quad (a^{-1}a)\alpha = [a^{-1}a]\beta$

$\Rightarrow \quad 1 \cdot \alpha = 1 \cdot \beta$

$\Rightarrow \quad \alpha = \beta$

10. Which of the following sets form vector spaces over real? If not why?

(i)   The set of all rationals over R.

(ii) $V = \{a + ib; \text{ for all } a, b \in Z\}$

(iii)   All polynomials over R with constant term zero.

(iv)   All polynomials over R with constant term 1.

(v)   All polynomials with positive real coefficients.

(vi)   All polynomials $f(x)$ over R such that $f(1) = 0$.

(vii)   All polynomials $f(x)$ over R such that $f(1) = 5$.

(viii) All upper (lower) triangular matrices of order n over R.

(ix)   All n–rowed symmetric (skew symmetric) matrices over C.

Solution:

(i)   No; not closed under scalar multiplication.

(ii)   No; not closed under, scalar multiplication.

(iii)   Yes.

(iv)   No, It is not closed under addition.

(v)   No zero element does not exist.

(vi)   Yes.

(vii)   No, not closed under addition.

(viii) Yes.

(ix)   Yes.

11. Does the set V of all ordered pairs of integers form a vector space over the field of real numbers with addition and scalar multiplication, defined as follows:

$$(a_1, a_2) + (b_1, b_2) = (a_1 + b_1, a_2 + b_2) \text{ for } (a_1, a_2), (b_1, b_2) \in V.$$

$$\alpha(a_1, a_2) = (\alpha a_1, \alpha a_2) \text{ for } \alpha \in R, (a_1, a_2) \in V?$$

Solution: $V = \{(a_i, a_j) a_i, a_j \in Z\}$ [1]

Since V is not closed for scalar multiplication as defined $\therefore$ $V(R)$ is not a vector space.

$$\left[\text{For example, } (5,6) \in V \text{ and } \frac{1}{7} \in R \right]$$

$\therefore$ by scalar multiplication, as defined,

we have $\dfrac{1}{7}(5,6) = \left(\dfrac{5}{7}, \dfrac{6}{7} \right) \notin V$

$\because \quad \dfrac{5}{7}, \dfrac{6}{7} \notin Z$

Definition (Linear Span): The set of all linear combinations of finite sets of elements of a non-empty subset S of a vector space V is called the linear span of S and is denoted by $L(S)$. Thus, we have.

$$L(S) = \{a_1 \mathbf{v}_1 + a_2 \mathbf{v}_2 + \ldots + a_m \mathbf{v}_m : \mathbf{v}_i \in S, \ i = 1, 2, \ldots m\}, \text{ where } m \text{ is finite}$$

Note: $L(\varnothing) = \{\mathbf{0}\}$.

Illustration

Let us consider the vector space $V_3(R)$ and

let $S = \{(1,0,1), (0,0,1)\}$

so that $S \subseteq V_3(R)$

Then, $L(S) = \{a(1,0,1) + b(0,0,1) : a, b \in R\}$

let $L(S) = \{a, 0 \cdot a) + (0, 0, b) : a, b \in R\}$

$\qquad = \{(a, 0, a + b) : a, b \in R\}$

$\qquad = \{(\alpha, 0, \beta) : \alpha, \beta \in R\}$

which is a subspace of $V_3(R)$.

Definition (Linear combination): Let U be a vector space over F. Let $\mathbf{u}_1, \mathbf{u}_2, \ldots \mathbf{u}_n \in U$. Then any vector '**u**' which can be written of the type

$$\mathbf{u} = a_1\mathbf{u}_1 + a_2\mathbf{u}_2 + ... + a_n\mathbf{u}_n$$

$$= \sum_{i=1}^{n} a_i\mathbf{u}_i \text{ for } a_i \in F, \text{ where } 1 \le i \le n.$$

is said to be a linear combination of the vectors $\mathbf{u}_1$, $\mathbf{u}_2$, ... $\mathbf{u}_n$ over F.

Since U is a vector space, therefore $\mathbf{u} \in U$.

Note: (i) For $\mathbf{u}_1$, $\mathbf{u}_2$,...$\mathbf{u}_n$, we get different linear combinations by taking different sets of scalars.

Note: (ii) Alternatively, we may define the linear combination as: The vectors in a subset $S = \{\mathbf{u}_1, \mathbf{u}_2,...\mathbf{u}_n\}$ of U, a vector space over a field F, span or generate U if for every $\mathbf{w} \in U$, we have $\mathbf{w} = a_1\mathbf{u}_1 + a_2\mathbf{u}_2 + ... + a_n\mathbf{u}_n$ for all $a_j \in F$ and $u_j \in S$, $j = 1, 2,...n$.

A vector $\sum\limits_{j=1}^{n} a_j\mathbf{u}_j =$ linear combination of $\mathbf{u}_j$

It may be noted that the vector $\mathbf{w}$ such that $\mathbf{w} = \sum\limits_{j=1}^{n} a_j\mathbf{u}_j$ is again a vector in U, as U over F is closed for both addition and scalar multiplication.

Illustration

Consider the vector space

$$U = R^3, F = R \text{ and Let}$$

$$\mathbf{u}_1 = (1, 1, 1); \mathbf{u}_2 = (1, 2, 3); \mathbf{u}_3 = (2, -1, 1).$$

We want to express a vector $\mathbf{u} = (1, -2, 5)$ as a linear combination of the given set of vectors $\mathbf{u}_1$, $\mathbf{u}_2$, $\mathbf{u}_3$.

Let $\mathbf{u} = a_1\mathbf{u}_1 + a_2\mathbf{u}_2 + a_3\mathbf{u}_3, a_i \in R$

$\therefore$ $(1,-2,5) = a_1(1,1,1) + a_2(1,2,3) + a_3(2,-1,1)$

$= (a_1, a_1, a_1) + (a_2, 2a_2, 3a_2) + (2a_3, -a_3, a_3)$

$= (a_1 + a_2 + 2a_3, a_1 + 2a_2 - a_3, a_1 + 3a_2 + a_3)$

(by coordinate-wise addition)

$\therefore$ $a_1 + a_2 + 2a_3 = 1$

$a_1 + 2a_2 - a_3 = -2$

$a_1 + 3a_2 + a_3 = 5$

Eliminating a_1, we get

$$a_2 - 3a_3 = -3$$

$$a_2 + 2a_3 = 7$$

Upon solving we get, $a_3 = 2$; $a_2 = 3$ and hence $a_1 = -6$

$\mathbf{u} = -6\mathbf{u}_1 + 3\mathbf{u}_2 + 2\mathbf{u}_3$ and such $\mathbf{u}$ is a linear combination of $\mathbf{u}_1$, $\mathbf{u}_2$, $\mathbf{u}_3$.

Linear span of a set

Definition: The linear span of a non-empty subset S of $V(F)$ is the set of all linear combination of any finite number of elements of S and is denoted by $L(S)$.

i.e., $L(S) = \{a_1\mathbf{u}_1 + a_2\mathbf{u}_2 + ... + a_n\mathbf{u}_n : \mathbf{u}_i \in S, a_i \in F\}$

$$i = 1, 2, .., n$$

Linear Dependence and Independence

Definition (Linear Dependency): A finite set $\{\mathbf{u}_1, \mathbf{u}_2, ..., \mathbf{u}_n\}$ of vectors of a vector space $V(F)$ is said to be linearly dependent (L.D.) if there exists a set of scalars $a_1, a_2, ..., a_n$ (not all zero) though some may be zero such that

$$a_1\mathbf{u}_1 + a_2\mathbf{u}_2 + ... + a_n\mathbf{u}_n = 0 \qquad [1]$$

Definition (Linearly Independency): If V is a vector space over field F, then a finite set of vectors $\mathbf{u}_1, \mathbf{u}_2, ..., \mathbf{u}_n \in V$ are said to be linearly independent (L.I) if $\exists$ elements $a_1, a_2, ..., a_n \in F$ (all zero) such that $\mathbf{u}_1 a_1 + \mathbf{u}_2 a_2 + ... + \mathbf{u}_n a_n = \mathbf{0}$.

i.e., $\sum \mathbf{u}_i a_i = 0 \Rightarrow a_i = 0$ for each i.

From above definition of linearly independent of a finite set, we conclude that an infinite set of vectors of V is linearly independent if every finite subset of this is linearly independent because otherwise it is linearly dependent.

Illustration

The vectors $\mathbf{u}_1 = (1, 0, 0)$

$$\mathbf{u}_2 = (0, 1, 0)$$

$$\mathbf{u}_3 = (0, 0, 1)$$

are linearly independent (L.I.).

Let a_1, a_2, a_3, be real numbers such that

$$a_1\mathbf{u}_1 + a_2\mathbf{u}_2 + a_3\mathbf{u}_3 = 0$$

$\Leftrightarrow \quad a_1(1, 0, 0) + a_2(0, 1, 0) + a_3(0, 0, 1) = (0, 0, 0)$

$\Leftrightarrow \quad (a_1, 0, 0) + (0, a_2, 0) + (0, 0, a_3) = (0, 0, 0)$

$\Leftrightarrow \quad (a_1, a_2, a_3) = (0, 0, 0)$

$\Leftrightarrow \quad a_1 = 0;\ a_2 = 0;\ a_3 = 0$

Criteria for linear dependence and independence

1. An infinite subspace S of a vector space is said to be L.I. if every subset of S is L.I.
2. Any super set of L.D. set is L.D.
3. Any subset of a L.I. set is L.I.
4. Any subset of a vector space is either L.D. or L.I.
5. A set containing only 0 vector that is $\{0\}$ is L.D.
6. A set containing the single non-zero vector is L.I.
7. A set having one of the vectors as zero vector is L.D.
8. If two vectors are L.D. then one of them is a scalar multiple of the other.

Definition (Basis of a vector space): A subset S of vectors of a vector space V over a field F is said to be basis of V over F, if

(i) S is linearly independent set of vectors in V.

(ii) S spans or generates $V(F)$, (i.e., $L(S) = V$ or linear span of S is V). In other words every vector in V is a linear combination of a finite number of elements of S.

Note: A zero vector cannot be an element of any basis set, since a set of vectors with zero vector is always linearly dependent.

Illustration

Let us consider a system S consisting of n vectors

$\mathbf{e}_1 = (1, 0, 0, \dots 0);$

$\mathbf{e}_2 = (0, 1, 0 \dots 0);$

$\vdots$

$\mathbf{e}_n = (0, 0, 0, \dots 1).$

We want to verify that the above system of vectors is a basis of $V_n\ (F)$.

Let $S = \{\mathbf{e}_1,\ \mathbf{e}_2, \dots \mathbf{e}_n\}$, then by definition of basis, S will be a basis set of $V_n\ (F)$, if (i) S is Linearly Independent set and (ii) $L(S) = V_n\ (F)$, i.e., each vector in V is a linear combination of elements of S.

(i) For Linear Independence.

$$a_1 e_1 + a_2 e_2 + ... + a_n e_n = 0 = (0, 0, ...0)$$

or $\quad a_1 (1, 0, 0, ..., 0) + ... + a_n (0, 0, ..., 1) = (0, 0, ..., 0)$

$\Rightarrow \quad (a_1 0, 0, .., 0) + ... + (0, 0, ..., a_n) = (0, 0, ..., 0)$

$\Rightarrow \quad (a_1, a_2, ..., a_n) = (0, 0, 0, ..., 0)$

$\Rightarrow \quad a_1 = 0; a_2 = 0; ..., a_n = 0$

$\Rightarrow \quad S$ is L.I. set of vectors

(ii) $L(S) = V_n(F)$

We always have $L(S) \subseteq V_n(F)$.

So we should prove that $V_n(F) \subseteq L(S)$

i.e., each vector in $V_n(F)$ is a linear combination of elements of S.

Let $\quad \mathbf{v} = (a_1, a_2, ...a_n)$ be any vector is $V_n(F)$ We can write:

$$\mathbf{v} = (a_1, a_2, ... a_n) = a_1 (1, 0, ...0) + a_2 (0, 1, 0, ...0) + ... + a_n (0, , ...1)$$

i.e., $\quad \mathbf{v} = a_1 e_1 + a_2 e_2 + ... + a_n e_n.$

Hence S is a basis set of $V_n(F)$. We shall call this particular basis the standard basis of $V_n(F)$ or F^n.

Note 1: We can prove that the set of unit vectors $\{(1, 0, 0) (0, 1, 0)$ and $(0, 0, 1)\}$ is a basis of $V_3(F)$ and $\{(1, 0), (0, 1)\}$ is basis for $V_2(F)$ and the set $\{1\}$ is a basis for $F(F)$ where 1 is the unit element of F.

Subspaces

Definition: A non-empty subset W of a vector space V is said to be a subspace of V over a field F if W is a vector space over F w.r.t. the same operations as in V.

Illustration

The set V of all ordered triplets (x_1, x_2, x_3) over the field of real numbers, is a vector space w.r.t. addition and scalar multiplication.

The set W of all ordered triplets of the form $(x_1, x_2, 0)$ is a subset of V and W is a subspace of V.

Here, W satisfies all the postulates of vector space.

Note: Every vector space always has two subspaces $\{0\}$ and V. These are called trivial subspaces and any other subspace is called a non-trivial subspace of V.

Theorem 1: A non-empty subset W of a vector space V is a subspace of V iff

    (i) $\alpha \in W, \beta \in W \Rightarrow \alpha + \beta \in W$ and

    (ii) $c \in F, \alpha \in W \Rightarrow c\alpha \in W$

Proof: (a) Let W be a vector space over F. Then

$\Rightarrow$ W satisfies all the vector space axioms, i.e.,

$\Rightarrow$ W is closed w.r.t addition and multiplication.

$\therefore$ $\forall \alpha, \beta \in W, \alpha + \beta \in W$

and $\forall \alpha \in W$ and $c \in F,$

    $c\alpha \in W.$

(b) Conversely, let W be a non-empty subset of V such that the conditions (i) and (ii) are satisfied. We have to prove that W is a subspace of V. For this, we have to prove that W satisfies all the vector space axioms.

(V_1): (i) $\alpha + \beta \in W, \quad \forall \alpha, \beta \in W$

    (ii) since $\alpha + (\beta + \gamma) = (\alpha + \beta) + \gamma$

        is defined in V, it is satisfied in the subset W also.

    (iii) $\forall \alpha \in W, c\alpha \in W.$ Take $c = -1$

$\therefore$ $\forall \alpha \in W, (-1)\alpha = -\alpha \in W$

$\therefore$ From condition (a)

    $\alpha + (-\alpha) \in W$

    is $0 \in W$

    (iv) $\forall \alpha \in W, \exists\ c = -1 \in F$ such that

        $c\alpha = (-1)\alpha = -\alpha \in W$

    (v) $\alpha + \beta = \beta + \alpha$ is satisfied in V, and hence it is satisfied in the subset W also.

(V_2): $c(\alpha + \beta) = (c\alpha + c\beta)$

and $(c_1 + c_2)\alpha = c_1\alpha + c_2\alpha$ is satisfied in V. Hence they are satisfied in the subset also.

(V_3): $(c_1 c_2)\ \alpha = c_1(c_2\alpha)$ is satisfied in V and hence it is satisfied in the subset W also.

(V_4): $1 \cdot \alpha = \alpha,\ \forall \alpha \in W$ and $1 \in F$

EXAMPLES

1. If V_1 is a subspace of V_2 and V_2 is a subspace of V, show that V_1 is a subspace of V.

   Solution: Subgroup of a subgroup is a subgroup. So V_1 is an abelian subgroup of V.
   Also for $\mathbf{v} \in V_1$ and $a \in F$, $a\mathbf{v} \in V_2 \subset V$.

2. Which of the following spaces are subspaces of R^n?

   (i) $\{\mathbf{u} = (u_1, u_2, ..., u_n) / u_1 > u_2\}$.

   (ii) $\{\mathbf{u} = (u_1, u_2, ..., u_n) / u_1 + u_2 + ... + u_n = 0\}$.

   (iii) $\{\mathbf{u} = (u_1, u_2, ..., u_n / u_1 + u_2 + ... + u_n = 3\}$

   (iv) $\{\mathbf{u} = (u_1, u_2, ... u_n) / u_1 = 0$ and $u_n = 0\}$

   (v) $\{\mathbf{u} = (u_1, u_2, ... u_n) / u_1 = 2u_2 + 3u_3 + ... + nu_n\}$.

   Solution:

   (i) No　　(ii) Yes　　(iii) No　　(iv) Yes　　(v) Yes.

3. Let V be any vector space.
   Describe the "smallest" and "largest" subspace of V.

   Solution: The set $\{0\}$ consisting of the zero vector alone is subspace of V contained in every other subspace of V, and the entire space V is a subspace of V which contains every other subspace of V.

4. Show that W is not a subspace of R^3 where W consists of those vectors whose length does not exceed 1.

   i.e., $W = \{(a, b, c)\ a^2 + b^2 + c^2 \le 1\}$.

Solution: Let $\mathbf{v} = (1, 0, 0) \in W$

and $\mathbf{w} = (0, 1, 0) \in W$

Ant $\mathbf{v} + \mathbf{w} = (1, 0, 0) + (0, 1, 0)$

$= (1, 1, 0)$ does not belong to W since $1^2 + 1^2 + 0^2 = 2 > 1$.

Hence, W is not a subspace of V.

Theorem 2: A non-empty subset W of a vector space V is a subspace of V iff

$\alpha, \beta \in W, c_1\, c_2 \in F \Rightarrow c_1\alpha + c_2\beta \in W$.

Proof: Given, W is a subspace of $V(F)$.

To prove: $\forall c_1, c_2 \in F$ and $\forall \alpha, \beta \in W$

$\Rightarrow$ $c_1\alpha + c_2\beta \in W$

and $c_1 \in F, \alpha \in W \Rightarrow c_1\alpha \in W$

$c_2 \in F, \beta \in W \Rightarrow c_2\beta \in W$

$[\because W$ is closed under scalar multiplication$]$

Now $c_1\alpha \in W, c_2\beta \in W \Rightarrow c_1\alpha + c_2\beta \in W$

$[\because W$ is closed under additions$]$

Hence $\forall c_1, c_2 \in F$ and $\forall \alpha, \beta \in W$

$\Rightarrow$ $c_1\alpha + c_2\beta \in W$

Conversely: Given, $\forall c_1, c_2 \in F$ and $\forall \alpha, \beta \in W$

$\Rightarrow$ $c_1\alpha + c_2\beta \in W$

To prove: W is a subspace of $V(F)$

Let us take $c_1 = 1$ and $c_2 = -1$.

Hence $1 \cdot \alpha + (-1)\beta \in W \Rightarrow \alpha - \beta \in W$.   Let us take $c_2 = 0$

Hence $c_1\alpha + 0 \cdot \beta \in W \Rightarrow c_1\alpha + \mathbf{0} \in W$ $[\because 0\beta = \mathbf{0}]$

$\Rightarrow$ $c_1\alpha \in W$

Hence W is a subspace of $V(F)$.

EXERCISES

1. Verify the following for a vector space : The set of all polynomials with real coefficients over the field of real numbers w.r.t. addition of a polynomial and scalar multiplication of polynomials.

2. Prove that every field F can be considered as a vector space over F w.r.t. the operations in F.

3. Prove that the set of all $m \times n$ matrices with real elements is a vector space over the field of real numbers w.r.t. addition and scalar multiplication of matrices.

4. Show that W is not a subspace of $V = R^3$ where W consists of those vectors whose components are rational numbers
   i.e., $W = \{(a,b,c); a,b,c \in Q\}$.

5. Show that W is a subspace of $V = R^3$ where W is the xy plane which consists of those vectors whose third component is 0, i.e,
   $W = \{(a,b,0) : a,b, \in R\}$.

6. Show that W is a subspace of V where W consists of the symmetric matrices
   i.e., all matrices $A = (a_{ii})$ for which $a_{ij} = a_{ji}$

7. Show that W is not a subspace of V when W consists of all matrices with zero determinant.

8. Show that W is a subspace of V where W consists of all matrices which commute with a given matrix T
   i.e., $W = \{A \in V : AT = TA\}$.

EXAMPLES (On linear Dependence)

1. Determine whether or not the following vectors in R^3 are linearly dependent.

   (i) $(1,-2,1), (2,1,-1), (7,-4,1)$

   (ii) $(1,2,-3), (1,-3,2), (2,-1,5)$

   [VTU MED. ELEN, June, 2002]

Solution:

(i) Let $\quad a_1(1,-2,1) + a_2(2,1,-1) + a_3(7,-4,1) = 0$

$\Rightarrow \quad (a_1 + 2a_2 + 7a_3, -2a_1 + a_2 - 4a_3, a_1 - a_2 + a_3) = (0,0,0)$

$\therefore \quad$ we have $\quad a_1 + 2a_2 + 7a_3 = 0; -2a_1 + a_2 - 4a_3 = 0; a_1 - a_2 + a_3 = 0$

We solve these equations by cross multiplication method. Now, using equations first and third, we can solve for a_1, a_2 and a_3 as follows:

$$a_1 + 2a_2 + 7a_3 = 0$$

$$a_1 - a_2 + a_3 = 0$$

$$\Rightarrow \quad \frac{a_1}{\begin{vmatrix} 2 & 7 \\ -1 & 1 \end{vmatrix}} = \frac{-a_2}{\begin{vmatrix} 1 & 7 \\ 1 & 1 \end{vmatrix}} = \frac{a_3}{\begin{vmatrix} 1 & 2 \\ 1 & -1 \end{vmatrix}}$$

$$\Rightarrow \quad \frac{a_1}{9} = \frac{-a_2}{-6} = \frac{a_3}{-3}$$

$$\Rightarrow \quad \frac{a_1}{3} = \frac{a_2}{2} = \frac{a_3}{-1};$$

$$\Rightarrow \quad a_1 = -3a_3; \, a_2 = -2a_3, \text{ and } a_3 \text{ can take any value.}$$

Hence, the given system of vectors is linearly dependent.

(ii) Let $a_1(1, 2, -3) + a_2(1, -3, 2) + a_3(2, -1, 5) = 0$

$$\Rightarrow \quad (a_1 + a_2 + 2a_3, \, 2a_1 - 3a_2 - a_3, \, -3a_1 + 2a_2 + 5a_3) = (0, 0, 0,)$$

$$\Rightarrow \quad a_1 + a_2 + 2a_3 = 0; \, 2a_1 - 3a_2 - a_3 = 0; \, -3a_1 + 2a_2 + 5a_3 = 0$$

Solving these equations by using cross multiplication method, using equation first and second we get,

$$a_1 + a_2 + 2a_3 = 0$$

$$2a_1 - 3a_2 - a_3 = 0$$

$$\Rightarrow \quad \frac{a_1}{\begin{vmatrix} 1 & 2 \\ -3 & -1 \end{vmatrix}} = \frac{-a_2}{\begin{vmatrix} 1 & 2 \\ 2 & -1 \end{vmatrix}} = \frac{a_3}{\begin{vmatrix} 1 & 1 \\ 2 & -3 \end{vmatrix}}$$

$$\Rightarrow \quad \frac{a_1}{5} = \frac{-a_2}{-5} = \frac{a_3}{-5}$$

$$\Rightarrow \quad \frac{a_1}{1} = \frac{a_2}{1} = \frac{a_3}{-1};$$

$$\Rightarrow \quad a_1 = -a_3; \, a_2 = -a_3; \text{ and } a_3 \text{ can take any value.}$$

Hence, the given system of vectors is linearly dependent.

2. Find '*a*' if the vectors

$$a_1 = \begin{bmatrix} 1 \\ -1 \\ 3 \end{bmatrix}; a_2 = \begin{bmatrix} 1 \\ 2 \\ -3 \end{bmatrix}; a_3 = \begin{bmatrix} a \\ 0 \\ 1 \end{bmatrix} \text{ are linearly dependent.}$$

Solution: Let *x*, *y*, *z* be scalars (as yet unknown) in *R* such that

$$x\begin{bmatrix} 1 \\ -1 \\ 3 \end{bmatrix} + y\begin{bmatrix} 1 \\ 2 \\ -3 \end{bmatrix} + z\begin{bmatrix} a \\ 0 \\ 1 \end{bmatrix} = \begin{bmatrix} 0 \\ 0 \\ 0 \end{bmatrix}$$

$$\Rightarrow \begin{bmatrix} x+y+az \\ -x+2y \\ 3x-3y+z \end{bmatrix} = \begin{bmatrix} 0 \\ 0 \\ 0 \end{bmatrix}$$

$$\Rightarrow \quad x+y+az = 0 \qquad\qquad\qquad [1]$$

$$-x+2y = 0 \qquad\qquad\qquad [2]$$

$$3x-3y+z = 0 \qquad\qquad\qquad [3]$$

From [2], $x = 2y$ $\qquad\qquad\qquad\qquad\qquad [4]$

Substituting in [3], $6y - 3y + z = 0 \Rightarrow 3y + z = 0$

$$\Rightarrow \quad y = -\frac{z}{3}$$

Substituting in [4], $x = -\dfrac{2z}{3}$.

Substituting in [1], we have

$$-\frac{2z}{3} - \frac{z}{3} + az = 0 \cdot$$

$$\Rightarrow \quad az - z = 0$$

$$\Rightarrow \quad (a-1) = 0$$

($\because z \neq 0$, otherwise if $z = 0$, then $x = y = 0$ also and then the system is linearly independent)

$$\therefore \quad a = 1$$

3. If a_1, b_1 be scalars belong to *C* and $(1, a_1)$, and $(1, b_1)$ are the linearly dependent vectors in $V_2(C)$, then prove

$$a_1 = b_1.$$

Solution: Given, $(1, a_1)$ and $(1, b_1)$ are linearly dependent

$\therefore$ $(1, a_1) = \alpha(1, b_1)$ for $\alpha \in C$

$\Rightarrow$ $(1, a_1) = (\alpha, \alpha b_1)$

$\Rightarrow$ $1 = \alpha$ [1]

         $a_1 = \alpha b_1$ [2]

From [1] and [2], $a_1 = b_1$, Hence the result

4. Determine whether or not **x** and **y** are linearly dependent.

(i) $\mathbf{x} = \begin{bmatrix} 4 \\ 3 \\ -2 \end{bmatrix}$; $\mathbf{y} = \begin{bmatrix} 2 \\ -6 \\ 7 \end{bmatrix}$

(ii) $\mathbf{x} = \begin{bmatrix} 1 \\ 2 \\ 3 \\ 4 \end{bmatrix}$; $\mathbf{y} = \begin{bmatrix} 2 \\ 4 \\ 6 \\ 8 \end{bmatrix}$

(iii) $\mathbf{x} = \begin{bmatrix} 1 & -2 & 4 \\ 3 & 0 & -1 \end{bmatrix}$; $\mathbf{y} = \begin{bmatrix} 1 & -4 & 8 \\ 6 & 0 & -2 \end{bmatrix}$

(iv) $\mathbf{a}_1 = \begin{bmatrix} 1 \\ 2 \\ 4 \end{bmatrix}$; $\mathbf{a}_2 = \begin{bmatrix} 1 \\ 0 \\ 0 \end{bmatrix}$; $\mathbf{a}_3 = \begin{bmatrix} 0 \\ 1 \\ 0 \end{bmatrix}$; $\mathbf{a}_4 = \begin{bmatrix} 0 \\ 0 \\ 1 \end{bmatrix}$

Solution: We know that two vectors are linearly dependent if one is a multiple of the other.

(i) We have $\mathbf{x} = \begin{bmatrix} 4 \\ 3 \\ -2 \end{bmatrix}$ and $\mathbf{y} = \begin{bmatrix} 2 \\ -6 \\ 7 \end{bmatrix}$

Since **x** cannot be expressed as a multiple of **y**.

$\Rightarrow$ **x**, **y** are not linearly dependent

(ii) We have

$$\mathbf{x} = \begin{bmatrix} 1 \\ 2 \\ 3 \\ 4 \end{bmatrix} \text{ and } \mathbf{y} = \begin{bmatrix} 2 \\ 4 \\ 6 \\ 8 \end{bmatrix} = 2\begin{bmatrix} 1 \\ 2 \\ 3 \\ 4 \end{bmatrix} = 2\dot{\mathbf{x}}$$

$\therefore \qquad \mathbf{y} = 2\mathbf{x}$

Hence **x**, **y** are linearly dependent.

(iii) We have

$$\mathbf{x} = \begin{bmatrix} 1 & -2 & 4 \\ 3 & 0 & -1 \end{bmatrix}; \quad \mathbf{y} = \begin{bmatrix} 2 & -4 & 8 \\ 6 & 0 & -2 \end{bmatrix}$$

$$\therefore \qquad \mathbf{y} = \begin{bmatrix} 2 & -4 & 8 \\ 6 & 0 & -2 \end{bmatrix} = 2 \begin{bmatrix} 1 & -2 & 4 \\ 3 & 0 & -1 \end{bmatrix} = 2\mathbf{x}$$

Hence **x** and **y** are linearly dependent.

(iv) Let $a_1 x + a_2 y + a_3 z + a_4 t = 0$

where x, y, z, t are as yet unknowns.

$$\Rightarrow \quad x \begin{bmatrix} 1 \\ 2 \\ 4 \end{bmatrix} + \begin{bmatrix} 1 \\ 0 \\ 0 \end{bmatrix} y + z \begin{bmatrix} 0 \\ 1 \\ 0 \end{bmatrix} + t \begin{bmatrix} 0 \\ 0 \\ 1 \end{bmatrix} = \begin{bmatrix} 0 \\ 0 \\ 0 \end{bmatrix}$$

$$\Rightarrow \quad \left. \begin{aligned} x + y &= 0 \\ 2x + z &= 0 \\ 4x + t &= 0 \end{aligned} \right\} \Rightarrow y = -x, z = -2x, t = -4x$$

$\therefore$ If we take $x = 2$, then $y = -2$,

$\qquad z = -4; \; t = -8.$

$$\Rightarrow \quad a_1 x + a_2 y + a_3 z + a_4 t = 0,$$

where x, y, z, t are not all zero.

Hence, the given set of vectors is linearly dependent.

5. Under what conditions on the scalar '*a*' are the vectors

$$\begin{bmatrix} a \\ 1 \\ 0 \end{bmatrix}, \begin{bmatrix} 1 \\ a \\ 1 \end{bmatrix}, \begin{bmatrix} 0 \\ 1 \\ a \end{bmatrix} \text{ in } R^3 \text{ linearly dependent?}$$

Solution: Let there be scalars a_1, a_2, $a_3 \in R$, such that

$$a_1 \begin{bmatrix} a \\ 1 \\ 0 \end{bmatrix} + a_2 \begin{bmatrix} 1 \\ a \\ 1 \end{bmatrix} + a_3 \begin{bmatrix} 0 \\ 1 \\ a \end{bmatrix} = \begin{bmatrix} 0 \\ 0 \\ 0 \end{bmatrix}$$

$$\Rightarrow \quad \begin{bmatrix} aa_1 + a_2 \\ a_1 + aa_2 + a_3 \\ a_2 + aa_3 \end{bmatrix} = \begin{bmatrix} 0 \\ 0 \\ 0 \end{bmatrix}$$

$$\Rightarrow \quad \left. \begin{array}{l} aa_1 + a_2 = 0 \\ a_1 + aa_2 + a_3 = 0 \\ a_2 + aa_3 = 0 \end{array} \right\} \qquad\qquad [1]$$

From, $aa_1 + a_2 = 0$

and $a_2 + aa_3 = 0$,

we get, $aa_1 - aa_3 = 0$, on subtracting.

$\Rightarrow a(a_1 - a_3) = 0$ i.e., either $a = 0$ or $a_1 = a_3$ [2]

If $a = 0$, then from [1], we get $a_2 = 0$,

i.e., $a_2 = 0$ and $a_3 = -a_1$

$\therefore$ in this case $a = 0$, if we take $a_1 = b$,

$a_2 = 0$ and $a_3 = -b$, the given vectors are linearly dependent.

Again if $a \neq 0$, then from [2],

we have, $a_1 = a_3$ and so from [1],

we get, $a_1 = a_3$; $2a_1 + aa_2 = 0$, $aa_1 + a_2 = 0$.

Solving, $2a_1 + aa_2 = 0$ and $aa_1 + a_2 = 0$, we get

$$2a_1 + a(-aa_1) = 0$$

or $\quad a_1(2 - a^2) = 0$

or $\quad a^2 = 2$ or $a \pm\sqrt{2}$

$\therefore \quad a = \pm\sqrt{2}$

$\therefore$ For $a_1 = a_3; a_2 = \pm a_1\sqrt{2}$, $a = \pm\sqrt{2}$,

The given vectors are linearly dependent.

Hence the given vectors are linearly dependent if $a = 0$ or $a = \pm\sqrt{2}$.

6. Under what condition on scalar $a_1 \in C$ are the vectors $(1 + a_1, 1 - a_1)$ and $(1 - a_1, 1 + a_1)$ in $V_2(C)$ linearly dependent ?

Solution: By data, the given vectors are linearly dependent

$\therefore$ $\qquad$ $(1+a_1, 1-a_1) = \alpha(1-a_1, 1+a_1)$ for $\alpha \in C$

$\Rightarrow$ $\qquad$ $(1+a_1, 1-a_1) = (a(1-a_1), \alpha(1+a_1))$

$\therefore$ $\qquad$ $1+a_1 = \alpha - \alpha a_1$ $\hfill$ [1]

and $\quad 1-a_1 = \alpha + \alpha a_1$ $\hfill$ [2]

By [1] and [2], for addition in F, we have

$\qquad 2 = 2\alpha \Rightarrow \alpha = 1$

Then by [2] for $\alpha = 1$, we have

$\qquad 1 - a_1 = 1 + a_1$

$\Rightarrow \qquad 2a_1 = 0$

$\Rightarrow \qquad a_1 = 0$

Hence $a_1 = 0$ is the required condition.

7. Show that the vectors

$$\mathbf{v}_1 = \begin{bmatrix} 1 \\ 1 \\ 2 \\ 4 \end{bmatrix}; \ \mathbf{v}_2 = \begin{bmatrix} 2 \\ -1 \\ -5 \\ 2 \end{bmatrix}; \ \mathbf{v}_3 = \begin{bmatrix} 1 \\ -1 \\ -4 \\ 0 \end{bmatrix} \text{ and } \mathbf{v}_4 = \begin{bmatrix} 2 \\ 1 \\ 1 \\ 6 \end{bmatrix}$$

are linearly dependent in R^4.

Solution: Let $a_1\mathbf{v}_1 + a_2\mathbf{v}_2 + a_3\mathbf{v}_3 + a_4\mathbf{v}_4 = 0$, when $a_i \in R$

$$\Rightarrow \quad a_1\begin{bmatrix} 1 \\ 1 \\ 2 \\ 4 \end{bmatrix} + a_2\begin{bmatrix} 2 \\ -1 \\ -5 \\ 2 \end{bmatrix} + a_3\begin{bmatrix} 1 \\ -1 \\ -4 \\ 0 \end{bmatrix} + a_4\begin{bmatrix} 2 \\ 1 \\ 1 \\ 6 \end{bmatrix} = \begin{bmatrix} 0 \\ 0 \\ 0 \\ 0 \end{bmatrix}$$

$$\Rightarrow \quad \left. \begin{aligned} a_1 + 2a_2 + a_3 + 2a_4 &= 0 \\ a_1 - a_2 - a_3 + a_4 &= 0 \\ 2a_1 - 5a_2 - 4a_3 + a_4 &= 0 \\ 4a_1 + 2a_2 + 6a_4 &= 0 \end{aligned} \right\}$$

Upon solving, we get $a_1 = 0; \ a_2 = -3; \ a_3 = 4; \ a_4 = 1$

Hence the given set of vectors is linearly dependent.

8. If F is a field of real numbers, prove that the vectors

$\begin{bmatrix} a_1 \\ a_2 \end{bmatrix}$ and $\begin{bmatrix} b_1 \\ b_2 \end{bmatrix}$ in $V_2(F)$ are linearly dependent iff $a_1 b_2 - a_2 b_1 = 0$.

Solution: Let $x, y \in F$, then

$$x \begin{bmatrix} a_1 \\ a_2 \end{bmatrix} + y \begin{bmatrix} b_1 \\ b_2 \end{bmatrix} = \begin{bmatrix} 0 \\ 0 \end{bmatrix}$$

$$\Rightarrow \begin{bmatrix} a_1 x + b_1 y = 0 \\ a_2 x + b_2 y = 0 \end{bmatrix} = \begin{bmatrix} 0 \\ 0 \end{bmatrix}$$

$$\Rightarrow \left. \begin{array}{l} a_1 x + b_1 y = 0 \\ a_2 x + b_2 y = 0 \end{array} \right\}$$

The necessary and sufficient condition for these equations to possess a non-zero solution is that

$$\begin{vmatrix} a_1 & b_1 \\ a_2 & b_2 \end{vmatrix} = 0$$

$$\Rightarrow \quad a_1 b_2 - a_2 b_1 = 0$$

Hence the given system is linearly dependent
iff $a_1 b_2 - a_2 b_1 = 0$.

9. If $\mathbf{v}_1$ and $\mathbf{v}_2$ are vectors of $V(F)$, and $a, b \in F$, show that the set $\{\mathbf{v}_1, \mathbf{v}_2, a\mathbf{v}_1 + b\mathbf{v}_2\}$ is linearly dependent.

Solution: Let $(-a)\mathbf{v}_1 + (-b)\mathbf{v}_2 + 1(a\mathbf{v}_1 + b\mathbf{v}_2)$

$= (-a + a)\mathbf{v}_1 + (-b + b)\mathbf{v}_2$ whatever may be the scalars $-a$ and $-b$ since

$= 0\mathbf{v}_1 + 0\mathbf{v}_2 = \mathbf{0};$ (zero vector)

$1 \neq 0$ therefore, the given set of vectors is linearly dependent.

10. Determine whether the polynomials $\mathbf{u}$ and $\mathbf{v}$ are linearly dependent, where

(i) $\mathbf{u} = 2 - 5t + 6t^2 - t^3$ (ii) $\mathbf{u} = 1 - 3t + 2t^2 - 3t^3$

$\quad\;\; \mathbf{v} = 3 + 2t - 4t^2 + 5t^3$ $\quad\;\; \mathbf{v} = -3 + 9t - 6t^2 + 9t^3$

Solution:

(i) They are not dependent, since neither is a multiple of the other.

(ii) Yes because $\mathbf{v} = -3\mathbf{u}$.

11. Show that the vectors $(1, -2, 1)$, $(2, 1, -1)$, $(7, -4, 1)$ are linearly dependent.

Solution: Method: (1)

$$\left\{\begin{array}{l} \text{Let} \quad x(1,-2,1) + y(2,1,-1) + z(7,-41) = (0,0,0) \\ \Rightarrow \quad (x_1 - 2x, x) + (2y, y, -y) + (7z, -4z, z) = (0,0,0) \\ \Rightarrow \quad (x + 2y + 7z, -2x + y - 4z, x - y + z) = (0,0,0) \end{array}\right\}$$

Where this $\Rightarrow \left.\begin{array}{l} x + 2y + 7z = 0 \\ -2x + y - 4z = 0 \\ x - y + z = 0 \end{array}\right\} \Rightarrow \left.\begin{array}{l} x + 2y + 7z = 0 \\ 5y + 10z = 0 \\ -3y - 6z = 0 \end{array}\right\} \Rightarrow \begin{array}{l} x + 2y + 7z = 0 \\ y + 2z = 0 \end{array}$

The above system has a non-zero solution.

Method: (2)

We form the matrix:

$$\begin{bmatrix} 1 & -2 & 1 \\ 2 & 1 & -1 \\ 7 & -4 & 1 \end{bmatrix} \text{ to } \begin{bmatrix} 1 & -2 & 1 \\ 0 & 5 & -3 \\ 0 & 10 & -6 \end{bmatrix},$$

and, to $\begin{bmatrix} 1 & -2 & 1 \\ 0 & 5 & -3 \\ 0 & 0 & 0 \end{bmatrix}$

$\Rightarrow$ The vectors are linearly dependent as the echelon matrix has a zero row.

12. Let V be the vector space of polynomials of degree 3 over R.

Find whether
$$\mathbf{u} = t^3 - 3t^2 + 5t + 1$$
$$\mathbf{v} = t^3 - t^2 + 8t + 2,$$
$$\mathbf{w} = 2t^3 + 4t^2 + 9t + 5$$
are linearly dependent.

Solution: Consider the linear combination of $\mathbf{u}$, $\mathbf{v}$ and $\mathbf{w}$ using unknown scalars x, y and z. i.e., we set, $x\mathbf{u} + y\mathbf{v} + z\mathbf{w} = 0$

$\Rightarrow \quad x(t^3 - 3t^2 + 5t + 1) + y(t^3 - t^2 + 8t + 1) + z(2t^3 - 4t^2 + 9t + 5) = 0$

$\Rightarrow \quad xt^3 - 3xt^3 + 5xt + x + yt^3 - yt^2 + 8yt + 2y + 2zt^3 - 4zt^2 - 4zt^2 + 9zt + 5z = 0$

$\Rightarrow \quad (x + y + 2z)t^3 + (-3x - y - 4z)t^2 + (5x + 8y + 9z)t + (x + 2y + 5z) = 0$

$$x + y + 2z = 0$$

$\Rightarrow$ $\left. \begin{array}{l} x + y + 2z = 0 \\ -3x - y - 4z = 0 \\ 5x + 8y + 9z = 0 \\ x + 2y + 5z = 0 \end{array} \right\}$ {on equating the coefficients of t^3, t^2, t and 1}

The coefficients of the powers of t must each be zero. On solving the above system, we obtain: $x = 0$, $y = 0$, $z = 0$.

Hence **u**, **v** and **w** are independent.

13. Find whether the polynomials **u**, **v**, **w** are dependent where

$$\mathbf{u} = t^3 + 4t^2 - 2t + 3,$$
$$\mathbf{v} = t^3 + 6t^2 - t + 4,$$
$$\mathbf{w} = 3t^3 + 8t^2 - 8t + 7$$

Solution: Consider the set $x\mathbf{u} + y\mathbf{v} + z\mathbf{w} = 0$ (x, y, z are unknown scalars)

$$x(t^3 + 4t^2 - 2t + 3) + y(t^3 + 6t^2 - t + 4) + z(3t^3 + 8t^2 - 8t + 7) = 0$$

$\Rightarrow$ $xt^3 + 4xt^2 - 2xt + 3x + yt^3 + 6yt^2 - yt + 4y + 3zt^3 + 8zt^2 - 8zt + 7z = 0$

or $(x + y + 3z)t^3 + (4x + 6y + 8z)t^2 + (-2x - y - 8z)t + (3x + 4y + 7z) = 0$

Equating to zero, the coefficients of various powers of 't', we get the system.

$$x + y + 3z = 0$$
$$4x + 6y + 8z = 0$$
$$-2x - y - 8z = 0$$
$$3x + 4y + 7z = 0$$

or $\quad x + y + 3z = 0$
$\quad\quad 2y - 4z = 0$
$\quad\quad y - 2z = 0$

or $\left\{ \begin{array}{l} x + y + 3z = 0 \\ y - 2z = 0 \end{array} \right\}$

This system has a free variable, and hence a non-zero solution.

$\therefore x\mathbf{u} + y\mathbf{v} + z\mathbf{w} = 0$ does not imply that $x = 0$, $y = 0$, $z = 0$; hence the polynomials are linearly independent.

EXERCISES

1. Which of the following sets of vectors are linearly dependent (L.D.) or linearly independent (L.I.)?

   (a) $\{(2, -1, 4), \quad (3, 6, 2), \quad (2, 10, -4)\}$

   (b) $\{(1, 1, 1), \quad (2, 2, 0), \quad (3, 0, 0)\}$

   (c) $\{(1, 3, 3), \quad (0, 1, 4), \quad (5, 6, 3), \quad (7, 2, -1)\}$

   (d) $(1, 2, 1, 2), (3, 2, 3, 2), (-1, -3\ 0, 4), (0, 4, -1, -3)\}$

   (e) $\{(1, 0, 0, 0), \quad (1, 1, 0, 0), (1, 1, 1, 1), (0, 0, 1, 1)\}$.

   {**Ans:** (a) L.D., (b) L.I., (c) L.D., (d) L.I. (e) L.I.}

2. Prove that $(1, 3, 2), (1, -7, -8), (2, 1, -1)$ are linearly dependent in R^3.

3. Determine whether $(1, -3, 7), (2, 0, -6), (3, -1, -1)$ $(2, 4, -5)$ are L. D.

   {**Ans:** yes}

4. Determine whether $(1, 2, -3), (1, -3, 2), (2, -1, 5)$ are L. D.

   (**Ans:** No. as the echelon matrices has no zero rows)

5. Determine whether $(2, -3, 7), (0, 0, 0), (3, -1, -4)$ are L. D.

   {**Ans:** yes, since $= (0, 0, 0)$ is one of the vectors}

6. Determine whether matrices A, B, C are dependent where

$$A = \begin{bmatrix} 1 & 2 \\ 3 & 1 \end{bmatrix}; \quad B = \begin{bmatrix} 3 & -1 \\ 2 & 2 \end{bmatrix}; \quad C = \begin{bmatrix} 1 & -5 \\ -4 & 0 \end{bmatrix} \qquad \text{{Ans. L.D.}}$$

EXAMPLES (on linear combination)

14. Find x and y if $x (1, 1) + y (2, -1) = (1, 4)$

   Solution:

   $$x (1, 1) + y (2, -1) = (x, x) + (2y, -y) = (x + 2y, x - y) = (1, 4)$$

   $\Rightarrow \quad x + 2y = 1; \ x - y = 4$

   on solving, we get $x = 3; \ y = -1$

15. If $\mathbf{v} = (1, 4)$ find a linear combination of the vectors $\mathbf{u}_1 = (1, 1)$ and $\mathbf{u}_2 = (2, -1)$.

Solution: We know that a vector $\mathbf{v}$ is a linear combination of vectors $\mathbf{u}_1, \mathbf{u}_2, ...\mathbf{u}_m$ if $\exists$ a set of scalars $a_1, a_2,....,a_m$ such that

$$\mathbf{v} = a_1\mathbf{u}_1 + a_2\mathbf{u}_2 + ... + a_m\mathbf{u}_m = \sum_{i=1}^{m} a_i\mathbf{u}_i \qquad [1]$$

Now, we want to express $\mathbf{v}$ in the form:

$$\mathbf{v} = x\mathbf{u}_1 + y\mathbf{u}_2 \qquad [2]$$

where x and y are as yet unknowns.

Hence, we require $(1, 4) = x(1, 1) + y(2, -1)$

$$\Rightarrow \quad x(1,1) + y(2,-1) = (x,x) + (2y,-y)$$

$$= (x+2y, x-y)$$

$$= (1,4)$$

This yields $\left. \begin{matrix} x+2y=1 \\ x-y=4 \end{matrix} \right\}$

on solving for x and y, we get $(x = 3 \; ; \; y = -1)$

Substituting into [2], we have

$$\boxed{\mathbf{v} = 3u_1 - u_2}$$

16. If $\mathbf{v} = (1, -2, 5)$ then find a linear combination of the vectors $\mathbf{u}_1 = (1, 1, 1)$; $\mathbf{u}_2 = (1, 2, 3)$ and $\mathbf{u}_3 = (2, -1, 1)$

Solution: Let $\mathbf{v} = x\mathbf{u}_1 + y\mathbf{u}_2 + z\mathbf{u}_3$, (where x, y, z are yet unknowns)

Thus, we have $\begin{bmatrix} 1 \\ -2 \\ 5 \end{bmatrix} = x\begin{bmatrix} 1 \\ 1 \\ 1 \end{bmatrix} + y\begin{bmatrix} 1 \\ 2 \\ 3 \end{bmatrix} + z\begin{bmatrix} 2 \\ -1 \\ 1 \end{bmatrix}$

$$= \begin{bmatrix} x+y+2z \\ x+2y-z \\ x+3y+z \end{bmatrix}$$

Setting corresponding components equal to each other we obtain

$$\left. \begin{matrix} x+y+2z = 1 \rightarrow (1) \\ x+2y-z = -2 \rightarrow (2) \\ x+3y+z = 5 \rightarrow (3) \end{matrix} \right\} \qquad \left. \begin{matrix} x+y+2z = 1 \rightarrow (1) \\ y-3z = -3; \quad [(2)-(1)] \\ 2y-z = 4; \quad [(3)-(1)] \end{matrix} \right\}$$

$$x + y + 2z = 1 \rightarrow (1)$$

$$\Rightarrow \quad y - 3z = -3$$

$$5z = 10$$

$\because$ from $y - 3z = -3$; we get $y = -3 + 3z$;

and from $2y - z = 4$ we get $2(-3 + 3z) - z = 4$

$$\Rightarrow -6 + 6z - z = 4$$

$$\Rightarrow 5z = 10$$

which gives the unique solutions :

$$(x = -6; \ y = 3; \ z = 2)$$

Hence $\boxed{\mathbf{v} = -6\mathbf{u}_1 + 3\mathbf{u}_2 + 2\mathbf{u}_3.}$

17. Let $\mathbf{a}_1 = \begin{bmatrix} 1 \\ -2 \\ -5 \end{bmatrix}$, $\mathbf{a}_2 = \begin{bmatrix} 2 \\ 5 \\ 6 \end{bmatrix}$; and $\mathbf{b} = \begin{bmatrix} 7 \\ 4 \\ -3 \end{bmatrix}$

Determine whether $\mathbf{b}$ can be generated (or written) as a linear combination of $\mathbf{a}_1$ and $\mathbf{a}_2$. [VTU MED. ELEN. May/June, 2004]

***Solution*:** We want to express $\mathbf{b}$ in the form $\mathbf{b} = x\mathbf{a}_1 + y\mathbf{a}_2$, with x, y are yet unknowns

Thus we have,

$$\begin{bmatrix} 7 \\ 4 \\ -3 \end{bmatrix} = x \begin{bmatrix} 1 \\ -2 \\ -5 \end{bmatrix} + y \begin{bmatrix} 2 \\ 5 \\ 6 \end{bmatrix} = \begin{bmatrix} x + 2y \\ -2x + 5y \\ -5x + 6y \end{bmatrix}$$

setting corresponding components equal to each other, we obtain:

$$\begin{aligned} x + 2y &= 7 &\rightarrow (1) \\ -2x + 5y &= 4 &\rightarrow (2) \\ -5x + 6y &= -3 &\rightarrow (3) \end{aligned} \Rightarrow$$

$$\Rightarrow \quad \therefore \text{ from (2);}$$

$$x + 2y = 7 \rightarrow (1) \ (\Rightarrow x = 7 - 2y)$$

$$-2(7 - 2y) + 5y = 4$$

$$\Rightarrow \quad -14 + 4y + 5y = 4$$

$$\Rightarrow 9y = 18; \Rightarrow \quad (y = 2 \text{ and } x = 3).$$

Therefore, we have, a unique solution:

$$(x = 3; \ y = 2)$$

Thus, $\boxed{\mathbf{b} = 3\mathbf{a}_1 + 2\mathbf{a}_2}$

18. Let $\mathbf{a_1} = \begin{bmatrix} 1 \\ 2 \\ -3 \end{bmatrix}$; $\mathbf{a_2} = \begin{bmatrix} 2 \\ -1 \\ -4 \end{bmatrix}$; $\mathbf{a_3} = \begin{bmatrix} 1 \\ 7 \\ -5 \end{bmatrix}$ and $\mathbf{b} = \begin{bmatrix} 2 \\ 3 \\ -5 \end{bmatrix}$

Determine whether b can be generated (or written) as a linear combination of $\mathbf{a_1}$, $\mathbf{a_2}$ and $\mathbf{a_3}$.

Solution: We want to express **b** in the form:

$$\mathbf{b} = \begin{bmatrix} 2 \\ 3 \\ -3 \end{bmatrix} = x \begin{bmatrix} 1 \\ 2 \\ -3 \end{bmatrix} + y \begin{bmatrix} 2 \\ -1 \\ -4 \end{bmatrix} + z \begin{bmatrix} 1 \\ 7 \\ -5 \end{bmatrix} = \begin{bmatrix} x+2y+z \\ 2x-y+7z \\ -3x-4y-5z \end{bmatrix}$$

where x, y, and z are as yet unknowns.

Setting corresponding components equal to each other or obtain:

$$\left. \begin{array}{l} x+2y+z = 2 \quad \rightarrow (1) \\ 2x-y+7z = 3 \quad \rightarrow (2) \\ -3x-4y-5z = - \quad \rightarrow (3) \end{array} \right\} \Rightarrow \left. \begin{array}{l} x+2y+z = 2 \\ -5y+5z = -1 \\ 2y-2z = 1 \end{array} \right\} \Rightarrow \begin{array}{l} x+2y+z = 2 \\ -5y+5z = -1 \\ 0 = 3 \end{array}$$

$0 = 3$ is not possible, which indicates that the system has no solution. This implies that **b** cannot be written as a linear combination of the vectors $\mathbf{a_1}$, $\mathbf{a_2}$ and $\mathbf{a_3}$.

19. If $a_1 = (3,2,1)$, $a_2 = (2,1,0)$ and $a_3 = (1,0,0)$ be three vectors in R^3, then express the vector $b = (3,5,2) \in R^3$ as a linear combination of $\mathbf{a_1}$, $\mathbf{a_2}$, $\mathbf{a_3}$.

Solution: If $\mathbf{b} = (3, 5, 2) = x\mathbf{a_1} + y\mathbf{a_2} + z\mathbf{a_3}$, then, we have $(3, 5, 2) = (3, 2, 1) x + y (2, 1, 0) + z(1, 0, 0)$, where x, y, z are as yet unknowns.

$\Rightarrow (3, 5, 2) = (3x, 2x, x) + (2y, y, 0) + (z, 0, 0)$

$\quad = (3x + 2y + z, 2x + y + 0, x + 0 + 0)$

$\Rightarrow \quad (3, 5, 2) = (3x + 2y + z, 2x + y, x)$

$\Rightarrow \quad 3x + 2y + z = 3; \ 2x + y = 5, x = 2$

$\Rightarrow \quad x = 2, y = 1, z = -5,$

On solving these 3 equations

$\boxed{\therefore \ (3,5,2) = x\mathbf{a_1} + y\mathbf{a_2} + z\mathbf{a_3} = 2\mathbf{a_1} + \mathbf{a_2} - 5\mathbf{a_3}.}$

20. Let $\mathbf{a_1} = \begin{bmatrix} 1 \\ -3 \\ 2 \end{bmatrix}$; $\mathbf{a_2} = \begin{bmatrix} 2 \\ -4 \\ -1 \end{bmatrix}$; $\mathbf{a_3} = \begin{bmatrix} 1 \\ -5 \\ -7 \end{bmatrix}$ and $\mathbf{b} = \begin{bmatrix} 2 \\ -5 \\ 3 \end{bmatrix}$

Determine whether **b** can be generated (or written) as a linear combination of $\mathbf{a}_1$, $\mathbf{a}_2$ and $\mathbf{a}_3$.

Solution: Let $\mathbf{b} = \mathbf{a}_1 x + \mathbf{a}_2 y + \mathbf{a}_3 z$, where $x, y, z \in R$ are scalars to be determined. Then we have

$$\begin{bmatrix} 2 \\ -5 \\ 3 \end{bmatrix} = x \begin{bmatrix} 1 \\ -3 \\ 2 \end{bmatrix} + y \begin{bmatrix} 2 \\ -4 \\ -1 \end{bmatrix} + z \begin{bmatrix} 1 \\ -5 \\ -7 \end{bmatrix} = \begin{bmatrix} x+2y+z \\ -3x-4y-5z \\ 2x-y-7z \end{bmatrix}$$

$$\left. \begin{cases} x+2y+z = 2 ...(1) \\ -3x-4y-5z = -5 ...(2) \\ 2x-y-7z = 3 ...(3) \end{cases} \right\} \Rightarrow x = \left(\frac{37}{28}\right); \quad y = \left(\frac{11}{28}\right); \quad z = \left(\frac{-3}{28}\right)$$

On solving these equations

$$\therefore \qquad \mathbf{b} = \left(\frac{37}{28}\right)\mathbf{a}_1 + \left(\frac{11}{28}\right)\mathbf{a}_2 + \left(-\frac{3}{28}\right)\mathbf{a}_3$$

$\Rightarrow$ '**b**' is a linear combination of vectors $\mathbf{a}_1$, $\mathbf{a}_2$, $\mathbf{a}_3$.

21. Let $\mathbf{e}_1 = \begin{bmatrix} 3 \\ 2 \\ 1 \end{bmatrix}$; $\mathbf{e}_2 = \begin{bmatrix} 1 \\ 0 \\ 0 \end{bmatrix}$; $\mathbf{e}_3 = \begin{bmatrix} 2 \\ 0 \\ 1 \end{bmatrix}$

Show that the set $\{\mathbf{e}_1, \mathbf{e}_2, \mathbf{e}_3\}$ generates R^3.

Solution: Let $\begin{bmatrix} x \\ y \\ z \end{bmatrix}$ be any arbitrary column vector in R^3. We are to show that it is a linear combination of

$\mathbf{e}_1, \mathbf{e}_2, \mathbf{e}_3$. Let $\begin{bmatrix} x \\ y \\ z \end{bmatrix} = a\mathbf{e}_1 + b\mathbf{e}_2 + c\mathbf{e}_3$, where a, b, c are scalars to be determined.

Thus, we have

$$\begin{bmatrix} x \\ y \\ z \end{bmatrix} = \begin{bmatrix} 3a \\ 2a \\ a \end{bmatrix} + \begin{bmatrix} b \\ 0 \\ 0 \end{bmatrix} + \begin{bmatrix} 2c \\ 0 \\ c \end{bmatrix} = \begin{bmatrix} 3a+b+2c \\ 2a+0+0 \\ a+0+c \end{bmatrix} = \begin{bmatrix} 3a+b+2c \\ 2a \\ a+c \end{bmatrix}$$

$$\Rightarrow \quad \begin{rcases} x = 3a + b + 2c; \\ y = 2a; \\ z = a + c; \end{rcases} \quad \begin{aligned} &\Rightarrow a = \frac{1}{2}y; \quad b = x - \frac{1}{2}y - 2z; \\ & c = z - \frac{1}{2}y \end{aligned}$$

Hence, any vector in R^3 can be expressed as linear combination of the given vectors e_1, e_2, e_3.

22. Let $a_1 = \begin{bmatrix} 3 \\ 2 \\ 1 \end{bmatrix};$ $a_2 = \begin{bmatrix} 2 \\ 1 \\ 0 \end{bmatrix}$ and $b = \begin{bmatrix} m \\ 3 \\ 1 \end{bmatrix}.$

'b' is a linear combination of a_1 and a_2. Find 'm'

Solution: Let $b = a_1 x + a_2 y;$ where x and y are scalars to be determined. Then, we have

$$\begin{bmatrix} m \\ 3 \\ 1 \end{bmatrix} = \begin{bmatrix} 3 \\ 2 \\ 1 \end{bmatrix} x + \begin{bmatrix} 2 \\ 1 \\ 0 \end{bmatrix} y = \begin{bmatrix} 3x + 2y \\ 2x + y \\ x \end{bmatrix}$$

$$\Rightarrow \quad \begin{rcases} m = 3x + 2y \\ 3 = 2x + y \\ x = 1 \end{rcases}$$

$$\Rightarrow \quad x = 1; \quad y = 1; \quad m = 3x + 2y$$

$$\Rightarrow \quad m = 3(1) + 2(1) = 5.$$

$$\Rightarrow \quad \boxed{m = 5}$$

EXAMPLES (on Linear Independency of Vectors)

23. Let $v_1 = \begin{bmatrix} 1 \\ 2 \\ 3 \end{bmatrix};$ $v_2 = \begin{bmatrix} 4 \\ 5 \\ 6 \end{bmatrix}$ and $v_3 = \begin{bmatrix} 2 \\ 1 \\ 0 \end{bmatrix}$

Determine if the set $\{v_1, v_2, v_3\}$ is linearly independent.

[VTU, ELEC & ELEN, May/June, 2004]

Solution: Let a, b, c. be scalars, i.e., real numbers such that $a v_1 + b v_2 + c v_3 = 0$

i.e., $\quad a \begin{bmatrix} 1 \\ 2 \\ 3 \end{bmatrix} + b \begin{bmatrix} 4 \\ 5 \\ 6 \end{bmatrix} + c \begin{bmatrix} 2 \\ 1 \\ 0 \end{bmatrix} = \begin{bmatrix} 0 \\ 0 \\ 0 \end{bmatrix}$

$\Rightarrow \quad \begin{bmatrix} a + 4b + 2c \\ 2a + 5b + c \\ 3a + 6b \end{bmatrix} = \begin{bmatrix} 0 \\ 0 \\ 0 \end{bmatrix}$

$\quad\quad a + 4b + 2c = 0 \quad\quad\quad\quad\quad\quad\quad\quad\quad\quad [1]$

$\Rightarrow \quad 2a + 5b + c = 0 \quad\quad\quad\quad\quad\quad\quad\quad\quad [2]$

$\quad\quad 3a + 6b = 0 \quad\quad\quad\quad\quad\quad\quad\quad\quad\quad\quad [3]$

These equations will have a non-zero solution i.e., a solution in which a, b, c are not all zero if the rank of the coefficient matrix is less than 3, i.e., the number of unknowns a, b, c. If the rank is 3, then zero solution: $a = 0$, $b = 0$, $c = 0$, will be the only solution.

Consider the coefficient matrix:

$$\mathbf{A} = \begin{bmatrix} 1 & 4 & 2 \\ 2 & 5 & 1 \\ 3 & 6 & 0 \end{bmatrix}$$

Reducing **A** to canonical form as follows:

$$\xrightarrow[\substack{R_3 \to R_3 - 3R_1}]{\text{Applying: } R_2 \to R_2 - 2R_1} \begin{bmatrix} 1 & 4 & 2 \\ 0 & -3 & 0 \\ 0 & -6 & -6 \end{bmatrix} \xrightarrow{R_3 \to R_3 - 2R_2} \begin{bmatrix} 1 & 4 & 2 \\ 0 & -3 & 0 \\ 0 & 0 & -6 \end{bmatrix}$$

$$\xrightarrow{R_3 \to \frac{-1}{6} R_3} \begin{bmatrix} 1 & 4 & 2 \\ 0 & -3 & 0 \\ 0 & 0 & 1 \end{bmatrix} \xrightarrow{R_2 \to -\frac{1}{3} R_2} \begin{bmatrix} 1 & 4 & 2 \\ 0 & 1 & 0 \\ 0 & 0 & 1 \end{bmatrix}$$

Clearly $\rho(\mathbf{A}) = 3$; $\therefore \rho(\mathbf{A}) = r$;

$\Rightarrow$ vectors are linearly independent.

(**Note:** $r = 3$; $n = 3$)

24. Let $\mathbf{v}_1 = \begin{bmatrix} 6 \\ 2 \\ -1 \\ 2 \end{bmatrix}$; $\mathbf{v}_2 = \begin{bmatrix} -1 \\ 3 \\ 5 \\ 1 \end{bmatrix}$ and $\mathbf{v}_3 = \begin{bmatrix} -3 \\ 7 \\ 8 \\ 3 \end{bmatrix}$

Determine if the set $\{\mathbf{v}_1, \mathbf{v}_2, \mathbf{v}_3\}$ is linearly independent in R^4.

Solution: Let a, b, c, be the real numbers(scalars) such that

$$a\mathbf{v}_1 + b\mathbf{v}_2 + c\mathbf{v}_3 = 0 \qquad [1]$$

i.e., $a\begin{bmatrix} 6 \\ 2 \\ -1 \\ 2 \end{bmatrix} + b\begin{bmatrix} -1 \\ 3 \\ 5 \\ 1 \end{bmatrix} + c\begin{bmatrix} -3 \\ 7 \\ 8 \\ 3 \end{bmatrix} = \begin{bmatrix} 0 \\ 0 \\ 0 \\ 0 \end{bmatrix}$

$\Rightarrow \quad \begin{bmatrix} 6a - b - 3c \\ 2a + 3b + 7c \\ -a + 5b + 8c \\ 2a + b + 3c \end{bmatrix} = \begin{bmatrix} 0 \\ 0 \\ 0 \\ 0 \end{bmatrix}$

$\Rightarrow \quad \begin{cases} 6a - b - 3c = 0 & [1] \\ 2a + 3b + 7c = 0 & [2] \\ -a + 5b + 8c = 0 & [3] \\ 2a + b + 3c = 0 & [4] \end{cases}$

i.e., $\mathbf{A} = \begin{bmatrix} 6 & -1 & -3 \\ 2 & 3 & 7 \\ -1 & 5 & 8 \\ 2 & 1 & 3 \end{bmatrix}$

Reduce **A** to canonical form:

Applying $\xrightarrow{R_1 \rightarrow R_1 + 5R_3}$ $\begin{bmatrix} 1 & 14 & 37 \\ 2 & 3 & 7 \\ -1 & 5 & 8 \\ 2 & 1 & 3 \end{bmatrix}$

Applying $\dfrac{R_2 \to R_2 - 2R_1, R_5 \to R_3 + R_1}{R_4 \to R_4 - 2R_1}$
$$\begin{bmatrix} 1 & 14 & 37 \\ 0 & -25 & -67 \\ 0 & 19 & 45 \\ 0 & -27 & -74 \end{bmatrix}$$

Applying $\dfrac{R_2 \to R_2 - R_4}{}$
$$\begin{bmatrix} 1 & 14 & 37 \\ 0 & 2 & 4 \\ 0 & 19 & 45 \\ 0 & -27 & -74 \end{bmatrix}$$

25. Show that the set of vectors

$\mathbf{v}_1 = (0, 1, -2)$, $\mathbf{v}_2 = (1, -1, 1)$, $\mathbf{v}_3 = (1, 2, 1)$ are linearly independent.

Solution: Let $a_1\ (0,\ 1,\ -2) + a_2\ (1,\ -1,\ 1) + a_3\ (1,\ 2,\ 1) = 0$

where a_i's are unknown scalars.

Then, $(0, a_1, -2a_1) + (a_2, -a_2, a_2) + (a_3, 2a_3, a_3) = 0$

$\Rightarrow \quad (a_2 + a_3,\ a_1 - a_2 + 2a_3,\ -2a_1 + a_2 + a_3) = 0 = (0, 0, 0)$

$\Rightarrow \quad a_2 + a_3 = 0;\ a_1 - a_2 + 2a_3 = 0, -2a_1 + a_2 + a_3 = 0$

$\Rightarrow \quad a_1 = 0;\ a_2 = 0;\ a_3 = 0,$ on solving these equations.

$\Rightarrow$ All the coefficients a_1, a_2, a_3 are zero. Hence, the given set of vectors are linearly independent.

26. Determine whether the following system of vectors is linearly dependent or not.

$$\mathbf{v}_1 = \begin{bmatrix} 1 & 1 \\ 1 & 1 \end{bmatrix};\ \mathbf{v}_2 = \begin{bmatrix} 1 & 0 \\ 0 & 1 \end{bmatrix};\ \mathbf{v}_3 = \begin{bmatrix} 1 & 1 \\ 0 & 0 \end{bmatrix}$$

Solution: Let $a_1 \begin{bmatrix} 1 & 1 \\ 1 & 1 \end{bmatrix} + a_2 \begin{bmatrix} 1 & 0 \\ 0 & 1 \end{bmatrix} + a_3 \begin{bmatrix} 1 & 1 \\ 0 & 0 \end{bmatrix} = 0 = \begin{bmatrix} 0 & 0 \\ 0 & 0 \end{bmatrix}$

where a_i's are unknown scalars.

Then, $\begin{bmatrix} a_1 & a_1 \\ a_1 & a_1 \end{bmatrix} + \begin{bmatrix} a_2 & 0 \\ 0 & a_2 \end{bmatrix} + \begin{bmatrix} a_3 & a_3 \\ 0 & 0 \end{bmatrix} = \begin{bmatrix} 0 & 0 \\ 0 & 0 \end{bmatrix}$

$\Rightarrow \quad \begin{bmatrix} a_1 + a_2 + a_3 & a_1 + 0 + a_3 \\ a_1 + 0 + 0 & a_1 + a_2 + 0 \end{bmatrix} = \begin{bmatrix} 0 & 0 \\ 0 & 0 \end{bmatrix}$

$\Rightarrow \quad a_1 + a_2 + a_3 = 0; \quad a_1 + a_3 = 0; \quad a_1 + a_2 = 0$

$\Rightarrow \quad a_1 = 0; \quad a_2 = 0; \quad a_3 = 0.$

$\Rightarrow \quad$ all the coefficients a_1, a_2, a_3 are zero

Hence from definition the given set of vectors are linearly independent.

27. Verify that (a) row vectors (b) column vectors comprising the matrix:

$$\begin{bmatrix} 2 & 7 & 5 \\ 3 & -6 & 2 \\ 1 & 17 & 7 \end{bmatrix}$$

are linearly independent.

Solution:

(a) The row vectors in the matrix are

$$\mathbf{u}_1 = \begin{bmatrix} 2 & 7 & 5 \end{bmatrix}; \quad \mathbf{u}_2 = \begin{bmatrix} 3 & -6 & 2 \end{bmatrix} \text{ and } \mathbf{u}_3 = \begin{bmatrix} 1 & 17 & 7 \end{bmatrix}.$$

Let a, b, c be scalars in R such that $a\mathbf{u}_1 + b\mathbf{u}_2 + c\mathbf{u}_3 = \mathbf{0}$

$\Rightarrow \quad a\begin{bmatrix} 2 & 7 & 5 \end{bmatrix} + b\begin{bmatrix} 3 & -6 & 2 \end{bmatrix} + c\begin{bmatrix} 1 & 17 & 7 \end{bmatrix} = 0$

$\Rightarrow \quad \begin{bmatrix} 2a+3b+c & 7a-6b+17c & 5a+2b+7c \end{bmatrix} = \begin{bmatrix} 0 & 0 & 0 \end{bmatrix};$ \hfill [1]

$\Rightarrow \quad 2a+3b+c = 0; \quad 7a-6b+17c = 0; \quad 5a+2b+7c = 0$

$\Rightarrow \quad a = b = c = 0;$ (on solving these equations)

Hence the row vectors are linearly independent.

(b) The column vectors are

$$\begin{bmatrix} 2 \\ 3 \\ 1 \end{bmatrix}; \quad \begin{bmatrix} 7 \\ 6 \\ 17 \end{bmatrix} \text{ and } \begin{bmatrix} 5 \\ 2 \\ 7 \end{bmatrix}.$$

Let a, b, c be the scalars in R such that

$$a\begin{bmatrix} 2 \\ 3 \\ 1 \end{bmatrix} + b\begin{bmatrix} 7 \\ -6 \\ 17 \end{bmatrix} + c\begin{bmatrix} 5 \\ 2 \\ 7 \end{bmatrix} = \begin{bmatrix} 0 \\ 0 \\ 0 \end{bmatrix}$$

$$\Rightarrow \quad \begin{bmatrix} 2a+7b+5c = 0 \\ 3a-6b+2c \\ a+17b+7c \end{bmatrix} = \begin{bmatrix} 0 \\ 0 \\ 0 \end{bmatrix}$$

$$2a + 7b + 5c = 0 \qquad [1]$$

$$\Rightarrow \quad 3a - 6b + 2c = 0 \qquad [2]$$

$$a + 17b + 7c = 0 \qquad [3]$$

On solving these, we obtain;

$$a = b = c = 0 \qquad [4]$$

$\Rightarrow$ column vectors are linearly independent.

28. Let $A_1 = \begin{bmatrix} 2 & 1 & -1 \\ 3 & -2 & 4 \end{bmatrix}$; $A_2 = \begin{bmatrix} 1 & 1 & -3 \\ -2 & 0 & 5 \end{bmatrix}$

and $A_3 = \begin{bmatrix} 4 & -1 & 2 \\ 1 & -2 & 3 \end{bmatrix}$

Determine whether the set $\{A_1, A_2, A_3\}$ is linearly independent of the vector space $V(R)$ of 2×3 matrices over R.

Solution: Let a, b, c be the scalars in R such that

$$a \begin{bmatrix} 2 & 1 & -1 \\ 3 & -2 & 4 \end{bmatrix} + b \begin{bmatrix} 1 & 1 & -3 \\ -2 & 0 & 5 \end{bmatrix} + c \begin{bmatrix} 4 & -1 & 2 \\ 1 & -2 & 3 \end{bmatrix} = 0$$

$$\Rightarrow \quad \begin{bmatrix} 2a+b+4c & a+b-c & -a-3b+2c \\ 3a-2b+c & -2a-2c & 4a+5b+3c \end{bmatrix} = \begin{bmatrix} 0 & 0 & 0 \\ 0 & 0 & 0 \end{bmatrix}$$

$$\Rightarrow \quad 2a+b+4c = 0; \quad a+b-c = 0; \quad -a-3b+2c = 0$$

$$3a-2b+c = 0; \quad -2a-2c = 0; \quad 4a+5b+3c = 0$$

By second and fifth, we get

$2a + b = 0$, then by first, we get $c = 0$. and so by fifth, we get $a = 0$; $b = 0$. Thus, showing that [1] is true only if $a = b = c = 0$ and so the matrices A_1, A_2, A_3 in $V(R)$ are linearly independent.

29. If x_1, y_2, z_3 are linearly independent vectors space $V(F)$, then prove that

(a) $x + y$, $y + z$, $z + x$

(b) $x + y$, $x - y$, $x - 2y + z$

are also linearly independent.

Solution:

(a) Let a, b, c be scalars such that

$$a(x + y) + b(y + z) + c(z + x) = 0$$

$\Rightarrow \quad (a + c) x + (a + b) y + (b + c) z = 0$ $\qquad$ [1]

But x, y, z are linearly independent, (given)

$\therefore$ [1] $\Rightarrow$ $\quad a + 0b + c = 0$ $\qquad$ [2]

$\quad a + b + 0c = 0$ $\qquad$ [3]

$\quad 0a + b + c = 0$ $\qquad$ [4]

The coefficient matrix **A** of these equations is

$$A = \begin{bmatrix} 1 & 0 & 1 \\ 1 & 1 & 0 \\ 0 & 1 & 1 \end{bmatrix}$$

we have rank $\rho(A) = 3$, i.e., $\rho(A)$

the number of unknowns a, b, c.

$\therefore$ $a = 0$; $b = 0$; $c = 0$ is the only solution of the given equations.

Hence $x + y$, $y + z$, $z + x$ are also linearly independent.

(b) Let a, b, c be scalars such that

$\quad a(x + y) + b(x - y) + c(x - 2y + z) = 0$ $\qquad$ [1]

$\quad (a + b + c) x + (a - b - 2) y + cz = 0$

But x, y, z are linearly independent (given)

$\therefore \quad a + b + c = 0$ $\qquad$ [2]

$\quad a - b - 2c = 0$ $\qquad$ [3]

and $\quad c = 0$ $\qquad$ [4]

$\Rightarrow \quad a = b = c = 0$

which shows that the vectors $x + y$, $x - y$, $x - 2y + z$ are linearly independent.

30. Show that the set $\{1, x, 1 + x + x^2\}$ is a linearly independent set of vectors in the vector space of all polynomials over the real number field.

Solution: Let a, b, c be scalars (real numbers) such that

$\quad a(1) + bx + c(1 + x + x^2) = 0.$

$\Rightarrow \quad (a + c) + (b + c)x + cx^2 = 0$

$\Rightarrow \quad a + c = 0$; $b + c = 0$; $c = 0$

$\Rightarrow \quad c = 0$; $b = 0$; $a = 0$.

$\therefore$ the vectors $1, x, 1 + x + x^2$ are linearly independent over the field of real numbers.

31. Show that the set $\{1, x, x(1-x)\}$ is a linearly independent set of vectors in the space of all polynomials over the real number field.

Solution: Let a, b, c be scalars such that
$$a(1) + b(x) + c\{x(1-x)\} = 0$$
$$\Rightarrow \quad a + ax + cx - cx^2 = 0$$
$$\Rightarrow \quad a + (b+c)x - cx^2 = 0$$
$$\Rightarrow \quad a = 0;\ b+c = 0;\ c = 0.$$
$$\Rightarrow \quad a = 0;\ b = 0;\ c = 0.$$
Hence the set $\{1, x, x(1-x)\}$ is linearly independent.

32. Find whether the vectors $2x^3 + x^2 + x + 1$, $x^3 + 3x^2 + x - 2$, $x^3 + 2x^2 - x + 3$ of $V_4(R)$ are linearly independent or not ?

Solution: Let $v_1 = 2x^3 + x^2 + x + 1$;
$$v_2 = x^3 + 3x^2 + x - 2;$$
$$v_3 = x^3 + 2x^2 - x + 3$$
and let $a_1, a_2, a_3 \in R$

Then $a_1 v_1 + a_2 v_2 + a_3 v_3 = 0$; (Zero polynomial)
$$\Rightarrow \quad a_1(2x^3 + x^2 + x + 1) + a_2(x^3 + 3x^2 + x - 2) + a_3(x^3 + 2x^2 - x + 3) = 0.$$
$$\Rightarrow (2a_1 + a_2 + a_3)x^3 + (a_1 + 3a_2 + 2a_3)x^2 + (a_1 + a_2 - a_3)x + (a_1 - 2a_2 + 2a_3) = 0 = (0,0,0,0)$$
$\therefore$ by the definition of equality of two polynomials, we get
$$2a_1 + a_2 + 2a_3 = 0;\quad a_1 + 3a_2 + 2a_3 = 0;\quad a_1 + a_2 - a_3 = 0.$$ On solving these, we get
$$a_1 = 0 = a_2 = a_3.$$
$\therefore$ the given vectors are linearly independent.

33. Let V be the vector space of polynomials of degree ≤ 3, determine whether the following vectors of V are linearly independent or linearly dependent.
$$u = t^3 - 3t^2 + 5t + 1,$$
$$v = t^3 - t^2 + 8t + 2$$
$$w = 2t^3 - 4t^2 + 9t + 5.$$

***Solution*: Method (I):**

Let $\mathbf{u} = t^3 - 3t^2 + 8t + 1$

$\mathbf{v} = t^3 - t^2 + 8t + 2$

$\mathbf{w} = 2t^3 - 4t^2 + 9t + 5$

and let $a_1, a_2, a_3 \in R$

Then $a_1\mathbf{u} + a_2\mathbf{v} + a_3\mathbf{w} = \mathbf{0}$; (zero polynomial)

$\Rightarrow \quad a_1(t^3 - 3t^2 + 5t + 1) + a_2(t^3 - t^2 + 8t + 2) + a_3(2t^3 - 4t^2 + 9t + 5) = 0$

$\Rightarrow \quad (a_1 + a_2 + 2a_3)t^3 + (-3a_1 - a_2 - 4a_3)t^2 + (5a_1 + 8a_2 + 9a_3)t + (a_1 + 2a_2 + 5a_3)$
$$= (0,0,0,0)$$

By the definition of equality of two polynomials .

we get, $(a_1 + a_2 + 2a_3) = 0$; $(-3a_1 - a_2 - 4a_3) = 0$

$(5a_1 + 8a_2 + 9a_3) = 0$; $(a_1 + 2a_2 + 5a_3) = 0$.

On solving these, we get, $a_1 = 0 = a_2 = a_3$

∴ the given vectors are linearly independent.

Method (II):

Given, $\mathbf{u} = t^3 - 3t^2 + 5t + 1$;

$\mathbf{v} = t^3 - t^2 + 8t + 2$

$\mathbf{w} = 2t^3 - 4t^2 + 9t + 5$

∴ $\mathbf{v} - \mathbf{u} = 2t^2 + 3t + 1$,

$\mathbf{w} - 2\mathbf{u} = 2t^2 - t + 3$,

and $(\mathbf{v} - \mathbf{u}) - (\mathbf{w} - 2\mathbf{u}) = 4t - 2$.

This cannot be reduced any further since the R.H.S is different from zero polynomial, the given vectors are linearly independent.

34. In the vector space V of polynomials of degree ≤ 4, determine the following vectors of V which are linearly independent or linearly dependent.

$\mathbf{v}_1 = 1$;

$\mathbf{v}_2 = 1 + x$;

$\mathbf{v}_3 = (1 + x)^2$;

$\mathbf{v}_4 = (1 + x)^3$;

$\mathbf{v}_5 = (1 + x)^4$;

Solution: Suppose if it is possible that for all values of x,

$$c_0 \mathbf{v}_1 + c_1 \mathbf{v}_2 + c_2 \mathbf{v}_3 + c_3 \mathbf{v}_4 + c_4 \mathbf{v}_5 = \mathbf{0}; \text{ (zero polynomial)}$$

$$\Rightarrow \quad c_0(1) + c_1(1+x) + c_2(1+x)^2 + c_3(1+x)^3 + c_4(1+x)^4 = 0 \qquad [1]$$

where c_0, c_1, c_2, c_3, c_4 are some real numbers. On putting $x = 0$, in [1], we get $c_0 = 0$

$$c_1 + c_2 + c_3 + c_4 = 0$$

Differentiating [1], we get

$$c_1 + 2c_2(1+x)(1) + 3c_3(1+x)^2(1) + 4c_4(1+x)^3 = 0 \qquad [2]$$

Putting $x = 0$ in this we get, $c_1 = 0$

Differentiating [2] again and putting $x = 0$, we get, $c_2 = 0$, Proceeding in this manner, we can show that $c_3 = c_4 = 0$

Hence, the set of functions

$$\{1, 1+x, (1+x)^2, (1+x)^3, (1+x)^4\} = \{\mathbf{v}_1, \mathbf{v}_2, \mathbf{v}_3, \mathbf{v}_4, \mathbf{v}_5\}$$

is linearly independent.

35. Show that the set of functions $\{1, t, t^2, \ldots, t^n\}$ is linearly independent over the field of real numbers.

Solution: (We shall prove it by the method of contradiction). If possible, let us suppose that for all values of t

$$c_0 1 + c_1 t + c_2 t^2 + \ldots + c_n t^n = 0 \qquad [1]$$

where $c_0, c_1, \ldots, c_n$ are some real numbers on putting $t = 0$ in [1], we get $c_0 = 0$.

Differentiating [1], we get, $c_1 + 2c_2 t + 3c_3 t^2 + \ldots + c_n t^{n-1} = 0$

Putting $t = 0$, in this, we get $c_1 = 0$ $\qquad [2]$

Differentiating [2] again and putting $t = 0$, we get $c_2 = 0$. Proceeding in this manner, we can show that $c_3 = c_4 = \ldots = c_n = 0$. All the coefficients are zero.

$\Rightarrow$ the set of functions $\{1, t, t^2, \ldots, t^n\}$ is linearly independent.

36. If V be a vector space over R of all polynomials in t with real coefficients and of degree $\leq n$, then find the dimension of V and give a basis.

Can the set $\{1, 1-t, (1-t)^2, (1-t)^3, \ldots (1-t)^n\}$ be taken as a basis of V?

Solution: By the given data, we shall assume the set of polynomials in t as

$$\{1, t, t^2, \ldots, t^n\}. \qquad [1]$$

Proceeding as in the previous example (34) we can show that this set is linearly independent. Moreover

$$c_0 + c_1 t + c_2 t^2 + ... + c_n t^n = c_0(1) + c_1(t) + ... + c_n(t^n)$$

i.e., any vector of V is spanned by the vectors of set [1].

$\therefore$ [1] is a basis of V. It contains $n + 1$ vectors; hence the dimension of V is $n + 1$.

The set $\{1, 1 - t, (1 - t)^2, (1 - t)^3, ... (1 - t)^n\}$ [2]

can also be taken as a basis of V, because

(i)   it is linearly independent, and

(ii) it spans V.

To prove (i), we suppose that

$$c_0(1) + c_1(1 - t) + c_2(1 - t)^2 + ... + c_n(1 - t)^n = 0$$ [3]

Putting $t = 1$, in [3], we get $c_0 = 0$.

Differentiating [3] twice and then putting $t = 1$, we get $c_1 = 0$. Differentiating [3] twice and then putting $t = 1$, we get $c_2 = 0$. Differentiating it again and again and putting $t = 1$, we similarly obtain

$$c_3 = c_4 = ... = c_n = 0.$$

To prove [ii],

Let $c_0 + c_1 t^2 + c_2 t^3 + ... c_n t^n$ be any vector of V and suppose that

$$c_0 + c_1 t + c_2 t^2 + ... + c_n t^n = a_0 + a_1(1 - t) + a_2(1 - t)^2 + ... + a_n(1 - t)^n,$$

Equating the coefficients of $1, t, t^2, ..., t^n$ we get the following $n + 1$ equations for determining $a_0, a_1, .., a_n$

$$c_0 = a_0 + a_1 + a_2 + ... + a_n,$$

$$c_1 = -a_1 - 2a_2 - ... - na_n$$

$$c_2 = a_2 + {}^3C_2 a_3 + ... + n_2 a_n ....$$

$$c_{n-1} = (-1)^{n-1}\{a_{n-1} + na_n\}$$

$$c_n = (-1)^n a_n.$$

These determine $a_n, a_{n-1}.., a_1, a_0$ uniquely.

37. Let V be a vector space of functions from R into R.

Show that $\mathbf{f}, \mathbf{g}, \mathbf{h} \in V$ are linearly independent where

$$\mathbf{f}(t) = e^{2t}, \ \mathbf{g}(t) = t^2, \ \mathbf{h}(t) = t.$$

Solution: Let $x\mathbf{f} + y\mathbf{g} + z\mathbf{h} = 0$

We show that $x = 0,\ y = 0,\ z = 0$

where $x,\ y,\ z,$ are scalars which are unknown.

In the equation $xe^{2t} + yt^2 + zt = 0.$

substitute

$$\begin{cases} t = 0 \Rightarrow xe^0 + y0 + z0 = 0 \quad \text{or} \quad x = 0 \\ t = 1 \Rightarrow xe^2 + y + z = 0 \\ t = 2 \Rightarrow xe^4 + 4y + 2z = 0 \end{cases}$$

Solve the system $\begin{cases} x \qquad\quad = 0 \\ xe^2 + y + z = 0 \\ xe^4 + 4y + 2z = 0 \end{cases}$ to obtain only

the zero solution: $x = 0;\ y = 0;\ z = 0.$

$\Rightarrow \mathbf{f,\ g,\ h}$ are independent.

38. Show that the functions
$\mathbf{f}(t) = \sin t;\quad \mathbf{g}(t) = \cos t;\quad \mathbf{h}(t) = t$ are linearly independent.

Solution: $x\mathbf{f} + y\mathbf{g} + z\mathbf{h} = \mathbf{0}$

$\Rightarrow \quad x \sin t + y \cos t + zt = 0$

using unknowns $x,\ y,\ z$ and then show $x = 0,\ y = 0,\ z = 0.$

$x \sin t + y \cos t + zt = 0,$

For $\quad t = 0 \qquad \Rightarrow x \cdot 0 + y \cdot 1 + z \cdot 0 = 0 \qquad \Rightarrow y = 0$

For $\quad t = \dfrac{\pi}{2} \quad \Rightarrow x \cdot 1 + y \cdot 0 + z\left(\dfrac{\pi}{2}\right) = 0 \quad \Rightarrow x + \left(\dfrac{\pi}{2}\right)z = 0$

For $\quad t = \pi \qquad \Rightarrow x \cdot 0 + y(-1) + z \cdot \pi = 0 \quad \Rightarrow -y + \pi z = 0$

On solving, we obtain only the zero solution:

$x = 0;\ y = 0;\ z = 0.$

$\Rightarrow \mathbf{f,\ g,\ h}$ are linearly independent

39. Let $\mathbf{v} = (1 + i,\ 2i)$

$\mathbf{w} = (1,\ 1 + i)$ be the vectors in C^2

are linearly dependent over C but are linearly independent over the real field R.

Solution: We know that two vectors are linearly dependent if one is a multiple of the other. Since the first coordinate of **w** is 1, **v** can be multiple of **w** iff **v** = (1 + *i*) **w**. But 1 + *i* ∉ *R*; hence **v** and **w** are independent over *R*.

Since (1 + *i*) **w** = (1 + *i*) (1, 1+ *i*)

$$= (1 + i, 2i) = \mathbf{v}$$

and 1 + *i* ∈ *C*, they are dependent over *C*.

EXERCISES

1. If **u**, **v** and **w** be L.I. vectors, show that **u** + **v**, **u** − **v** and **u** − 2**v** + **w** are also L.I.

2. Find whether **u** and **v** are L.D.
   where   (a) **u** = (3, 4); **v** = (1, −3)
   (b) **u** = (2, −3); **v** = (6, − 9)

   (Hint: (a) No, neither is a multiple of the other   (b) yes, v = 3u)

3. Determine whether **u** and **v** are L.D.
   where   (a) **u** = (4, 3, −2) ; **v** = (2, −6, 7)
   (b) **u** = (−4, 6, −2); **v** = (2, −3, 1)

   (Hint: (a) No, since neither is a matrices of the other   (b) yes, u = −2v)

4. Let *V* be the vector space of 2×2 matrices over *R*.
   Determine whether the matrices
   A, B, C ∈ *V* are L.D.

   $$A = \begin{bmatrix} 1 & 1 \\ 1 & 1 \end{bmatrix}; \quad B = \begin{bmatrix} 1 & 0 \\ 0 & 1 \end{bmatrix}; \quad C = \begin{bmatrix} 1 & 1 \\ 0 & 0 \end{bmatrix}$$ [*Ans.* L.I.]

5. Determine whether the matrices *A*, *B*, *C* are L.D.
   where $A = \begin{bmatrix} 1 & 2 \\ 3 & 1 \end{bmatrix}; \quad B = \begin{bmatrix} 3 & -1 \\ 2 & 2 \end{bmatrix}; \quad C = \begin{bmatrix} 1 & -5 \\ -4 & 0 \end{bmatrix}$ [*Ans.* L.D.]

6. Prove that (1, 1, −1), (2, −3, 5), (−2, 1, 4) are L.I. in R^3

Inner product spaces

Let $V(F)$ be a vector space over the field F then, we have the following two maps (functions)

- (a) $V \times V \to V$ (Vector addition)
- (b) $F \times V \to V$ (Scalar multiplication)

1. Real Inner product

If $x = (a_1, a_2, a_3)$, $y = (b_1, b_2, b_3)$ are two vectors then we know the following:

(a) $|x| = (a_1^2 + a_2^2 + a_3^2)^{\frac{1}{2}}$

(b) $|x| = 0$ if $a_1 = 0;\ a_2 = 0;\ a_3 = 0$

i.e., $x = 0$ (vector)

Definition: The inner product, dot product, or scalar product of two vectors **u** and **v** in three dimensional space is written as **u.v** and is defined as

$$\mathbf{u} \cdot \mathbf{v} = |\mathbf{u}||\mathbf{v}|\cos\theta \quad \text{(when } \mathbf{u} \neq 0,\ \mathbf{v} \neq 0)$$

$$\mathbf{u.v} = 0 \quad \text{(when } \mathbf{u} = 0 \text{ or } \mathbf{v} = 0)$$

here θ $(0 \leq \theta \leq \pi)$ is the angle between **u** and **v** (computed when the vectors have their initial point coinciding).

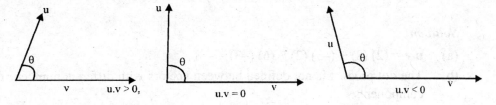

Angle between vectors and value of inner product.

Definition (orthogonality): Two non-zero vectors are orthogonal (perpendicular) iff their product (their dot product) is zero,

Putting $\mathbf{u} = \mathbf{v}$ in $\mathbf{u} \cdot \mathbf{v} = |\mathbf{u}||\mathbf{v}|\cos\theta$

we have, $\mathbf{u} \cdot \mathbf{u} = |\mathbf{u}|^2$, and this shows that the length (Euclidean norm) of a vector can be written in terms of the inner product,

$$|\mathbf{u}| = \sqrt{\mathbf{u} \cdot \mathbf{u}} \quad (\geq 0)$$

From [1] and $\mathbf{u} \cdot \mathbf{v} = |\mathbf{u}||\mathbf{v}|\cos\theta$ we obtain the useful formula for the angle between two non-zero vector

$$\cos\theta = \frac{\mathbf{u} \cdot \mathbf{v}}{|\mathbf{u}||\mathbf{v}|} = \frac{\mathbf{u.v}}{\sqrt{\mathbf{u} \cdot \mathbf{u}}\sqrt{\mathbf{v} \cdot \mathbf{v}}}$$

From the above definition, we also see that the inner product has the properties.

(a) $[q_1\mathbf{u} + q_2\mathbf{v}] \cdot \mathbf{c} = q_1\mathbf{u} \cdot \mathbf{c} + q_2\mathbf{v} \cdot \mathbf{c}$ (linearity)

(b) $\mathbf{u} \cdot \mathbf{v} = \mathbf{v} \cdot \mathbf{u}$ (symmetry)

$\left.\begin{array}{l} \mathbf{u} \cdot \mathbf{u} \geq 0 \\ \mathbf{u} \cdot \mathbf{u} = 0 \ \text{ iff } \quad \mathbf{u} = \mathbf{0} \end{array}\right\}$ (positive definiteness).

Note (1) If $\mathbf{u} = (a_1, a_2, \ldots a_n); \ \mathbf{v} = \left(b_1, b_2 \ldots, b_n \right)$

then the inner (dot) product is defined as $\mathbf{u} \cdot \mathbf{v} = a_1 b_1 + a_2 b_2 + \ldots + a_n b_n = \displaystyle\sum_{i=1}^{n} a_i b_i$

Note (2) Norm (or length) of a vector :

The length of a vector $\mathbf{u}$ is defined as norm (length) : $\|\mathbf{u}\| = \sqrt{\mathbf{u} \cdot \mathbf{u}} = |\mathbf{u}|$

$$= \sqrt{a_1^2 + a_2^2 + \ldots + a_n^2}$$

where $\mathbf{u} = (a_1, a_2, \ldots, a_n); \mathbf{v} = (b_1, b_2 \ldots, b_n)$ are vectors in R^n.

EXAMPLES

1. Compute $\mathbf{u} \cdot \mathbf{v}$, where   (a) $\mathbf{u} = (2, -3, 6); \quad \mathbf{v} = (8, 2, -3)$

                               (b) $\mathbf{u} = (1, -8, 0, 5); \ \mathbf{v} = (3, 6, 4)$

Solution:

(a) $\mathbf{u} \cdot \mathbf{v} = (2)(8) + (-3)(2) + (6)(-3) = -8$

(b)   The dot product is not defined between vectors with different number of components.

2. Find $\mathbf{u} \cdot \mathbf{v}$

where (a) $\mathbf{u} = (3, -5, 2, 1); \quad \mathbf{v} = (4, 1, -2, 5)$

          (b) $\mathbf{u} = (1, -2, 3, -4); \ \mathbf{v} = (6, 7, 1, -2)$

Solution:

(a) $\mathbf{u} \cdot \mathbf{v} = (3)(4) + (-5)(1) + (2)(-2)(-2) + (1)(5)$

         $= 12 - 5 - 4 + 5 = 8$

(b) $\mathbf{u} \cdot \mathbf{v} = 6 - 14 + 3 + 8 = 3$.

3. Find (a) $(\mathbf{u} + \mathbf{v}) \cdot \mathbf{w}$

       (b) $\mathbf{u} \cdot \mathbf{w} + \mathbf{v} \cdot \mathbf{w}$; where $\mathbf{u} = (3, 2, 1) \, ; \mathbf{v} = (5, -3, 4); \mathbf{w} = (1, 6, -7)$

Solution:

(a) $\mathbf{u} + \mathbf{v} = (3 + 5, 2 - 3, 1 + 4) = (8, -1, 5)$

Also, $(\mathbf{u} + \mathbf{v}) \cdot \mathbf{w} = (8)(1) + (-1)(6) + (5)(-7)$

$\qquad = 8 - 6 - 35 = -33$

(b) $\mathbf{u} \cdot \mathbf{w} = 3 + 12 - 7 = 8$

$\quad \mathbf{u} \cdot \mathbf{w} = 5 - 18 - 28 = -41.$

Then $\mathbf{u} \cdot \mathbf{w} + \mathbf{v} \cdot \mathbf{w} = 8 - 41 = -33$

Definition (Angle θ): The angle θ between two vectors $\mathbf{u}$ and $\mathbf{v}$ is given by

$$\cos\theta = \frac{(\mathbf{u} \cdot \mathbf{v})}{\|\mathbf{u}\|\|\mathbf{v}\|}$$

where $\|\mathbf{u}\|$ represents the 'norm' or the modulus of a vector and

$$\|\mathbf{u}\| = \left|\sqrt{(u_1^2 + u_2^2 + \ldots + u_m^2)}\right|$$

Note : $\|\mathbf{u} - \mathbf{v}\| \le \|\mathbf{u} - \mathbf{w}\| + \|\mathbf{w} - \mathbf{v}\|, \forall\ \mathbf{w}$, a vector.

Note: Alternatively, we can say that product (x, y) on $V(F)$ i.e., a real valued function $V \times V \to F$ (Real) satisfying the following properties.

[1] $(\mathbf{x}, \mathbf{x}) \ge 0$ and $(\mathbf{x}, \mathbf{x}) = 0$ if $\mathbf{x} = \mathbf{0}$; (non-negative)

[2] $(\mathbf{x}, \mathbf{y}) = (\mathbf{y}, \mathbf{x})$ (symmetric)

[3] $(a\mathbf{x} + b\mathbf{y}, \mathbf{z}) = a(\mathbf{x}, \mathbf{z}) + b(\mathbf{y}, \mathbf{z})$

Projections: If $\mathbf{u}$ and $\mathbf{v} \ne 0$ be vectors in R^n, then the (vector) projection of $\mathbf{u}$ onto $\mathbf{v}'$ is the vector denoted by $Proj\ (\mathbf{u}, \mathbf{v}) = \dfrac{\mathbf{u} \cdot \mathbf{v}}{\|\mathbf{v}\|^2}\mathbf{v}$ [1]

Illustration: From the figure, the (perpendicular) projection of $\mathbf{u}$ onto $\mathbf{v}$ is the vector $\mathbf{u}^*$, of magnitude.

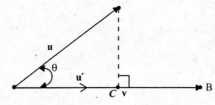

$$|\mathbf{u}^*| = |\mathbf{u}|\cos\theta$$

$$= |\mathbf{u}|\frac{\mathbf{u} \cdot \mathbf{v}}{|\mathbf{u}||\mathbf{v}|}$$

$$= \frac{\mathbf{u} \cdot \mathbf{v}}{|\mathbf{v}|}$$

To obtain $\mathbf{u}^*$, we multiply its magnitude by the unit vector in the direction of $\mathbf{v}$:

$$\left|\mathbf{u}^*\right| = \left|\mathbf{u}^*\right| \frac{\mathbf{v}}{|\mathbf{v}|} = \frac{\mathbf{u} \cdot \mathbf{v}}{|\mathbf{v}|^2} \mathbf{v}$$

which satisfies equation [1].

EXAMPLE

Let $\mathbf{u} = (1, -2, 3); \mathbf{v} = (:, 5, 4)$
Find proj $(\mathbf{u}, \mathbf{v})$

Solution: Here, $\mathbf{u} \cdot \mathbf{v} = 2 - 10 + 12 = 4$ and $\left|\mathbf{v}^2\right| = 4 + 25 + 16 = 45$.

Then by using Proj $(\mathbf{u}, \mathbf{v}) = \frac{\mathbf{u} \cdot \mathbf{v}}{\|\mathbf{v}\|^2} \mathbf{v}$

$$= \frac{4}{45}(2, 5, 4)$$

$$= \left(\frac{8}{45}, \frac{20}{45}, \frac{16}{45} \right)$$

$$= \left(\frac{8}{45}, \frac{4}{9}, \frac{16}{45} \right)$$

Given, $\mathbf{u} = (4, -3, 1, 5); \mathbf{v} = (3, 6, -4, 1)$.

then, evaluate proj $(\mathbf{u}, \mathbf{v}) = \frac{\mathbf{u} \cdot \mathbf{v}}{\|\mathbf{v}\|^2} \mathbf{v}$

$$\mathbf{u} \cdot \mathbf{v} = 12 - 18 - 4 + 5 = -5$$

and $\|\mathbf{v}\|^2 = 9 + 36 + 16 + 1 = 62,$

$$\therefore \quad \text{Proj}\,(\mathbf{u}, \mathbf{v}) = \frac{\mathbf{u} \cdot \mathbf{v}}{\|\mathbf{v}\|^2} \mathbf{v}$$

$$= \frac{-5}{62}(3, 6, -4, 1)$$

$$= \left(\frac{-15}{62}, \frac{-15}{31}, \frac{10}{31}, \frac{-5}{62} \right)$$

Distance between two vectors

The distance between **u** and **v**, (where **u** and **v** be any vectors in R^n) denoted by $d(\mathbf{u}, \mathbf{v})$, is defined as $d(\mathbf{u}, \mathbf{v}) = \|\mathbf{u} - \mathbf{v}\|$ [1]

Illustration: From the figure, we have $\mathbf{u} = (a, b)$; $\mathbf{v} = (c, d)$, in R^2; the distance between

$$P(a, b); \text{ and } Q(c, d) \text{ is } d = \sqrt{(a-c)^2 + (b-d)^2}$$

or we have by [1],

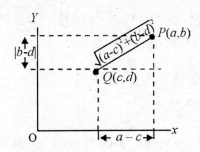

$$d(\mathbf{u}, \mathbf{v}) = \|\mathbf{u} - \mathbf{v}\| = \|(a-c, b-d)\|$$

$$= \sqrt{(a-c)^2 + (b-d)^2}$$

which corresponds to the usual notion of Euclidean distance in R^2.

EXAMPLES

1. Determine k such that $d(\mathbf{u}, \mathbf{v}) = 6$,
    if $\mathbf{u} = (2, k, 1, -4)$ and $\mathbf{v} = (3, -3, 6, -3)$.

    Solution: $(d(\mathbf{u}, \mathbf{v}))^2 = \|\mathbf{u} - \mathbf{v}\|^2 = (2-3)^2 + (k+1)^2 + (1-6)^2 + (-4+3)^2$

    $$= k^2 + 2k + 28;$$

    on solving, we get, $k^2 + 2k + 28 = 6^2$

    $$k = 2, -4.$$

2. Prove the following:
    (a) $d(\mathbf{x}, \mathbf{y}) \geq 0$ and $d(\mathbf{x}, \mathbf{y}) = 0$ iff $\mathbf{x} = \mathbf{y}$
    (b) $d(\mathbf{x}, \mathbf{y}) = d(\mathbf{y}, \mathbf{x})$
    (c) $d(\mathbf{x}, \mathbf{y}) \leq d(\mathbf{x}, \mathbf{z}) + d(\mathbf{z}, \mathbf{y})$
    (d) $d(\mathbf{x}, \mathbf{y}) = d(\mathbf{x} + \mathbf{z}, \mathbf{y} + \mathbf{z})$

Proof: If $\mathbf{x}$, $\mathbf{y}$ be any two vectors in an inner product vector space then, we define $d(\mathbf{x}, \mathbf{y})$ the distance from $\mathbf{x}$ to $\mathbf{y}$ as $d(\mathbf{x}, \mathbf{y}) = \|\mathbf{x} - \mathbf{y}\|$ [1]

(a) $d(\mathbf{x}, \mathbf{y}) = \|\mathbf{x} - \mathbf{y}\| \geq 0$ and $= 0$

      iff $\mathbf{x} - \mathbf{y} = 0$ iff $\mathbf{x} = \mathbf{y}$

(b) $d(\mathbf{x}, \mathbf{y}) = \|\mathbf{x} - \mathbf{y}\| = \|-1(\mathbf{y} - \mathbf{x})\| = |-1|\|\mathbf{y} - \mathbf{x}\|$

              $= \|\mathbf{y} - \mathbf{x}\| = d(\mathbf{y}, \mathbf{x})$

(c) $d(\mathbf{x}, \mathbf{y}) = \|\mathbf{x} - \mathbf{y}\| = \|\mathbf{x} - \mathbf{z} + \mathbf{z} - \mathbf{y}\| \leq \|\mathbf{x} - \mathbf{z}\| + \|\mathbf{z} - \mathbf{y}\|$ by triangular inequality

              $= d(\mathbf{x}, \mathbf{z}) + d(\mathbf{z}, \mathbf{y})$

(d) $d(\mathbf{x}, \mathbf{y}) = \|\mathbf{x} - \mathbf{y}\| = \|(\mathbf{x} + \mathbf{z}) - (\mathbf{y} + \mathbf{z})\|$

              $= d(\mathbf{x} + \mathbf{z}, \mathbf{y} + \mathbf{z})$.

Normed Vector Space: If in a vector space V, to each vector $\mathbf{u}$ in V, there corresponds a real number denoted by $\|\mathbf{u}\|$, called the norm of $\mathbf{u}$, in such a manner, that

(1) $\|\mathbf{u}\| \geq 0$ and $\|\mathbf{u}\| = 0 \Leftrightarrow \mathbf{u} = 0$

(2) $\|\alpha\,\mathbf{u}\| = |\alpha|\,\|\mathbf{u}\|$, $\alpha \in F$

(3) $\|\mathbf{u} + \mathbf{v}\| \leq \|\mathbf{u}\| + \|\mathbf{v}\|$ (Triangular inequality)

If the vector space $V(F)$ is an inner product vector space, then norm of $\mathbf{u}$ i.e., $\|\mathbf{u}\|$ is defined as $+\sqrt{(\mathbf{u}, \mathbf{u})}$.

Orthogonal Sets and Bases

Let V be an inner product vector space and let $S = \{u_1, u_2, ..., u_k\}$ be a set of vectors in V. Then S is said to be orthogonal if each of its vectors are non-zero and if its vectors are mutually orthogonal. That is, if $(\mathbf{u}_i, \mathbf{u}_i) \neq 0$ but $(\mathbf{u}_i, \mathbf{u}_j) = 0$ for $i \neq j \in S$ is said to be orthonormal if S is orthogonal and if each of its vectors have unit length, or in other words, if

$$(\mathbf{u}_i, \mathbf{u}_j) = \delta_{ij} = \begin{cases} 1 & \text{if } i = j \\ 0 & \text{if } i \neq j \end{cases}$$

The process of dividing each vector in an orthogonal set S by its length so that S is transformed into an orthonormal set. An orthogonal (orthonormal) basis refers to a basis S which is orthogonal (orthonormal).

Illustration: Let $S = \{(1, 2, -3, 4), (3, 4, 1, -2), (3, -2, 1, 1)\}$ in R^4. Show that S is orthogonal.

Solution: Let $\mathbf{u} = (1, 2, -3, 4)$; $\mathbf{v} = (3, 4, 1, -2)$; $\mathbf{w}$ $(3, -2, 1, 1)$

Now, $(\mathbf{u}, \mathbf{v}) = 1 \cdot 3 + 2 \cdot 4 + (-3) \cdot 1 + 4(-2)$

$$= 3 + 8 - 3 - 8 = 0$$

$(\mathbf{u}, \mathbf{w}) = 1 \cdot 3 + 2(-2) + (-3)(1) + 4(1)$

$$= 3 - 4 - 3 + 4 = 0$$

$(\mathbf{v}, \mathbf{w}) = 3 \cdot 3 + 4 \cdot (-2) + 1 \cdot 1 + (-2) \cdot 1$

$$= 9 - 8 + 1 - 2 = 0$$

$\Rightarrow$ each pair of vectors is orthogonal

$\Rightarrow$ S is orthogonal.

Definition (1): (orthogonality) Two non-zero vectors are orthogonal (Perpendicular) iff their inner product (dot product) is zero, i.e., if $\mathbf{u}$ and $\mathbf{v}$ be vectors in R^n, then $\mathbf{u}$ is said to be orthogonal (perpendicular) to $\mathbf{v}$ if $\mathbf{u} \cdot \mathbf{v} = 0$, and denoted by $\mathbf{u} \perp \mathbf{v}$.

Definition (2): (orthonormality) Let $S = \{\mathbf{u}_1, \mathbf{u}_2, ..., \mathbf{u}_k\}$, be a set of vectors in an inner product space V. S is said to be orthonormal if S is orthogonal and if each of its vectors have unit length or in other words,

if $(\mathbf{u}_i, \mathbf{u}_j) = \delta_{ij} = \begin{cases} 1 & \text{is } i = j \\ 0 & \text{is } i \neq j \end{cases}$

Properties

P_1: If $\mathbf{u} \perp \mathbf{v}$, then $\mathbf{v} \perp \mathbf{u}$

Proof: given $\mathbf{u} \perp \mathbf{v}$, then $(\mathbf{u}, \mathbf{v}) = 0$.
Hence $(\mathbf{v}, \mathbf{u}) = (\mathbf{u}, \mathbf{v}) = 0$ and so $\mathbf{v} \perp \mathbf{u}$.

P_2: $0 \in \mathbf{v}$ is orthogonal to every $v \in V$

Proof: $(0, \mathbf{v}) = (0\mathbf{v}, \mathbf{v}) = 0$;
Hence, 0 is orthogonal to every $\mathbf{v} \in V$

P_3: To every $v \in V$ $(\mathbf{u}, \mathbf{v}) = 0$ then $\mathbf{u} = 0$

Proof: $(\mathbf{u}, \mathbf{v}) = 0$ for every $v \in V$,
Then $(\mathbf{u}, \mathbf{u}) = 0$ and hence $\mathbf{u} = 0$.

EXAMPLES

1. Find a unit vector orthogonal to $v_1 = (1, 1, 2)$ and $v_2 = (0, 1, 3)$ in R^3.

Solution: Let $\mathbf{w} = (x, y, z)$.
Now, $0 = (\mathbf{w}, v_1) = x + y + 2z$
and $0 = (\mathbf{w}, v_2) = y + 3z$

$\Rightarrow \quad x + y + 2z = 0$

$\qquad y + 3z = 0$

Now put $z = 1$, then $y = -3$.

and $x = 1$; then $w = (1, -3, 1)$.

Now, normalizing $\mathbf{w}_1$ to get $\mathbf{w}'$ orthogonal to $\mathbf{v}_1$ and $\mathbf{v}_2$:

$$\mathbf{w}' = \frac{\mathbf{w}}{\|\mathbf{w}\|} = \left(\frac{1}{\sqrt{11}}, \frac{-3}{\sqrt{11}}, \frac{1}{\sqrt{11}} \right)$$

2. Let $S = \{\mathbf{u}_1 = (1, 2, 1), \mathbf{u}_1 = (2, 1, -4), \mathbf{u}_3 = (3, -2, 1)\}$ be a set of vectors in R^3:

   (a) Show that S is orthogonal

   (b) Is S a basis of R^3?

Solution:

(a) Since $\left. \begin{array}{l} \mathbf{u}_1 \cdot \mathbf{u}_2 = 2 + 2 - 4 = 0; \\ \mathbf{u}_1 \cdot \mathbf{u}_3 = 3 - 4 + 1 = 0; \\ \mathbf{u}_2 \cdot \mathbf{u}_3 = 6 - 2 - 4 = 0. \end{array} \right\}$

$\Rightarrow S$ is orthogonal

(b) We know that any three linearly independent vectors form a basis for R^3. Here, S is shown to be orthogonal it is linearly independent. Hence, S form a basis for R^3.

3. Given, $S = \{\mathbf{u} = (1, 2, -3, 4); \mathbf{v} = (3, 4, 1, -2); \mathbf{w} = (3, -2, 1, 1)\}$ be an orthogonal set in R^4, normalize S to obtain an orthonormal set.

Solution: Let us divide each vector in S by its length.

$$\left. \begin{array}{l} \|\mathbf{u}\|^2 = 1 + 4 + 9 + 16 = 30; \\ \|\mathbf{v}\|^2 = 9 + 16 + 1 + 4 = 30; \\ \|\mathbf{w}\|^2 = 9 + 4 + 1 + 1 = 15; \end{array} \right\}$$

Then, $\hat{\mathbf{u}} = \left(\frac{1}{\sqrt{30}}, \frac{2}{\sqrt{30}}, \frac{-3}{\sqrt{30}}, \frac{4}{\sqrt{30}} \right)$;

$\hat{\mathbf{v}} = \left(\frac{3}{\sqrt{30}}, \frac{4}{\sqrt{30}}, \frac{1}{\sqrt{30}}, \frac{-2}{\sqrt{30}} \right)$;

$\hat{\mathbf{w}} = \left(\frac{3}{\sqrt{15}}, \frac{-2}{\sqrt{30}}, \frac{1}{\sqrt{15}}, \frac{1}{\sqrt{15}} \right)$

form the required orthonormal set of vectors,

4. Given, $S = \{e_1, e_2, e_3\}$ be the usual basis of Euclidean 3 space R^3.

where $e_1 = (1, 0, 0)$; $e_2 = (0, 1, 0)$; $e_3 = (0, 0, 1)$.

    (a) Is S orthogonal

    (b) Is S orthonormal?

Solution: We have $\begin{cases} (e_1, e_2) = 0 \\ (e_1, e_3) = 0 \\ (e_2, e_3) = 0 \end{cases}$

$\Rightarrow$ S is orthogonal

and $\begin{cases} (e_1, e_1) = 1; \\ (e_2, e_2) = 1 \\ (e_3, e_3) = 1 \end{cases}$

$\Rightarrow$ S is orthonormal basis of R^3.

Note: The above results are true in general. i.e., the usual basis of R^n is orthonormal for every n.

5. If V be the vector space of real continuous functions on the interval $-\pi \leq t \leq \pi$ with inner product defined by

$(f, g) = \int\limits_{-\pi}^{\pi} f(t)g(t)dt$. The following set S of functions plays a fundamental role in the theory of Fourier series: $S = \{1, \sin t, \cos t, \sin 2t, \cos 2t, ...\}$. Is S orthogonal?

Solution: Let f and g functions belong to S.

We have $\int\limits_{-\pi}^{\pi} f(t)g(t)dt = 0$

$\Rightarrow$ S is orthogonal.

Again, by taking $f(t) = \cos t = g(t)$

$(\cos t,\ \cos t) = \int\limits_{-\pi}^{\pi} \cos^2 t\, dt = \pi.$

6. Given, $S = \{(1, 2, 1), (2, 1, -4), (3, -2, 1)\}$.

Is S orthogonal ?

$$\textbf{\textit{Solution:}} \begin{cases} (1,2,1)\cdot(2,1,-4) & = 2+2-4=0; \\ (1,2,1)\cdot(3,-2,1) & = 3-4+1=0; \\ (2,1,-4)\cdot(3,-2,1) = 6-2-4=0; \end{cases}$$

7. Given, $S = \{\mathbf{u}_1, \mathbf{u}_2, ..., \mathbf{u}_r\}$ is an orthogonal set

and $a_1\mathbf{u}_1 + a_2\mathbf{u}_2 + ... + a_r\mathbf{u}_r = \mathbf{0}$.

Show that S is linearly independent.

Solution: Consider the inner product of $a_1\mathbf{u}_1 + a_2\mathbf{u}_2 + ...a_r\mathbf{u}_r = 0$ with $\mathbf{u}_1$, we get

$$0 = (0, \mathbf{u}_1) = (a_1\mathbf{u}_1 + a_2\mathbf{u}_2 + ... + a_r\mathbf{u}_r, \mathbf{u}_1)$$

$$= a_1(\mathbf{u}_1, \mathbf{u}_1) + a_2(\mathbf{u}_2, \mathbf{u}_1) + ... + a_r(\mathbf{u}_r, \mathbf{u}_1)$$

$$= a_1(\mathbf{u}_1, \mathbf{u}_1) + a_2 \cdot 0 + ... + a_r \cdot 0$$

$$= a_1(\mathbf{u}_1, \mathbf{u}_1) \cdot \text{ since } S \text{ is orthogonal,}$$

$$(\mathbf{u}_1, \mathbf{u}_1) \neq 0; \Rightarrow a_1 = 0$$

Similarly, for $i = 2, ..., r$, taking the inner product of [1] with u_i,

$$0 = (0, \mathbf{u}_i) = (a_1\mathbf{u}_1 + ... + a_r\mathbf{u}_r, \mathbf{u}_r)$$

$$= a_1(\mathbf{u}_1, \mathbf{u}_1) + ... + a_i(\mathbf{u}_i, \mathbf{u}_i)$$

$$+ ... + a_r(\mathbf{u}_r, \mathbf{u}_r) = a_i(\mathbf{u}_i, \mathbf{u}_i).$$

But $(\mathbf{u}_i, \mathbf{u}_i) \neq 0$ and hence $a_i = 0$.

Thus S is linearly independent.

8. Verify the parallelogram law for vectors $\mathbf{u}$ and $\mathbf{v}$ in R^n.

$$\|\mathbf{u} + \mathbf{v}\|^2 + \|\mathbf{u} - \mathbf{v}\|^2 = 2\|\mathbf{u}\|^2 + 2\|\mathbf{v}\|^2$$

[VTU MED. ELEN. May/June 2004].

Solution: Suppose $\mathbf{u}$ and $\mathbf{v}$ be vectors in the vector space $V_2(R)$ with standard inner product defined in it.

If the vector $\mathbf{u}$ is represented by the side AB and the vector $\mathbf{v}$ by the side BC of a parallelogram $ABCD$, then the vectors $\mathbf{u} + \mathbf{v}$ and $\mathbf{u}-\mathbf{v}$ represent the diagonals AC and DB of the parallelogram.

$$\boxed{\therefore AC^2 + DB^2 = 2AB^2 + 2BC^2}$$ [1]

> The sum of the squares of the sides of a parallelogram is equal to the sum of the squares of its diagonals.

Here, we have

$$\|u+v\|^2 = (u+v, u+v); \qquad \text{[by definition of norm]}$$

$$= (u, u+v) + (v, u+v); \quad \text{[by linearty property]}$$

$$= (u, u) + (u, v) + (v, u) + (v, v)$$

$$\|u\|^2 + (u, v) + (v, u) + \|v\|^2$$

> Hence, $\|u+v\|^2 = \|u\|^2 + (u, v) + (v, u) + \|v\|^2$

[2]

Also $\|u - v\|^2 = (u-v, u-v) = (u, u-v) - (v, u-v)$

$$= (u, u) - (u, v) - (v, u) + (v, v)$$

$$= \|u\|^2 - (u, v) - (v, u) + \|v\|^2$$

> Hence $\|u-v\|^2 = \|u\|^2 - (u, v) - (v, u) + \|v\|^2$

[3]

Adding [2] and [3], we get

$$\|u + v\|^2 + \|u - v\|^2 = 2\|u\|^2 + 2\|v\|^2$$

9. Prove that $\|u + v\|^2 = \|u\|^2 + 2(u, v) + \|v\|^2$.

   Solution: We have, $\|u + v\|^2 = (u + v, u + v)$

$$= (u, u) + (u, v) + (v, u) + v, v)$$

$$= (u, u) + (u, v) + (v, u) + (v, v)$$

$$= (u, u) + (u, v) + (u, v) + (v, v)$$

$$= \|u\|^2 + 2(u, v) + \|v\|^2$$

10. Prove that $\|u - v\|^2 = \|u\|^2 - 2(u, v) + \|v\|^2$.

   Solution: $\|u - v\|^2 = (u - v, u - v)$

$$= (u, u) - (u, v) - (v, u) + (v, v)$$

$$= (\mathbf{u}, \mathbf{u}) - (\mathbf{u}, \mathbf{v}) - (\mathbf{u}, \mathbf{v}) + (\mathbf{v}, \mathbf{v})$$

$$= \|\mathbf{u}\|^2 - 2(\mathbf{u}, \mathbf{v}) + \|\mathbf{v}\|^2$$

11. Prove that $(\mathbf{u} + \mathbf{v}, \mathbf{u} - \mathbf{v}) = \|\mathbf{u}\|^2 - \|\mathbf{v}\|^2$.

Solution: $(\mathbf{u} + \mathbf{v}, \mathbf{u} - \mathbf{v}) = (\mathbf{u}, \mathbf{u}) - (\mathbf{u}, \mathbf{v}) + (\mathbf{v}, \mathbf{u}) - (\mathbf{v}, \mathbf{v})$

$$= \|\mathbf{u}\|^2 - (\mathbf{u}, \mathbf{v}) + (\mathbf{u}, \mathbf{v}) - \|\mathbf{v}\|^2$$

$$= \|\mathbf{u}\|^2 - \|\mathbf{v}\|^2$$

12. Prove that: $\left(\sum_{i=1}^{r} a_i \mathbf{u}_i, \sum_{i=1}^{s} b_j \mathbf{v}_j \right) = \sum_{i=1}^{r} \sum_{i=1}^{s} a_i b_j (\mathbf{u}_i, \mathbf{v}_j)$.

Solution: We know that by symmetry,

$$\boxed{(\mathbf{u}, \mathbf{v}) = (\mathbf{v}, \mathbf{u}).}$$ [1]

Now, $\left(\sum_{i=1}^{r} a_i \mathbf{u}_i, \sum_{i=1}^{s} b_j \mathbf{v}_j \right) = \sum_{i=1}^{r} a_i \left(\mathbf{u}_i, \sum_{j=1}^{s} b_j \mathbf{v}_j \right)$

$$= \sum_{i=1}^{r} a_i \left(\sum_{j=1}^{s} b_j \mathbf{v}_j, \mathbf{u}_j \right)$$

$$= \sum_{i=1}^{r} a_i \sum_{j=1}^{s} a_i b_j (\mathbf{v}_j, \mathbf{u}_i)$$

$$= \sum_{i=1}^{r} \sum_{j=1}^{s} a_i b_j (\mathbf{u}_i, \mathbf{v}_j)$$

13. Cauchy–Schwarz Inequality

> For any vectors $\mathbf{u}, \mathbf{v} \in V$,
> $$(\mathbf{u}, \mathbf{v})^2 \leq \|\mathbf{u}\|^2 \|\mathbf{v}\|^2$$
> or
> $$\boxed{|(\mathbf{u}, \mathbf{v})| \leq \|\mathbf{u}\| \|\mathbf{v}\|}$$

Proof: For any real number t,

$$(t\mathbf{u} + \mathbf{v}, \, t\mathbf{u} + \mathbf{v})$$

$$= t^2(\mathbf{u}, \mathbf{u}) + 2t(\mathbf{u}, \mathbf{v}) + \mathbf{v}, \mathbf{v})$$

$$= t^2\|\mathbf{u}\|^2 + 2t(\mathbf{u}, \mathbf{v}) + \|\mathbf{v}\|^2$$

Let $\quad a = \|\mathbf{u}\|^2, \quad b = 2(\mathbf{u}, \mathbf{v}) \quad$ and $\quad c = \|\mathbf{v}\|^2.$

Now, $\|t\mathbf{u} + \mathbf{v}\|^2 > 0$

We have, $at^2 + bt + c > 0$, for every value of t.

$\Rightarrow$ Quadratic polynomial cannot have two real roots.

$\Rightarrow \quad b^2 - 4ac \leq 0$

$\Rightarrow \quad b^2 \leq 4ac.$

Thus,

$$4(\mathbf{u}, \mathbf{v})^2 \leq 4\|\mathbf{u}\|^2 \|\mathbf{v}\|^2$$

$$\Rightarrow \quad (\mathbf{u}, \mathbf{v})^2 \leq \|\mathbf{u}\|^2 \|\mathbf{v}\|^2$$

$$\Rightarrow \quad |(\mathbf{u}, \mathbf{v})| \leq \|\mathbf{u}\|\|\mathbf{v}\|$$

14. Cauchy Schwarz inequality for any complex number z.

$$\boxed{|(\mathbf{u}, \mathbf{v})| \leq \|\mathbf{u}\|\|\mathbf{v}\|}$$

If $\mathbf{v} = 0$, the inequality reduces to $0 \leq 0$ and hence is valid.

Now, let $\mathbf{v} \neq 0$, but by using

$z\bar{z} = |z|^2$ (for any complex number z)

and $(\mathbf{u}, \mathbf{v}) = \overline{(\mathbf{u}, \mathbf{v})}$

we expand $\|\mathbf{u} - (\mathbf{u}, \mathbf{v})t\mathbf{v}\|^2 \geq 0$, ($t$ is any real value)

Now, $0 \leq \|\mathbf{u} - (\mathbf{u}, \mathbf{v})t\mathbf{v}\|^2$

$$= (\mathbf{u} - (\mathbf{u}, \mathbf{v})t\mathbf{v}, \, \mathbf{u} - (\mathbf{u}, \mathbf{v})t\mathbf{v})$$

$$= (\mathbf{u}, \mathbf{v}) - \overline{(\mathbf{u}, \mathbf{v})}t(\mathbf{u}, \mathbf{v}) - (\mathbf{u}, \mathbf{v})t\overline{(\mathbf{v}, \mathbf{u})} + (\mathbf{u}, \mathbf{v})\overline{(\mathbf{u}, \mathbf{v})}t^2(\mathbf{v}, \mathbf{v})$$

$$= \|\mathbf{u}\|^2 - 2t|(\mathbf{u}, \mathbf{v})|^2 + |(\mathbf{u}, \mathbf{v})|^2 t^2 \|\mathbf{v}\|^2$$

set $\quad t = \dfrac{1}{\|\mathbf{v}\|^2}$ to find $0 \leq \|\mathbf{u}\|^2 - (\,|(\mathbf{u}, \mathbf{v})|^2 - \|\mathbf{v}\|^2\,)$, from which $|(\mathbf{u}, \mathbf{v})|^2 \leq \|\mathbf{u}\|^2 \|\mathbf{v}\|^2.$

$$\Rightarrow \quad \boxed{|(\mathbf{u}, \mathbf{v})| \leq \|\mathbf{u}\|\|\mathbf{v}\|}$$

15. Minkowski's inequality:

$\|u + v\| \le \|u\| + \|v\|$, for arbitrary u and v in R^n.

Proof: We know that by Cauchy–Schwarz inequality and the other properties of the inner product,

$$\|u + v\|^2 = (u + v) \cdot (u + v) = u \cdot u + 2(u \cdot v) + v \cdot v$$

$$\le \|u\|^2 + 2\|u\|\|v\| + \|v\|^2$$

$$= (\|u\| + \|v\|)^2$$

$$\Rightarrow \quad \|u + v\| \le \|u\| + \|v\|,$$

on taking the square roots of both sides.

Gram–Schmidt orthogonalization process

Suppose we are given a basis for a vector space, we wish to find an orthonormal basis of that space. This is done by the famous Gram-Schmidt Orthogonalization process.

Explanation: Let v_1, v_2, ..., v_m be a given basis for a vector space $V_n^m(R)$ of n-vectors over R and of dimension m.

To find an orthonormal basis of $V_n^m(R)$, we first find a set of mutually orthogonal vectors w_1, w_2, ..., w_m as follows:

Take $\quad w_1 = v_1$

Let $\quad w_2 = v_2 + a w_1$, $\hfill [1]$

where 'a' is a scalar to be chosen such that w_1 and w_2 are mutually orthogonal.

$\therefore \quad w_1 \cdot w_2 = 0$

i.e., $\quad w_1 \cdot (v_2 + a w_1) = 0$

$\Rightarrow \quad w_1 \cdot v_2 + a w_1 \cdot w_1 = 0$

$\Rightarrow \quad a = -\dfrac{w_1 \cdot v_2}{w_1 \cdot w_1}$ $\hfill [2]$

Using [2] in [1], we have

$$w_2 = v_2 - \frac{w_1 \cdot w_2}{w_1 \cdot w_1} \cdot w_1.$$

Let $\quad w_3 = v_3 + a w_2 + b w_1$ $\hfill [3]$

where a and b are scalars such that w_1, w_2, w_3 are mutually orthogonal.

$$\therefore \quad \mathbf{w}_1 \cdot \mathbf{w}_3 = 0 \text{ and } \mathbf{w}_2 \cdot \mathbf{w}_3 = 0$$

$$\Rightarrow \quad \mathbf{w}_1 \cdot (\mathbf{v}_3 + a\mathbf{w}_2 + b\mathbf{w}_1) = 0$$

$$\text{and} \quad \mathbf{w}_2 \cdot (\mathbf{v}_3 + a\mathbf{w}_2 + b\mathbf{w}_1) = 0$$

$$\Rightarrow \quad \mathbf{w}_1 \mathbf{v}_3 + b\mathbf{w}_1 \mathbf{w}_1 = 0$$

$$\text{and} \quad \mathbf{w}_2 \cdot \mathbf{v}_3 + a\mathbf{w}_2 \cdot \mathbf{w}_2 = 0$$

$$(\because \mathbf{w}_1 \cdot \mathbf{v}_2 = \mathbf{w}_2 \cdot \mathbf{w}_1 = 0)$$

$$\Rightarrow \quad b = -\frac{\mathbf{w}_1 \cdot \mathbf{w}_3}{\mathbf{w}_1 \cdot \mathbf{w}_1} \text{ and } a = -\frac{\mathbf{w}_2 \cdot \mathbf{w}_2}{\mathbf{w}_2 \cdot \mathbf{w}_2}.$$

Substituting for a and b in [3], we have

$$\mathbf{w}_3 = \mathbf{v}_3 - \frac{\mathbf{w}_2 \cdot \mathbf{w}_3}{\mathbf{w}_2 \cdot \mathbf{w}_2} \mathbf{w}_2 - \frac{\mathbf{w}_1 \cdot \mathbf{v}_3}{\mathbf{w}_1 \cdot \mathbf{w}_1} \mathbf{w}_1 \ldots \text{ and so on.}$$

Continuing like this, we have

$$\mathbf{w}_m = \mathbf{v}_m - \frac{\mathbf{w}_{m-1} \cdot \mathbf{v}_m}{\mathbf{w}_{m-1} \cdot \mathbf{w}_{m-1}} \mathbf{w}_{m-1} \cdots - \frac{\mathbf{w}_1 \cdot \mathbf{v}_m}{\mathbf{w}_1 \cdot \mathbf{w}_1} \mathbf{w}_1$$

Then, the vectors $\frac{\mathbf{w}_i}{\|\mathbf{w}_i\|}$, $(i = 1, 2, 3, \ldots, n)$ are mutually orthogonal unit vectors and form an orthonormal basis of $V_n^m(R)$.

EXAMPLES

1. Using the Gram-Schmidt process, construct an orthonormal basis of V_3, whose basis is $\mathbf{v}_1 = (1, 1, 1)$; $\mathbf{v}_2 = (1, -2, 1)$; $\mathbf{v}_3 = (1, 2, 3)$.

Solution: Take $\mathbf{w}_1 = \mathbf{v}_1 = (1, 1, 1)$

$$\mathbf{w}_2 = \mathbf{v}_2 - \frac{\mathbf{w}_1 \cdot \mathbf{w}_2}{\mathbf{w}_1 \cdot \mathbf{w}_1} \cdot \mathbf{w}_1$$

$$= (1, -2, 1) - \frac{1, 1, 1(-2) + 1 \cdot 1}{1 \cdot 1 + 1 \cdot 1 + 1 \cdot 1} \mathbf{w}_1$$

$$= (1, -2, 1) - \frac{0}{3} \mathbf{w}_1 \quad (1, -2, 1)$$

$$\mathbf{w}_3 = \mathbf{v}_3 - \frac{\mathbf{w}_2 \cdot \mathbf{w}_3}{\mathbf{w}_2 \cdot \mathbf{w}_2} \cdot \mathbf{w}_2 - \frac{\mathbf{w}_1 \cdot \mathbf{w}_3}{\mathbf{w}_1 \cdot \mathbf{w}_1} \cdot \mathbf{w}_1$$

$$= (1, 2, 3) - \frac{1 \cdot 1 + (-2) \cdot 2 + 1 \cdot 3}{1 \cdot 1 + (-2)(-2) + 1 \cdot 1} \mathbf{w}_2 - \frac{1 \cdot 1 + 1 \cdot 2 + 1 \cdot 3}{1 \cdot 1 + 1 \cdot 1 + 1 \cdot 1} \mathbf{w}_1$$

$$= (1, 2, 3) - \frac{0}{6} \mathbf{w}_2 - \frac{3}{3} \mathbf{w}_1$$

$$= (1, 2, 3) - 2(1, 1, 1) = (-1, 0, 1)$$

Normalizing the w's, we have the unit vectors

$$\frac{\mathbf{w}_1}{\|\mathbf{w}_1\|} = \left(\frac{1}{\sqrt{3}}, \frac{1}{\sqrt{3}}, \frac{1}{\sqrt{3}} \right); \quad \frac{\mathbf{w}_2}{\|\mathbf{w}_2\|} = \left(\frac{1}{\sqrt{6}}, \frac{-2}{\sqrt{6}}, \frac{1}{\sqrt{6}} \right); \quad \frac{\mathbf{w}_3}{\|\mathbf{w}_3\|} = \left(\frac{-1}{\sqrt{2}}, 0, \frac{1}{\sqrt{2}} \right);$$

Clearly, each product $\dfrac{\mathbf{w}_i}{\|\mathbf{w}_i\|} \cdot \dfrac{\mathbf{w}_j}{\|\mathbf{w}_j\|} = 0$ and each $\dfrac{\mathbf{w}_i}{\|\mathbf{w}_i\|}$ is a unit vector.

$\therefore$ The vectors $\left(\dfrac{1}{\sqrt{3}}, \dfrac{1}{\sqrt{3}}, \dfrac{1}{\sqrt{3}} \right), \left(\dfrac{1}{\sqrt{6}}, \dfrac{-2}{\sqrt{6}}, \dfrac{1}{\sqrt{6}} \right), \left(\dfrac{-1}{\sqrt{2}}, 0, \dfrac{1}{\sqrt{2}} \right)$ form an

orthonormal basis of V_3

remark: Here, $\mathbf{w}_2 = \mathbf{v}_2 \; \because \; \mathbf{v}_1$ and $\mathbf{v}_2$ are orthogonal.

2. Using the Gram-Schmidt process, construct an orthonormal basis of V_3, using the given vectors as basis:

   (a) $(2, 1, 3), \ (1, 2, 3), \ (1, 1, 1)$.

   (b) $(1, -1, 0), \ (2, -1, -2), \ (1, -1, -2)$.

   (c) $(0, 1, 1), \ (3, 1, 1), \ (2, 3, 1)$.

Solution: (a) Let $\mathbf{v}_1 = (2, 1, 3); \quad \mathbf{v}_2 = (1, 2, 3); \quad \mathbf{v}_3 = (1, 1, 1)$

Choose

$$\mathbf{w}_1 = \mathbf{v}_1 = (2, 1, 3)$$

$$\mathbf{w}_2 = \mathbf{v}_2 - \frac{\mathbf{w}_1 \cdot \mathbf{w}_2}{\mathbf{w}_1 \cdot \mathbf{w}_1} \cdot \mathbf{w}_1$$

$$= (1, 2, 3) - \frac{2 \cdot 1 + 1 \cdot 2 + 3 \cdot 3}{2 \cdot 2 + 1 \cdot 1 + 3 \cdot 3} \cdot (2, 1, 3)$$

$$= (1, 2, 3) - \frac{13}{14} \cdot (2, 1, 3)$$

$$= (1, 2, 3) - \left(\frac{26}{14}, \frac{13}{14}, \frac{39}{14} \right)$$

$$= \left(1 - \frac{26}{14}, 2 - \frac{13}{14}, 3 - \frac{39}{14} \right)$$

$$= \left(-\frac{12}{14}, \ \frac{15}{14}, \ \frac{3}{14} \right)$$

$$\mathbf{w}_3 = \mathbf{v}_3 - \frac{\mathbf{w}_2 \cdot \mathbf{w}_3}{\mathbf{w}_2 \cdot \mathbf{w}_2} \cdot \mathbf{w}_2 - \frac{\mathbf{w}_1 \cdot \mathbf{w}_3}{\mathbf{w}_1 \cdot \mathbf{w}_1} \cdot \mathbf{w}_1$$

$$= (1,1,1) - \frac{\left(-\frac{12}{14}\right) \cdot 1 + \frac{15}{14} \cdot 1 + \frac{3}{14} \cdot 1}{\left(\frac{-12}{14}\right) \cdot \left(\frac{-12}{14}\right) + \frac{15}{14} \cdot \frac{15}{14} + \frac{3}{14} \cdot \frac{3}{14}}$$

$$\times \left(\frac{-12}{14}, \ \frac{15}{14}, \ \frac{3}{14} \right) - \frac{2 \cdot 1 + 1 \cdot 1 + 3 \cdot 1}{2 \cdot 2 + 1 \cdot 1 + 3 \cdot 3} \cdot (2, 1, 3)$$

$$= (1, \ 1, \ 1) \ - \frac{\dfrac{6}{14}}{\dfrac{144 + 225 \ 9}{14 \times 14}} \times \left(\frac{-12}{14}, \ \frac{15}{14}, \ \frac{3}{14}\right) - \frac{6}{14}(2, \ 1 \ 3)$$

$$= (1, \ 1, \ 1) \ - \frac{84}{378}\left(\frac{-12}{14}, \ \frac{15}{14}, \ \frac{3}{14}\right) - \frac{6}{14}(2, \ 1 \ 3)$$

$$= (1, \ 1, \ 1) \ - \left(\frac{-12}{63}, \ \frac{15}{63}, \ \frac{3}{63}\right) - \left(\frac{12}{14}, \ \frac{6}{14}, \ \frac{3}{14}\right)$$

$$= \left(1 + \frac{12}{63}, -\frac{12}{63}, -\frac{12}{14}, 1 - \frac{15}{63} - \frac{6}{14}, \ 1 - \frac{3}{63} - \frac{18}{14} \right)$$

$$= \left(\frac{1}{3}, \ \frac{1}{3}, \frac{1}{3} \right)$$

$$\|\mathbf{w}_1\| = \sqrt{2 \cdot 2 + 1 \cdot 1 + 3 \cdot 3} = \sqrt{14}$$

$$\|\mathbf{w}_2\| = \sqrt{\left(\frac{-12}{14}\right)^2 + \left(\frac{15}{14}\right)^2 + \left(\frac{3}{14}\right)^2} = \sqrt{\frac{27}{14}}$$

$$\|\mathbf{w}_3\| = \sqrt{\left(\frac{1}{3}\right)^2 + \left(\frac{1}{3}\right)^2 + \left(\frac{1}{3}\right)^2} = \frac{1}{\sqrt{3}}$$

Normalizing w's we have unit vectors

Now, $\dfrac{\mathbf{w}_1}{\|\mathbf{w}_2\|} = \left(\dfrac{2}{\sqrt{14}}, \dfrac{1}{\sqrt{14}}, \dfrac{3}{\sqrt{14}} \right)$

$$\frac{\mathbf{w}_2}{\|\mathbf{w}_2\|} = \left(\frac{-4}{\sqrt{42}}, \frac{5}{\sqrt{42}}, \frac{1}{\sqrt{42}}\right)$$

$$\frac{\mathbf{w}_3}{\|\mathbf{w}_3\|} = \left(\frac{1}{\sqrt{3}}, \frac{1}{\sqrt{3}}, \frac{-1}{\sqrt{3}}\right)$$

Hence, the vectors

$$\left(\frac{2}{\sqrt{14}}, \frac{1}{\sqrt{14}}, \frac{3}{\sqrt{14}}\right), \left(\frac{-4}{\sqrt{42}}, \frac{5}{\sqrt{42}}, \frac{1}{\sqrt{42}}\right),$$

$$\left(\frac{1}{\sqrt{3}}, \frac{1}{\sqrt{3}}, \frac{-1}{\sqrt{3}}\right)$$

form an orthonormal basis of V_3

(b) Let $\mathbf{v}_1 = (1, -1, 0);\ \mathbf{v}_2 = (2, -1, -2);\ \mathbf{v}_3 = (1, -1, -2)$

Take $\mathbf{w}_2 = \mathbf{v}_2 - \dfrac{\mathbf{w}_1 \cdot \mathbf{w}_2}{\mathbf{w}_1 \cdot \mathbf{w}_1} \cdot \mathbf{w}_1$

$$= (2, -1, -2) - \frac{1 \cdot 2 + (-1) \cdot (-1) + 0 \cdot (-2)}{1 \cdot 1 + (-1) \cdot (-1) + 0 \cdot 0} \times (1, -1, 0)$$

$$= (2, -1, -2) - \frac{3}{2}(1, -1, 0)$$

$$= (2, -1, -2) - \left(\frac{3}{2}, -\frac{3}{2}, 0\right)$$

$$= \left(\frac{1}{2}, \frac{1}{2}, -2\right)$$

Take $\mathbf{w}_3 = \mathbf{v}_3 - \dfrac{\mathbf{w}_2 \cdot \mathbf{w}_3}{\mathbf{w}_2 \cdot \mathbf{w}_2} \cdot \mathbf{w}_2 - \dfrac{\mathbf{w}_1 \cdot \mathbf{w}_3}{\mathbf{w}_1 \cdot \mathbf{w}_1} \cdot \mathbf{w}_1$

$$= (1, -1, -2) - \frac{\dfrac{1}{2} \cdot 1 + (-1) + (-2) \cdot (-2)}{\dfrac{1}{2} \cdot \dfrac{1}{2} + \dfrac{1}{2} \cdot \dfrac{1}{2} + (-2) \cdot (-2)} \left(\frac{1}{2}, \frac{1}{2}, -2\right)$$

$$= -\frac{1 \cdot 1 + (-1) \cdot (-1) + 0 \cdot (-2)}{1 \cdot 1 + (-) \cdot (-1) + 0 \cdot 0}(1, -1, 0)$$

$$= (1, -1, -2) - \frac{8}{7}\left(\frac{1}{2}, \frac{1}{2}, -2\right) - (1, -1, 0)$$

$$= \left(\frac{-4}{7}, \frac{-4}{7}, \frac{2}{7}\right)$$

Now, $\|w_1\| = \sqrt{(1)^2 + (-1)^2 + 0^2} = \sqrt{2}$

$$\|w_2\| = \sqrt{\left(\frac{1}{2}\right)^2 + \left(\frac{1}{2}\right)^2 + (-2)^2} = \frac{3}{\sqrt{2}}$$

$$\|w_3\| = \sqrt{\left(\frac{-4}{7}\right)^2 + \left(\frac{-4}{7}\right)^2 + \left(\frac{2}{7}\right)^2} = \frac{6}{7}$$

Normalizing w's, we have unit vectors

$$\left(\frac{\sqrt{2}}{2}, \frac{-\sqrt{2}}{2}, 0\right), \left(\frac{\sqrt{2}}{6}, \frac{-\sqrt{2}}{6}, \frac{-2\sqrt{6}}{6}\right),$$

$$\left(\frac{-2}{3}, \frac{-2}{3}, \frac{1}{3}\right)$$

which form an orthonormal basis of V_3.

(c) Let $v_1 = (0, 1, 1)$; $v_2 = (3, 1, 1)$; $v_3 = (2, 3, 1)$;

Choose $w_1 = v_1 = (0, 1, 1)$

$$w_2 = v_2 - \frac{w_1 \cdot w_2}{w_1 \cdot w_1} \cdot w_1$$

$$= (3, -1, 1) - \frac{0 \cdot 3 + 1 \cdot 1 + 1 \cdot 1}{0 \cdot 0 + 1 \cdot 1 + 1 \cdot 1}(0, 1, 1)$$

$$w_3 = v_3 - \frac{w_2 \cdot w_3}{w_2 \cdot w_2} \cdot w_2 - \frac{w_1 \cdot w_3}{w_1 \cdot w_1} \cdot w_1$$

$$= (2, 3, 1) - \frac{3 \cdot 2 + 0 \cdot 3 + 0 \cdot 1}{3 \cdot 3 + 0 \cdot 0 + 0 \cdot 0}(3, 0, 0) - \frac{0 \cdot 2 + 1 \cdot 3 + 1 \cdot 1}{0 \cdot 1 + 1 \cdot 1 + 1 \cdot 1}(0, 1, 1)$$

$$= (2, 3, 1) - \frac{6}{9}(3, 0, 0) - \frac{4}{2}(0, 1, 1)$$

$$= (0, 1, -1)$$

Now, $\|w_1\| = \sqrt{0^2 + 1^2 + 1^2} = \sqrt{2}$

$$\|w_2\| = \sqrt{3^2 + 0^2 + 0^2} = 3,$$

$$\|w_3\| = \sqrt{0^2 + 1^2 + (-1)^2} = \sqrt{2},$$

$\therefore$ Normalizing w's, we have unit vectors

$$\left(0, \frac{1}{\sqrt{2}}, \frac{1}{\sqrt{2}}\right), \ (1, 0, 0), \ \left(0, \frac{1}{\sqrt{2}}, \frac{-1}{\sqrt{2}}\right)$$

which form an orthonormal basis of V_3.

3. (a) Construct an orthogonal basis of $V_3 = R^3$, given the basis $\mathbf{v}_1 = (3, 0, 4)$; $\mathbf{v}_2 = (-1, 0, 7)$; $\mathbf{v}_3 = (2, 9, 11)$; Also express any vector (x_1, x_2, x_3) as a linear combination of the orthogonal basis.

Solution: Let $\mathbf{w}_1 = \mathbf{v}_1 = (3, 0, 4)$;

$$\mathbf{w}_2 = \mathbf{v}_2 - \frac{\mathbf{w}_1 \cdot \mathbf{w}_2}{\mathbf{w}_1 \cdot \mathbf{w}_1} \cdot \mathbf{w}_1$$

$$= (-1, 0, 7) - \frac{3 \cdot (-1) + 0 \cdot 0 + 4 \cdot 7}{3 \cdot 3 + 0 \cdot 0 + 4 \cdot 4} (3, 0, 4)$$

$$= (-1, 0, 7)\,(-3, 0, 4) = (-4, 0, 3)$$

$$= (-1, 0, 7)\,(-3, 0, 4) = (-4, 0, 3)$$

$$\mathbf{w}_3 = \mathbf{v}_3 - \frac{\mathbf{w}_2 \cdot \mathbf{w}_3}{\mathbf{w}_2 \cdot \mathbf{w}_2} \cdot \mathbf{w}_2 - \frac{\mathbf{w}_1 \cdot \mathbf{w}_3}{\mathbf{w}_1 \cdot \mathbf{w}_1} \cdot \mathbf{w}_1$$

$$= (2, 9, 11) - \frac{(-4) \cdot 2 + 0 \cdot 9 + 3 \cdot 11}{(-4) \cdot (-4) + 0 \cdot 0 + 3 \cdot 3} (-4, 0, 3) - \frac{3 \cdot 2 + 0 \cdot 9 + 4 \cdot 11}{3 \cdot 3 + 0 \cdot 0 + 4 \cdot 4} (3, 0, 4)$$

$$= (2, 9, 11) - (-4, 0, 3) - 2(3, 0, 4) = (0, 9, 0)$$

Clearly, the vectors $\mathbf{w}_1, \mathbf{w}_2, \mathbf{w}_3$ are non-zero and mutually orthogonal and hence form an orthogonal basis for R^3.

To express any vector $\mathbf{z} = (x_1, x_2, x_3)$ in R^3 as a linear combination of $\mathbf{w}_1, \mathbf{w}_2, \mathbf{w}_3$ we need not to solve any linear equations.

But, we have

$$\mathbf{z} = \frac{\mathbf{z} \cdot \mathbf{w}_1}{\|\mathbf{w}_1\|^2} \mathbf{w}_1 + \frac{\mathbf{z} \cdot \mathbf{w}_2}{\|\mathbf{w}_2\|^2} \mathbf{w}_2 + \frac{\mathbf{z} \cdot \mathbf{w}_3}{\|\mathbf{w}_3\|^2} \mathbf{w}_3$$

$$= \frac{3x_1 + 4x_1}{25} \mathbf{w}_1 \frac{-4x_1 + 3x_3}{25} \mathbf{w}_2 + \frac{x_2}{9} \mathbf{w}_3$$

Note: From $\mathbf{w}_1, \mathbf{w}_2, \mathbf{w}_3$, we get the orthonormal basis:

$$\frac{1}{5}(3, 0, 4), \frac{1}{5}(-4, 0, 3), (0, 1, 0),$$

3. (b) Show that in the Gram-schmidt process, span $(v_1, ... v_k) = \text{span}(w_1, ... w_k)$ for $k = 1, ..., r$.

Solution: We shall prove this result by the principle of mathematical induction. For $k = 1$, $w_1 = v_1$ and so span $(v_1) = $ span (w_1). suppose $k > 1$. Since v_k is a linear combination of $w_1, ..., w_k$, we have, span $(v_1 ..., v_k) \subseteq$ span $(w_1, ..., w_k)$. [1]

On the other hand, w_k is a linear combination of v_k and $w_1, ..., w_{k-1}$. By induction, span $(w_1, ..., w_{k-1}) =$ span $(v_1, ... v_{k-1})$ this w_k is a linear combination of $v_1, ..., v_k$ and hence span $(w_1 ..., w_k) \subseteq$ span $(v_1, ..., v_k)$. [2]

From [1] and [2], we get

$$\boxed{\text{span } (v_1, v_2, .., v_k) = \text{span}(w_1, ... w_k)}$$

Orthogonal and Orthonormal Basis

A set of orthogonal vectors spanning a vector space V_m is called an Orthogonal basis. If $(v_1, v_2, ..., v_m)$ be the orthogonal basis (obtained by gram-schmidt orthogonalization process)

then, $\dfrac{w_1}{\|w_1\|}, \dfrac{w_2}{\|w_2\|}, ..., \dfrac{w_m}{\|w_m\|}$

represent an orthonormal basis of all the vector space or the subspace.

EXAMPLES

1. Find an orthonormal basis for the subspace U of R^4 spanned by

$$v_1 = (1,1,1,1), \; v_2 = (1,2,4,5), \; v_3 = (1,-3,-4,-2)$$

Solution: We first find an orthogonal basis of U using the Gram-schmidt algorithm.

First put $w_1 = v_1 = (1,1,1,1)$

Next find, $v_2 - \dfrac{(v_2, w_1)}{\|w_1\|^2} \cdot w_1$

$$= (1,2,4,5) - \dfrac{12}{4}(1,1,1,1)$$

$$= (-2,-1,1,2)$$

Again put, $w_2 = (-2, -1, 1, 2)$. then find

$$v_3 - \frac{(v_3, w_1)}{\|w_1\|^2} w_1 - \frac{(v_3, w_2)}{\|w_2\|^2} w_2$$

$$= (1, -3, -4, -2) - \frac{-8}{4}(1,1,1,1) - \frac{-7}{10}(-2,-1,1,2)$$

$$= \left(\frac{8}{5}, \frac{-17}{10}, \frac{-13}{10}, \frac{7}{5}\right).$$

Clear fraction to obtain:

$$w_3 = (16, -17, -13, 14).$$

Lastly, normalize the orthogonal basis

$$w_1 = (1,1,1,1),$$

$$w_2 = (-2,-1,1,2),$$

$$w_3 = (16,-17,-13,14).$$

Since $\|w_1\|^2 = 4, \|w_2\|^2 = 10, \|w_3\|^2 = 910,$

The following vectors form an orthonormal basis of U:

$$u_1 = \frac{1}{2}(1,1,1,1)$$

$$u_2 = \frac{1}{\sqrt{10}}(-2,-1,1,2)$$

$$u_3 = \frac{1}{\sqrt{910}}(16,-17,-13,14).$$

2. Let $\{v_1 = (1,1,1), v_2 = (0,1,1), v_3 = (0,0,1)\}$ be a basis of the euclidean space R^3. Use the Gram–Schmidt algorithm to transform $\{v_i\}$ into an orthonormal basis $\{u_i\}$ of R^3.

Solution: First set $w_1 = v_1 = (1,1,1)$. Then find

$$v_2 - \frac{(v_2, w_1)}{\|w_1\|^2} w_1 = (0,1,1) - \frac{2}{3}(1,1,1) = \left(-\frac{2}{3}, \frac{1}{3}, \frac{1}{3}\right)$$

or $\quad w_2 = (-2, 1, 1)$

Next find $\quad v_3 - \frac{(v_3, w_1)}{\|w_1\|^2} - \frac{(v_3, w_2)}{\|w_2\|^2}$

$$= (0,0,1) - \frac{1}{3}(1,1,1) - \frac{1}{6}(-2,1,1)$$

$$= \left(0, -\frac{1}{2}, \frac{1}{2}\right)$$

or $\quad \mathbf{w}_3 = (0,-1,1)$.

Normalizing $\{\mathbf{w}_1, \mathbf{w}_2, \mathbf{w}_3\}$ to obtain the following required orthonormal basis of R^3.

$$\left\{ \mathbf{u}_1 = \left(\frac{1}{\sqrt{3}}, \frac{1}{\sqrt{3}}, \frac{1}{\sqrt{3}}\right), \mathbf{u}_2 = \left(-\frac{2}{\sqrt{6}}, \frac{1}{\sqrt{6}}, \frac{1}{\sqrt{6}}\right), \mathbf{u}_3 = \left(0, -\frac{1}{\sqrt{2}}, \frac{1}{\sqrt{2}}\right) \right\}.$$

3. Obtain an orthonormal basis of the subspace W of R^5 spanned by

$$\mathbf{v}_1 = (1,1,1,0,1); \quad \mathbf{v}_2 = (1,0,0,-1,1), \quad \mathbf{v}_3 = (3,1,1,-2,3); \quad \mathbf{v}_4 = (0,2,1,1,-1).$$

Solution: Let $\mathbf{w}_1 = \mathbf{u}_1 = (1,1,1,0,1)$. Then find

$$\mathbf{v}_2 - \frac{(\mathbf{v}_2, \mathbf{w}_1)}{\|\mathbf{w}_1\|^2} \mathbf{w}_1 = (1,0,0,-1,1) - \frac{2}{4}(1,1,1,0,1)$$

$$= \left(\frac{1}{2}, -\frac{1}{2}, -\frac{1}{2}, -1, \frac{1}{2}\right)$$

or $\quad \mathbf{w}_2 = (1,-1,-1,-2,1)$.

Next, find $\mathbf{v}_3 - \dfrac{(\mathbf{v}_3, \mathbf{w}_1)}{\|\mathbf{w}_1\|^2} - \dfrac{(\mathbf{v}_3, \mathbf{w}_2)}{\|\mathbf{w}_2\|^2}$

$$= (3,1,1,-2,3) - \frac{8}{4}(1,1,1,0,1) - \frac{8}{8}(1,-1,-1,-2,1) = (0,0,0,0,0)$$

$\Rightarrow$ $\mathbf{v}_3$ is a linear combination of $\mathbf{v}_1$ and $\mathbf{v}_2$ and hence $\mathbf{v}_3$ is omitted.

Next form $\mathbf{v}_4 - \dfrac{(\mathbf{v}_4, \mathbf{w}_1)}{\|\mathbf{w}_1\|^2} \mathbf{w}_1 - \dfrac{(\mathbf{v}_4, \mathbf{w}_2)}{\|\mathbf{w}_2\|^2} \mathbf{w}_2$

$$= (0,2,1,1-1) - \frac{2}{4}(1,1,1,0,1) - \frac{-6}{8}(1,-1,-1,-2,1)$$

$$= \left(\frac{1}{4}, \frac{3}{4}, -\frac{1}{4}, -\frac{1}{2}, -\frac{3}{4}\right).$$

or $\quad \mathbf{w}_3 = (1, 3, -1, -2, -3)$.

Normalizing $\{w_1, w_2, w_3\}$ we obtain the required orthonormal basis of W:

$$u_1 = \frac{1}{2}(1,1,1,0,1) \quad u_2 = \frac{1}{2\sqrt{2}}(1,-1,-1,-2,1)$$

$$u_3 = \frac{1}{2\sqrt{6}}(1,3,-1,-2,-3)$$

4. Let V be the vector space of polynomials $f(t)$ with inner product $(f, g) = \int_{-1}^{1} f(t)g(t)dt$. Apply the Gram–Schmidt algorithm to the set $\{1, t, t^2, t^3\}$ to obtain an orthonormal set $\{f_0, f_1, f_2, f_3\}$.

Solution: Let us make use of the fact if $r + s = n$ then,

$$(t^r, t^s) = \int_{-1}^{1} t^n dt = \left[\frac{t^{n+1}}{n+1}\right]_{-1}^{1} = \begin{cases} \dfrac{2}{n+1} & \text{if } n \text{ is even} \\ 0 & \text{if } n \text{ is odd} \end{cases}$$

Let us set $f_0 = 1$. Then find

$$f_1 = t - \frac{(t,1)}{(1,1)} \cdot 1 = t - \frac{0}{2} \cdot 1 = t - \frac{0}{2} \cdot 1 = t$$

Next, find $f_2 = t^2 - \dfrac{(t^2,1)}{(1,1)} \cdot 1 - \dfrac{(t^2,t)}{(t,t)} \cdot t$

$$= t^2 - \frac{\left(\dfrac{2}{3}\right)}{2} \cdot 1 - \frac{0}{\left(\dfrac{2}{3}\right)} \cdot t$$

$$= t^2 - \frac{1}{3}.$$

and $f_3 = t^3 - \dfrac{(t^3-1)}{(1,1)} \cdot 1 - \dfrac{(t^3,t)}{(t,t)} t - \dfrac{\left(t^3, t^2 - \dfrac{1}{3}\right) \cdot \left(t^2 - \dfrac{1}{3}\right)}{\left(t^2 - \dfrac{1}{3}, t^2 - \dfrac{1}{3}\right)}$

$$= t^3 - 0 \cdot 1 - \frac{\dfrac{2}{5}}{\dfrac{2}{3}} t - 0\left(t^2 - \frac{1}{3}\right)$$

$$= t^3 - \frac{3}{5}t$$

i.e., $\left\{1, t, t^2 - \frac{1}{3}, t^3 - \frac{3}{5}t\right\}$ is the required orthonormal set of polynomials.

Bessel's Inequality

Let $\{u_1, u_2, ..., u_r\}$ be an orthonormal set of vectors in V. Let v be any vector in V and let c_i be the Fourier coefficient of V w.r.t. u_i

Then $\boxed{\displaystyle\sum_{k=1}^{r} c_k^2 \le \|v\|^2}$

Proof: Let $c_i = (v, u_i)$ and $\|u_i\| = 1$

By using $(u_i, u_j) = 0$ for $i \ne j$,

we get $0 \le \left(v - \sum c_k u_k, v - \sum c_k u_k\right)$

$$= (v, v) - 2\left(v, \sum c_k u_k\right) + \sum c_k^2$$

$$= (v, v) - \sum 2c_k(v, v_k) + \sum c_k^2$$

$$= (v, v) - \sum 2c_k^2 + \sum c_k^2$$

$$= (v, v) - \sum c_k^2$$

$\Rightarrow$ $\boxed{\displaystyle\sum_{k=1}^{r} c_k^2 \le \|v\|^2}$

EXERCISES

1. Using the Gram-Schmidt orthogonalization process, construct an orthonormal basis from the given basis $v_1 = (2, 3, 0)$, $v_2 = (6, 1, 0)$; and $v_3 = (0, 2, 4)$

   Ans: $w_1 = (2, 3, 0)$, $w_2 = (3.69, -2.460)$ and
   $w_1 = (0.26, -2.16, 4)$ is an orthonormal basis

2. Construct an orthogonal basis of $(-1, -3, 3, 1)$, $(1, 1, -1, 0)$, $(3, -5, 2, 1)$ and $(-1, 1, 0, 1)$

Linear Transformation

Definition: If U and V be two vector spaces over the same field F, then a function T of U into V i.e., $T: U \rightarrow V$ is called a linear transformation (or vector space Homomorphism) from U into V if it satisfies the following properties.

(I) Additive property: $T(\alpha + \beta) = T(\alpha) + T(\beta), \forall \alpha, \beta \in U$

i.e., T carries the sum of two vectors of U to the sum of the images of the vectors.

(II) Homogeneous property: $T(a\alpha) = aT(\alpha), \forall \alpha, \beta \in U$ and $a \in F$

i.e., T carries the scalar multiple of a vector $\alpha \in U$ to the same scalar multiple of the T-image of that vector.

The above-mentioned two properties are combined into single property, namely linear property (or linearity of T) as :

$$T(a\alpha + \beta) = aT(\alpha) + T(\beta), \ \forall \alpha, \beta \in U \text{ and } a \in F.$$

or $\quad T(a\alpha + b\beta) = aT(\alpha) + bT(\beta), \forall \alpha, \beta \in U$ and, $a, b \in F.$

Definition (Linear operator on U) (L.O). If in the above definition of linear transformation, V is the same as U, then the linear transformation $T : U \rightarrow U$ is called a linear operator such that

$$T(c\alpha + \beta) = cT(\alpha) + T(\beta)$$

$$\forall \alpha, \beta \in U, c \in F$$

Note: A linear operator is a function or mapping from U into itself, whenever it is referred that T is a linear transformation on U it would mean that T is a linear operator.

Definition (Linear Functional on U)

Let U be a vector space over the field F and T be a mapping from U into F

i.e., $\quad T : U \rightarrow F$

such that $T(a\alpha + b\beta) = aT(\alpha) + bT(\beta),$

$$\forall \alpha, \beta \in U \text{ and } a, b \in F,$$

then the mapping T is called a linear functional on U. This is also known as scalar valued function.

Theorem 1. (Identity transformation I on U)

If U is a vector space over the field F, then the function (or mapping) T is defined as

$$T(\alpha) = \alpha, \forall \alpha \in U \qquad\qquad [1]$$

Now, for $\alpha, \beta \in U$ and $a, b \in F$

$\Rightarrow \qquad a\alpha + b\beta \in U$

$\therefore \qquad T(a\alpha + b\beta) = a\alpha + b\beta$

$$= aT(\alpha) + bT(\beta)$$

(Using [1])

$\Rightarrow$ T is linear operator, called identity operator denoted by I.

Note: $I(\alpha) = \alpha \ \forall \ \alpha \in U$

Theorem 2. (Zero operator or Transformation)

If U and V are vector spaces over the same field F, then a mapping (or function) T defined as:

$$T: U \to V, T\ (\alpha) = 0, \forall \alpha \in U$$

is a linear transformation (or operator)

Proof: Let $T: U \to V$ (or U) be a linear transformation, ($\because$ 0 is a common element of U and V)

Now, for $\alpha, \beta \in U, a, b \in F$

$\Rightarrow \qquad a\alpha + b\beta \in U$

($\because$ U is a vector space)

thus, by definition of T, We have

$$T(a\alpha + b\beta) = 0 = aT(\alpha) + bT(\beta)$$

$$= a.0 + b.0 = 0$$

$\Rightarrow$ by definition of L.T, T is a linear transformation.

Note: $0(\alpha) = 0 \forall \alpha \in U$.

Theorem 3. (Negative Transformation).

If $V(F)$ and $W(F)$ are vector spaces and L in a linear transformation from V to W, then the mapping $-L$ is defined by

$$(-L)\mathbf{x} = -[L(\mathbf{x}),] \ \forall \mathbf{x} \in V \ \text{is a linear transformation.}$$

Proof: First of all, $-L : V \to W$ is defined as a

$$(-L)\mathbf{x} = -[L(\mathbf{x})] \; \forall \; \mathbf{x} \in V$$

Now for $\mathbf{x}, \mathbf{y} \in V$, and $c_1, c_2 \in F$

$$c_1\mathbf{x} + c_2\mathbf{y} \in V$$

$$\therefore \qquad (-L)(c_1\mathbf{x} + c_2\mathbf{y}) = -[L(c_1\mathbf{x} + c_2\mathbf{y})] \qquad [\because \text{of (1)}]$$

$$= -[c_1 L(\mathbf{x}) + c_2 L(\mathbf{y})] \qquad [\because L \text{ is } L.T]$$

$$= -c_1 L(\mathbf{x}) - c_2 L(\mathbf{y})$$

$$= c_1[(-L(\mathbf{x}))] + c_2[-L(\mathbf{y})]$$

$$= c_1[(-L(\mathbf{x})] + c_2[(-L)\mathbf{y}]$$

$\Rightarrow$ $-L$ is a linear transformation

Hence $-L$ is a linear transformation corresponding to linear transformation L.

Theorem 4.

Let $L : V \to W$ be a linear transformation and suppose $\mathbf{x}_1, \mathbf{x}_2, ..., \mathbf{x}_n \in V$ have the property that the images $L(\mathbf{x}_1), L(\mathbf{x}_2) ..., L(\mathbf{x}_n)$ are linearly independent. Show that the vectors $\mathbf{x}_1, \mathbf{x}_2, ..., \mathbf{x}_n$ are linearly independent.

Proof: Let there exist $c_1, c_2, ... c_n \in F$

such that. $c_1\mathbf{x}_1 + c_2\mathbf{x}_2 + ... + c_n\mathbf{x}_n = \mathbf{0}$

Now $L(c_1\mathbf{x}_1 + c_2\mathbf{x}_2 + ... + c_n\mathbf{x}_n) = L(\mathbf{0}) = 0$

$\Rightarrow \qquad c_1 L(\mathbf{x}_1) + c_2 L(\mathbf{x}_2) + ... + c_n L(\mathbf{x}_n) = \mathbf{0} \qquad (\because L \text{ is L.T})$

$\Rightarrow \qquad c_1 = 0, c_2 = 0, ..., c_n = 0 \qquad (\because L(\mathbf{x}_1), L(\mathbf{x}_2), ... L(\mathbf{x}_n) \text{ are linearly independent})$

Hence $\mathbf{x}_1, \mathbf{x}_2, ..., \mathbf{x}_n$ are also linearly independent.

EXAMPLES

1. Find out which of the following are linear transformations:

   (a) $T : R^2 \to R^3$ defined by $T(a, b) = (a + b, a - b, b)$
   (b) $T : R^2 \to R$ defined by $T(a, b) = (a - b)$
   (c) $T : R^3 \to R$ defined by $T(a, b, c) = 2a - 3b + 4c$.
   (d) $T : R^2 \to R$ defined by $T(a, b) = (ab)$
   (e) $T : R \to R^2$ defined by $T(a) = (2a, 3a)$
   (f) $T : R^3 \to R^3$ defined by $T(x, y, z) = (x + 1, y, z)$
   (g) $T : R^2 \to R$ defined by $T(a, b) = |2a - 3b|$.

***Solution*:**

(a) Here we have $T : R^2 \rightarrow R^3$

such that $T(a,b) = (a + b, a - b, b)$, $\forall a, b \in R$ [1]

Let $\mathbf{u}_1 = (a_1, b_1)$; $\mathbf{u}_2 = (a_2, b_2)$ be any two elements of R^2.

Then from [1],

$$\left.\begin{array}{l} T(\mathbf{u}_1) = T(a_1, b_1) = (a_1 + b_1, a_1 - b_1, b_1) \\ T(\mathbf{u}_2) = T(a_2, b_2) = (a_2 + b_2, a_2 - b_2, b_2) \end{array}\right\} \qquad [2]$$

Also let $a, b \in R$, then $a\mathbf{u}_1 + b\mathbf{u}_2 \in R^2$

$\therefore \quad T(a\mathbf{u}_1 + b\mathbf{u}_2) = T[a(a_1, b_1) + b(a_2, b_2)]$

$\qquad\qquad\qquad = T(aa_1 + ba_2, ab_1 + bb_2)$

$\qquad\qquad = (aa_1 + ba_2 + ab_1 + bb_2, aa_1 + ba_2 - ab_1 - bb_2, ab_1 + bb_2)$ using [2]

$\qquad\qquad = (a(a_1 + b_1) + b(a_2 + b_2), a(a_1 - b_1) + b(a_2 - b_2), ab_1 + bb_2)$

$\qquad\qquad = a(a_1 + b_1, a_1 - b_1, b_1) + b(a_2 + b_2, a_2 - b_2, b_2)$ using [2]

$\qquad\qquad = aT(a_1, b_1) + bT(a_2, b_2)$

$\qquad\qquad = aT(\mathbf{u}_1) + bT(\mathbf{u}_2),$ from [2]

Hence T is a linear transformation.

(b) Here, we have $T : R^2 \rightarrow R$

such that $T(a, b) = a - b$, $\forall a, b \in R$ [1]

Let $\mathbf{u}_1 = (a_1, b_1)$; $\mathbf{u}_2 = (a_2, b_2)$ be any two elements of R^2.

Then from [1] $\left.\begin{array}{l} T(\mathbf{u}_1) = T(a_1, b_2) = a_1 - b_1 \\ \text{and} \quad T(\mathbf{u}_2) = T(a_2, b_2) = a_2 - b_2 \end{array}\right\}$ [2]

$\therefore \quad T(a\mathbf{u}_1 + b\mathbf{u}_2) = T[a(a_1, b_1) + b(a_2, b_2)]$

$\qquad\qquad\qquad = T(aa_1 + ba_2, ab_1 + bb_2)$

$\qquad\qquad\qquad = (aa_1 + ba_2) - (ab_1 + bb_2),$ using [1]

$\qquad\qquad\qquad = a(a_1 - b_1) + b(a_2 - b_2)$

$\qquad\qquad\qquad = aT(a_1, b_1) + bT(a_2, b_2)$ using [2]

$\qquad\qquad\qquad = aT(\mathbf{u}_1) + bT(\mathbf{u}_2)$ using [2]

This shows that T is a linear transformation.

(c) Here, we have $T : R^3 \to R$

such that $T(a,b,c) = 2a - 3b + 4c, \ a,b,c \in R$ [1]

Let $\mathbf{u}_1 = (a_1, b_1, c_1);\ \mathbf{u}_2 = (a_2, b_2, c_2)$ be any two elements of R^3

Then from [1], $T(\mathbf{u}_1) = T(a_1, b_1, c_1) = 2a_1 - 3b_1 + 4c_1$
and $T(\mathbf{u}_2) = T(a_2, b_2, c_2) = 2a_2 - 3b_2 + 4c_2$ [2]

Also, let $a, b \in R$, then $a\mathbf{u}_1 + b\mathbf{u}_2 \in R^3$

$\therefore \quad T(a\mathbf{u}_1 + b\mathbf{u}_2) = T[a(a_1, b_1, c_1) + b(a_2, b_2, c_2)]$

$\qquad = T(aa_1 + ba_2, ab_1 + bb_2, ac_1 + bc_2)$

$\qquad = 2(aa_1 + ba_2) - 3(ab_1 + bb_2) + 4(ac_1 + bc_2)$ using [1]

$\qquad = a(2a_1 - 3b_1 + 4c_1) + b(2a_2 - 3b_2 + 4c_2)$

$\qquad = aT(\mathbf{u}_1) + bT(\mathbf{u}_2),$ using [2]

This shows that T is a linear transformation.

(d) Here, we have $T : R^2 \to R$

Such that $T(a,b) = ab, \forall a,b \in R$ [1]

Let $\mathbf{u}_1 = (a_1, b_1);\ \mathbf{u}_2 = (a_2, b_2)$ be any two elements of R^2.

Then from [1], $T(\mathbf{u}_1) = T(a_1, b_1) = a_1 b_1$
$T(\mathbf{u}_2) = T(a_2, b_2) = a_2 b_2$ [2]

Also let $a, b \in R$, Then $a\mathbf{u}_1 + b\mathbf{u}_2 \in R^2$

$\therefore \quad T(a\mathbf{u}_1 + b\mathbf{u}_2) = T[a(a_1, b_1) + b(a_2, b_2)]$

$\qquad = T(aa_1 + ba_2, ab_1 + bb_2)$

$\qquad = (aa_1 + ba_2)(ab_1 + bb_2)$ using [1]

$\qquad \neq a(a_1 b_1) + b(a_2 b_2)$

i.e., $\neq aT(\mathbf{u}_1) + bT(\mathbf{u}_2)$

This shows that T cannot be linear.

(e) Here, we have $T : R \to R^2$

such that $T(a) = (2a, \ 3a)$

Let $a, \ b, \in R$, then

$\qquad T(a) = (2a, 3a)$

$\qquad T(b) = (2b, 3b)$

$\therefore \qquad T(a+b) = [2(a+b), 3(a+b)]$

(by the definition of linear transformation)

$$= (2a, 3a) + (2b, 3b)$$

i.e., $T(a+b) = T(a) + T(b)$, by definition of T.

Also, for any scalar k, we have

$$T(ka) = T(2ka, 3ka) = kT(a)$$

$\Rightarrow$ T is a linear transformation.

(f) We have: $T: R^3 \to R^3$ defined by

$$T(x, y, z) = (x+1, y, z)$$

Let $\mathbf{v}_1 = (x_1, y_1, z_1) \in V_3(R)$

and $\mathbf{v}_2 = (x_2, y_2, z_2) \in V_3(R)$

and a, b are any two real numbers

$$\mathbf{v}_1 a + \mathbf{v}_2 b = a(x_1, y_1 z_1) + b(x_2, y_2, z_2)$$
$$= (ax_1 + bx_2, ay_1 + by_2, az_1 + bz_2)$$

$\therefore$ $T(\mathbf{v}_1 a + \mathbf{v}_2 b) = T(ax_1 + bx_2, ay_1 + by_2, az_1 + bz_2)$
$$= (ax_1 + bx_2 + 1, ay_1 + by_2, az_1 + bz_2) \qquad [1]$$

and $aT(\mathbf{v}_1) + bT(\mathbf{v}_2)$

$$= aT(x_1, y_1, z_1) + bT(x_2, y_2, z_2)$$
$$= a(x_1 + 1, y_1, z_1) + b(x_2 + 1, y_2, z_2)$$
$$= (ax_1 + a, ay_1, az_1) + (bx_2 + b, by_2, bz_2)$$
$$= (ax_1 + bx_2 + a + b, ay_1 + by_2, az_1 + bz_2) \qquad [2]$$

From [1], and (2),

$$T(a\mathbf{v}_1 + b\mathbf{v}_2) \neq aT(\mathbf{v}_1) + bT(\mathbf{v}_2)$$

Hence T is not a linear transformations

(g) We have $T: R^2 \to R$ defined by

$$T(a, b) = |2a - 3b|$$

$\mathbf{x} = (a_1, b_1) \in V_2(R)$ and $\mathbf{y} = (a_2, b_2) \in V_2(R)$

and α, β are any two real numbers.

$$\mathbf{x}\alpha + \mathbf{y}\beta = \alpha(a_1, b_1) + \beta(a_2, b_2)$$
$$= (\alpha a_1 + \beta a_2, \alpha b_1 + \beta b_2)$$

$$T(\mathbf{x}\alpha + \mathbf{y}\beta)$$

$$= T(\alpha a_1 + \beta a_2, \ \alpha b_1 + \beta b_2)$$

$$\left| 2(\alpha a_1 + \beta a_2) - 3(\alpha b_1 + \beta b_2) \right| \tag{1}$$

$$= \left| \alpha(2a_1 - 3b_1) + \beta(2a_2 - 3b_2) \right|$$

and $\alpha T(\mathbf{x}) + \beta T(\mathbf{y})$

$$= \alpha T(a_1, b_1) + \beta T(a_2, b_2)$$

$$= \alpha \left| 2a_1 - 3b_1 \right| + \beta \left| 2a_2 - 3b_2 \right|$$

$$= \left| \alpha(2a_1 - 3b_1) \right| + \left| \beta(2a_2 - 3b_2) \right| \tag{2}$$

From [1] and [2], we get

$$T(\mathbf{x}\alpha + \mathbf{y}\beta) \neq \alpha T(\mathbf{x}) + \beta T(\mathbf{y})$$

Hence $T : R^2 \to R$ is not a linear transformation.

2. Let $\mathbf{x}_1 = \begin{bmatrix} 1 \\ 2 \\ -1 \end{bmatrix}$; $\mathbf{x}_2 = \begin{bmatrix} 2 \\ -3 \\ 2 \end{bmatrix}$; $\mathbf{x}_3 = \begin{bmatrix} 4 \\ 1 \\ 3 \end{bmatrix}$

and $\mathbf{x}_4 = \begin{bmatrix} -3 \\ 1 \\ 2 \end{bmatrix}$ be the vectors in $V_3\ (R)$.

Show that $L(\{\mathbf{x}_1, \mathbf{x}_2\}) \neq L(\{\mathbf{x}_3, \mathbf{x}_4\})$.

Solution: If possible, let us assume that

$$L(\{\mathbf{x}_1, \mathbf{x}_2\}) = L(\{\mathbf{x}_3, \mathbf{x}_4\})$$

This means that there exist scalars $\alpha_1, \alpha_2 \in R$ for arbitrary $a_1, a_2 \in R$ such that

$$\alpha_1 \mathbf{x}_1 + \alpha_2 \mathbf{x}_2 = a_1 \mathbf{x}_3 + a_2 \mathbf{x}_4$$

$$\Rightarrow \quad \alpha_1 \begin{bmatrix} 1 \\ 2 \\ -1 \end{bmatrix} + \alpha_2 \begin{bmatrix} 2 \\ -3 \\ 2 \end{bmatrix} = a_1 \begin{bmatrix} 4 \\ 1 \\ 3 \end{bmatrix} + a_2 \begin{bmatrix} -3 \\ 1 \\ 2 \end{bmatrix}$$

$$\Rightarrow \quad \begin{bmatrix} \alpha_1 + 2\alpha_2 \\ 2\alpha_1 - 3\alpha_2 \\ -\alpha_1 + 2\alpha_2 \end{bmatrix} = \begin{bmatrix} 4a_1 - 3a_2 \\ a_1 + a_2 \\ 3a_1 + 2a_2 \end{bmatrix}$$

$$\Rightarrow \quad \alpha_1 + 2\alpha_2 = 4a_1 - 3a_2 \tag{1}$$

$$2\alpha_1 - 3\alpha_2 = a_1 + a_2 \tag{2}$$

$$-\alpha_1 + 2\alpha_2 = 3a_1 + 2a_2 \tag{3}$$

Solving [1] and [3], $\alpha_2 = \dfrac{1}{2}(a_1 - 5a_2); \alpha_2 = \dfrac{1}{4}(7a_1 - a_2)$,

Substituting in [2], we get,

$$2\alpha_1 - 3\alpha_2 = 2\left[\frac{1}{2}(a_1 - 5a_2)\right] - 3\frac{1}{4}(7a_1 - a_2)$$

$$= (a_1 - 5a_2) - \frac{3}{4}(7a_1 - a_2)$$

$$= \frac{-17}{4}a_1 - \frac{17}{4}a_2 \neq a_1 + a_2$$

Hence, [2] is not satisfied.

$$\therefore \quad L(\{\mathbf{x}_1, \mathbf{x}_2\}) \neq L(\{\mathbf{x}_3, \mathbf{x}_4\})$$

Rank and Nullity of a linear transformation

Definition (Rank of T): If T be a linear transformation from a finite dimensional vector space U over F into a vector space V over F, then the rank of T is the dimension of the range space of T and is denoted by $\rho(T)$

i.e., Rank of $T = \rho(T) = \dim$ [Range (T)]

$\qquad = \dim$ [R(T)]

Definition (Nullity of T): If $T : U \to V$ be a linear transformation from a finite dimensional vector space $U(F)$ into a vector space $V(F)$, then the nullity of T is the dimension of the null space of T and is denoted by $v(T)$

i.e, Nullity of $T = v(T) = \dim$. [Null space T]

$\qquad = \dim$ [$N(T)$]

Nullity of a matrix

If $\mathbf{A}$ is a non-singular matrix, then $\mathbf{Ax} = \mathbf{0}$ clearly implies $\mathbf{x} = \mathbf{0}$.

Thus, only the null vector maps into null vector under transformation $\mathbf{A}$.

If $\mathbf{A}$ is a singular matrix, then there are non-zero vectors $\mathbf{x}$ for which $\mathbf{Ax} = \mathbf{0}$.

All the vectors $\mathbf{x}$ in E_n which maps into the null vector on transformation under $\mathbf{A}$, form a subspace of E_n. If $\mathbf{x}$ and $\mathbf{y}$ are two such vectors, then

$$\mathbf{Ax} = \mathbf{0}, \ \mathbf{Ay} = \mathbf{0} \text{ imply } \mathbf{A}(\mathbf{x} + \mathbf{y}) = \mathbf{0}, \ \mathbf{A}(\alpha \mathbf{x}) = \mathbf{0}.$$

So, closure law under addition and multiplication by a scalar is satisfied. This space is called the null space of **A**, and its dimension is called the nullity of **A**.

Theorem 3: (Negative of transformation)

If U and V are vector spaces over the same field F and T is a linear transformation from U into V, then the mapping $-T$ defined by $(-T)\alpha = -[T(\alpha)] \quad \forall \alpha \in V$ is a linear transformation.

Proof: $-T : U \to V$ is defined as

$$(-T)\alpha = -[T(\alpha)], \ \forall \alpha \in U \tag{1}$$

Now for $\alpha, \beta \in U$ and $a, b \in F$

$$a\alpha + b\beta \in U$$

$\therefore \quad (-T)(a\alpha + b\beta) = -[T(a\alpha + b\beta)]$ \hfill (of [1])

$\qquad = -[aT(\alpha) + bT(\beta)]$ \hfill ($\because T$ is linear transformation)

$\qquad = -aT(\alpha) - bT(\beta)$

$\qquad = a[(-T(\alpha)) + b(-T(\beta))]$

$\Rightarrow \quad -T$ is a linear transformation

$\Rightarrow \quad -T$ is L.T corresponding to linear transformation T.

Properties of Linear Transformations

P_1: Let $T : U \to V$ be a linear transformation from the vector space U over the field F to the vector space V over the same field F,

then **(a)** $T(0) = 0$, where left hand $0 \in U$ and right hand $0 \in V$.

(b) $T(-\alpha) = -T(\alpha) \quad \forall \alpha \in U$

(c) $T(\alpha - \beta) = T(\alpha) - T(\beta) \ \forall \alpha, \beta \in U$

Proof: (a) $T(\alpha) = \alpha'$ for $\alpha \in U, \alpha' \in V$ \hfill [1]

Then, $T(\alpha) = T(\alpha + 0)$

$\qquad = T(\alpha) + T(0);$ \hfill ($\because T$ is linear transformation)

$\Rightarrow \quad \alpha' = \alpha' + T(0);$ \hfill (using [1])

$\Rightarrow \quad T(0) = 0;$ \hfill (using cancellation law)

(b) $\quad T(-\alpha) = T((-1)\alpha);$ $\qquad\qquad\qquad$ ($\because T$ is linear transformation)

$\qquad\qquad = (-1)T(\alpha);$ $\qquad\qquad\qquad\qquad$ (by definition)

$\qquad\qquad = -T(\alpha)$

(c) $\quad T(\alpha - \beta) = T(\alpha + (-\beta)) = T(\alpha) + T(-\beta),$ $\qquad$ ($\because T$ is linear transformation)

$\qquad\qquad\qquad\qquad\quad = T(\alpha) - T(\beta),$

P_2: (Linear transformations for same dimensional vector space)

If U and V are n-dimensional vector spaces over the same field F having their bases as

$B_1 = \{u_1, u_2, ..., u_n\}$ and $B_2 = \{v_1, v_2, ...v_n\}$ respectively, then there exist a unique linear transformation T form $U(F)$ to $V(F)$, such that

$$T(\mathbf{u}_i) = \mathbf{v}_i, \quad i = 1, 2, 3, ..., n \qquad\qquad [1]$$

Proof: Since B_1 is basis of U, so **u**, any vector in $U(F)$ can be expressed as a linear combination of the elements of B_1

i.e., $\quad \mathbf{u} = \sum_{i=1}^{n} a_i \mathbf{u}_i, a_i\text{'s in } F \qquad\qquad\qquad\qquad [2]$

(i) Existence of T:

For $\mathbf{u} \in U(F)$, let us define a mapping

$$T(\mathbf{u}) = T(\sum a_i \mathbf{u}_i) = \sum a_i T(\mathbf{u}_i), \text{ by property of } T$$

$$= \sum_{i=1}^{n} a_i (\mathbf{v}_i), \text{ from [1]} \qquad\qquad\qquad [3]$$

$\qquad$ = a linear combination of basis B_2 of $V(F)$.

This shows that $T(\mathbf{u})$ is a unique element of $V(F)$ and thus T is well defined rule for associating a unique vector $T(\mathbf{u})$ in V with each vector $\mathbf{u} \in U$.

$\therefore T$ is a mapping from U into V.

(ii) T is a linear transformation:

Let $\mathbf{u}, \mathbf{v} \in U(F)$ and $a, b \in F$. Then, we have

$$T(a\mathbf{u} + b\mathbf{v}) = T(a\sum a_i \mathbf{u}_i + b\sum b_i \mathbf{u}_i), \text{ from [2]}$$

(for $\mathbf{u} = \sum a_i \mathbf{u}_i, v = \sum b_i \mathbf{u}_i$)

$$= T[(\sum aa_i)\mathbf{u}_i + (\sum bb_i)\mathbf{u}_i]$$

$$= T[(\sum aa_i + bb_i)T(\mathbf{u}_i)$$

$$= \sum (aa_i + bb_i)\mathbf{v}_i \quad \text{from [1]},$$

$$= \sum aa_i\mathbf{v}_i + \sum bb_i\mathbf{v}_i$$

$$= a\sum a_i\mathbf{v}_i + b\sum b_i\mathbf{v}_i$$

$$= aT(\mathbf{u}) + bT(\mathbf{v})$$

This shows that T is a linear transformation. i.e., there exist a linear transformation T from $U \to V$ such that

$$T(\mathbf{u}_i) = \mathbf{v}_i, i = 1,2,3,...n$$

(iii) Uniqueness of T:

If possible, let $T' : U \to V$ be another transformation such that

$$T'(\mathbf{u}_i) = \mathbf{v}_i, i = 1,2,3,...n \tag{4}$$

then $\quad T'(\mathbf{u}) = T'(\sum a_i\mathbf{u}_i) \ \forall \mathbf{u} \in U, a_i, \in F \quad$ from [2]

$$= \sum_{i=1}^{n} a_i\mathbf{v}_i; \quad \text{from [4]}$$

$$= T(\mathbf{u}); \quad \text{From [3]}$$

As above equality is true for each $\mathbf{u} \in U$ so $T = T'$

showing the uniqueness of T.

$\boldsymbol{P_3}$: Let $T : U \to V$ be a linear transformation and suppose $\mathbf{u}_1, \mathbf{u}_2, ...\mathbf{u}_n \in U$ have the property that their images $T(\mathbf{u}_1)$, $T(\mathbf{u}_2)$, ..., $T(\mathbf{u}_n)$ are linearly independent. Show that the vectors $\mathbf{u}_1, \mathbf{u}_2, ..., \mathbf{u}_n$ are linearly independent.

Proof: Let there exist scalars

$$a_1, a_2, ...a_n \in F \text{ such that}$$

$$a_1\mathbf{u}_1 + a_2\mathbf{u}_2 + ... + a_n\mathbf{u}_n = 0$$

$$a_1\mathbf{u}_1 + a_2\mathbf{u}_2 + ... + a_n\mathbf{u}_n = 0$$

Now, $\ T(a_1\mathbf{u}_1 + a_2\mathbf{u}_2 + ... + a_n\mathbf{u}_n) = \ T(0) = 0$

$\Rightarrow \quad a_1T(\mathbf{u}_1) + a_2T(\mathbf{u}_2) \ + ... + a_nT(\mathbf{u}_n) = 0 \qquad (\because T \text{ is linearly independent})$

$\Rightarrow \quad a_1 = 0; \ a_2 = 0; ...a_n = 0$

$\quad (\because T(\mathbf{u}_1), \ T(\mathbf{u}_2)..., T(\mathbf{u}_n)$ are linearly independent

Hence $\mathbf{u}_1, \ \mathbf{u}_2, \ ..., \ \mathbf{u}_n$ are also linearly independent.

EXAMPLES

1. Let $R^2 \to R^2$ be defined by $T(x, y) = (2x - 3y, x + y)$. Compute the matrix of T relative to the basis:

   (a) $B = \{(1, 0), (0, 1)\}$

   (b) $B = \{(1, 2), (2, 3)\}$

   Solution: Let x_j is the basis member for each j in $T(x_j)$

   (a) $T(x,y) = (2x - 3y, x + y)$; [Given]   [1]

   $\Rightarrow$ $T(x_1) = T(1, 0)$

   $= (2{\cdot}1 - 3{\cdot}0, 1 + 0) = (2, 1)$

   $= 2(1, 0) + 1(0, 1)$

   $= 2x_1 + 1x_2$ [2]

   $T(x_2) = T(0, 1)$

   $= (2{\cdot}0 - 3{\cdot}1, 0 + 1)$

   $= (-3, 1)$

   $= -3(1, 0) + 1(0, 1)$

   $= -3x_1 + 1x_2$ [3]

   $\therefore$ coefficient matrix is: $\begin{bmatrix} 2 & 1 \\ -3 & 1 \end{bmatrix}$

   Hence the matrix T w.r.t B is the transpose of the coefficient matrix.

   $\therefore$ from [2] and [3],

   $$[T : B] = \begin{bmatrix} 2 & 1 \\ -3 & 1 \end{bmatrix}$$

   (b) Given: $T(x,y) = (2x - 3y, x + y)$ [1]

   $T(x_1) = T(1, 2)$

   $= (2{\cdot}1 - 3{\cdot}2, 1 + 2)$

   $= (-4, 3)$

   Let $(-4, 3) = a_1(1, 2) + b_1(2, 3)$

   $\therefore$ $-4 = a_1 + 2b_1$; $3 = 2a_1 + 3b_1$

   Solving $a_1 = 18$ and $b_1 = -11$

   Thus, $T(x_1) = T(1, 2)$

   $= (-4, 3)$

   $= 18(1, 2) - 11(2, 3)$ [2]

and $T(x_2) = T(2, 3) = (2. 2 - 3. 3, 2 + 3)$

$\qquad = (-5, 5)$

Let $(-5, 5) = a_2(1, 2) + b_2(2, 3)$

$\therefore \quad 5 = a_2 + 2b_2, \ 5 = 2a_2 + 3b_2$

Solving, $a_2 = 25$ and $b_2 = -15$

Thus, $T(x_2) = T(2, 3) = (-5, 5)$

$\qquad = 25 (1, 2) + (-15) (2, 3)$ [3]

From [2] and [3], we get

$$[T : B] = \begin{bmatrix} 18 & 25 \\ -11 & -15 \end{bmatrix}$$

2. Let $T : R^3 \rightarrow R^3$ be a linear transformation defined by $T(x, y, z) = (a,b,c)$ where $a = 2x;\ b = 4y;\ c = 5z$. Find the matrix of T with respect to the basis $\left(\dfrac{2}{3},0,0\right)$, $\left(0,\dfrac{1}{2},0\right)$ and $\left(0,0,\dfrac{1}{4}\right)$.

Solution: Here, we have $T : R^3 \rightarrow R^3$ such that $T(x,y,z) = (a,b,c) = (2x,4y,5z)$

Now, $\quad T\left(\dfrac{2}{3},0,0\right) = \left(\dfrac{4}{3},0,0\right) = 2\left(\dfrac{2}{3},0,0\right)$

$\qquad T\left(0,\dfrac{1}{2},0\right) = (0, 2, 0) = 4\left(0,\dfrac{1}{2},0\right)$

$\qquad T\left(0,0,\dfrac{1}{4}\right) = \left(0,0,\dfrac{5}{4}\right) = 5\left(0,0,\dfrac{1}{4}\right)$

Hence, the required matrix is $\begin{bmatrix} 2 & 0 & 0 \\ 0 & 4 & 0 \\ 0 & 0 & 5 \end{bmatrix}$.

3. $T : R^3 \rightarrow R^3$ and let $\mathbf{A} = \begin{bmatrix} 1 & 2 & 3 \\ 3 & 1 & -5 \\ 0 & 0 & 1 \end{bmatrix}$ be the matrix of $T : R^3 \rightarrow R^3$. w.r.t the standard basis $(1, 0, 0)$, $(0, 1, 0)$ and $(0, 0, 1)$. Find the matrix T w.r.t the basis $(1, 1, 0)$, $(0, 1, 0)$, and $(0, 1, 1)$.

Solution:

Now $(1, 1, 0) = (1, 0, 0) + (0, 1, 0)$ and $(0, 1, 1) = (0, 1, 0) + (0, 0, 1)$
So, the matrix **C** which takes the standard basis to the new basis is

$$\mathbf{C} = \begin{bmatrix} 1 & 1 & 0 \\ 0 & 1 & 0 \\ 0 & 1 & 1 \end{bmatrix}.$$

The required matrix w.r.t. the new basis is $B = CAC^{-1}$, which can be computed as follows.

Now, find $\mathbf{C}^{-1}$ and then $\mathbf{CAC}^{-1} = \mathbf{B}$.

4. Describe explicitly the linear transformation $T : R^2 \rightarrow R^2$ such that $T(e_1)=(a,b)$; $T(e_2) = (c,d)$ where $e_1 = (1, 0)$ and $e_2 = (0, 1)$ are unit vectors.

Solution: Let $(x_1, x_2) \in R^2$

To find $T(x_1, x_2)$ under the conditions

$T(e_1) = (a, b)$ and $T(e_2) = (c, d)$

We know that $\{e_1, e_2\}$ is a basis set for R^2. Therefore, any vector $(x_1, x_2) \in R^2$ can be expressed as a linear combination of the elements of the basis set.

Now $(x_1, x_2) = x_1 (1, 0) + x_2 (0, 1)$

$\qquad = x_1 e_1 + x_2 e_2$

$\therefore \qquad T(x_1, x_2) = T(x_1 e_1 + x_2 e_2)$

$\qquad = x_1 T(e_1) + x_2 T(e_2)$

$\qquad = x_1 (a, b) + x_2 (c, d)$

$\qquad = (ax_1, bx_1) + (cx_2, dx_2)$

$\qquad = (ax_1 + cx_2, bx_1 + dx_2)$,

which is the required L.T.

5. Let $\mathbf{A} = \begin{bmatrix} 1 & 2 \\ 3 & 4 \end{bmatrix}$. Let T be the linear operator on R^3 defined by $T(\mathbf{v}) = \mathbf{Av}$, where $\mathbf{v}$ is written as a column vector. Find the matrix of T in each of the following bases.

   (a) $B_1 = \{(1, 0), (0, 1)\}$;
   (b) $B_2 = \{(1, 3), (2, 5)\}$.

Solution:

(a) $T(1,0) = \begin{bmatrix} 1 & 2 \\ 3 & 4 \end{bmatrix} \begin{bmatrix} 1 \\ 0 \end{bmatrix} = \begin{bmatrix} 1 \\ 3 \end{bmatrix}$

$\qquad\qquad = 1(1,\ 0) + 3\ (0,\ 1)$

$\qquad T(0,1) = \begin{bmatrix} 1 & 2 \\ 3 & 4 \end{bmatrix} \begin{bmatrix} 0 \\ 1 \end{bmatrix} = \begin{bmatrix} 2 \\ 4 \end{bmatrix}$

$\qquad\qquad = 2\ (1,\ 0) + 4\ (0,\ 1)$

Thus, $[\text{T} : \mathbf{B}] = \begin{bmatrix} 1 & 2 \\ 3 & 4 \end{bmatrix}$

(b) Let $V = (a,b) \in R^2$ and $\mathbf{v} = (a,b) = \alpha(1,3) + \beta(2,5) = (\alpha+2\beta, 3\alpha+5\beta)$

$\therefore \qquad \alpha = \alpha + 2\beta;\quad b = 3\alpha + 5\beta$

Solving $\alpha = 2b - 5a;$

$\qquad \beta = 3a - b$

$\therefore \qquad (a,\ b) = (2b - 5a)\ (1,\ 3) + (3a - b)\ (2,\ 5) \rightarrow \qquad [1]$

$\qquad T\ (1,\ 3) = \begin{bmatrix} 1 & 2 \\ 3 & 4 \end{bmatrix} \begin{bmatrix} 1 \\ 3 \end{bmatrix} = \begin{bmatrix} 7 \\ 15 \end{bmatrix}$

$\qquad\qquad = -5\ (1,\ 3) + 6\ (2,\ 5)$

(putting $a = 7$, $b = 15$ in [1])

$\qquad T\ (2,\ 5) = \begin{bmatrix} 1 & 2 \\ 3 & 4 \end{bmatrix} \begin{bmatrix} 2 \\ 5 \end{bmatrix} = \begin{bmatrix} 12 \\ 26 \end{bmatrix}$

$\qquad\qquad = -\ 8\ (1,\ 3) + 10(2,\ 5)$

(putting $a = 12$; $b = 26$ in [1])

Hence $[\text{T}]_{B_1} = \begin{bmatrix} -5 & -8 \\ 6 & 10 \end{bmatrix}$

Examples on Kernel and Image of a Linear Transformation

6. Let $L : R^4 \rightarrow R^3$ be the linear transformation defined by

$L\left(\begin{bmatrix} x \\ y \\ s \\ t \end{bmatrix}\right) = \begin{bmatrix} x - y + s + t \\ x + 2s - t \\ x + y + 3s - 3t \end{bmatrix}$. Find a basis and the dimension of the image

U of L.

Solution: Consider the image of the usual basis vectors of R^4:

$$L \begin{bmatrix} 1 \\ 0 \\ 0 \\ 0 \end{bmatrix} = \begin{bmatrix} 1 \\ 1 \\ 1 \\ 1 \end{bmatrix} ; \; L \begin{bmatrix} 0 \\ 1 \\ 0 \\ 0 \end{bmatrix} = \begin{bmatrix} -1 \\ 0 \\ 0 \\ 1 \end{bmatrix} ; \; L \begin{bmatrix} 0 \\ 0 \\ 1 \\ 0 \end{bmatrix} = \begin{bmatrix} 1 \\ 2 \\ 3 \end{bmatrix} ; \; L = \begin{bmatrix} 0 \\ 0 \\ 0 \\ 1 \end{bmatrix} = \begin{bmatrix} 1 \\ -1 \\ -3 \end{bmatrix}$$

The image vectors span U ; hence form the matrix whose column are these image vectors and row reduce to echelon form :

$$\begin{bmatrix} 1 & 1 & 1 \\ -1 & 0 & 1 \\ 1 & 2 & 3 \\ 1 & -1 & -3 \end{bmatrix} \text{ to } \begin{bmatrix} 1 & 1 & 1 \\ 0 & 1 & 2 \\ 0 & 0 & 0 \\ 0 & 0 & 0 \end{bmatrix} \text{Thus,} \left\{ \begin{bmatrix} 1 \\ 1 \\ 1 \end{bmatrix}, \begin{bmatrix} 0 \\ 1 \\ 2 \end{bmatrix} \right\} \text{is a basis of } U; \text{ hence dim } U = 2.$$

Note: $\begin{bmatrix} 1 & 1 & 1 \\ -1 & 0 & 1 \\ 1 & 2 & 3 \\ 1 & -1 & -3 \end{bmatrix}$ is the transpose of

$\begin{bmatrix} 1 & -1 & 1 & 1 \\ 1 & 0 & 2 & -1 \\ 1 & 1 & 3 & -3 \end{bmatrix}$, which is obtained.

7. Determine a basis and the dimension of the kernel W of the transformation L in $L\ (x,\ y,\ s,\ t) = (x - y + s + t,\ x +2s - t,\ x + y + 3s - 3t)$.

Solution: $L(\mathbf{v}) = \mathbf{0}$, where $\mathbf{v} = (x,\ y,\ s,\ t)$

$L(x,y,s,t) = (x - y + s + t,\ x + 2s - t,\ x + y + 2s - 3t) = (0,\ 0,\ 0)$

$\Rightarrow$ The following system whose solution space is the kernel W of L:

$$\begin{cases} x - y + s + t = 0 \\ x + 2s - t = 0 \\ x + y + 3s - 3t = 0 \end{cases} \Rightarrow \begin{cases} x - y + s + t = 0 \\ y + s - 2t = 0 \\ 2y + 2s - 4t = 0 \end{cases}$$

$$\Rightarrow \begin{cases} x - y + s + t = 0 \\ y + s - 2t = 0 \end{cases}$$

The free variables are s and t; hence dim $W = 2$.

Set (a) $s = -1$, $t = 0$ to get $(2, 1, -1, 0)$

(b) $s = 0$; $t = 1$, to get $(1, 2, 0, 1)$

Thus, $\{(2,1,-1,0),(1,2,0,1)\}$ is a basis W.

Note: $\begin{cases} \dim U + \dim W = 2+2 = 4 \\ \text{which is the dimension} \\ \text{of the domain } R^4 \text{ of } L \end{cases}$

8. Let $L : R^3 \rightarrow R^3$ be the linear transformation defined by

$$L \begin{bmatrix} x \\ y \\ z \end{bmatrix} = \begin{bmatrix} x+2y-z \\ y+z \\ x+y-2z \end{bmatrix}$$

Find **(a)** basis of (image U of L)

(b) dimension of (image of U of L)

Solution: **(a)** We find the image of vectors which span the domain R^3:

$$L \begin{bmatrix} 1 \\ 0 \\ 0 \end{bmatrix} = \begin{bmatrix} 1 \\ 0 \\ 1 \end{bmatrix};$$

$$L \begin{bmatrix} 0 \\ 1 \\ 0 \end{bmatrix} = \begin{bmatrix} 2 \\ 1 \\ 1 \end{bmatrix};$$

$$L \begin{bmatrix} 0 \\ 0 \\ 1 \end{bmatrix} = \begin{bmatrix} -1 \\ 1 \\ -2 \end{bmatrix};$$

The images span the image U of L hence from the matrix whose column vectors are the image vectors and column reduce to echelon form.

$$\begin{bmatrix} 1 & 2 & -1 \\ 0 & 1 & 1 \\ 1 & 1 & -2 \end{bmatrix}, \text{ its transpose is}$$

$$\begin{bmatrix} 1 & 0 & 0 \\ 2 & 1 & 1 \\ -1 & 1 & -2 \end{bmatrix} \text{ to } \begin{bmatrix} 1 & 0 & 1 \\ 0 & 1 & -1 \\ 0 & 1 & -1 \end{bmatrix} \text{ to } \begin{bmatrix} 1 & 0 & 1 \\ 0 & 1 & -1 \\ 0 & 0 & 0 \end{bmatrix}$$

Thus, $\{(1,0,1),(0,1-1)\}$ is basis of U, and so dim $U = 2$.

9. Let $L : R^3 \to R^4$ be defined by $L(x, y, z) = (x + y + z, x + 2y - 3z, 2x + 3y - 2z, 3x + 4y - z)$.

Find a basis and the dimension of the image of L.

   Solution: We first find the image of vectors which span the domain R^3 of L:

   $L(1, 0, 0) = (1, 1, 2, 3)$

   $L(0, 1, 0) = (1, 2, 3, 4)$

   $L(0, 0, 1) = (1, -3, -2, -1)$

   (the 3 image vectors span image L).

   Next, we form the matrix whose rows are the image vectors and row reduce to echelon form:

   $$\begin{bmatrix} 1 & 1 & 2 & 3 \\ 1 & 2 & 3 & 4 \\ 1 & -3 & -2 & -1 \end{bmatrix} \text{ to } \begin{bmatrix} 1 & 1 & 2 & 3 \\ 0 & 1 & 1 & 1 \\ 0 & -4 & -4 & -4 \end{bmatrix} \text{ to } \begin{bmatrix} 1 & 1 & 2 & 3 \\ 0 & 1 & 1 & 1 \\ 0 & 0 & 0 & 0 \end{bmatrix}$$

   Thus, $\{(1,1,2,3),(0,1,1,1)\}$ is a basis of Im L and dim (Im L) = 2.

10. Let $L : R^3 \to R^4$ be defined $L(x, y, z)$
    $= (x + 2y - z, y + z, x + y - 2z)$

    Find **(a)** a basis of the Ker (L)

    (b) a dimension of Ker (L).

    Solution: **(a)** Let $L(\mathbf{v}) = \mathbf{0}$; where $\mathbf{v} = (x, y, z)$;

    $L(x, y, z) = (x + 2y - z, y + z, x + y - 2z) = (0, 0, 0)$.

    Equate the corresponding components whose solution space is the Ker (L).

    $$\left. \begin{array}{l} x+2y-z=0 \\ y+z=0 \\ x+z-2z=0 \end{array} \right\} \Rightarrow \left. \begin{array}{l} x+2y-z=0 \\ y+z=0 \\ -y-z=0 \end{array} \right\} \Rightarrow \begin{array}{l} x+2y-z \doteq 0 \\ y+z=0 \end{array}$$

    z is the only free variable.

    Hence, dim (Ker L) = 1.

    Let $z = 1$; then $y = -1$ and $x = 3$.

    Thus $\{(3,-1,1)\}$ is a basis of Ker (L)

Note: We know that dim (range L) + dim (Ker L) = 2 + 1 = 3, which is the dimension of R^3 of L.

11. Find the dimension and a basis for the image of $\mathbf{A} = \begin{bmatrix} 1 & 2 & 3 & 1 \\ 1 & 3 & 5 & -2 \\ 3 & 8 & 13 & -3 \end{bmatrix}$

Solution: Since the column space of $\mathbf{A}$ is equal to Im $\mathbf{A}$. Thus, reduce $\mathbf{A}^T$ to echelon form:

$$\mathbf{A}^T = \begin{bmatrix} 1 & 1 & 3 \\ 2 & 3 & 8 \\ 3 & 5 & 13 \\ 1 & -2 & -3 \end{bmatrix} \text{ to } \begin{bmatrix} 1 & 1 & 3 \\ 0 & 1 & 2 \\ 0 & 2 & 4 \\ 0 & -3 & -6 \end{bmatrix} \text{ to } \begin{bmatrix} 1 & 1 & 3 \\ 0 & 1 & 2 \\ 0 & 0 & 0 \\ 0 & 0 & 0 \end{bmatrix}$$

Thus, $\{(1,1,3),(0,1,2)\}$ is a basis of Im A and dim (Im A) = 2.

12. Consider the vector space $V(R)$ of all 2×2 matrices over the field R of real numbers, let L be the linear transformation on V that sends each matrix $\mathbf{X}$ into $\mathbf{AX}$ where $\mathbf{A} = \begin{bmatrix} 1 & 1 \\ 1 & 1 \end{bmatrix}$. Find the matrix of L w.r.t the ordered basis $S = \{\alpha_1, \alpha_2, \alpha_3, \alpha_4\}$ for V where $\alpha_1 = \begin{bmatrix} 1 & 0 \\ 0 & 0 \end{bmatrix}$; $\alpha_2 = \begin{bmatrix} 0 & 1 \\ 0 & 0 \end{bmatrix}$; $\alpha_3 = \begin{bmatrix} 0 & 0 \\ 1 & 0 \end{bmatrix}$;

$\alpha_4 = \begin{bmatrix} 0 & 0 \\ 0 & 1 \end{bmatrix}$

Solution:

$$L(\alpha_1) = \mathbf{A}\alpha_1 = \begin{bmatrix} 1 & 1 \\ 1 & 1 \end{bmatrix}\begin{bmatrix} 1 & 0 \\ 0 & 0 \end{bmatrix} = \begin{bmatrix} 1 & 0 \\ 1 & 0 \end{bmatrix} \text{ or}$$

$$L(\alpha_1) = 1\begin{bmatrix} 1 & 0 \\ 0 & 0 \end{bmatrix} + 0\begin{bmatrix} 0 & 1 \\ 0 & 0 \end{bmatrix} + 1\begin{bmatrix} 0 & 0 \\ 1 & 0 \end{bmatrix} + 0\begin{bmatrix} 0 & 0 \\ 0 & 1 \end{bmatrix}$$

$$L(\alpha_1) = 1\alpha_1 + 0\alpha_2 + 1\alpha_3 + 0\alpha_4$$

Similarly, we can show that,

$$\begin{cases} L(\alpha_2) = 0\alpha_1 + 1\alpha_2 + 0\alpha_3 + 0\alpha_4 \\ L(\alpha_3) = 1\alpha_1 + 0\alpha_2 + 1\alpha_3 + 0\alpha_4 \\ L(\alpha_4) = 0\alpha_1 + 1\alpha_2 + 0\alpha_3 + 1\alpha_4 \end{cases}$$

Hence, the coefficient matrix is
$$\begin{bmatrix} 1 & 0 & 1 & 0 \\ 0 & 1 & 0 & 1 \\ 1 & 0 & 1 & 0 \\ 0 & 1 & 0 & 1 \end{bmatrix}$$

Therefore, the matrix of L relative to given basis is transpose of the above coefficient matrix.

$$[L]_s = \begin{bmatrix} 1 & 0 & 1 & 0 \\ 0 & 1 & 0 & 1 \\ 1 & 0 & 1 & 0 \\ 0 & 1 & 0 & 1 \end{bmatrix}$$

13. Show that the mapping $L : V_2(R_2) \to V_3(R)$ defined as $T(a,b) = (a + b, a - b, b)$ is a linear transformation from $V_2(R)$ into $V_3(R)$. Find the range, rank, null-space and nullity of T.

Solution: Let $\alpha = (a_1, b_1)$; $\beta = (a_2, b_2) \in V_2(R)$.
Then $T(\alpha) = T(a_1, b_1) = a_1 + b_1, a_1 - b_1, b_1)$ and $T(\beta)$
$\qquad T(\beta) = (a_2 + b_2, a_2 - b_2, b_2)$
Also Let $a, b \in R$. Then $a\alpha + b\beta \in V_2 (R)$ and $T (a\alpha + b\beta)$
$\qquad T [a(a_1, b_1) + b(a_2, b_2)]$
$\qquad = T(aa_1 + ba_2, ab_1 ab_1 + bb_2)$
$\qquad = (aa_1 + ba_2 + ab_1 + bb_2, aa_1 + ba_2 - ab_1 - bb_2, ab_1 + bb_2)$
$\qquad = \left(a[a_1+b_1]+b[a_2+b_2], a[a_1-b_1]+b[a_2-b_2], ab_1+bb_2\right)$
$\qquad = a (a_1 + b_1, a_1 - b_1, b_1) + b (a_2 + b_2, a_2 - b_2, b_2)$
$\qquad = aT(\alpha) + bT(\beta)$.
$\therefore$ T is a linear transformation from V_2 into $V_3 (R)$.

Now, $\{(1,0),(0,1)\}$ is a basis for $V_2 (R)$
We have $L(1, 0) = (1 + 0, 1 - 0, 0) = (1, 1, 0)$ and
$\qquad L(0, 1) = (0 + 1, 0 - 1, 0) = (1, -1, 0)$

The vectors $L(1,0)$, $L(0,1)$ span the range of T. Thus, the range of T is the subspace of $V_3 (R)$ spanned by the vectors $(1, 1, 0)$, $(1, -1, 1)$.
Now the vectors $(1, 1, 0)$, $(1, -1, 1) \in V_3 (R)$ are linearly independent because if $x, y \in R$, then

x (1, 1, 0) + y (1, –1, 1) = (0, 0, 0)

$\Rightarrow$ $(x + y, x - y, y)$ = (0, 0, 0)

$\Rightarrow$ $x + y = 0;$ $x - y = 0;$ $y = 0$

$\Rightarrow$ $x = 0, y = 0$

$\therefore$ the vectors (1, 1, 0), (1, –1, 1) form a basis for range of T. Hence rank T = dim of range of T = 2.

Nullity of T = dim of V_2 (R) – rank T = 2 – 2 = 0

$\therefore$ null space of T is the zero subspace of $V_2(R)$.

Alternatively , (a, b) $\in$ null space of T

$\Rightarrow$ $T(a, b)$ = (0, 0, 0)

$\Rightarrow$ $(a + b, a - b, b)$ = (0, 0, 0)

$\Rightarrow$ $a + b = 0;$ $a - b = 0;$ $b = 0$

$\Rightarrow$ $a = 0, b = 0$

$\therefore$ (0, 0) is the only element of $V_2(R)$ which belongs to null space of T.

$\therefore$ null space of T is the zero subspace of $V_2(R)$.

14. Consider the basis $S = \{\alpha_1, \alpha_2, \alpha_3\}$ of R^3

where α_1 = (1, 1, 1) α_2 = (1, 1, 0),

α_3 = (1, 0, 0). Express (2, –3, 5) in terms of the basis $\{\alpha_1, \alpha_2, \alpha_3\}$. Let $T: R^3 \to R^2$ be defined as $T(\alpha_1)$ = (1, 0); $T(\alpha_2)$ = (2, –1), $T(\alpha_3)$ = (4,3). Find $T(2, -3, 5)$.

Solution: Let (2, –3, 5) = $a\alpha_1 + b\alpha_2 + c\alpha_3$.

= a(1, 1, 1) + b(1, 1, 0) + c(1, 0, 0)

Then $a + b + c = 2, a + b = -3, a = 5$.

Solving these equations, we get

$a = 5, b = -8, c = 5$.

$\therefore$ (2, –3, 5) = $5\alpha_1 - 8\alpha_2 + 5\alpha_3$

Now $T(2, -3, 5) = T(5\alpha_1 - 8\alpha_2 + 5\alpha_3)$

= $5 T(\alpha_1) - 8 T(\alpha_2) + 5T (\alpha_3)$

($\because T$ is a linear transformation)

= 5(1, 0) – 8(2, –1) + 5(4, 3)

= (5, 0) – 8(2, –1) + 5(4, 3)

= (5, 0) – (16, –8) + (20, 15) = (9, 23)

15. If $L : R^2 \to R^3$ defined by

$$L \begin{bmatrix} x_1 \\ x_2 \end{bmatrix} = \begin{bmatrix} x_1 - x_2 \\ x_2 - x_1 \\ -x_1 \end{bmatrix} \text{ find}$$

(a) basis for range L

(b) basis for Ker L

(c) verify.

dim (Ker L) + dim (range L) = dim V

Solution: We know that the set $A = \{e_1, e_2\}$ is a basis for R^2

where $e_1 = \begin{bmatrix} 1 \\ 0 \end{bmatrix}$ and $e_2 = \begin{bmatrix} 0 \\ 1 \end{bmatrix}$

By def $L(e_1) = T \begin{bmatrix} 1 \\ 0 \end{bmatrix} = \begin{bmatrix} 1-0 \\ 0-1 \\ -1 \end{bmatrix} = \begin{bmatrix} 1 \\ -1 \\ -1 \end{bmatrix}$

and $L(e_2) = T \begin{bmatrix} 0 \\ 1 \end{bmatrix} = \begin{bmatrix} 0-1 \\ 1-0 \\ -0 \end{bmatrix} = \begin{bmatrix} -1 \\ 1 \\ 0 \end{bmatrix}$

Now for $x \in R^2 = a_1 e_1 + a_2 e_2$ as a basis

$\therefore \quad x \in R(L) = L(x) = L(a_1 e_1 + a_2 e_2)$

$\qquad = a_1 L(e_1) + a_2 L(e_2)$, (by linearity of L)

$\qquad = a_1 \begin{bmatrix} 1 \\ -1 \\ -1 \end{bmatrix} + a_2 \begin{bmatrix} -1 \\ 1 \\ 0 \end{bmatrix}.$

To verify whether $y \in R(L)$ expressed as a linear combination of two vectors $\in R^3$ can be expressed as linear combination of fewer number of vectors or not.

For this, we compute a matrix whose columns are these two vectors.

$$B = \begin{bmatrix} 1 & -1 \\ -1 & 1 \\ -1 & 0 \end{bmatrix} \text{ transpose of } B \text{ is } \begin{bmatrix} 1 & -1 & 1 \\ -1 & 1 & 0 \end{bmatrix}, \text{ which is not in}$$

echelon form of matrix. Thus, $\{(1,-1,-1),(-1,1,0)\}$ is the basis for $R(L)$. Hence dim $R(L)$ i.e., rank $(L) = 2$.

To find the basis and dimension for $N(L)$.

Let $\mathbf{x} \in N(L)$ if $L(\mathbf{x}) = \mathbf{0}$

Now $L \begin{bmatrix} x_1 \\ x_2 \end{bmatrix} = \mathbf{0}$

$\Rightarrow \quad \begin{bmatrix} x_1 + x_2 \\ x_2 - x_1 \\ -x_1 \end{bmatrix} = \begin{bmatrix} 0 \\ 0 \\ 0 \end{bmatrix}$

$\Rightarrow \quad x_1 + x_2 = 0$

$\qquad x_2 - x_1 = 0$

$\qquad -x_1 = 0$

$\Rightarrow \quad x_1 = 0;\ x_2 = 0$

$\Rightarrow \quad \begin{bmatrix} x_1 \\ x_2 \end{bmatrix} = \begin{bmatrix} 0 \\ 0 \end{bmatrix} = \mathbf{0} \in R^2.$

Hence the null space consists of only zero vectors. $\therefore\ N(L) = \mathbf{0}$

Now dim $R^2 = 2$, dim $R(L) = 2$, dim $N(L) = 0$

$\therefore$ Rank (L) + Nullity (L) = dim R^2.

16. If $V(R)$ be the vector space of 2×2 matrices and $\mathbf{M} = \begin{bmatrix} 1 & 2 \\ 0 & 3 \end{bmatrix}$ and if $T: V \to V$ be a linear transformation defined by $T(\mathbf{A}) = \mathbf{AM} - \mathbf{MA}$, $\forall A \in V(R)$ then find the basis and dimension of the Kernel K of T.

Solution: We know that kernel of T means the null space of T i.e., $K = N(T)$.

To find $K = N(T)$ = Kernel of T.

Let $\mathbf{V} = \begin{bmatrix} a & b \\ c & d \end{bmatrix} \in V(R)$ such that $T(\mathbf{V}) = \mathbf{0}$, (zero element of V)

$\Rightarrow \quad T \begin{bmatrix} a & b \\ c & d \end{bmatrix} = \mathbf{0} = \begin{bmatrix} 0 & 0 \\ 0 & 0 \end{bmatrix}$

$\Rightarrow \quad \begin{bmatrix} a & b \\ c & d \end{bmatrix} \begin{bmatrix} 1 & 2 \\ 0 & 3 \end{bmatrix} - \begin{bmatrix} 1 & 2 \\ 0 & 3 \end{bmatrix} \begin{bmatrix} a & b \\ c & d \end{bmatrix} = \begin{bmatrix} 0 & 0 \\ 0 & 0 \end{bmatrix}$ (by data)

$\Rightarrow \quad \begin{bmatrix} a+0 & 2a+3b \\ c+0 & 2c+3d \end{bmatrix} - \begin{bmatrix} a+2c & b+2d \\ 0+3c & 0+3d \end{bmatrix} = \begin{bmatrix} 0 & 0 \\ 0 & 0 \end{bmatrix}$

$$\Rightarrow \quad \begin{bmatrix} a-(a+2c) & (2a+3b)-(b+2d) \\ c-3c & (2c+3d)-(3d) \end{bmatrix} = \begin{bmatrix} 0 & 0 \\ 0 & 0 \end{bmatrix}$$

$$\Rightarrow \quad \begin{bmatrix} -2c & 2a+2b-2d \\ -2c & 2c \end{bmatrix} = \begin{bmatrix} 0 & 0 \\ 0 & 0 \end{bmatrix}$$

$$\Rightarrow \quad 2c = 0,\ 2a + 2b - 2d = 0$$

$$\Rightarrow \quad c = 0;\ a = d - b$$

From the above equation, we find that the free variables are b and d, so dim K = dim $[N(T)]$ = number of free variables = 2.

Again, by fixing $b = 0$; $d = 1$; then $a = 1$, $c = 0$ which yield $\begin{bmatrix} 1 & 0 \\ 0 & 1 \end{bmatrix}$ and

if we take $b = -1$, $d = 0$, then $a = 1$, $c = 0$ which yield $\begin{bmatrix} 1 & -1 \\ 0 & 0 \end{bmatrix}$

$$\therefore \quad \left\{ \begin{bmatrix} 1 & 0 \\ 0 & 1 \end{bmatrix}, \begin{bmatrix} 1 & -1 \\ 0 & 0 \end{bmatrix} \right\} \text{ form the basis set of } N(T) \text{ i.e., Kernel } K \text{ of } T.$$

17. Let V be the vector space of 2×2 matrices over R and $\mathbf{M} = \begin{bmatrix} 1 & -1 \\ -2 & 2 \end{bmatrix}$ be a fixed matrix in V. If $T : V \to V$ be a linear transformation defined by $T(\mathbf{A}) = \mathbf{MA} \ \forall \ \mathbf{A} \in V$, then find the basis and dimensions of (i) $R(T)$ and (ii) $N(T)$.

Solution: $R(T)$ = Range of T = $\{\mathbf{u} \in V : \mathbf{u} = T(\mathbf{v}),\ \mathbf{v} \in V\}$ (by definition)

Now, the basis of $V(R)$ is the set

$$B = \left\{ \begin{bmatrix} 1 & 0 \\ 0 & 0 \end{bmatrix}, \begin{bmatrix} 0 & 1 \\ 0 & 0 \end{bmatrix}, \begin{bmatrix} 0 & 0 \\ 1 & 0 \end{bmatrix}, \begin{bmatrix} 0 & 0 \\ 0 & 1 \end{bmatrix} \right\}$$

By data, we have $T\left(\begin{bmatrix} 1 & 0 \\ 0 & 0 \end{bmatrix} \right) = \begin{bmatrix} 1 & -1 \\ -2 & 2 \end{bmatrix} \begin{bmatrix} 1 & 0 \\ 0 & 0 \end{bmatrix}, = \begin{bmatrix} 1 & 0 \\ -2 & 0 \end{bmatrix}$

Similarly, $T\left(\begin{bmatrix} 0 & 1 \\ 0 & 0 \end{bmatrix} \right) = \begin{bmatrix} 1 & -1 \\ -2 & 2 \end{bmatrix} \begin{bmatrix} 0 & 1 \\ 0 & 0 \end{bmatrix} = \begin{bmatrix} 0 & 1 \\ 0 & -2 \end{bmatrix}$

$$T = \left(\begin{bmatrix} 0 & 0 \\ 1 & 0 \end{bmatrix} \right) = \begin{bmatrix} 1 & -1 \\ -2 & 2 \end{bmatrix} \begin{bmatrix} 0 & 0 \\ 1 & 0 \end{bmatrix} = \begin{bmatrix} -1 & 0 \\ 2 & 0 \end{bmatrix}$$

and $\quad T = \left(\begin{bmatrix} 0 & 0 \\ 0 & 1 \end{bmatrix} \right) = \begin{bmatrix} 1 & -1 \\ -2 & 2 \end{bmatrix} \begin{bmatrix} 0 & 0 \\ 0 & 1 \end{bmatrix} = \begin{bmatrix} 0 & -1 \\ 0 & 2 \end{bmatrix}$

Now we form a matrix whose rows are elements of generator of $R(T)$ and then reduce it to echelon form.

i.e., $\begin{bmatrix} 1 & 0 & -2 & 0 \\ 0 & 1 & 0 & -2 \\ -1 & 0 & 2 & 0 \\ 0 & -1 & 0 & 2 \end{bmatrix} \sim \begin{bmatrix} 1 & 0 & -2 & 0 \\ 0 & 1 & 0 & -2 \\ 0 & 0 & 0 & 0 \\ 0 & 0 & 0 & 0 \end{bmatrix}$

Applying $R_3 + R_1$ and $R_4 + R_2$

Hence the basis of $R(T)$ is the set $\begin{bmatrix} 1 & 0 \\ -2 & 0 \end{bmatrix}, \begin{bmatrix} 0 & 1 \\ 0 & -2 \end{bmatrix}$ and so we have

$\dim(R(T)) =$ Rank of $T = 2$.

(ii) Null space of T i.e., $N(T)$.

By definition, we have $\quad N(T) = \{ v \in V(R) : T(v) = 0 \in V(R) \}$

If $v \in N(T)$, then $T(v) = 0$ Let $\quad v = \begin{bmatrix} a & b \\ c & d \end{bmatrix} \in V(R)$, then $T(v) = 0$

$\Rightarrow \quad T \begin{bmatrix} a & b \\ c & d \end{bmatrix} = 0 = \begin{bmatrix} 0 & 0 \\ 0 & 0 \end{bmatrix}$

$\Rightarrow \quad \begin{bmatrix} 1 & -1 \\ -2 & 2 \end{bmatrix} \begin{bmatrix} a & b \\ c & d \end{bmatrix} = \begin{bmatrix} 0 & 0 \\ 0 & 0 \end{bmatrix},$ (by definition of T)

$\Rightarrow \quad \begin{bmatrix} a-c & b-d \\ -2a+2c & -2b+2d \end{bmatrix} = \begin{bmatrix} 0 & 0 \\ 0 & 0 \end{bmatrix}$

$\Rightarrow \quad a - c = 0, \ b - d = 0, \ -2a + 2c = 0, 2b + 2d = 0$

$\Rightarrow \quad a = c, \ b = d.$ [1]

From [1], we find that the values of a and b depend upon c and d, so the free variables are c and d, which are two in number.

$\therefore \quad$ Nullity of $T = \dim [N(T)] =$ number of free variables $= 2$.

If we fix $c = 1, d = 0$, then $a = 1, b = 0$ which yield $\begin{bmatrix} 1 & 0 \\ 1 & 0 \end{bmatrix}$ and if we

fix $c = 0, d = 1$, then $a = 0, b = 1$ which yields $\begin{bmatrix} 0 & 1 \\ 0 & 1 \end{bmatrix}$. Thus, $\left\{ \begin{bmatrix} 1 & 0 \\ 1 & 0 \end{bmatrix}, \begin{bmatrix} 0 & 1 \\ 0 & 1 \end{bmatrix} \right\}$

forms the basis set of $N(T)$. Also, Rank (T) + Nullity (T) = dim $[R(T)]$ + dim $[N(T)]$ = 2 + 2 = 4 = dim $V(R)$.

18. If $L : R^3 \rightarrow R^3$ be defined by $L\left[\begin{pmatrix} x \\ y \\ z \end{pmatrix}\right] = \begin{bmatrix} x-y \\ x+2y \\ z \end{bmatrix}$ find,

(i) basis for Ker L

(ii) basis for range L

(iii) verify

dim (Ker L) + dim (range L) = dim V.

[VTU Med. Elen. 2002 (8th sem).]

Solution:

(i) We know that Ker L means the null space of L, Ker $L = N(L)$

$$N(L) = \{v \in R^3 : L(v) = 0 \in R^3\}$$

If $v \in N(L)$, then $L(v) = 0$ for $v \in R^3$ and $0 \in R^3$

Let $v = L\begin{bmatrix} x \\ y \\ z \end{bmatrix}$ then $L = 0$ $\begin{bmatrix} x-y \\ x+2y \\ z \end{bmatrix} = 0 = \begin{bmatrix} 0 \\ 0 \\ 0 \end{bmatrix}$

$$\Rightarrow \quad \left. \begin{aligned} x - y &= 0 \\ x + 2y &= 0 \\ z &= 0 \end{aligned} \right\} \qquad \qquad [1]$$

Now, we shall form the matrix corresponding to the system of equations given by [1] and then shall reduce it to the equation form i.e.,

$$\begin{bmatrix} 1 & -1 & 0 \\ 1 & 2 & 0 \\ 0 & 0 & 1 \end{bmatrix} \quad \text{Applying } R_2 \rightarrow R_2 \rightarrow R_1 \quad \begin{bmatrix} 1 & -1 & 0 \\ 0 & 3 & 0 \\ 0 & 0 & 1 \end{bmatrix}$$

Thus, we obtain the echelon matrix which gives the equivalent system of equation as:

$$\left. \begin{aligned} x - y &= 0 \\ 3y &= 0 \\ z &= 0 \end{aligned} \right\}$$

$\Rightarrow \quad x - 0 = 0 \; y = 0, \; z = 0;$

$\Rightarrow \quad (x = 0; \; y = 0, z = 0)$

$$\Rightarrow \quad \mathbf{v} = \begin{bmatrix} x \\ y \\ z \end{bmatrix} = \begin{bmatrix} 0 \\ 0 \\ 0 \end{bmatrix} \in N(L) \text{ i.e., Ker } L = N(L) = \{0\}, \text{ which forms, the}$$

basis of $N(L)$.

Also dim $[N(L)] = 0$

(ii) We know that range L means the range space of L, range $L = R(L)$.

$R(L) = \{\mathbf{u} \in R^3 : \mathbf{u} = T(\mathbf{v}), \ \mathbf{v} \in R^3\}$

Now a basis of R^3 is $\{(1, 0, 0), (0, 1, 0), (0, 0, 1)\}$

Also $L \begin{bmatrix} 1 \\ 0 \\ 0 \end{bmatrix} = \begin{bmatrix} 1-0 \\ 1+0 \\ 0 \end{bmatrix} = \begin{bmatrix} 1 \\ 1 \\ 0 \end{bmatrix}$, from the given definition of L.

Similarly, $L \begin{bmatrix} 0 \\ 0 \\ 1 \end{bmatrix} = \begin{bmatrix} 0-1 \\ 0+2.1 \\ 0 \end{bmatrix} = \begin{bmatrix} -1 \\ 2 \\ 0 \end{bmatrix}$

$\rightarrow \quad L \begin{bmatrix} 0 \\ 0 \\ 1 \end{bmatrix} = \begin{bmatrix} 0-0 \\ 0+0 \\ 1 \end{bmatrix} = \begin{bmatrix} 0 \\ 0 \\ 1 \end{bmatrix}$

$\therefore R(L)$ is a subspace of R^3 generated by

$$\left\{ \begin{bmatrix} 1 \\ 1 \\ 0 \end{bmatrix}, \begin{bmatrix} -1 \\ 2 \\ 0 \end{bmatrix}, \begin{bmatrix} 0 \\ 0 \\ 1 \end{bmatrix} \right\}$$

Now, we shall form a matrix with columns as the generators of $R(L)$ and then reduce it to echelon form i.e.,

$$\begin{bmatrix} 1 & -1 & 0 \\ 1 & 2 & 0 \\ 0 & 0 & 1 \end{bmatrix} \sim \begin{bmatrix} 1 & -1 & 0 \\ 0 & 3 & 0 \\ 0 & 0 & 1 \end{bmatrix}, \text{ applying } R_2 \rightarrow R_2 - R_1$$

Hence the set of non-zero vectors in the above echelon matrix viz.,

$$\left\{ \begin{bmatrix} 1 \\ 0 \\ 0 \end{bmatrix}, \begin{bmatrix} -1 \\ 3 \\ 0 \end{bmatrix}, \begin{bmatrix} 0 \\ 0 \\ 1 \end{bmatrix} \right\} \text{ is a basis of } R(L).$$

$\therefore$ dim $[R(L)]$ = rank of $L = 3$.

Hence dim (Ker L) + dim (range L)

$\qquad = 0 + 3 = $ dim V.

19. Find the matrix representation of each of the following operators L on R^2 relative to the basis

(a) $B_1 = \left\{ \begin{bmatrix} 1 \\ 3 \end{bmatrix}, \begin{bmatrix} 2 \\ 5 \end{bmatrix} \right\}$;

(b) $B_2 = \left\{ \begin{bmatrix} 1 \\ 0 \end{bmatrix}, \begin{bmatrix} 0 \\ 1 \end{bmatrix} \right\}$

(i) $L \begin{bmatrix} x \\ y \end{bmatrix} = \begin{bmatrix} 2y \\ 3x - y \end{bmatrix}$

(ii) $L \begin{bmatrix} x \\ y \end{bmatrix} = \begin{bmatrix} 3x - 4y \\ x + 5y \end{bmatrix}$

Solution: Let us assume $L(\mathbf{x}_j)$, where $\mathbf{x}_j$ is the basis member.

(a) (i) By data

$$L \begin{bmatrix} x \\ y \end{bmatrix} = \begin{bmatrix} 2y \\ 3x - y \end{bmatrix} \qquad [1]$$

$$L\,(\mathbf{x}_1) = L \begin{bmatrix} 1 \\ 3 \end{bmatrix} = \begin{bmatrix} 2.3 \\ 3.1 - 3 \end{bmatrix} = \begin{bmatrix} 6 \\ 0 \end{bmatrix}$$

Let $\begin{bmatrix} 6 \\ 0 \end{bmatrix} = a_1 \begin{bmatrix} 1 \\ 3 \end{bmatrix} + b_1 \begin{bmatrix} 2 \\ 5 \end{bmatrix}$

$$\therefore \quad \left. \begin{aligned} 6 &= a_1 + 2b_1 \\ \text{and} \quad 0 &= 3a_1 + 5b_1 \end{aligned} \right\}$$

solving, $a_1 = -30;\ b_1 = 18$.

Thus $L(\mathbf{x}_1) = L \begin{bmatrix} 1 \\ 3 \end{bmatrix} = \begin{bmatrix} 6 \\ 0 \end{bmatrix} = -30 \begin{bmatrix} 1 \\ 3 \end{bmatrix} + 18 \begin{bmatrix} 2 \\ 5 \end{bmatrix} \qquad [2]$

and $L(\mathbf{x}_2) = L \begin{bmatrix} 1 \\ 3 \end{bmatrix} = \begin{bmatrix} 2.5 \\ 3.2 - 5 \end{bmatrix} = \begin{bmatrix} 10 \\ 1 \end{bmatrix}$

Let $\begin{bmatrix} 10 \\ 1 \end{bmatrix} = a_2 \begin{bmatrix} 1 \\ 3 \end{bmatrix} + b_2 \begin{bmatrix} 1 \\ 3 \end{bmatrix}$

$$\therefore \quad 10 = a_2 + 2b_2$$
$$1 = 3a_2 + 5b_2$$

solving, $a_2 = -48;\ b_2 = 29$.

Thus, $L(\mathbf{x}_2) = L \begin{bmatrix} 2 \\ 5 \end{bmatrix} = \begin{bmatrix} 10 \\ 1 \end{bmatrix}$

$$= -48 \begin{bmatrix} 1 \\ 3 \end{bmatrix} + 29 \begin{bmatrix} 2 \\ 5 \end{bmatrix} \qquad [3]$$

From [2] and [3],

$$[L : B_1] = \begin{bmatrix} -30 & -48 \\ 18 & 29 \end{bmatrix}$$

20. If $L : R^3 \to R^3$ be defined by $L \begin{bmatrix} x_1 \\ x_2 \\ x_3 \end{bmatrix} = \begin{bmatrix} x_1 + 2x_2 \\ x_2 - x_3 \\ x_1 + 2x_3 \end{bmatrix}$ find

(i) basis for Ker L

(ii) Basis for range L

(iii) verify

   dim (Ker L) + dim (range L) = dim V.

Solution: We know that Ker L means the null space of L, Ker $L = N(L)$

and Ker $L = N(L) = \{ v \in R^3 : L(v) = 0 \in R^3 \}$

If $v \in N(L)$, then $L (v) = 0$ for $v \in R^3$ and $0 \in R^3$.

Let $v = \begin{bmatrix} x_1 \\ x_2 \\ x_3 \end{bmatrix}$, then $L(v) = 0$

$$\Rightarrow L \begin{bmatrix} x_1 \\ x_2 \\ x_3 \end{bmatrix} = \begin{bmatrix} x_1 + 2x_2 \\ x_2 - x_3 \\ x_1 + 2x_3 \end{bmatrix} = 0 = \begin{bmatrix} 0 \\ 0 \\ 0 \end{bmatrix}$$

$$\Rightarrow \left. \begin{aligned} x_1 + 2x_2 &= 0 \\ x_2 - x_3 &= 0 \\ x_1 + 2x_3 &= 0 \end{aligned} \right\} \qquad\qquad [1]$$

Coefficient matrix : $\begin{bmatrix} 1 & 2 & 0 \\ 0 & 1 & -1 \\ 1 & 0 & 2 \end{bmatrix}$

Applying $\xrightarrow{R_3 \to R_3 - R_1}$ $\begin{bmatrix} 1 & 2 & 0 \\ 0 & 1 & -1 \\ 0 & -2 & 2 \end{bmatrix}$

Applying $\xrightarrow{R_3 \rightarrow R_3 + 2R_2}$ $\begin{bmatrix} 1 & 2 & 0 \\ 0 & 1 & -1 \\ 0 & 0 & 0 \end{bmatrix}$

Thus, the system [1] is equivalent to

$$x_1 + 2x_2 = 0 \qquad\qquad [2]$$

$$x_2 - x_3 = 0 \qquad\qquad [3]$$

From, [3], $x_2 = x_3$

Similarly, (2) $x_1 + 2x_3 = 0$

$$x_1 = - 2x_3$$

Here x_3 is a free variable

Hence nullity $L = \dim N(L)$

$\qquad$ = number of free variable

$\qquad$ = 1

Choosing $x_2 = -1$; $x_3 = -1$, $x_1 = 2$,

$\{(2,-1,-1)\}$ constitutes a basis for $N(L)$: $\therefore$ the above system is linearly independent also

$$\left[\{(2,-1,-1)\}, \dim(\ker L) = 1 \right]$$

(ii) We know that the set

$\qquad A = \{e_1, e_2, e_3\}$ is a basis set for R^3 where $e_1 = (1, 0, 0)$;

$\qquad e_2 = (0, 1, 0)$; $e_3 = (0, 0, 1)$

By def: $L(e_1) = L \begin{bmatrix} 1 \\ 0 \\ 0 \end{bmatrix} = \begin{bmatrix} 1+0 \\ 0-0 \\ 1+0 \end{bmatrix} = \begin{bmatrix} 1 \\ 0 \\ 1 \end{bmatrix}$

Similarly $L(e_2) = L \begin{bmatrix} 0 \\ 1 \\ 0 \end{bmatrix} = \begin{bmatrix} 0+2.1 \\ 1-0 \\ 0+0 \end{bmatrix} = \begin{bmatrix} 2 \\ 1 \\ 0 \end{bmatrix}$

$\therefore \quad L(e_1) = \begin{bmatrix} 2 \\ 1 \\ 0 \end{bmatrix}$

$$L(e_3) = L \begin{bmatrix} 0 \\ 0 \\ 1 \end{bmatrix} = \begin{bmatrix} 0+0 \\ 0-1 \\ 0+2.1 \end{bmatrix} = \begin{bmatrix} 0 \\ -1 \\ 2 \end{bmatrix}$$

Now, for any $\mathbf{x} \in R^3 = a_1 e_1 + a_2 e_2 + a_3 e_3$ as A is basis

$$\therefore \quad \mathbf{y} \in R(L) = L(\mathbf{x}) = L(a_1 e_1 + a_2 e_2 + a_3 e_3)$$
$$= a_1 L(e_1) + a_2 L(e_2) + a_3 L(e_3)$$

(by linearity of L)

$$= a_1 \begin{bmatrix} 1 \\ 0 \\ 1 \end{bmatrix} + a_2 \begin{bmatrix} 2 \\ 1 \\ 0 \end{bmatrix} + a_3 \begin{bmatrix} 0 \\ -1 \\ 2 \end{bmatrix}$$

To verify whether $\mathbf{y} \in R(L)$ expressed as linearly combination of 3 vectors $\in R^3$ can be expressed as a linearly combination of fewer number of vectors or not. For this, we compute a matrix whose rows are these three vectors

$$\mathbf{B} = \begin{bmatrix} 1 & 2 & 0 \\ 0 & 1 & -1 \\ 1 & 0 & 2 \end{bmatrix}, \text{ transpose of this matrix is : } \begin{bmatrix} 1 & 0 & 1 \\ 2 & 1 & 0 \\ 0 & -1 & 2 \end{bmatrix}$$

Applying $\dfrac{R_2 \to R_2 - 2R_1}{R_3 \to R_3 + R_2}$, $\begin{bmatrix} 1 & 0 & 1 \\ 0 & 1 & -2 \\ 2 & 0 & 2 \end{bmatrix}$

Applying $\xrightarrow{R_3 \to R_3 - 2R_1}$ $\begin{bmatrix} 1 & 0 & 1 \\ 0 & 1 & -2 \\ 0 & 0 & 0 \end{bmatrix}$ which is echelon form of matrix.

Thus, the non-zero vectors $\{(1,0,1),(0,1,-2)\}$ is the basis for $R(L)$ dim (Range L) = rank (L) = 2.

Now, dim $R^3 = 3$, dim (Ker L) = 1; dim (Range L) = 2

$\therefore$ dim (Ker L) + dim (Range L) = dim R^3.

21. Let L be a linear operator on R^3 defined by $L\left(\begin{bmatrix} x_1 \\ x_2 \\ x_3 \end{bmatrix} \right) = \begin{bmatrix} 3x_1 + x_3 \\ -2x_1 + x_2 \\ -x_1 + 2x_2 + 4x_3 \end{bmatrix}$

What is the matrix of T in the ordered basis $S = \{\alpha_1, \alpha_2, \alpha_3\}$

where $\alpha_1 = \begin{bmatrix} 1 \\ 0 \\ 1 \end{bmatrix}$; $\alpha_2 = \begin{bmatrix} -1 \\ 2 \\ 1 \end{bmatrix}$; $\alpha_3 = \begin{bmatrix} 2 \\ 1 \\ 1 \end{bmatrix}$?

Solution:

$$L(\alpha_1) = L \begin{bmatrix} 1 \\ 0 \\ 1 \end{bmatrix} = \begin{bmatrix} 3.1+1 \\ -2.1+0 \\ -1+2.0+4.1 \end{bmatrix} = \begin{bmatrix} 4 \\ -2 \\ 3 \end{bmatrix}$$

$$L(\alpha_2) = L \begin{bmatrix} -1 \\ 2 \\ 1 \end{bmatrix} = \begin{bmatrix} 3(-1)+1 \\ -2(-1)+2 \\ -(-1)+2(2)+4(1) \end{bmatrix} = \begin{bmatrix} -2 \\ 4 \\ 9 \end{bmatrix}$$

$$L(\alpha_3) = L \begin{bmatrix} 2 \\ 1 \\ 1 \end{bmatrix} = \begin{bmatrix} 3(2)+1 \\ -2(2)+1 \\ -2+2(1)+4(1) \end{bmatrix} = \begin{bmatrix} 7 \\ -3 \\ 4 \end{bmatrix}$$

We have to press each of these in terms of α_1, α_2, α_3

Let $\begin{bmatrix} p \\ q \\ r \end{bmatrix} = x\alpha_1 + y\alpha_2 + z\alpha_3 = x \begin{bmatrix} 1 \\ 0 \\ 1 \end{bmatrix} + y \begin{bmatrix} -1 \\ 2 \\ 1 \end{bmatrix} + z \begin{bmatrix} 2 \\ 1 \\ 1 \end{bmatrix};$

$$\begin{bmatrix} p \\ q \\ r \end{bmatrix} = \begin{bmatrix} x-y+2z \\ 2y+z \\ x+y+z \end{bmatrix}$$

$$\therefore \quad \left.\begin{array}{l} x-y+2z = p \\ 2y+z = q \\ x+y+z = r \end{array}\right\}$$

Solving the three equations, we get

$$x = \frac{2r-q}{2}; \ y = \frac{q+v-p}{4}, \ z = \frac{q-r+p}{4}$$

$$\therefore \quad \begin{bmatrix} p \\ q \\ r \end{bmatrix} = \left(\frac{2v-q}{2}\right)\alpha_1 + \frac{q+v-p}{4}\alpha_2 + \frac{q-r+p}{4}\alpha_3$$

Putting $p = 4$; $q = -2$; $r = 3$, we get

$$L \begin{bmatrix} 4 \\ -2 \\ 3 \end{bmatrix} = 4\alpha_1 - \frac{3}{4}\alpha_2 - \frac{1}{4}\alpha_3$$

$$L \begin{bmatrix} -2 \\ 4 \\ 9 \end{bmatrix} = 7\alpha_1 + \frac{15}{4}\alpha_2 - \frac{7}{4}\alpha_3$$

$$L \begin{bmatrix} 7 \\ -3 \\ 4 \end{bmatrix} = \frac{11}{2}\alpha_1 - \frac{3}{2}\alpha_2 + 0\alpha_3$$

Hence, the coefficient matrix is

$$\begin{bmatrix} 4 & -\dfrac{3}{4} & -\dfrac{1}{4} \\ 7 & \dfrac{15}{4} & -\dfrac{7}{4} \\ \dfrac{4}{2} & -\dfrac{3}{2} & 0 \end{bmatrix}$$

∴ The matrix of T relative to basis $S = \{\alpha_1, \alpha_2, \alpha_3\}$ is the transpose of the coefficient matrix.

$$\therefore \quad [L]_S = \begin{bmatrix} 4 & 7 & \dfrac{11}{2} \\ -\dfrac{3}{4} & \dfrac{15}{4} & -\dfrac{3}{2} \\ -\dfrac{1}{4} & -\dfrac{7}{4} & 0 \end{bmatrix}$$

EXERCISES

1. Let $L : R^4 \to R^3$ be defined by $T(x,y,z,t) = (x - y + z + t,\ x + y + 3z - 3t)$
Find the dimensions of:

(i) Range (L)

(ii) Ker (L)

(iii) Verify

Range (L) + Ker (L) = dim (R^4).

Ans: (i) {(1,0), (0,1)}

(ii) {(1,–1,1)}

2. Let $L : R^3 \to R^4$ be defined by

$T(e_1) = (0, 1, 0, 2)$; $T(e_2) = (0,1,1,0)$ and

$T(e_3) = (0,1,-1,4)$ where $\{e_1, e_2, e_3\}$ is the standard basis of R^3. Find the range (T) and Ker (T).

> ***Ans:*** $(-2,1,1)$ spans null space, and $\{(0,1,0,2),$
> $(0,0,1,-2)\}$ spans range (T)

3. Let T be the linear operator on R^3 defined by

$T(x_1,x_2,x_3) = (3x_1 + x_3, - 2x_1 + x_2 - x_1 + 2x_2 + 2x_3)$

What is matrix sin of T in the ordered basis

$S = \{\alpha_1,\alpha_2,\alpha_3\}$ where $\alpha_1 = (1,0,1,)$, $\alpha_2 = (-1, 2, 1)$ and $\alpha_3 = (2,1,1)$?

$$\textbf{\textit{Ans:}}\ [T]_s = \begin{bmatrix} \dfrac{17}{4} & \dfrac{35}{4} & \dfrac{11}{2} \\ \dfrac{-3}{4} & \dfrac{15}{4} & -\dfrac{3}{2} \\ \dfrac{1}{2} & -\dfrac{7}{2} & 0 \end{bmatrix}$$

Eigen Values and Eigen-vectors of linear transformation.

Definition (1): Let $A = [a_{ij}]$ be an $n \times n$ matrix over a field F. The matrix $[A - \lambda I]$ or $[\lambda I - A]$ where I is the unit matrix of the same order as that of A and λ is an indeterminate, is called the characteristic matrix of a square matrix A.

Definition (2): Let $A =[a_{ij}]$ be a square matrix of order $n \times n$ the determinant $|A - \lambda I|$ or $|\lambda I - A|$ is a non-zero polynomial of degree n is λ. This polynomial is called characteristic polynomial of A.

Definition (3): The equation $|A - \lambda I| = 0$ is called the characteristic equation of A or eigen equation of A.

Definition (4) : The roots of the characteristic equation i.e., the roots of the equation $|A - \lambda I| = 0$ are called the characteristic roots or latent roots or eigen values of square matrix A.

$$\text{If} \quad A = \begin{bmatrix} a_{11} & a_{12} & \dots & a_{1n} \\ a_{21} & a_{22} & \dots & a_{2n} \\ \dots & \dots & \dots & \dots \\ a_{n1} & a_{n2} & \dots & a_{nn} \end{bmatrix}$$

then $|\mathbf{A} - \lambda\mathbf{I}| = 0 = |\lambda\mathbf{I} - \mathbf{A}|$

$$\Rightarrow \begin{bmatrix} a_{11}-\lambda & a_{12} & .... & a_{1n} \\ a_{21} & a_{22}-\lambda & .... & a_{2n} \\ .... & .... & .... & .... \\ a_{n1} & a_{n2} & .... & a_{nn}-\lambda \end{bmatrix} = 0 = \begin{vmatrix} \lambda-a_{11} & a_{12} & .... & a_{1n} \\ a_{21} & \lambda-a_{22} & .... & a_{2n} \\ .... & .... & .... & .... \\ a_{n1} & a_{n2} & .... & \lambda-a_{nn} \end{vmatrix}$$

$\Rightarrow$ $(a_{11} - \lambda)(a_{22}- \lambda)....(a_{nn} - \lambda)$ + terms with almost $(n-2)$ factors of the form $(a_{ii}- \lambda)$ or $(\lambda -a_{ii})$

$\therefore$ $c(\lambda) = (-1)^n [\lambda^n + c_{n-1}\lambda^{n-1} + c_{n-2} \lambda^{n-2} + ... + c_1\lambda + c_0] = 0$

where $c_{n-1}, c_{n-2}, ... , c_1, c_0$ are constants.

EXAMPLES

1. If $\mathbf{A}$ is a square matrix, then prove that $\mathbf{A}$ and $\mathbf{A}^T$ have the same eigen values.

   Solution: Let $(\mathbf{A} - \lambda\mathbf{I})^T = \mathbf{A}^T - (\mathbf{A}\mathbf{I})^T$

   $= \mathbf{A}^T - \lambda\mathbf{I}$

   but $|\mathbf{A} - \lambda\mathbf{I}| = |(\mathbf{A} - \lambda\mathbf{I})^T| = |\mathbf{A}^T - \lambda\mathbf{I}|$

   $\therefore$ $\mathbf{A}$ and $\mathbf{A}^T$ have the same characteristic (or eigen) equation and hence the same eigen values.

2. Let $\mathbf{M} = \begin{bmatrix} \mathbf{A}_1 & \mathbf{B} \\ \mathbf{O} & \mathbf{A}_2 \end{bmatrix}$; where $\mathbf{A}_1$ and $\mathbf{A}_2$ are square matrices. Show that the characteristics polynomial of $\mathbf{M}$ is the product of the characteristic polynomials $\mathbf{A}_1$ and $\mathbf{A}_2$.

   Solution: $[\lambda\mathbf{I} - \mathbf{M}] = \begin{bmatrix} \lambda\mathbf{I}-\mathbf{A}_1 & -\mathbf{B} \\ \mathbf{O} & \lambda\mathbf{I}-\mathbf{A}_2 \end{bmatrix}$.

   $\Rightarrow$ $|\lambda\mathbf{I} - \mathbf{M}| = \begin{bmatrix} \lambda\mathbf{I}-\mathbf{A}_1 & -\mathbf{B} \\ \mathbf{O} & \lambda\mathbf{I}-\mathbf{A}_2 \end{bmatrix} = |\lambda\mathbf{I} - \mathbf{A}||\lambda\mathbf{I} - \mathbf{B}|$, as required.

   ($\because$ the determinant of a block triangular matrix is the product of the determinant of the diagonal blocks).

3. Find the characteristic polynomial $c(\lambda)$ of a triangular matrix.

   $$\mathbf{A} = \begin{bmatrix} a_{11} & a_{12} & .... & a_{1n} \\ 0 & a_{22} & .... & a_{2n} \\ .... & .... & .... & .... \\ 0 & 0 & .... & a_{nn} \end{bmatrix}$$

Solution: If **A** is triangular and $\lambda\mathbf{I}$ is diagonal, $\lambda\mathbf{I} - \mathbf{A}$ is also triangular with diagonal elements $\lambda - a_{ii}$;

$$\lambda\mathbf{I} - \mathbf{A} = \begin{bmatrix} \lambda - a_{11} & -a_{12} & \cdots & -a_{1n} \\ 0 & \lambda - a_{22} & \cdots & -a_{2n} \\ \cdots & \cdots & \cdots & \cdots \\ 0 & 0 & \cdots & \lambda - a_{nn} \end{bmatrix}$$

then $C(\lambda) = |\lambda\mathbf{I} - \mathbf{A}|$ is the product of the diagonal elements

$\lambda - a_{ii} : C(\lambda) = (\lambda - a_{11})(\lambda - a_{22}) \cdots (\lambda - a_{nn})$,

4. **Prove that the similar matrices have the same characteristic polynomial.**

Solution: Let **A** and **B** are similar matrices, say $\mathbf{B} = \mathbf{P}^{-1}\mathbf{A}\mathbf{P}$ where **P** is invertible

Using $\lambda\mathbf{I} = \mathbf{P}^{-1}\lambda\mathbf{I}\mathbf{P}$, $|\lambda\mathbf{I} - \mathbf{B}| = |\lambda\mathbf{I} - \mathbf{P}^{-1}\mathbf{A}\mathbf{P}|$

$\qquad = |\mathbf{P}^{-1}\lambda\mathbf{I}\mathbf{P} - \mathbf{P}^{-1}\mathbf{A}\mathbf{P}| = |\mathbf{P}^{-1}(\lambda\mathbf{I} - \mathbf{A})\mathbf{P}|$

$\qquad = |\mathbf{P}^{-1}| \, \|\lambda\mathbf{I} - \mathbf{A}\| \, |\mathbf{P}|.$

Also, $|\mathbf{P}^{-1}| \, |\mathbf{P}| = 1$,

Finally, we get $|\lambda\mathbf{I} - \mathbf{B}| = |\lambda\mathbf{I} - \mathbf{A}|.$

$\Rightarrow$ **A** and **B** have the same characteristic polynomial.

5. **Find the eigen values of:**

(a) $\begin{bmatrix} 7 & 6 \\ 5 & 8 \end{bmatrix}$ 　　　　　(b) $\begin{bmatrix} 1 & 0 & -1 \\ 1 & 2 & 1 \\ 2 & 2 & 3 \end{bmatrix}$

Solution: (a) Let $\mathbf{A} = \begin{bmatrix} 7 & 6 \\ 5 & 8 \end{bmatrix}$

$\therefore \quad [\lambda\mathbf{I} - \mathbf{A}] = \begin{bmatrix} \lambda - 7 & -6 \\ -5 & \lambda - 8 \end{bmatrix} = [\mathbf{A} - \lambda\mathbf{I}] = \begin{bmatrix} 7 - \lambda & 6 \\ 5 & 8 - \lambda \end{bmatrix}$

$\therefore \quad |\mathbf{A} - \lambda\mathbf{I}| = 0 \Rightarrow \begin{vmatrix} 7 - \lambda & 6 \\ 5 & 8 - \lambda \end{vmatrix} = 0$

$\left.\begin{aligned} &\Rightarrow (7 - \lambda)(8 - \lambda) - 30 = 0 \\ &\Rightarrow \lambda^2 - 15\lambda + 26 = 0 \\ &\Rightarrow (\lambda - 2)(\lambda - 13) = 0 \\ &\Rightarrow \lambda = 2; \ \lambda = 13 \end{aligned}\right\}$

$\therefore$ 2 and 13 are the eigen values.

(b) Let $\mathbf{A} = \begin{bmatrix} 1 & 0 & -1 \\ 1 & 2 & 1 \\ 2 & 2 & 3 \end{bmatrix}$

$\therefore \quad \mathbf{A} - \lambda \mathbf{I} = \begin{bmatrix} 1-\lambda & 0 & -1 \\ 1 & 2-\lambda & 1 \\ 2 & 2 & 3-\lambda \end{bmatrix}$

$\therefore \quad |\mathbf{A} - \lambda \mathbf{I}| = 0 \Rightarrow \begin{vmatrix} 1-\lambda & 0 & -1 \\ 1 & 2-\lambda & 1 \\ 2 & 2 & 3-\lambda \end{vmatrix} = 0.$

$\Rightarrow \quad (1-\lambda)[(2-\lambda)(3-\lambda) - 2] - 1[2 - 2(2-\lambda)] = 0$

$\Rightarrow \quad (1-\lambda)(\lambda^2 - 5\lambda + 4) - (-2 + 2\lambda) = 0$

$\Rightarrow \quad \lambda^2 - 5\lambda + 4 - \lambda^3 + 5\lambda^2 - 4\lambda + 2 - 2\lambda = 0$

$\Rightarrow \quad -\lambda^3 + 6\lambda^2 - 11\lambda + 6 = 0$

$\Rightarrow \quad \lambda^3 - 6\lambda^2 + 11\lambda - 6 = 0$

$\Rightarrow \quad \lambda = 1, 2, 3$

$\therefore \quad$ 1, 2, 3, are the eigen values.

Eigen Values of a Linear Transformation

Suppose $T : V \rightarrow V$ be a linear transformation of an n dimensional vector space V, and $\mathbf{A}$ be the matrix of the linear transformation T. Then the characteristic equation (or eigen equation) of T is defined as the characteristic equation of $\mathbf{A}$ i.e., $|\mathbf{A} - \lambda \mathbf{I}| = 0$. The roots of the characteristic equation (or the eigen equation) $|\mathbf{A} - \lambda \mathbf{I}| = 0$ are called the characteristic roots or the eigen values of T.

Eigen Vector of a Linear Transformation

Let $T : V \rightarrow V$ be a linear transformation of an n–dimensional vector space V, $\mathbf{A}$ is an $n \times n$ matrix of T, and λ is an eigen value of T, then the vector $\mathbf{x} = (x_1, x_2....., x_n)$ which satisfies the equation $\mathbf{Ax} = \lambda \mathbf{x}$ is called the Eigen vector corresponding to the value of λ.

The vector $\mathbf{x} = (x_1, x_2, ..., x_n)$ can be represented as the column matrix $\begin{bmatrix} x_1 \\ x_2 \\ ... \\ x_n \end{bmatrix}$

The matrix equation $\mathbf{Ax} = \lambda \mathbf{x}$ where $\lambda = \lambda_1, \lambda_2, ..., \lambda_n$ is given by

$$\begin{bmatrix} a_{11} & a_{12} & .... & a_{1n} \\ a_{21} & a_{22} & .... & a_{2n} \\ .... & .... & .... & .... \\ a_{n1} & a_{n2} & .... & a_{nn} \end{bmatrix} \begin{bmatrix} x_1 \\ x_2 \\ ... \\ x_n \end{bmatrix} = \begin{bmatrix} \lambda x_1 \\ \lambda x_2 \\ .... \\ \lambda x_n \end{bmatrix}$$

Definition: (Eigen Space) The set of all vectors $x \in R^n$ satisfying the equation $Ax = \lambda x$ for a given λ form a subspace of R^n called the eigen space of A corresponding to λ.

Determination of Eigen vectors of a Linear transformation.

Working Rule:

(a) Let $T: V \to V$ be a linear transformation. Find the matrix A of this linear transformation.

(b) We find $|A - \lambda I| = 0$, the eigen equation.

(c) On solving $|A - \lambda I| = 0$, we find $\lambda = \lambda_1, \lambda_2, ..., \lambda_n$, the eigen values.

(d) Corresponding to $\lambda = \lambda_1$, put $\lambda = \lambda_1$ in $[A - \lambda I] x = 0$, we find the eigen vector. we get 'n' equation in n unknowns. The solution of this system of equations will give the eigen vector $(x_1, x_2, ..., x_n)$ corresponding to λ_1. Similarly we can find the eigen vectors corresponding to $\lambda = \lambda_2$, $\lambda = \lambda_3$, etc.

EXAMPLES

1. If $I: V \to V$ be the identity mapping on any non-zero vector space V. Show that $\lambda = 1$ is an eigen value of I. What is the eigen space E_1 of $\lambda = I$?

   Solution: Corresponding to each $v \in V$, we have $I(v) = v = 1v$.

   Since $\lambda = 1$ (Given) eigen value of I, and $E_1 = V$ every vector in V is an eigen vector belonging to I.

   Let $A = \begin{bmatrix} 1 & 2 \\ 3 & 2 \end{bmatrix}$. Show that (a) $v_1 = [2, 3]^T$ is an eigen vector of A belonging to the eigen value $\lambda_1 = 4$ of A;

   $v_2 = [1,1]^T$ is an eigen vector of A belonging to the eigen value $\lambda_2 = -1$ of A.

   (a) $Av_1 = \begin{bmatrix} 1 & 2 \\ 3 & 2 \end{bmatrix} \begin{bmatrix} 2 \\ 3 \end{bmatrix} = \begin{bmatrix} 8 \\ 12 \end{bmatrix} = 4 \begin{bmatrix} 2 \\ 3 \end{bmatrix} = 4v_1$

   $\Rightarrow v_1$ is an eigen vector of A belonging to $\lambda_1 = 4$.

(b) $\mathbf{Av}_2 = \begin{bmatrix} 1 & 2 \\ 3 & 2 \end{bmatrix} \begin{bmatrix} 1 \\ -1 \end{bmatrix} = \begin{bmatrix} -1 \\ 1 \end{bmatrix} = (-1)\ \mathbf{v}_2$

$\Rightarrow \mathbf{v}_2$ is an eigen vector of $\mathbf{A}$ belonging to $\lambda = -1$.

2. Find the eigen space of the linear transformation $T : R^3 \to R^3$ defined by
$T(x,\ y,\ z) = (2x + y,\ y - z,\ 2y + 4z)$

Solution: Given:- $T(x,\ y,\ z) = (2x + y,\ y - z,\ 2y + 4z)$

$\therefore\ T(1,\ 0,\ 0) = (2.1 + 0,\ 0 - 0,\ 2.0 + 4.0)$

$\begin{cases} \text{or} & T(1,0,0) = (2,0,0); \\ & T(0,1,0) = (1,1,2) \\ \text{and} & T(0,0,1) = (0,-1,4) \end{cases}$

The matrix of L.T. is

$$\mathbf{A} = \begin{bmatrix} 2 & 0 & 0 \\ 1 & 1 & 2 \\ 0 & -1 & 4 \end{bmatrix}$$

$\therefore$ Eigen equation is $|\mathbf{A} - \lambda \mathbf{I}| = 0$

$$\begin{vmatrix} 2-\lambda & 0 & 0 \\ 1 & 1-\lambda & 2 \\ 0 & -1 & 4-\lambda \end{vmatrix} = 0$$

$\Rightarrow\quad (2-\lambda)\,[(1-\lambda)(4-\lambda) + 2] = 0$

$\Rightarrow\quad (2-\lambda)\,(\lambda^2 - 5\lambda + 6) = 0$

$\Rightarrow\quad (2-\lambda)\,(\lambda - 2)\,(\lambda - 3) = 0$

$\Rightarrow\quad (\lambda - 2)^2\,(\lambda - 3) = 0$

$\Rightarrow\quad \lambda = 2, 2, 3.$

$\therefore$ 2, 3 are the eigen values.

Consider $\mathbf{Ax} = \lambda x$

$\Rightarrow\quad (\mathbf{A} - \lambda \mathbf{I})\,x = 0$

$$\Rightarrow \begin{bmatrix} 2-\lambda & 0 & 0 \\ 1 & 1-\lambda & 2 \\ 1 & -1 & 4-\lambda \end{bmatrix} \begin{bmatrix} x_1 \\ x_2 \\ x_3 \end{bmatrix} = \begin{bmatrix} 0 \\ 0 \\ 0 \end{bmatrix}$$

$\Rightarrow\quad (2 - \lambda)\,x_1 + 0x_2 + 0x_3 = 0$

$\Rightarrow \quad x_1 = 0$

and $\quad x_1 + (1 - \lambda) \, x_2 + 2x_3 = 0; \Rightarrow (1-\lambda) \, x_2 + 2x_3 = 0$

$\quad\quad ox_1 - x_2 + (4 - \lambda) \, x_3 = 0 \Rightarrow -x_2 + (4 - \lambda) \, x_3 = 0$

Put $\lambda = 2$;

$\therefore \quad x_2 + 2x_3 = 0;$

$\Rightarrow \quad x_2 = 2x_3$

$\therefore$ If $x_3 = k$; $\quad x_2 = 2k$

$\therefore$ The vector is $(0, 2k, k)$

$\therefore$ $(0, 2, 1)$ is a basis of the eigen space corresponding to $\lambda = 2$.

Put $\lambda = 3$, then $-2x_2 + 2x_3 = 0$

$\Rightarrow \quad - x_2 + x_3 = 0$

and $\quad - x_2 + x_3 = 0$

$\therefore \quad x_2 = x_3 = k$

$\therefore$ The vector is $(0, k, k)$

$\therefore$ $(0, 1, 1)$ is a basis of the eigen space corresponding to $\lambda = 3$.

3. Find the basis for the eigen space of the L.T., $T : R^2 \to R^2$ defined as $T(x,y) = (x + y, y)$

   Solution: Here, we shall first find the matrix of T w.r.t the standard basis
   $[(1, 0), (0, 1)]$

   $\quad T(1, 0) = (1, 1)$

   $\therefore \quad$ The matrix of the L.T is $A = \begin{bmatrix} 1 & 0 \\ 1 & 1 \end{bmatrix}$

   $\Rightarrow \quad |A - \lambda I| = 0$ is the eigen equation

   $\Rightarrow \quad \begin{vmatrix} 1-\lambda & 0 \\ 1 & 1-\lambda \end{vmatrix} = 0$

   $\Rightarrow \quad (1- \lambda) \, (1-\lambda) - 0 = 0$

   $\Rightarrow \quad \lambda = 1, \lambda = 1$

   Let $\quad x = (x_1, x_2)$ be a vector in R^2 then $Ax = \lambda x$

   $\Rightarrow \quad (A - \lambda I) = 0$

   $\Rightarrow \quad \begin{bmatrix} 1-\lambda & 0 \\ 1 & 1-\lambda \end{bmatrix} \begin{bmatrix} x_1 \\ x_2 \end{bmatrix} = \begin{bmatrix} 0 \\ 0 \end{bmatrix}$

$$\Rightarrow \quad \begin{bmatrix} (1-\lambda)x_1 \\ x_1 + (1-\lambda)x_2 \end{bmatrix} = \begin{bmatrix} 0 \\ 0 \end{bmatrix}$$

$\Rightarrow \quad (1 - \lambda)\, x_1 = 0$

$\quad\quad x_1 + (1 - \lambda)\, x_2 = 0$

Put $\lambda = 1$, we get $x_1 = 0$; $x_2 = 0$

$\therefore$ (0, 0) is the eigen vector

The eigen space is $\{(0, 0)\}$

4. Find the eigen values and eigen vectors of the linear transformations $T : R^3 \rightarrow R^3$ defined by

$$T\,(e_1) = (1, 1, 0)\ ;$$
$$T\,(e_2) = (0, 1, 1)\ ;$$
$$T\,(e_3) = (1, 2, 1)\ ;$$

Solution: Here, the matrix of the linear transformation $T : R^3$ is

$$A = \begin{bmatrix} 1 & 1 & 0 \\ 0 & 1 & 1 \\ 1 & 2 & 1 \end{bmatrix} \qquad\qquad [1]$$

$\therefore \quad |A - \lambda I| = 0$ is the eigen equation

$$\Rightarrow \quad \begin{vmatrix} 1-\lambda & 1 & 0 \\ 0 & 1-\lambda & 1 \\ 1 & 2 & 1-\lambda \end{vmatrix} = 0$$

$\Rightarrow \quad (1 - \lambda)\,[(1-\lambda)^2 - 2] - 1(0 - 1) + 0 = 0$

$\Rightarrow \quad (1 - \lambda)\,(\lambda^2 - 2\lambda - 1) + 1 = 0$

$\Rightarrow \quad \lambda^2 - 2\lambda - 1 - \lambda^3 + 2\lambda^2 + \lambda + 1 = 0$

$\Rightarrow \quad \lambda\,(\lambda^2 - 3\lambda + 1) = 0$

$\Rightarrow \quad \lambda = 0,\ \lambda = \dfrac{3 \pm \sqrt{9-4}}{2}$

$\qquad = \dfrac{3 \pm \sqrt{5}}{2}$

$\therefore \quad \lambda = 0,\ \dfrac{3+\sqrt{5}}{2},\ \dfrac{3-\sqrt{5}}{2}$ are the eigen values

$$Ax = \lambda x \Rightarrow (A - \lambda I)x = 0$$

$$\Rightarrow \begin{bmatrix} 1-\lambda & 1 & 0 \\ 0 & 1-\lambda & 1 \\ 1 & 2 & 1-\lambda \end{bmatrix} \begin{bmatrix} x_1 \\ x_2 \\ x_3 \end{bmatrix} = \begin{bmatrix} 0 \\ 0 \\ 0 \end{bmatrix}$$

$\Rightarrow \quad (1 - \lambda) x_1 + x_2 = 0$

$\quad (1 - \lambda) x_2 + 1x_3 = 0$

$\quad 1x_1 + 2x_2 + (1 - \lambda) x_3 = 0$

Put $\lambda = 0;$ $\therefore x_1 + x_2 = 0$ [1]

$\quad x_2 + x_3 = 0$ [2]

$\quad x_1 + 2x_2 + x_2 = 0$ [3]

[1] is $x_1 + x_2 = 0;$ $\therefore x_2 = - x_1$

$\therefore$ from [2] we get $x_3 = - x_2$

i.e., $x_3 = x_1$

$\Rightarrow \quad (x_1, x_2, x_3) (x_1, - x_1, x_1)$

$\quad = x_1 (1, -1, 1)$

$\therefore \quad \{(1, -1, 1)\}$ is a basis of the subspace corresponding to $\lambda = 0$

Put $\lambda = \dfrac{3+\sqrt{5}}{2};$

$\therefore \quad \left[1-\dfrac{3+\sqrt{5}}{2}\right] x_1 + x_2 = 0$ [4]

$\quad \left[1-\dfrac{3+\sqrt{5}}{2}\right] x_2 + x_3 = 0$ [5]

$\quad x_1 + 2x_2 + \left[1-\dfrac{3+\sqrt{5}}{2}\right] x_3 = 0$ [6]

From [4], $x_2 = -\left[1-\dfrac{3+\sqrt{5}}{2}\right] x_1$

$\quad = \left[\dfrac{1+\sqrt{5}}{2}\right] x_1$

From [5] $x_3 = \left[1-\dfrac{3+\sqrt{5}}{2}\right] \left[\dfrac{1+\sqrt{5}}{2}\right] x_1$

$$= \left[\frac{1+\sqrt{5}}{2}\right]\left[\frac{1+\sqrt{5}}{2}\right]x_1$$

i.e., $x_3 = \dfrac{6+2\sqrt{5}}{4}x_1$

$$\Rightarrow \left[x_1, \left(\frac{1+\sqrt{5}}{2}\right)x_1, \left(\frac{\sqrt{5}+3}{2}\right)x_1\right] = x_1 \left(1, \frac{1+\sqrt{5}}{2}, \frac{\sqrt{5}+3}{2}\right)$$

$$\therefore \quad \left\{\left(1, \frac{1+\sqrt{5}}{2}, \frac{\sqrt{5}+3}{2}\right)\right\} \quad \text{is a basis of the subspace.}$$

Put $\lambda = \dfrac{3-\sqrt{5}}{2}$

$$\therefore \quad \left(1-\frac{3-\sqrt{5}}{2}\right)x_1 + x_2 = 0 \tag{7}$$

$$\left(1-\frac{3-\sqrt{5}}{2}\right)x_2 + x_3 = 0 \tag{8}$$

$$x_1 + 2x_2 + \left(1-\frac{3-\sqrt{5}}{2}\right)x_3 = 0 \tag{9}$$

$$x_2 = -\left(\frac{-1+\sqrt{5}}{2}\right)x_1 = \left(\frac{1-\sqrt{5}}{2}\right)x_1$$

$$x_3 = -\left(\frac{-1+\sqrt{5}}{2}\right)x_2$$

$$= \left(\frac{1-\sqrt{5}}{2}\right)\left(\frac{1-\sqrt{5}}{2}\right)x_1$$

$$= \left(\frac{6-2\sqrt{5}}{4}\right)x_1 = \left(\frac{3-\sqrt{5}}{2}\right)x_1$$

$$\Rightarrow (x_1, x_2, x_3) = \left(x_1, \left(\frac{1-\sqrt{5}}{2}\right)x_1, \left(\frac{3-\sqrt{5}}{2}\right)x_1\right)$$

$$= x_1 \left(1, \frac{1-\sqrt{5}}{2}, \frac{3-\sqrt{5}}{2}\right)$$

$$\therefore \quad \left\{\left(1, \frac{1-\sqrt{5}}{2}, \frac{3-\sqrt{5}}{2}\right)\right\} \text{ is a basis of the sequence.}$$

5. If $L : R^2 \to R^2$ be the linear operator which rotates each vector $\mathbf{v} \in R^2$ by an angle $\theta = \pi/2 = 90°$, then prove geometrically that L has no eigen values and hence no eigen vectors.

   Solution: It can be observed that no non-zero vector is a multiple of itself, which is the defining condition for an eigen value. Thus, L has no eigen values and hence no eigen vectors.

6. Let $T : V \to V$ be a linear operator and λ be an eigen value. Let E_λ be the eigen space of λ, i.e., the set of all eigen vectors of T belonging to λ. Show that E_λ is a subspace of V, i.e.,

   (i) If $\mathbf{v} \in E_\lambda$ for any scalar $k \in K$.

   (ii) If $\mathbf{u}_1 \ \mathbf{v} \in E_\lambda$, then $\mathbf{u} + \mathbf{v} \in E_\lambda$

   Solution:

   (i) Since $\mathbf{v} \in E_\lambda$ we have $T(\mathbf{v}) = \lambda\mathbf{v}$.
   Then $T(k\mathbf{v}) = kT(\mathbf{v}) = k(\lambda\mathbf{v}) = \lambda(k\mathbf{v})$
   Thus $k\mathbf{v} \in E_\lambda$.

   (ii) Since $\mathbf{u}, \mathbf{v} \in E_\lambda$, we have $T(\mathbf{u}) = \lambda\mathbf{v}$ and $T(\mathbf{v}) = \lambda\mathbf{v}$.
   Then $T(\mathbf{u}+\mathbf{v}) = T(\mathbf{u}) + T(\mathbf{v})$
   $\qquad\qquad = \lambda\mathbf{u} + \lambda\mathbf{v} = \lambda(\mathbf{u} + \mathbf{v})$.
   Thus $\mathbf{u} + \mathbf{v} \in E_\lambda$.

7. If $L : V \to V$ be a linear operator on a vector space over K, then $\lambda \in K$ is an eigen value of L iff the operator $\lambda I - L$ is singular. The eigen value of λ is then the kernel $\lambda I - L$.

   Proof: The scalar I is an eigen value of L iff $\exists$ a non-vector v, such that
   $$L(\mathbf{v}) = \lambda\mathbf{v} \text{ or } (\lambda I)(\mathbf{v}) - L(\mathbf{v}) = 0$$
   $$(\lambda I - L)(\mathbf{v}) = 0.$$
   i.e., $\lambda I - L$ is singular. We also have that $\mathbf{v}$ is the eigen space of λ iff the above relation hold; hence $\mathbf{v}$ is the kernel of $\lambda I - L$.

8. Prove that a linear operator $L : V \to V$ can be represented by a diagonal matrix **B** iff V has a basis consisting of eigen vectors of L.

Solution:

Let us represent L by a diagonal matrix $\begin{bmatrix} c_1 & 0 & \cdots & 0 \\ 0 & c_2 & \cdots & 0 \\ \cdots & \cdots & \cdots & \cdots \\ 0 & 0 & \cdots & c_n \end{bmatrix}$

iff $\exists$ a basis $\{v_1, v_2, ..., v_n\}$ of V for which $L(v_1) = c_1 v_1$, $L(v_2) = c_2 v_2$ $L(v_n) = c_n v_n$ i.e., such that vectors $v_1, v_2, ..., v_n$ are eigen vectors of L belonging to eigen values $c_1, c_2, ..., c_n$.

In this case the diagonal elements of **B** are the corresponding eigen values.

Non-zero eigen vectors belonging to distinct values are L.I.

Proof: Let $v_1, v_2, ..., v_n$ be non-zero eigen vectors of a linear operator $L; V \to V$ belonging to distinct eigen values $1_1, 1_2, ..., 1_n$ respectively. We claim $v_1, v_2, ..., v_n$ are L.I.

We shall prove this result by mathematical induction when $n = 1$, here v_1 is L.I. $\therefore$ $v_1 \neq 0$.

$\therefore$ The result is true for $n = 1$,

Let us assume that the result is true when the number of vectors < n.

Let $\alpha_1 v_1 + \alpha_2 v_2 + ... + \alpha_n v_n = 0$ $\qquad$ [1]

where $\alpha_1, \alpha_2, ..., \alpha_n \in F$

$\Rightarrow \quad \alpha_1 L(v_1) + \alpha_1 L(v_2) + ... + \alpha_n L(v_n) = L(0).$

$\Rightarrow \quad \alpha_1 L(v_1) + \alpha_2 L(v_2) + \alpha_n L(v_n) = 0$

Since $L(v_i) = \lambda_i v_i$ for $i = 1, 2, ..., n$

$\therefore \quad \alpha_1 \lambda_1 v_1 + \alpha_2 \lambda_2 v_2 + ... + \alpha_n \lambda_n v_n = 0$ $\qquad$ [2]

Multiply [1] by λ_n, we get

$\therefore \quad \alpha_1 \lambda_n v_1 + \alpha_2 \lambda_n v_2 + ... + \alpha_n \lambda_n v_n = 0$

Subtracting [3] from [2], we get

$\quad \alpha_1 (\lambda_1 - \lambda_n) v_1 + \alpha_2 (\lambda_2 - \lambda_n) v_2 + ... + \lambda_{n-i} (\lambda_{n-1} - \lambda_n) v_{n-1} = 0$ [3]

Subtracting [3] from [2], we get

$\quad \alpha_i (\lambda_1 - \lambda_n) v_1 + \alpha_2 (\lambda_2 - \lambda_n) v_2 + ... + a_{n-1} (\lambda_{n-1} \lambda_n) v_{n-1} = 0$

$\Rightarrow \quad \alpha_1(\lambda_1 - \lambda_n) = 0; \quad \alpha_2(\lambda_2 - \lambda_n) = 0, \ldots$

$\qquad \alpha_{n-1}(\lambda_{n-1} - \lambda_n) = 0$ [4]

$[v_1, v_2, \ldots, v_{n-1}$ are L.I. (assumed)].

But since λ_i are distinct

$\therefore \quad \lambda_1 - \lambda_n \neq 0; \ \lambda_2 - \lambda_n \neq 0; \ \ldots, \ \lambda_{n-1} - \lambda_n = 0$

$\therefore \quad [4] \Rightarrow \alpha_1 = 0, \ \alpha_2 = 0, \ \ldots, \ \alpha_{n-1} = 0$

Putting in [1], $\alpha_n v_n = 0$

$\Rightarrow \quad \alpha_n = 0 \qquad\qquad (\because \ v_n \neq 0)$

Thus $\alpha_1 = 0, \ \alpha_2 = 0, \ \ldots, \ \alpha_n = 0$

Hence, the vectors $v_1, v_2, \ldots, v_n$ are L.I.

9. If λ is an eigen value of an invertible operator L on a vector space V over F, then λ^{-1} is an eigen value of L^{-1}.

Proof:

Since L is invertible   (Given)

$\therefore \quad L$ is non-singular

$\therefore \quad \exists$ an eigen value $\lambda \neq 0$

$\Rightarrow \quad \lambda^{-1}$ exists

$\Rightarrow \quad \exists$ a non-zero vector $v \in V$ s.t. $L(v) = \lambda v$

$\Rightarrow \quad v = L^{-1}(\lambda v);$ (operating L^{-1} on both sides)

$\Rightarrow \quad v = \lambda L^{-1}(v)$ $(\because \ L$ is linear $\Rightarrow L^{-1}$ is linear)

$\Rightarrow \quad L^{-1}(v) = \lambda^{-1} v$

$\Rightarrow \quad \lambda^{-1}$ is an eigen value of L^{-1}.

EXERCISES

1. Find the eigen values of

$$A = \begin{bmatrix} 1 & -3 & 3 \\ 3 & -5 & 3 \\ 6 & -6 & 4 \end{bmatrix}$$

Ans: $\lambda_1 = -2; \ \lambda_2 = 4$

2. Find all eigen values and corresponding eigen vectors of $A = \begin{bmatrix} 1 & -1 \\ 2 & -1 \end{bmatrix}$ assuming A is a real matrix.

    Ans: No eigen values, No eigen values in R.

3. Find a maximum set of L.I. eigen vectors of $\begin{bmatrix} 4 & 1 & -1 \\ 2 & 5 & -2 \\ 1 & 1 & 2 \end{bmatrix}$

4. Find the eigen values and eigen vectors of the following Linear transformation
    (i) $L : V_2(R) \rightarrow V_2 (R)$ defined by $L(1, 0) = (1, 2)$; $L(0, 1) = (3, 2)$

    Ans: $\lambda = 4, -1, ; (2, 3) (1, -1)$

    (ii) $L : V_2(R) \rightarrow V_2 (R)$ defined by
    $L(e_1) = (1, 4)$
    $L(e_2) = (2, 3)$

    Ans: $\lambda = 5, -1; (1, 1), (-2, 1)$

    (iii) $L : R^3 \rightarrow R^3$ defined by
    $L (e_1) = (4, 0, 1);$
    $L (e_2) = (-2, 1, 0)$
    $L (e_3) = (-2, 0, 1)$

    Ans: $\lambda = 1, 2, 3,; (0, 1, 0), (1, -2, -2)$

    (iv) $L : R^3 \rightarrow R^3$ defined by
    $L (1, 0, 0) = (1, -3, 3)$
    $L (0, 1, 0) = (3, -5, 3)$
    $L (0, 0, 1) = (6, -6, 4)$

    Ans: $\lambda = 4, -2; (1, 1, 2), (0, 1, 1)$

    (v) $L : R^3 \rightarrow R^3$ defined by $L (1, 0, 0) = (-3, 1, -1)$
    $L (0, 1, 0) = (-7, 5, -1)$; $L (0, 0, 1) = (-6, 6, 2)$

    Ans: $\lambda = 2, 4, -2; (-1, 2, 9), (1, 1, 0)$

    (vi) $L : R^3 \rightarrow R^3$ given by
    $L (e_1) = (3, 2, 4)$; $L (e_2) = (2, 0, 2)$
    $L (e_3) = (4, 2, 3)$

    Ans: $\lambda = 0, -1, 7; (1, 2, -2)$

(vii) $L : R^3 \rightarrow R^3$ given by

$L\ (x,\ y,\ z) = (3x + 2y + z,\ x + 4y +z,\ x +2y + 3z)$

Ans: $\lambda = 2,\ 6$; $(1,\ 2,\ -3),\ (1,\ 2,\ 1)$

(viii) $L : V_3(R) \rightarrow V_3(R)$ given by

$L : (x,\ y,\ z) = (x,\ x + y,\ z)$

Ans: $\lambda = 1;\ (1,\ 0,\ 2)$

(ix) $L : V_3(R) \rightarrow V_3(R)$ given by

$L\ (x,\ y,\ z) = (3x,\ 2y + z,\ -5y - 2z)$

Ans: $\lambda = 3;\ (1,\ 0,\ 0)$

(x) $L : R^3 \rightarrow R^3$ given by

$L\ (x,\ y,\ z) = (x + 3z,\ (2x + y - z,\ x - y + z)$

Ans: $\lambda = 2;\ (7,\ 6,\ -15)$

5

OPTIMIZATION

Introduction

This chapter is concerned with optimizing (maximizing / minimizing) a linear function of variables called the 'Objective function' subject to a set of linear equations and / or inequalities called the constraints or restrictions. The word linear is used here to describe the relationship among two or more variables which are directly proportional.

Owing to technical development over the years and increasing complexities in business and industry, the executives face situations of making a decision under intense competition not seen before. Linear programming technique is an interesting topic in operation research. It is extensively used in solving the problems related to management, commerce, economics, engineering, etc. In all business and industrial activities decision making is an important aspect. Nowadays Linear Programming technique is found to be a powerful tool for managerial decisions making problems though its early applications were for military operations. Its utility is increased by the development and use of computers in the recent years.

A linear programming is a technique of allocating the available resources in such an optimum manner so as to obtain a particular objective of minimizing the cost and maximizing the profit when alternative uses of the resources are available.

Basic concepts and Classification of Optimization Problems, Linear Programming

The basic concept of optimization problem is: What methods should be adopted so that the total cost is minimum or total profit is maximum?

In 1947, an American mathematician George B. Dantzig developed a mathematical technique (Simplex Method of Linear Programming) to solve the problems in the areas of management decision making which can be briefly classified as 1) Finance 2) Purchasing 3) To optimize the total output in all business and industrial activities etc.

The main object of Linear Programming Technique is to achieve optimal results with restricted resources. Hence it is an optimization technique. It gives all feasible solutions of the problem and select the best feasible solution.

Requirements to Formulate a Linear Programming Problem (L.P.P.)

In formulation of any L.P.P it is quite necessary to specify:

(a) Decision variables (Activity variables)

(b) Well-defined objective function

(c) Constraints

(d) Linearity

(e) Non-negativity of the decision variables

(f) Deterministic

(g) Feasible solution (FS)

(h) Basic solution (BS)

(a) Decision variables (Activity Variables): The problem should have number of decision variables for which the decisions are to be taken. These are x_1, x_2, ..., x_n, where ($x_1 \geq 0$, ..., $x_n \geq 0$, non-negative and interrelated).

(b) Well-defined objective function: The linear function z given by the equation: $z = c_1 x_1 + c_2 x_2 + ... + c_n x_n$ is called the objective function which is to be optimized (maximized / minimized). It is necessary that this function like, profit, cost, number of units produced etc., should be well-defined.

(c) Constraints: These are the conditions of the problem exposed as simultaneous linear equations or inequalities.

(d) Linearity: The objective function must be linear function involving constraints in it. It is usually denoted as: $z = c_1 x_1 + c_2 x_2 + ... + c_n x_n$, where c_i's are constant.

(e) Non-negativity of the decision variables: The decision variables x_1, x_2, ... x_n in the L.P.P. must be non-negative i.e., $x_1 \geq 0$, $x_2 \geq 0$, ..., $x_n \geq 0$. It is meaningless to study the negative variables.

(f) Deterministic: All the coefficient of the objective function i.e., c_i's in z, where $z = c_1 x_1 + c_2 x_2 + ... + c_n x_n$ and constraints are known with certainty.

(g) Feasible solution: Any set of variables say **x**, where $\mathbf{x} = (x_1, x_2, ..., x_n, x_{n+1}, x_{n+2}, ..., x_{n+m})$ is called a feasible solution of L.P.P. and also satisfying the non-negative restrictions of the problem.

(h) Basic solution: Out of $(n + m)$ variables, a solution obtained by setting any 'n' variables equal to zero and solving for remaining 'm' variables, provided the determinant of the coefficients of these m-variables is non-zero. Such 'm' variables (not all zero) are called basic variables and remaining n-(zero-valued) variables are called non-basic variables. In most optimization problems the objective function z depends on several variables,

i.e., $z = f(x_1, x_2, x_3 \ldots, x_n)$ – (linear)

$= c_1 x_1 + c_2 x_2 + \ldots + c_n x_n$

A linear form is meant for a mathematical expression of the type:

$$z = \; = \; c_1 x_1 + c_2 x_2 + \ldots + c_n x_n \qquad [1]$$

subject to the constraints

$$\left. \begin{aligned} a_{11}x_1 + a_{12}x_2 + \ldots + a_{1n}x_n &= b_1 \\ a_{21}x_1 + a_{22}x_2 + \ldots + a_{2n}x_n &= b_2 \\ \vdots \qquad \vdots \qquad \qquad \vdots \qquad \vdots \\ a_{m1}x_1 + a_{m2}x_2 + \ldots + a_{mn}x_n &= b_m \\ x_i \geq 0, \; (i = 1, 2, \ldots, n) \end{aligned} \right] \qquad [2]$$

Here $x_1, x_2, \ldots, x_n$ including the slack variables $x_{n+1}, x_{n+2}, \ldots, x_{n+m}$ (for which c_i's in z are zero.).

The theory of optimization (maximization/minimization) develops methods for optimal choices of $x_1, x_2, \ldots x_n$ i.e., for finding optimal values of $x_1, x_2, \ldots x_n$.

Some Important Notations/Symbols/Definitions

(1) $x_1 = x_2 = x_3 = \ldots = x_n = 0$ (Basic feasible solution) and $x_{n+1} = b_1, x_{n+2} = b_2, \ldots, x_{n+m} = b_m$

(2) Max $z = c_1 x_1 + c_2 x_2 + \ldots + c_n x_n = \mathbf{cv}$

subject to the matrix equation

$\mathbf{Ax = b, \; x \geq 0}$

where

$$\mathbf{A} = \begin{bmatrix} a_{11} & a_{12} & \ldots & a_{1n} \\ a_{21} & a_{22} & \ldots & a_{2n} \\ \vdots & \vdots & & \vdots \\ a_{n1} & a_{n2} & \ldots & a_{mn} \end{bmatrix}$$

$$\mathbf{x} = \begin{bmatrix} x_1 \\ x_2 \\ \vdots \\ x_n \end{bmatrix}, \; \mathbf{b} = \begin{bmatrix} b_1 \\ b_2 \\ \vdots \\ b_m \end{bmatrix}$$

$x_1 \geq 0, \; x_2 \geq 0, \; \ldots, \; x_n \geq 0$ (Note)

(3) A matrix **B** is defined by:

$$\mathbf{B} = \begin{bmatrix} 1 & 0 & 0 & \dots & 0 \\ 0 & 1 & 0 & \dots & 0 \\ \vdots & \vdots & \vdots & & \vdots \\ 0 & 0 & 0 & & 1 \end{bmatrix}$$

(identity matrix $\mathbf{I}_m$) is called a Basis Matrix.

(4) We denote the basic variables

$$x_{n+1} \text{ by } x_{b1},$$ [1]

$$x_{n+2} \text{ by } x_{b2}$$ [2]

$$\vdots$$

$$x_{n+m} \text{ by } x_{bm}$$

and the basic feasible solution is given by $x_b = (b_1, b_2, \dots, b_m)$.

(5) The objective function:

$z = c_1 x_1 + c_2 x_2 + \dots + c_n x_n = 0 \cdot x_{n+1} + 0 \cdot x_{n+2} + \dots + 0 \cdot x_{n+m}$ but the basic feasible solution is $x_1 = x_2 = x_3 = \dots = x_n = 0$, therefore

$$z = c_1 \cdot 0 + c_2 \cdot 0 + \dots + c_n \cdot 0 + c_{b_1} x_{b_1} + \dots + c_{b_m} x_{b_m}$$

or $\quad z = c_b x_b$

where $c_b = (0, 0, \dots, 0)$, initially we take the initial solutions as $z = 0$, $x_b = \mathbf{b}$

Definitions

Definition (1): A vector in n-space is an ordered set of n-real numbers. For example, $\mathbf{a} = (a_1, a_2, \dots a_n)$ is a vector of n-elements or n-components. The real numbers $a_1, a_2, \dots a_n$ are called the components of $\mathbf{a}$.

Definition (2) (Inner product): The inner product of n-vectors α and β, written $\alpha \cdot \beta$ or simply $\alpha\beta$ is a number given by $\alpha\beta = a_1 b_1 + a_2 b_2 \dots + a_n b_n$

e.g., $\quad \alpha = [1, 2, 3].$

$$\beta = \begin{bmatrix} 4 \\ 5 \\ 6 \end{bmatrix}$$

then $\alpha\beta = \begin{bmatrix} 1,2,3 \end{bmatrix} \begin{bmatrix} 4 \\ 5 \\ 6 \end{bmatrix} = 4 + 10 + 18 = 32$

It is also called scalar product.

Definition (3) (Linear combination): α is called a linear combination of the vectors α_i if

$$\alpha = \sum_{i=1}^{m} a_i \alpha_i, \ a_i \in R$$

when not all a_i's are zero then α_i are said to be linearly dependent.

If $\sum_{i=1}^{m} a_i \alpha_i = 0$, when $a_i = 0$, then α_i are said to be linearly independent.

Definition (4) (Euclidean space):

(a) Ordinary two or three dimensional space

(b) A space consisting of all sets (points) of n numbers $(x_1, x_2, \ldots x_n)$ where the distance $P(\mathbf{x}, \mathbf{y})$ between $\mathbf{x} = (x_1, x_2, \ldots x_n)$ and $\mathbf{y} = (y_1, y_2, \ldots y_n)$ is defined as and is given by

$$P(\mathbf{x}, \mathbf{y}) = \left[\sum_{i=1}^{n} |x_i - y_i|^2 \right]^{\frac{1}{2}}$$

Let R^n be a set of ordered n-tuples of real numbers. For every pair of n-tuples, $\mathbf{x}, \mathbf{y} \in R^n$ we have

(i) Sum $\mathbf{x} + \mathbf{y} = \mathbf{y} + \mathbf{x}$

$\qquad = (x_1 + y_1, x_2 + y_2, \ldots x_n + y_n) \in R^n$

(ii) Product $a\mathbf{x} = (ax_1, ax_2, \ldots ax_n) \in R^n, \ a \in R$

(iii) Inner product $\mathbf{x}^T \cdot \mathbf{y} = \mathbf{y}^T \cdot \mathbf{x}$

$= x_1 y_1 + x_2 y_2 + \ldots + x_n y_n \in R^n$ where $\mathbf{x}^T$ and $\mathbf{y}^T$ are tranposes of $\mathbf{x}$ and $\mathbf{y}$, be defined, then R^n, is called an Euclidean space.

(6) Length of a vector:

(a) The length or norm of the vector

$$\mathbf{x} \text{ is } \left[\sum_{i=1}^{n} |x_i|^2 \right]^{\frac{1}{2}} \tag{1}$$

Also, (ii) the distance between two points gives the length of a vector. The length of a vector is the distance between origin and the point identifying the vector. The length of a vector [as in [1]]

$\qquad \mathbf{a} = (a_1, a_2, \ldots a_n)$ in E^n is given by

$$|\mathbf{a}| = \sqrt{\left[a_1^2 + a_2^2 + \ldots + a_n^2 \right]}$$

Definition (5) (Orthogonal vectors): Two vectors are said to be orthogonal if

$\qquad \mathbf{a} \cdot \mathbf{b} = 0$

Definition (6): Normed vector space or normed linear space

A vector space is a normed vector space (or normed linear space) if there is a real number $\|\mathbf{x}\|$ (called the norm of x) associated with each "vector" $\mathbf{x}$ and $\|\mathbf{x}\| > 0$, $\|\mathbf{x}\| \neq 0$, $\forall \ \mathbf{x} \neq 0$, $\|a\mathbf{x}\| = |a| \|\mathbf{x}\|$, $\|\mathbf{x} + \mathbf{y}\| \leq \|\mathbf{x}\| + \|\mathbf{y}\|$. A normed vector space is also a linear topological space.

Note: If we choose $a = 0$,

then $a\mathbf{x} = 0\mathbf{x} = \mathbf{0}$

$$\|\mathbf{0}\| = |0| \, \|\mathbf{x}\| = 0$$

$\therefore \quad 0 = \|\mathbf{0}\| = \|\mathbf{x}-\mathbf{x}\| = \|\mathbf{x} + (-\mathbf{x})\|$

or $\quad 0 \le \|\mathbf{x}\| + \|-\mathbf{x}\| = \|\mathbf{x}\| + |-1| \, \|\mathbf{x}\| = 2\|\mathbf{x}\|$

$\quad 0 \le 2 \, \|\mathbf{x}\|$ or $\|\mathbf{x}\| \ge 0$

Hence in view of this, we may say that $\|\mathbf{x}\| \ne 0$ if $\mathbf{x} \ne 0$

Definition (7) (Line segments): In R^n, the line segments joining two points $\mathbf{x}_1$ and $\mathbf{x}_2$ is defined to be the set of points.

$$\{\mathbf{x} : \mathbf{x} = \lambda\mathbf{x}_1 + (1 - \lambda) \, \mathbf{x}_2\}$$

for $\quad 0 \le \lambda \le 1$

Definition (8) (Hyper plane): A subset H of a linear space L such that H contains all x for which there are numbers $\lambda_1, \lambda_2, ..., \lambda_n$, and elements $h_1, h_2, ... h_n$ of H, satisfying

$$\mathbf{x} = \Sigma \, \lambda_i h_i \text{ and } \Sigma \, \lambda_i = 1: \quad \text{or}$$

A set of points $\mathbf{x}$ satisfying $c_1 x_1 + c_2 x_2 + ... + c_n x_n = z$ (not all $c_i = 0$) $cx = z$ or $c^T x = z$ in matrix form

defines a hyper plane for prescribed values of $c_1, c_2, ... c_n$ and z. For optimum value of z, this hyper plane is called optimal hyper plane.

Definition (9) (Convex sets): A convex set is a non-empty set with the property that $\mathbf{x}$ and $\mathbf{y}$ be any two distinct points of it then $Z = \{(1 - t) \, \mathbf{x} + t\mathbf{y} : 0 \le t \le 1)\}$ also belongs to it.

We may also have $Z = \{p\mathbf{x} + q\mathbf{y} : p + q = 1, p \ge 0, q \ge 0\}$ also belongs to it as $p + q = 1 - t + t = 1$

Definition (10) (Convex Combination of vector): A convex combination of vectors or points $\mathbf{x}_1, \mathbf{x}_2, ..., \mathbf{x}_n$ is a point

$$\mathbf{x} = \lambda_1\mathbf{x}_1 + \lambda_2\mathbf{x}_2 + ... + \lambda_n\mathbf{x}_n = \Sigma\lambda_i\mathbf{x}_i$$

where λ_i is real and $\ge 0 \; \forall_i$

and $\quad \Sigma\lambda_i = \lambda_1 + \lambda_2 + ... + \lambda_n = 1$

The convex combination of two points $\mathbf{x}_1$ and $\mathbf{x}_2$ is given by

$$\mathbf{x} = \lambda_1\mathbf{x}_1 + \lambda_2\mathbf{x}_2,$$

and $\lambda_1 + \lambda_2 = 1$

This can also be written as

$$\mathbf{x} = \lambda\mathbf{x}_1 + (1 - \lambda)\mathbf{x}_2, \; 0 \le \lambda \le 1$$

EXAMPLES: Convex sets

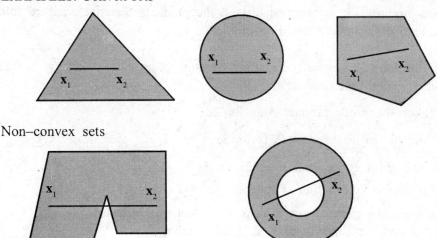

Non–convex sets

I. Convex hull of a_1, a_2, ... a_p in E_n

Definition: (11) The convex hull of p points a_1, a_2, ... a_p in E_n is the set of points $b = \lambda_1 a_1 + \lambda_2 a_2 + ... \lambda_p a_p$ for all non-negative $\lambda_1, \lambda_2, ... \lambda_p$, $\lambda_1 + \lambda_2 + ... \lambda_p = 1$

II. Two important results on convex sets

(a) For a given convex set C, any convex combination of points in C is also in C.

(b) Any point on the line joining two points in E_n can be expressed as a convex combination of the two points and conversely.

Model Examples to Formulate Linear Programming Problems

1. A manufacturer produces two products A and B. The profit per unit sold of each product are Rs. 2 and Rs. 3 respectively. The time required to manufacture one unit of each of the products and the daily capacity of the two machines C and D are given in the following table.

Machine	Time required per unit (in minutes) Product		Machine capacity (Minutes per day)
	A	B	
C	5	7	1200
D	4	6	1000

The manufacturer wants at least 60 units of product A and 30 units of product B to be produced. It is assumed that all the products manufactured are sold in the market. Formulate the L.P. problem.

Formulation: Let x_1 be the number of units of product A and x_2 be the number of units of product B.

(a) Since the profit product A is Rs $2x_1$.

(b) And the profit product B is Rs $3x_2$

∴ Total profit for x_1 and x_2 is $2x_1 + 3x_2$

∴ The objective function is maximize $z = 2x_1 + 3x_2$ [1]

Time required to manufacture x_1 units and x_2 units on machine C is $= 5x_1 + 7x_2$ minutes and the capacity of C is 1200 minutes

∴ $5x_1 + 7x_2 \leq 1200$ [2]

For machine D is

    $4x_1 + 6x_2 \leq 1000$ [3]

Since the manufacturer wants at least 60 units of A and 30 units of B products

∴ $x_1 \geq 60$ and $x_2 \geq 30$

∴ The required L.P.P is as follows

> Maximize: $z = 2x_1 + 3x_2$
> subject to constraints
> $5x_1 + 7x_2 \leq 1200$
> $4x_1 + 6x_2 \leq 1000$
> $x_1 \geq 60$ and $x_2 \geq 30$

Note: It is a product mix for allocation problem (B).

2. A dietician wishes to mix two types of food in such a way that the vitamin contents of the mixture contains at least 8 units of Vitamin A and 10 units of Vitamin B. Food I contains 2 units per kg of Vitamin A and 1 unit per kg of vitamin B while the food. II contains 1 unit per kg of Vitamin A and 2 units per kg of Vitamin B. It costs Rs 5 per kg to purchase food I and Rs 8 per kg to purchase food II. Prepare a mathematical model of the problem stated above.

Formulation: Let x_1 kg of food I and x_2 kg of food II be used in the food mixture so as to contain the minimum requirements of vitamin A and B.

We form the summary table as follows:

Food	Units of vitamin Per kg		Contents	Cost per kg(Rs.)
	A	B		
Food I	2	1		5
Food II	1	2		8
Daily min. requirement	8	10		

The total cost of mixture is $5x_1 + 8x_2$ and there should be at least 8 units of Vitamin A and 10 units of Vitamin B in the food mixture.

$\therefore$ The constraints are

$$2x_1 + x_2 \geq 8;$$

and $\quad x_1 + 2x_2 \geq 10 ;$

$$x_1 \geq 0, x_2 \geq 0 : \text{(Since } x_1 \text{ and } x_2 \text{ cannot be } -ve)$$

Hence the mathematical formulation is

Minimize $z = 5x_1 + 8x_2$ subject to
$$2x_1 + x_2 \leq 8$$
$$x_1 + 2x_2 \geq 10$$
$$x_1, x_2 \geq 0$$

Note : It is a diet problem

3. A manufacturer of wooden articles produces tables and chairs which require two types of inputs mainly, these being wood and labour. The manufacturers know that for a table 3 units of wood and 1 unit of labour are required while for a chair these are 2 units and 2 units respectively. The profit from each table is Rs 20 while it is Rs 16 from each chair. The total available resources for the manufacturer are 75 units of labour. The manufacturer wants to maximise his profit by distributing his resources for tables and chairs. Formulate this as a L.P.P.

    Formulation: Suppose x_1 be the number of tables and x_2 be the number of chairs manufactured by the manufacturer so, $x_1 \geq 0, x_2 \geq 0$
    (since they cannot be $-ve$)
    By data, the total wood required for x_1 table and x_2 chairs is $3x_1 + 2x_2$ units.
    Also total labourers required is $x_1 + 2x_2$ units.
    Now, the total available wood is 150 units and the total available labour is 75 units, so due to above constraints of availability of wood, and labour we have

    $$3x_1 + 2x_2 \leq 150$$

    and $\quad x_1 + 2x_2 \leq 75$

$\therefore$ Total profit from x_1 tables and x_2 chairs

$$= 20x_1 + 16x_2 = z \text{ (say)}.$$

Hence the required L.P.P. is

Maximize $z = 20x_1 + 16x_2$

subject to the constraints

$$3x_1 + 2x_2 \leq 150,$$
$$x_1 + 2x_2 \leq 75$$

and $x_1 \geq 0, x_2 \geq 0$

4. A person wishes to decide on the constituents of a diet which will satisfy his daily needs of proteins, fats and carbohydrates at the minimum cost. Choices from 3 different types of foods can be made. The yields per unit of these foods are given by

Food type	Yield per unit			Cost per unit (in Rs.)
	Proteins	Fats	Carbohydrates	
Bread	4	1	3	2
Butter	2	4	1	7
Milk	4	2	1	3
Daily requirement	6	2	3	

Formulate the problem mathematically.

Formulation: Let x_1 be the number of units of bread used, x_2 be the number of units of butter and x_3 be the number of units of milk respectively used daily by the person.

$\therefore$ from the given data, the minimum, daily requirement of the person are satisfied if

$$4x_1 + 2x_2 + 4x_3 \geq 6$$
$$1x_1 + 4x_2 + 2x_3 \geq 2$$

and $3x_1 + 1x_2 + 1x_3 \geq 3$

also, $x_1 \geq 0, x_2 \geq 0, x_3 \geq 0$

(no unit of food can be negative)

$\therefore$ Total $= 2x_1 + 7x_2 + 3x_2 = z$ (say)

(Total of the daily diet of the person)

Hence, the mathematical formulation of the L.P.P. as:

Minimize	$z = 2x_1 + 7x_2 + 3x_3$
subject to:	$4x_1 + 2x_2 + 4x_3 \geq 6,$
	$x_1 + 4x_2 + 2x_3 \geq 2,$
	$3x_1 + x_2 + x_3 \geq 3,$
and	$x_1 \geq 0, \ x_2 \geq 0, \ x_3 \geq 0,$
	(non $-$ negative)

EXERCISES

1. A farmer has 1000 acres of land on which he can grow corn, wheat or soya beans. Each acre of corn costs Rs. 100 for pre-preparation, requires 7 man-days of work and yields a profit of Rs. 30. An acre of wheat cost Rs 120 to prepare, requires 10 man-days of work and yields a profit of Rs. 40. An acre of soya beans costs Rs 70 to prepare, requires 8 man-days of work and yields a profit of Rs. 20. If the farmer has Rs. 1,00,000 for preparation and can count on 80,000 man-days work, formulate the mathematical model.

2. A firm manufactures 3 products A, B and C. The profits are Rs. 3, Rs. 2, and Rs. 4 respectively. The firm has two machines and given below is the required processing time in minutes for each machine on each product.

Machines	Products		
	A	B	C
M_1	4	3	5
M_2	2	2	4

Machines M_1 and M_2 have 2000 and 2500 machine minutes respectively. The firm must be manufacturing 100 A's 200 B's and 50 C's but not more than 150 A's. Formulate the mathematical model.

3. A company produces two types of Hats. Each hat of the first type requires twice as much labour time as the second type. If all hats are of the second type only, the company can produce a total of 500 hats a day. The market limits daily sales of the first and second type to 150 and 250 hats respectively. Assuming that the profits per hat are Rs. 8 for type A and Rs. 5 for type B, formulate the problem as a linear programming model in order to determine the number of hats to be produced of each type so as to maximize the profit.

Solution by Graphical Method

To determine the optimal (maximum / minimum) solution to a L.P.P. by graphical method the following working rule may be adopted.

Step 1:   Take each inequality constraints as equalities.

Step 2:   The graph of each constraint is a straight line. Plot each equation on the graph.

Step 3:   Determine the feasible region. This is the region that satisfies all the constants. Choose the convenient value of z (say $= 0$) and plot the objective function line.

Step 4:   Pull the objective function line until the extreme points of the feasible region. In the case of maximization problem value of objective function and the corresponding vertex determines the optimal solution. In the case of minimization problem the minimum value of the objective function and corresponding vertex determines the optimal solution.

EXAMPLES

1. Find a geometrical solution for the following L.P.P.

    Max: $z = 30x_1 + 20x_2$

    Subject to the constraints

    $2x_1 + x_2 \leq 800$ [1]

    $x_1 + 2x_2 \leq 1000$ [2]

    $x_1, x_2 \geq 0$.

    Solution: This problem can be solved by graphical method.

    We consider the equality of inequality [1]

    i.e., $2x_1 + x_2 = 800$ [3]

    when $x_1 = 0$, $x_2 = 800$

    and when $x_2 = 0$, $x_1 = 400$

    Therefore the points on the line; $2x_1 + x_2 = 800$ are $(0,800)$ and $(400,0)$

    Similarly considering the equality of inequality [2], we obtain:

    $x_1 + 2x_2 = 1000$ [4]

    when $x_1 = 0$, $x_2 = 500$

    and when $x_2 = 0$, $x_1 = 1000$

    Therefore the points on the line $x_1 + 2x_2 = 1000$ are : $(0,500)$ and $(1000,0)$

    Draw the graph of these equation [3] and [4]

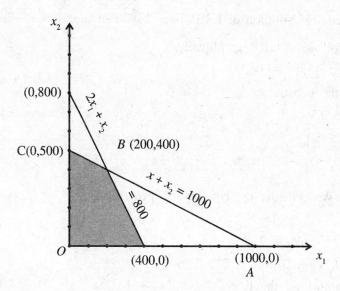

The feasible region is the shaded portion $OABC$.

The coordinates of the vertex B are obtained by solving the equation [3] and [4]. They are

$$2x_1 + x_2 = 800$$
$$x_1 + 2x_2 = 1000$$

[3] × 2: $4x_1 + 2x_2 = 1600$

[4] × 1: $x_1 + 2x_2 = 1000$

Subtracting $3x_1 + 0 = 600$

∴ $x_1 = 200$

$x_2 = 400$, using [3]

∴ $B = (200, 400)$

and corner $z = 30x_1 + 20x_2$. The optimal value of the objective function can be tabulated as follows:

Corner points	Objective function $z\ 30x_1 + 20x_2$	Value
At 0 (0,0)	$z = 30(0) + 20(0) = 0$	$z\ (0) = 0$
At A (400,0)	$z = 30(400) + 20(0) = 120000$	$z\ (A) = 12000$
At B (200,400)	$z = 30(200) + 20(400) = 14000$	$z\ (B) = 14000$
At C (0,500)	$z = 3{-}(0) + 20(500) = 10,000$	$z\ (C) = 10,000$

From these we find that the value of z maximum at the vertex B (200, 400)

∴   the required solution of L.P.P. is $z = 14000$ obtained at $x_1 = 200$, $x_2 = 400$.

2. Solve the following L.P.P. graphically

Maximize: $z = 5x_1 = 3x_2$

subject to the constraints

$3x_1 + 5x_2 \leq 15$ [1]

$5x_1 + 2x_2 \leq 10$ [2]

$x_1, x_2 \geq 0$.

Solution: We consider the equality of inequality[1]

$\qquad 3x_1 + 5x_2 = 15$ [3]

when $x_1 = 0$, $x_2 = 3$

and when $x_2 = 0$, $x_1 = 5$

∴ The points on the line : $3x_1 = 5x_2 = 15$ are : (0, 3) and (5, 0)

Similarly considering the equality of inequality [2]

We get $5x_1 + 2x_2 = 10$ [4]

When $x_1 = 0$, $x_2 = 5$

When $x_2 = 0$, $x_1 = 2$

∴ the points on the line : $5x_1 + 2x_2 = 10$ are : (0, 5) and (2, 0)

Draw the graph of these equations [3] and [4]

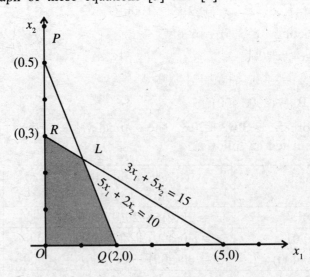

The coordinates of vertex L are obtained by solving equations [3] and [4]

$3x_1 + 5x_2 = 15$

$$5x_1 + 2x_2 = 10$$

[3] × 2: $6 + 2x_2 = 30$

[4] × 5: $25x_1 + 10x_2 = 50$

Subtracting $19x_1 = 20$

The shaded portion *OQLR* represents the feasible region

$$\left(\therefore \ x_1 = \frac{20}{19}; \ x_2 = \frac{45}{19} \right); \quad L\left(\frac{20}{19}, \frac{45}{19} \right)$$

The values of the objective function $z = 5x_1 + 3x_2$ can be obtained as follows:

Corner points	Objective function $z = 30x_1 + 20x_2$	Value
$O = (0, 0)$	$z = 5(0) + 3(0) = 0$	$z\ (0) = 0$
$Q = (2, 0)$	$z = 5(2) + 3(0) = 10$	$z\ (Q) = 10$
$R = (0, 3)$	$z = 5\left(\dfrac{20}{19}\right) + 3\left(\dfrac{45}{19}\right) = 9$	$z\ (R) = 9$
$L = \left(\dfrac{20}{19}, \dfrac{45}{19}\right)$	$= 12.37$	$z\ (L) = 12.37$

From these we find that the value of z is maximum at the vertex

$$L = \left(\frac{20}{19}, \frac{45}{19} \right)$$

∴ The required solution of L.P.P. is:

maximum: $z = 12.37$ obtained at $x_1 = \dfrac{20}{19}$ and $x_2 = \dfrac{45}{19}$

3. Solve the L.P.P.

Maximize: $z = 3x_1 + 4x_2$

subject to $4x_1 + 2x_2 \leq 80$ [1]

$2x_1 + 5x_2 \leq 180$ [2]

$x_1, x_2 \geq 0.$

Solution: We consider the equality of inequality [1]

$$4x_1 + 2x_2 = 80 \qquad\qquad [3]$$

When $\qquad x_1 = 0, \ x_2 = 40$

And when $x_2 = 0, \ x_1 = 20$

Therefore the points on the line: $4x_1 + 2x_2 = 80$ are: $(0, 40)$ and $(20, 0)$

Similarly, considering the equality of inequality [2],

$$2x_1 + 5x_2 = 180 \hspace{4cm} [4]$$

When $x_1 = 0$, $x_2 = 36$

and when $x_2 = 0$, $x_1 = 90$

Therefore the points on the line: $2x_1 + 5x_2 = 180$ are: $(0, 36)$ and $(90, 0)$

Draw the graph of these equations [3] and [4]

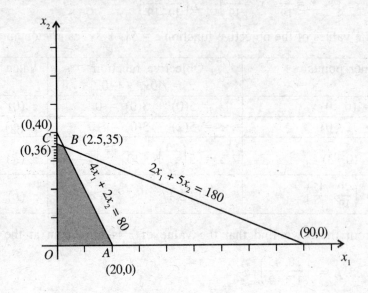

The feasible region is the shaded portion: *OABC*

The coordinates of vertex *L* are obtained by solving equation [3] and [4] they are:

$$4x_1 + 2x_2 = 80$$
$$2x_1 + 5x_2 = 180$$

[3] × 1: $4x_1 + 2x_2 = 80$

[4] × 2: $4x_1 + 10x_2 = 360$

Subtracting $8x_2 = 280$

$$x_2 = \frac{280}{8} = \frac{70}{2} = 35$$

From [3] ∴ $x_1 = \dfrac{80-70}{4} = \dfrac{10}{4} = 2.5$

∴ $B = (2.5, 35)$

And corner $z = 3x_1 + 4x_2$

The optimal value of the objective function can be calculated as follows.

Corner points	Objective function $z = 30x_1 + 4x_2$	Value
At O (0,0)	$z = 3(0) + 4(0) = 0$	$z(0) = 0$
At A (20,0)	$z = 3(20) + 4(0) = 60$	$z(A) = 60$
At B (5/2, 35)	$z = 3(5/2) + 4(35) = 15/2 + 140$ $= \dfrac{15+280}{2} = \dfrac{295}{2} = 147.5$	$z(B) = 147.5$
At C (0,36)	$z = 3(0) + 4(36) = 144$	$z(C) = 144$

From these, we find that the value of z is maximum at the vertex $B\left(\dfrac{5}{2},35\right)$.

The required solution of L.P.P. is $z_{max} = 147.5$ obtained at $x_1 = \dfrac{5}{2}$, $x_2 = 35$.

4. Minimize: $z = 4x_1 + x_2$
   subject to $3x_1 + 4x_2 \geq 20$
   $-x_1 - 15x_2 \leq -15$
   $x_1, x_2 \geq 0$

   Solution: Consider $3x_1 + 4x_2 = 20$
   When $x_1 = 0$, $x_2 = 5$
   When $x_2 = 0$

   $$x_1 = \frac{20}{3}$$

   $\therefore$ the points on the line are $(0, 5)$ and $\left(\dfrac{20}{3}, 0\right)$

   Consider the equation $-x_1 - 5x_2 = -15$
   i.e., $x_1 + 5x_2 = 15$
   When $x_1 = 0$, $x_2 = 3$
   And when $x_2 = 0$, $x_1 = 15$
   $\therefore$ the points on the line are : $(0, 3)$ and $(15, 0)$

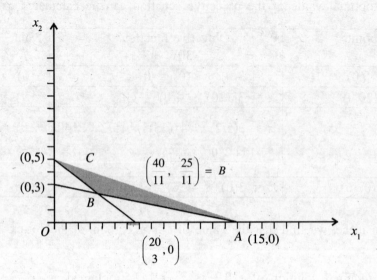

The feasible region (*ABC*) is the shaded portion in the graph.

The coordinates of *B* are obtained by solving equations

$$3x_1 + 4x_2 = 20 \qquad\qquad\qquad [1]$$

$$x_1 + 5x_2 = 15 \qquad\qquad\qquad [2]$$

$$[2] \times 3 \Rightarrow 3x_1 + 15x_2 = 45 \qquad\qquad\qquad [3]$$

$[3] - [1]$ gives $11x_2 = 25$

$$x_2 = \frac{25}{11}$$

$$x_1 = 15 - \frac{125}{11} = \frac{40}{11}$$

$$\therefore \quad B = \left(\frac{40}{25}, \frac{25}{11}\right)$$

Corner points	Objective function $z = 4x_1 + x_2$	Value
A (15,0)	$z = 4(15) + 0$	$60 = z(A)$
B (40/11, 25/11)	$z = 4\left(\dfrac{40}{11}\right) + \dfrac{25}{11}$	$z\,(B) = \dfrac{185}{11}$
C (0,5)	$z = 4(0) + 5$	$z\,(C) = 5$

$\therefore$ the optional solution is $x_1 = 0$, $x_2 = 5$ and min $z = 5$.

5. Find a geometrical solution for the following L.P.P.

$x_1 + x_2 \leq 1$ [1]

$3x_1 + x_2 \geq 3$ [2]

$x_1 \geq 0, \ x_2 \geq 0$

of a linear optimizing function

$z = x_1 + x_2$

    Solution: We consider the equality of inequality [1].

That is, $x_1 + x_2 = 1$ [3]

When $x_1 = 0, \ x_2 = 1$

And when $x_2 = 0, \ x_1 = 1$

$\therefore$ The points on the line: $x_1 + x_2 = 1$ are: (0, 1) and (1, 0)

Again, consider the equality of inequality [2]

i.e., $3x_1 + x_2 = 3$ [4]

When $x_1 = 0, \ x_2 = 3$

And when $x_2 = 0, \ x_1 = 1$

$\therefore$ The points on the line: $3x_1 + x_2 = 3$ are: (0, 3) and (1, 0)

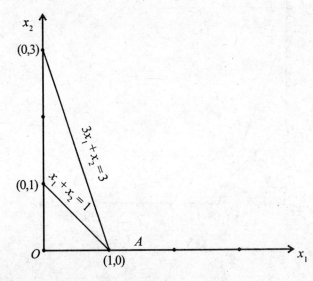

The feasible region is the point A.

Minimum value of $z = x_1 + x_2$ is 1.

6. Maximize: $z = 20x_1 + 30x_2$

subject to constraints

$3x_1 + 3x_2 \leq 36$

$5x_1 + 2x_2 \leq 50$

$$2x_1 + 6x_2 \le 60$$
$$x_1 + x_2 \ge 0$$

Solution: Consider the equation $3x_1 + 3x_2 = 36$
Put $x_1 = 0$, $x_2 = 12$
And $x_2 = 0$, $x_1 = 12$
∴ The points on the line are: (0, 12) and (12, 0)
Consider the equation $5x_1 + 2x_2 = 50$
Put $x_1 = 0$, $x_2 = 25$
And $x_2 = 0$, $x_1 = 10$
∴ (0, 25) and (10, 0) are the points on this line.
Consider the equation $2x_1 + 6x_2 = 60$
Put $x_1 = 0$, $x_2 = 60$
And $x_2 = 0$, $x_1 = 30$
∴(0, 10) and (30, 0) are the points on this line.

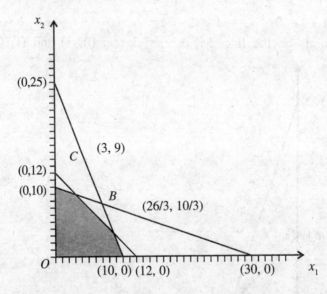

7. Maximize: $z = 2x_1 + 10x_2$
subject to $2x_1 + 5x_2 \le 16$
$6x_1 \le 30$
$x_1, x_2 \ge 0$

Solution: Consider $2x_1 + 5x_2 = 16$
Put $x_1 = 0$
$$x_2 = \frac{16}{5}$$

$$x_2 = 0, \ x_1 = 8$$

∴ The points on the line are $\left(0, \dfrac{16}{5}\right)$ and $(8, 0)$

Consider $6x_1 = 50$

Put $x_1 = 5$, (a line parallel to x_2 – axis)

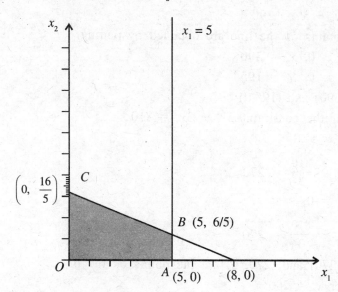

$OABC$ is the feasible region B is the intersection of the lines:

$$2x_1 + 5x_2 = 16$$
$$x_1 = 5$$

$$x_2 = \left(\dfrac{6}{5}\right), \ B = \left(5, \dfrac{6}{5}\right)$$

Corner points	$z = 2x_1 + 10x_2$	Value
O (0,0)	$z = 2(0) + 10(0)$	z (0) = 0
A (5,0)	$z = 2(5) + 10(0)$	z (A) = 10
B (5, 6/5)	$z = 2(5) + 10(6/5$	z (B) = 22
C (0,15)	$z = 2(0) + 10(16/5)$	z (C) = 32

∴ The optional solution is $x_1 = 0$

$$x_2 = \dfrac{16}{5} \ \text{ maximum } z = 32$$

8. Maximize: $z = 6x_1 + 4x_2$
subject to constraints
$$2x_1 + x_2 \leq 390$$

$$3x_1 + 3x_2 \leq 810$$
$$x_2 \leq 200$$
$$x_1, x_2 \geq 0$$

Solution: Consider the equation
$$2x_1 + x_2 = 390$$
∴ the points on the line are obtained by putting
$$x_1 = 0, \; x_2 = 390$$
$$x_2 = 0, \; x_1 = 195$$
and $(0,390)$ and $(195,0)$
Consider the constraint $3x_1 + 3x_2 = 810$
∴ put $x_1 = 0$,

$$x_2 = \frac{810}{3} = 270$$

and $x_2 = 0$,

$$x_1 = \frac{810}{3} = 270$$

∴ $(0, 270)$ and $(270, 0)$ are the points on the line.
Consider $x_2 = 200$
This is parallel to x − axis

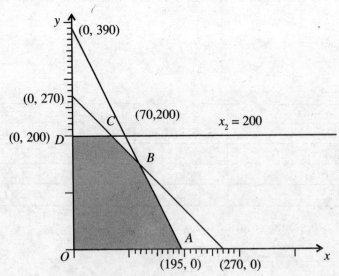

OABCD is the feasible region.
The coordinates of B are obtained by solving of the equations
$$x_1 + x_2 = 390$$

$$3x_1 + 3x_2 = 810$$

$$\therefore \quad x_1 = 120, \ x_2 = 150$$

$$\therefore \quad B \ (120, \ 150)$$

OABCD is the feasible region

The coordinates of *B* are obtained by solving of the equation.

$$5x_1 + 2x_2 = 50 \qquad\qquad\qquad [1]$$

$$3x_1 + 3x_2 = 36$$

i.e., $\quad x_1 + x_2 = 12 \qquad\qquad\qquad [2]$

$$5x_1 + 2x_2 = 50$$

$$2x_1 + 2x_2 = 24 \qquad \text{from [2]} \qquad [3]$$

$$\therefore \quad 3x_1 = 36$$

$$x_1 = \frac{26}{3}$$

and $\quad x_2 = \dfrac{10}{3}$

$$\therefore \quad B = \left(\frac{26}{3}, \frac{10}{3}\right)$$

C is obtained by solving the equations

$$2x_1 + 6x_2 = 60$$

i.e., $\quad x_1 + 3x_2 = 30$

$$3x_1 + 3x_2 = 36$$

Subtracting i.e., [3] − [2] gives

i.e., $\quad x_1 + x_2 = 12$

$$2x_2 = 18$$

i.e., $\quad x_2 = 9 \text{ and } \therefore x_1 = 3$

$\therefore \quad C = (3, 9)$ Thus $z = 20x_1 + 30$ can be found as:

Corner points	Objective function $z = 20x_1 + 30x_2$	Value
0 (0,0)	$z\,(O) = 20(0) + 30(0)$	$z\,(0) = 0$
$A\,(10,0)$	$z\,(A) = 20(10) + 30(0)$	$z\,(A) = 200$
$B\,(26/3, 10/3)$	$z\,(B) = 26/3\,(20) + 300/3$	$z\,(B) = 820/3$
$C\,(3,9)$	$z\,(C) = 60 + 270$	$z\,(C) = 330$
$D\,(0, 10)$	$z\,(D) = 0 + 330$	$z\,(D) = 300$

The optional solution is $x_1 = 3$, $x_2 = 9$ Max $z = 330$

Again, the coordinates of *C* are obtained by solving equation $x_1 + x_2 = 270$

and $x_2 = 200$

∴ $x_1 = 70$, C (70, 200)

Corner $z = 6x_1 + 4x_2$

Corner points	$z = 6x_1 + 4x_2$	Value
O (0,0)	z (O) = 6(0) + 4(0) + 0	z (0) = 0
A (195,0)	z (A) = 1170 + 0 = 1170	z (A) = 1170
B (120, 150)	z (B) = 720 + 600	z (B) = 1320
C (70, 200)	z (C) = 420 + 800	z (C) = 1220
D (0, 220)	z (D) = 0 + 800	z (D) = 800

The optional solution is $z = 1320$; $x_1 = 120$; $x_2 = 150$.

9. Maximize: $z = 0.10x_1 + 0.06x_2$

subject to constraints

$x_1 + x_2 \leq 50$

$2x_1 + x_2 \leq 54$

$x_1, x_2 \geq 0$

Solution: Consider the equation

$x_1 + x_2 = 50$

$x_1 = 0$, $x_2 = 50$

$x_2 = 0$, $x_1 = 50$

∴ the points on this line are (0, 50) and (50, 0) consider $2x_1 + x_2 = 54$

∴ put $x_1 = 0$, $x_2 = 54$

$x_2 = 0$, $x_1 = 50$

∴ the point on this line are

(27, 0) and (0, 54)

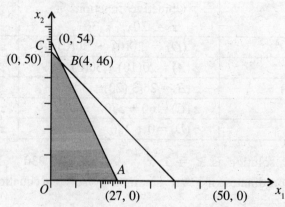

OABC is the feasible region.

To find coordinates of B we solve the equations

$$x_1 + x_2 = 50$$

and $2x_1 + x_2 = 54$

∴ B (4, 46)

Corner points	Objective function $z = 0.10x_1 + 0.06x_2$	Value
O (0,0)	$z = 0 + 0$	$z (O) = 0$
A (27,0)	$z = 0.27 + 0$	$z (A) = 0.27$
B (4,46)	$z = 0.40 + 2.76$	$z (B) = 3.16$
C (0,50)	$z = 0 + 3.00$	$z (C) = 3.00$

The optional solution is $x_1 = 4$, $x_2 = 46$ and min $z = 3.16$.

10. Solve by graphical method

Maximize: $z = 3x + 2y$

subject to $x + 2y \leq 6$ [1]

$2x + y \leq 8$ [2]

$y - x \leq 1$ [3]

$y \leq 2$

$x \geq 0$

$y \geq 0$

Solution: We consider the equality of inequality (constraint) [1].

$$x + 2y = 6$$

Put $x = 0, y = 3$

$y = 0, x = 6$

∴ the points on this line are: $x + 2y = 6$ are (0, 3) and (6, 0)

Again, consider $2x + y = 8$

Put $x = 0, y = 8$

$y = 0, x = 4$

∴ the points on this line : $2x + y = 8$ are (0, 8) and (4, 0)

and consider $y - x = 1$, $x = 0, y = 1$

$y = 0, x = -1$

∴ the points on this line $y - x = 1$ are (0, 1) and (−1, 0)

this is neglected ∵ $x \geq 0$ (given)

Consider $y = 2$

We draw a graph of $y = 2$

Consider $3x + 2y = z$

Assuming $3x + 2y = 6$

Put $x = 0, y = 3$

$y = 0, x = 2$

This defines the profit line.

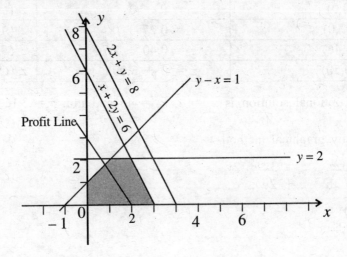

This triangle is neglected because

the given condition is

that $x > 0$ and $x < 0$

From this graph the profit line cuts the outermost point $x_1 = 1.33$, $x_2 = 2.33$ and hence $z = 3(1.33) + 2(2.33) = 8.65$

EXERCISES

Solve the following L.P.P. graphically

1. Minimize $z = 1.5x_1 + 2.5x_2$

   subject to $x_1 + 3x_2 > 3$,

   $x_1 + x_2 > 2$,

   $x_1 > 0, x_2 > 0$.

2. Maximize $z = 6x_1 + 4x_2$
subject to $2x_1 + 3x_2 \leq 100$
$4x_1 + 2x_2 \leq 120$
$x_1, x_2 \geq 0.$

3. Maximize $z = 500x_1 + 200x_2$
subject to $9x_1 + 6x_2 > 540$
$x_1 > 30, x_2 > 30.$
$x_1 < 50, x_2 < 80$

4. Minimize $z = 5x + 7y$
$12x + 12y \leq 840$
$3x + 6y \leq 300$
$8x + 4y \leq 480$
$x \geq 0, y \geq 0.$
$3x + 6y \leq 300$
$8x + 4y \leq 480$
$x \geq 0, y \geq 0.$

The Simplex Method

The simplex method, also know as iterative procedure is applied to almost all L.P.P. and are concerned with the optimization (maximization or minimization) of a linear objective function subject to set of linear constraints. The linear constraints are usually of the form ($\geq$, = or $\leq$).

The graphic method fails if there are more than two variables. In such situations this method (simplex method) is employed to find out the optimal solution to the complex problem.

Basic Terminology

(a) **Standard form:** All the constraints (inequalities) of a L.P.P. are written as equalities (equation) is termed, as the standard form of L.P.P.

(b) **Slack variables:** The non-negative variable which is added to the L.H.S. of the constraint to convert it into equation is called the slack variable. (or a new variable added to the L.H.S of '$\leq$' constraint to express the constraint as an equality).

(c)   **Surplus variable:** In order to make the constraint (inequality), an equality, we have to subtract something (non-negative new variable) from its L.H.S.

(d)   **Basic solution (BS):** A basic solution to a constraint is a solution obtained by setting any n variables. [out of $(m + n)$ variables] $= 0$ and solving for remaining m variables, provided the coefficient determinant. Of these 'm' variable is non-zero. Such 'm' variables (not all zero, some of them may be zero) are called <u>Non-Basic variables.</u>

(e)   **Basic feasible solution:** A basic feasible solution is a basic solution to the L.P.P. It is a vector $\mathbf{x} = (x_1, x_2, ..., x_n)$ which satisfy the given set of constraints. Remember (All basic variables are non-negative).

(f)   **Optimum basic feasible solution (or optimal solution):** A solution (basic feasible) which optimizes (maximizes or minimizes) the objective function of the general L.P.P. is said to be optimum (or optimal solution).

(g)   **Unbounded solution:** If the value of the objective function z can be increased or decreased indefinitely then such solutions are known as unbounded solutions.

Reformulation of General L.P.P.

After introducing the surplus variables or slack variables to the general L.P.P., we can reformulate the general L.P.P.

The reformulated L.P.P. stated can be written as:

Maximize: $z = c_1 x_1 + c_2 x_2 + c_n x_n + 0.x_{n+1} + 0.x_{n+2} + ... + 0.x_{n+m}$

subject to constraints:

$$a_{11} x_1 + a_{12} x_2 + ... + a_{1n} x_n + x_{n+1} = b_1$$
$$a_{21} x_1 + a_{22} x_2 + ... + a_{2n} x_n + x_{n+2} = b_2$$
$$\vdots \qquad \vdots \qquad \qquad \vdots \qquad \vdots \qquad \vdots$$
$$a_{m1} x_1 + a_{m2} x_2 + ... + a_{mn} x_n + x_{n+m} = b_m$$

and $x_1, x_2 ... x_n, x_{n+1}, x_{n+2} ... x_{n+m} \geq 0$

An initial basis feasible solution is obtained by setting $x_1 = x_2 = ... = x_n = 0$ and $x_{n+1} = b_1, x_{n+2} = b_2, ..., x_{n+m} = b_m$.

Note: This solution is given under the column of non-zero basic variables and solution.

Note: This solution is given under the column of non-zero basic variables and solution values column (i.e., $x_b = \mathbf{b}$), as shown in the Initial (Starting) Simplex Table.

Non-Zero Basic Variables	c_b	Solution Values $B(=x_b)$	Real Variables (Cofficient Matrix)				Slack Variable (Basic Matrix)				Min. Ratio
c_j			c_1	c_2	...	c_n	0	0	0	0	
			x_1	x_2	...	x_n	x_{n+1}	x_{n+2}	—	x_{n+m}	$x_b/x_k, x_k>0$
x_{n+1}	$c_1=0$	b_1	a_{11}	a_{12}	...	a_{1n}	1	0	—	0	
x_{n+2}	$c_2=0$	b_2	a_{21}	a_{22}	...	a_{2n}	0	1	—	0	
x_{n+3}	$c_3=0$	b_3									
⋮	⋮	⋮									
x_{n+m}	$c_m=0$	b_m	a_{m1}	a_{m2}	...	a_{mn}	0	0	—	1	
$x_1=x_2=x_3=\ldots$ $x_n=0$	$z=c_b x_b$		δ_1	δ_2	...	δ_n	0	0	—	1	$\delta_j = c_b x_j - c_j$

$z=c_b x_b$

$\delta_j = c_b x_j - c_j$

$z_j - c_j =$ Net contribution

Simple Algorithm for Simplex Method Computations

The solution steps in the simplex method are as follows:

1. Compute δ_j's which are same as $- c_j$'s. This is done in the first iteration only.

2. Find out min (δ_j) and indicate it '↑' which at once indicates the column needed for computing the minimum ratio $\left(\dfrac{x_b}{x_k}\right)$.

3. At the place where upward mark '↑' of min (δ_j) and the left directed arrow (←), of min. ratio $\dfrac{x_b}{x_k}$ intersect each other in the simplex table, the 'Key element' is found there.

4. 'Key element' indicates that Initial Simplex table must be transformed in such a way that the 'Key element' becomes 1 and all other element in that column become 0.

5. In transforming the table by row operations, the value of z and corresponding δ_j's are also computed at the same time.

Note: 1. Assign zero value to the decision variables (non-negative) (i.e., $x_1 = x_2 = x_3 = x_4 = \dots x_n = 0$) each in the initial, Simplex table.

      2. The variable on the top of 'Key column' is the entering variable (incoming variable).

      3. The basic variable corresponding to the minimum of these ratios is called the departing (outgoing) variable in the next simplex table.

EXAMPLES

1. Maximize $z = x_1 + x_2 + 3x_3$,
   subject to the constraints
   $$3x_1 + 2x_2 + x_3 \le 3$$
   $$2x_1 + x_2 + 2x_3 \le 2$$
   $$x_1, x_2, x_3 \ge 0$$

Method (1)

   Solution: Introducing the slack variable, we get the new 'Objective function' as:
$$z = x_1 + x_2 + 3x_3 + 0 \cdot x_4 + 0 \cdot x_5 \qquad [1]$$
and the constraint equations as:
$$3x_1 + 2x_2 + x_3 + 0.x_4 + 0.x_5 = 3 \qquad [2]$$
$$2x_1 + x_2 + 2x_3 + 0.x_4 + 0.x_5 = 5$$
We present the equation [2] in matrix form as :

$$\begin{bmatrix} 3 & 2 & 1 & 1 & 0 \\ 2 & 1 & 2 & 0 & 1 \end{bmatrix} \begin{bmatrix} x_1 \\ x_2 \\ x_3 \\ x_4 \end{bmatrix} = \begin{bmatrix} 3 \\ 2 \end{bmatrix}$$

$$\qquad \text{A} \qquad\qquad \text{x} \quad = \quad \text{b}$$

The Starting (Initial) Simplex Table

Non-Zero Basic Variables	Solution Values $c_b = x_b$	Real	Variables		Slack	Variables	Min Ratio
		x_1	x_2	x_3	x_4	x_5	$x_b/x_p x_k > 0$
x_4	0 $\quad$ 3	3	2	1	1	0	3/1
x_5	0 $\quad$ 2	2	1	2	0	1	2/2 ←
$x_1 = x_2 = x_3 = 0$	$z = 0$ $z = c_b x_b$ $= 0$	-1	-1	$-3\uparrow$	0	0	δ_j ←

Compute the ratio $\begin{bmatrix} \dfrac{3}{1}, \dfrac{3}{2} \end{bmatrix}$ i.e., [3, 1]. The smallest ratio is 1, which is along the second row of the above table. We next select the most negative value (or least negative coefficient) of δ_j ($\delta_j = c_b x_j - c_j$). Here it is (–3) in the 3rd column (of real variables) i.e., x_3 – column, so x_3 will enter the basis (x_5). Thus, the second row and 3rd column will intersect at the element 2. This element is called the 'Key element' which indicates that the current table must be transformed in such a way that the 'Key element' becomes 1 and all other elements in that column become zero.

This is done as follows:

We consider that intermediate coefficient matrix of the initial simplex table, (obtained after dividing each element of 2nd row by the Key element '2'.)

	x_b	x_1	x_2	x_3	x_4	x_5
R_1	3	3	2	1	1	0
R_2	1	1	1/2	1	0	1/2
R_3	$z = 0$	-1	-1	$-3\uparrow$	0	0

		c_j	1	1	3	0	0
	c_b	x_b	x_1	x_2	x_3	x_4	x_5
$R_1 \rightarrow R_1 - R_2$	0	-2	2	3/2	0	1	$-1/2$
	3	1	1	1/2	1	0	1/2
		$z = 3$	-1	-1	-3	0	0 $\overset{\leftarrow}{\delta_j}$

$$z = c_b x_1 = (0, 3)(2, 1)$$
$$= (0 \times 2) + (3 \times 1) = 3$$

$$\delta_1 = c_b x_2 = c_1$$
$$= (0, 3)(2, 1) - 1$$
$$= 0 \times 2 + (3 \times 1) - 1$$
$$= 2$$

$$\delta_2 = c_b x_3 = c_2$$
$$= (0, 3)\left(\frac{3}{2}, \frac{1}{2}\right) - 1$$
$$= 0 \times \frac{3}{2} + \frac{3}{2} - 1$$
$$= \frac{1}{2}$$

$$\delta_3 = c_b x_3 = c_3$$
$$= (0, 3)(0, 1) - 3$$
$$= 0 \times 0 + 3 \times 1 - 3$$
$$= 0$$

$$\delta_4 = c_b x_4 - 0$$
$$= (0, 3)(1, 0) - 0$$
$$= 0 \times 1 + 3 \times 0 - 0$$
$$= 0$$

$$\delta_5 = c_b x_5 - 0$$
$$= (0, 3)(-1/2, 1/1) - 0$$
$$= 0 \times -\frac{1}{2} + 3 \times \frac{1}{2} - 0$$
$$= \frac{3}{2}$$

Thus, we have the next simplex table.

Second Simplex Table

Basic variables	c_b	c_j x_b	1 x_1	1 x_2	3 x_3	0 x_4	0 x_5
x_4	0	2	2	3/2	0	1	−1/2
x_3	3	1	1	1/2	1	0	1/2
$x_1 = x_2 = 0$	$z = 3$		2	1/2	0	0	3/2

From this table it is evident that all δ_j's are tie and hence an optimum solution has been reached.

Thus the optimum solution is

$$x_3 = 1, \; x_1 = 0, \; x_2 = 0$$

and maximum $z = (0) + (0) + 3(1) = 3$

Method (II):
(Simple Method)

2. Maximize $z = x_1 + x_2 + 3x_3$,
   subject to the constraints
   $3x_1 + 2x_2 + x_3 \leq 3$
   $2x_1 + x_2 + 2x_3 \leq 2$
   $x_1, x_2, x_3 \geq 0$

   Solution: Step (1) Introducing the slack variable and constraints (inequalities) will become equalities as:

   $$3x_1 + 2x_2 + x_3 + s_1 = 3$$
   $$2x_1 + x_2 + 2x_3 \; s_2 = 2$$
   $$z - x_1 - x_2 - 3x_3 = 0$$

   Step (2) Writing the system of equations [in step (1)] in the form of a table called initial simplex table.

Starting (Initial) Simplex Table

Basic variables	Solution constants (x_b)	x_1	x_2	x_3	Min. Ratio $x_b/x_k, \; x_k > 0$	
s_1	3	3	2	1	3/1	
s_2	2	2	1	2	2/2 →	Pivot Row
z	0	−1	−1	−3 ↑		

Pivot Column

Identify the Pivot column (least negative entry in the last row). To locate the Pivot row (least positive ratio of the constants to values in marked Pivot column). The least ratio is 2/2 i.e., 1.

Step (3) Pivot Element = 2 To write a new Simplex table, change Pivot to $\left(\dfrac{1}{\text{Pivot}}\right)$ Divide Pivot row by + Pivot and Pivot column by—Pivot. Interchange the variable of Pivot row and Pivot column. This is done as follows.

				S_2
S_1	·	·	·	–1/2
x_3	1	1	1/2	1/2
z	·	·	·	3/2

Remaining elements are given by the formula:

New element $= \left\{ \text{Previous element} \dfrac{(\text{Element in P·R} \times \text{Element in P·C})}{\text{Pivot}} \right\}$

Hence, we have

$$3 \to 3 - \frac{2 \times 1}{2} = 2 \qquad 3 \to 3 - \frac{2 \times 1}{2} = 2 \qquad 2 \to 2 - \frac{1 \times 1}{2} = \frac{3}{2};$$

$$0 \to 0 - \frac{2 \times (-3)}{2} = 3 \qquad -1 \to -1 - \frac{2 \times -3}{2} = 2 \qquad -1 \to -1 - \frac{1 \times -3}{2} = \frac{1}{2}$$

Step (4) So, we have new Simplex table which shows the improvement in the solution.

Basic variables	Solution values	x_1	x_2	S_2
S_1	2	2	3/2	–1/2
x_3	1	1	1/2	1/2
z	3	2	1/2	3/2

Since last row does not contain negative values, stop the procedure. An optimum solution has been reached.

Solution: $x_1 = 0,\ x_2 = 0,\ x_3 = 1$

Maximize $z = 3$

Maximize $z = x_1 + x_2 + 3x_3$
$$= 0 + 0 + 3(1) = 3$$

3. Use Simplex method to solve the following L.P.P.

Maximize: $z = 7x_1 + 5x_2$

subject to the constraints

$x_1 + 2x_2 \leq 6,$

$$4x_1 + 3x_2 \leq 12,$$
$$x_1, \ x_2 \geq 0.$$

Solution: Introducing the slack variable, we get, 'Objective function' in the form:

$$z = 7x_1 + 5x_2 + 0 \cdot x_3 + 0 \cdot x_4 \tag{1}$$

and constraint equations as:

$$x_1 + 2x_2 + 1 \cdot x_3 + 0 \cdot x_4 = 6 \tag{2}$$
$$4x_1 + 3x_2 + 0x_3 + 1 \cdot x_4 = 12$$

Now, the matrix form of equation [2] is.

$$\begin{bmatrix} 1 & 2 & 1 & 0 \\ 4 & 3 & 0 & 1 \end{bmatrix} \begin{bmatrix} x_1 \\ x_2 \\ x_3 \\ x_4 \end{bmatrix} = \begin{bmatrix} 6 \\ 12 \end{bmatrix}$$

$$\mathbf{A} \quad \mathbf{x} = \mathbf{b}, \text{ where}$$

$$\mathbf{A} = \begin{bmatrix} 1 & 2 & 1 & 0 \\ 4 & 3 & 0 & 1 \end{bmatrix}, \ \mathbf{b} = \begin{bmatrix} 6 \\ 12 \end{bmatrix}$$

$$\mathbf{x} = \begin{bmatrix} x_1 \\ x_2 \\ x_3 \\ x_4 \end{bmatrix} 1$$

Starting Simplex Table

Non-zero basic variable	c_b	Solution values $b \,(= x_b)$	c_j	7	5	0	0	Min. Ratio $(x_b/x_k), \ x_k > 0$
				Real variables		Slack variables		
				x_1	x_2	x_3	x_4	
				Coefft. Matrix		Basis Matrix		
x_3	0	6		1	2	1	0	6/1
x_4	0	12		4	3	0	1	12/4 $\leftarrow$
$x_1 = x_2 = 0$	$z = 0$ $z = c_b x_b$			$\rightarrow\uparrow$ $\delta_1 = -7$	-5 $\delta_2 = -5$	0 $\delta_3 = 0$	0 $\delta_4 = 0$	$\delta_j \geq 0$

Compute the ratio $\left[\dfrac{6}{1}, \dfrac{12}{4}\right]$ i.e., [6, 3]. The minimum ratio (or smallest ratio) of these two is 3, which is along the second row of the initial simplex table. We next choose the most negative value (or least negative coefficient of δ_j. [$\delta_j = c_b x_j - c_j$] here it is (–7) in the first column (of real variables) i.e., x_1– column. So, x_1 will enter the basis (x_4). Thus, the second row and first column will intersect at 'the element. 4.' This element is called the key element or Pivotal element which indicates that the current table must be transformed in such a way that the 'Key element' becomes '1' and all other elements in that column become zero. This is done as follows:

We consider the intermediate Coefficient Matrix of the initial simplex table, [i.e., after dividing each element of 2nd row by the key element '4']

	x_b	x_1	x_2	x_3	x_4	
R_1	6	1	2	1	0	
R_2	3	1	3/4	0	1/4	
R_3	$z = 0$	7	5	0	0	$\delta_j \leftarrow$

Apply

$R_1 \rightarrow R_2 \rightarrow R_3 \rightarrow$

	x_b	x_1	x_2	x_3	x_4	
	3	0	5/4	1	−1/4	
	3	1	3/4	0	1/4	
	$z = 0$	− 7	− 5	0	0	$\delta_j \leftarrow$

Hence, we have the following:

Second Simplex Table

Basic variables	c_b	c_j	7	5	0	0	
		x_b	x_1	x_2	x_3	x_4	
x_3	0	3	0	5/4	1	−1/4	
x_1	7	3	1	3/4	0	1/4	
$x_2 = x_4 = 0$		$z = c_b x_b$ $z = 21$	0	1/4	0	1/4	$\delta_j \leftarrow$

$\delta_j = c_b x_j - c_j = z_j - c_j$

$z = c_b x_b = (0 \times 3) + (7 \times 3) = 21$

$$\delta_1 = c_b x_1 - c_1$$
$$= (7, 0)\,(0, 1) - 7$$
$$= [(0 \times 0) + (7 \times 1)] \text{-}7$$
$$= 0$$

$$\delta_2 = c_b x_2 - c_2$$
$$= (0, 7)\left(\frac{5}{4}, \frac{3}{4}\right) - 5$$
$$= 0\left(\frac{5}{4}\right) + 7\left(\frac{3}{4}\right) - 5$$
$$= \frac{1}{4}$$

$$\boxed{\begin{aligned} \delta_j &= (0, 7)\,(1, 0) - 0 \\ &= (0 \times 1) + (7 \times 0) - 0 \\ &= 0 \end{aligned}}$$

$$\boxed{\begin{aligned} \delta_4 &= c_b x_4 - c_4 \\ &= (0, 7)\left(\frac{-1}{4}, \frac{1}{4}\right) - 0 \\ &= 0\left(\frac{-1}{4}\right) + 7\left(\frac{1}{4}\right) = \frac{7}{4} \end{aligned}}$$

From the second simplex table, it is evident that all δ_j's are positive and hence an optimum solution has been reached. Thus optimal solution is: $x_1 = 3$, $x_2 = 0$ Max $z = 7(3) + 5(0) + 0(3) + 0(0) = 21$

$\therefore$ Max $z = 21$

Method (2) (Simplex method):

4. Maximize: $z = 7x_1 + 5x_2$
   subject to the constraints
   $x_1 + 2x_2 \leq 6$,
   $4x_1 + 3x_2 \leq 12$
   $x_1, x_2 \geq 0$

   Solution: Introducing the slack variable and constraints (inequalities) will become equalities as:

   $$x_1 + 2x_2 + s_1 = 6,$$
   $$4x_1 + 3x_2 + s_2 = 12$$
   $$z - 7x_1 - 5x_2 = 0$$

   Step (1) Writing the system of equations above in the form of a table known as simplex table.

Starting (Initial) Simplex Table

Basic variables	Solution constants $b(x_b)$	x_1	x_2	Min. Ratio x_b/x_k, $x_k > 0$
s_1	6	1	2	(6/1)
s_2	12	④	1	(12/4) ←
z	0	-7 ↑	-5	4

Identify the Pivot column (least negative entry in the last row). To locate the Pivot row (least positive ratio of the constants to value in the marked

Pivot column) the least positive ratio is $\left[\dfrac{12}{4} \text{ is } 3\right]$.

Step (2): Pivot Element $= 4$ To write a new simplex table, change Pivot to $\left(\dfrac{1}{\text{Pivot}}\right)$ Divide Pivot row by $+$ Pivot and Pivot column by $-$ Pivot, interchange variables of Pivot row and Pivot column.

		s_2	x_2
s_1	.	$-1/4$	.
x_3	3	$1/4$	$3/4$
z	.	$7/4$	.

Step (3): Remaining elements are given by

$$= \left\{ \text{Pr evious value} - \frac{(\text{Element in Pivot row} \times \text{Element in Pivot column})}{\text{Pivot}} \right\}$$

They are:

$$6 = 6 - \frac{12 \times 1}{4} = 3; \qquad 2 = 2 - \frac{3 \times 1}{4} = \frac{5}{4}$$

$$0 = 0 - \frac{12 \times (-7)}{4} = 21; \qquad -5 = -5 - \frac{3 \times (-7)}{4} = \frac{1}{4}$$

Step (4) We have, the next improvement in the Second Simplex table

Second (Final) Simplex Table

Basic variables	Solution values $b = x_b$	s_2	x_2
s_1	3	$-1/4$	$5/4$
x_3	3	$1/4$	$3/4$
z	21	$7/4$	$1/4$

Since last row does not contain negative values, an optimum solution has been reached.

Solution: $x_1 = 3$, $x_2 = 0$ $z = 21$ Max

$$z = 7(3) + 5(0) = 21$$

$\therefore$ Max $z = 21$

5. Maximize: $z = 4x_1 + 10x_2$

subject to $2x_1 + x_2 \leq 50$,

$2x_1 + 5x_2 \leq 100$,

$2x_1 + 3x_2 \leq 90$,

$x_1 \geq 0, \; x_2 \geq 0$.

Solution: Introducing the slack variable

Step (1): and constraints (inequalities) will become equalities as:

$2x_1 + x_2 + s_1 = 50$,

$2x_1 + 5x_2 + s_2 = 100$,

$2x_1 + 3x_2 + s_3 = 90$,

$z - 4x_1 - 10x_2 = 0$

Step (2): Writing the system of equations in Step (1) in the form of a table known as simplex table.

Starting Simplex Table

Basic variables	Solution constants $b(x_b)$	x_1	x_2	Min. Ratio $x_b/x_k, \; x_k > 0$	
s_1	50	2	1	50/1	
s_2	100	2	5	100/5 ←	Pivot Row
s_3	90	2	3	90/3	
z	0	−4	−10 ↑		

Identify the Pivot column (least negative entry in the last row). To locate the Pivot row (least positive ratio of the constants to value in the marked Pivot column) the least positive ratio is $\dfrac{100}{5} = 20$

Step (3): Pivot Element = 5

To write a new simplex table, change Pivot to $\dfrac{1}{\text{Pivot}}$. Divide Pivot row by + Pivot and Pivot column by − Pivot, Interchange variables of Pivot row and Pivot column.

		x_1	s_2
s_1	.	.	−1/5
x_2	100/5	2/5	1/5
s_3	.	.	−3/5
z	.	.	2

Step (4): Remaining elements:

Previous element =

$$\left\{ \text{Previous value} - \frac{(\text{Element in Pivot row} \times \text{Element in Pivot column})}{\text{Pivot}} \right\}$$

$$50 \rightarrow 50 - \frac{100}{5} = 30 \qquad\qquad 2 \rightarrow 2 - \frac{2 \times 1}{5} = \frac{8}{5}$$

$$90 \rightarrow 90 - \frac{100 \times 3}{5} = 30 \qquad\qquad 2 \rightarrow 2 - \frac{2 \times 3}{5} = \frac{4}{5}$$

$$0 \rightarrow 0 - \frac{100 \times (-10)}{5} = 200 \qquad -4 \rightarrow -4 - \frac{2 \times (-10)}{5} = 0$$

Step (5): So, we have new Simplex table which shows the improvement.

Second (Final) Simplex Table

Basic variables	Solution values $b = x_b$	x_1	s_2	
s_1	30	8/5	−1/5	
x_2	20	2/5	1/5	
s_3	30	4/5	−3/5	
z	200	0	2	$\delta_j \geq -0$

Since last row does not contain negative values, stop the procedure. An optimum solution has been reached:

Solution: $x_1 = 0$, $x_2 = 20$

Max $z = 200$

$(\therefore z = 4x_1 + 10x_2 = 4(0) + 10(20) = 200)$

6. Maximize: $z = x_1 + 2x_2 + x_3$

subject to the constraints

$x_1 + x_2 - x_3 \leq -2,$
$2x_1 - x_2 - 5x_3 \geq -6,$
$4x_1 + x_2 + x_3 \leq 6,$
$x_1, x_2, x_3 \geq 0.$

Step (1): Introducing the slack variable, the constraints can be written as equations; in the standard form:

$x_1 + x_2 - x_3 + s_1 = -2,$
$2x_1 - x_2 + 5x_3 + s_2 = -6,$
$4x_1 + x_2 + x_3 + s_3 = 6,$

Step (2): Writing the system of equations [in Step (1)] in the form of a table known as simplex table.

Starting Simplex Table

Non-Zero basic variable	Solution constants $b(= x_b)$	Real variables			Min. Ratio $x_b/x_k, x_k > 0$
		x_1	x_2	x_3	
s_1	-2	1	①	-1	$-2/1 \leftarrow$
s_2	6	-2	-1	5	$6/1$
s_3	6	4	1	1	$6/1 \leftarrow$
z	0	-1	-2	-1	$\delta_j \geq 0$

To Locate Pivot column (least negative entry in the last row). To locate the Pivot row (least positive ratio of the constants to value in marked Pivot column) Here the least positive ratio is $\dfrac{6}{1} = 6 \rightarrow$ Pivot row. The Pivotal element is 1 in this case.

To write a new (second) Simplex table of numbers, change Pivot to $\dfrac{1}{\text{Pivot}}$ Divide Pivot row by + Pivot and Pivot column by '−' Pivot. Interchange variables of Pivot row and Pivot column.

	x_1		s_3	x_3
s_1	.	.	$+1/-1$	.
s_2	.	.	$-1/-1$	.
x_2	$6/1$	$4/1$	$1/+1$	$1/1$
z	.	.	$-2/-1$	.

Remaining Elements are given by :

$$\left\{ \text{Previous value} - \frac{\text{Element in Pivot row} \times \text{Element in Pivot column}}{\text{Pivot}} \right\}$$

Hence we have

$$2 \rightarrow -2 - \frac{6 \times 1}{1} = -2 - 6 = -8 \qquad 1 \rightarrow 1 - \frac{4 \times 1}{1} = 1 - 4 = -3$$

$$-1 \rightarrow -1 - \frac{1 \times 1}{1} = -2 \qquad 6 \rightarrow 6 - \frac{6 \times (-1)}{1} = 6 + 6 = 12$$

$$-2 \rightarrow -2 \frac{4 \times (-1)}{1} = -2 + 4 = 2 \qquad 5 \rightarrow 5 - \frac{1 \times (-1)}{1} = 5 + 1 = 6$$

$$0 \rightarrow 0 - \frac{6 \times (-2)}{1} = 12 \qquad\qquad -1 \rightarrow -1 - \frac{4 \times (-2)}{1} = -1 + 8 = 7$$

$$1 \rightarrow -1 - \frac{1 \times (-2)}{1} = -1 + 2 = 1$$

Therefore, we have new Simplex table as:

Final Simplex Table

Basic variables	Solution values $b = (x_b)$	Real variables			
		x_1	s_3	x_3	
s_1	−8	−3	−1	−2	
s_2	12	2	1	−2	
x_2	6	4	+1	6	
z	12	7	2	1	$\delta_j \geq 0$

Since($\delta_j \geq 0$, j = 1, 2, 3, 4) the last row contains non–negative elements, stop at this stage. An optimum solution has been reached.

Solution: Max $z = 0 + 2(6) + 0 = 12$, $x_1 = 0$, $x_2 = 6$, $x_3 = 0$

$$\text{Max } z = 0 + 2(6) + 0 = 12$$

7. Maximize: $z = 10x_1 + 11x_2$

subject to the

$5x_1 + 2x_2 \leq 8,$

$3x_1 + 4x_2 \leq 9,$

$x_1 + 2x_2 \leq 1$

$x_1, x_2 \geq 0.$

Solution: Step (1): Introducing the slack variables.

$$5x_1 + 2x_2 + s_1 = 8,$$
$$3x_1 + 4x_2 + s_2 = 9,$$
$$x_1 - 2x_2 + s_3 = 1,$$
$$z - 10x_1 - 11x_2 = 0$$

Step (2): Writing the system of equations in Step (1), in the form of a table known as simplex table:

Starting (First) Simplex Table

Non-Zero basic variable	Solution values $b\ (= x_b)$	Real variables		Min. Ratio $x_b/x_k,\ x_k > 0$
		x_1	x_2	
s_1	8	5	2	8/2
s_2	9	3	4	9/4
s_3	1	1	+2	1/2 ←
z	0	−10	−11 ↑	$\delta_j \geq 0$

To Locate Pivot column (least negative entry in the last row). To locate the Pivot row least positive ratio of the constants to values in marked Pivot column) The least positive ratio is $\dfrac{1}{2}= 0.5$ of the three ratios $\left(\dfrac{8}{2},\dfrac{9}{4},\dfrac{1}{2}\right)$ =(4,2.25,0.5)

Pivot Element = 2: To write a new Simplex table of numbers change Pivot to $\left(\dfrac{1}{\text{Pivot}}\right)$. Divide Pivot row by + Pivot and Pivot column by − Pivot, Interchange variables of Pivot row and Pivot column.

		x_1			s_3	
s_1		.		.	−1	.
s_2		.		.	−2	.
x_2		0.5		0.5	0.5	.
z		.		.	5.5	.

Remaining Elements are given by:
$$= \left\{ \text{Previous existing value} - \frac{(\text{Element in Pivot row} \times \text{Element in Pivot column})}{\text{Pivot}} \right\}$$

$$8 \rightarrow 8 - \frac{1\times 2}{2} = 7;$$

$$5 \rightarrow 5 - \frac{1\times 2}{2} = 4;$$

$$9 \rightarrow 9 - \frac{4\times 1}{2} = 7$$

$$0 \rightarrow 0 - \frac{(-11)\times 1}{2} = \frac{11}{2} = 5.5;$$

$$-10 \rightarrow -10 - \frac{1\times(-11)}{2} = \frac{9}{2} = -4.5$$

Repeat the above procedure till no negative values appear in the z – row. So, we have new Simplex table.

Second Simplex Table

Basic variables	Solution values x_b	Real variables x_1		Min. Ratio s_3	
s_1	7	4	−1	$7/4 = 1.75$	
s_2	7	1	−2	$7/1 = 7$	
x_2	0.5	0.5	+2	$0.5/0.5 = 1 \leftarrow$	Pivot row
z	5.5 ↑	−4.5	5.5	$\delta_j \geq 0$	

The Pivot (key) element is 0.5. Change Pivot to $\dfrac{1}{0.5}$ Divide Pivot row elements by $+ 0.5$ and Pivot column elements by $−0.5$. Interchange the variables of Pivot row and Pivot column.

		x_1	s_3	
s_1		4/−0.5		
s_2		1/−0.5		← Pivot row
x_2	0.5/0.5	1/0.5	0.5/0.5	
z		−4.5/0.5 P.C		

Remaining elements are replaced by:

$$= \left\{ \text{Previous element} - \frac{(\text{Element in Pivot row} \times \text{Element in Pivot column})}{\text{Pivot}} \right\}$$

They are

$$7 \to 7 - \frac{(0.5) \times 4}{(0.5)} = 3; \quad -1 \to -1 - \frac{0.5 \times 4}{0.5} = -5; \quad 7 \to 7 - \frac{0.5 \times 1}{0.5} = 6$$

$$-2 \to -2 - \frac{0.5 \times 1}{0.5} = -3; \quad 5.5 \to 5.5 - \frac{0.5 \times (-4.5)}{0.5} = 10$$

$$5.5 \to 5.5 - \frac{0.5 \times (-4.5)}{0.5} = 10$$

Final Simplex Table

	x_b	x_2	s_3	
s_1	3	−8	−5	
s_2	6	−2	−3	
x_1	1	2	1	
z	10	9	10	$\delta_j \geq 0$

Since the least row ($\delta_j \geq 0$) contains no negative elements so an optimum solution has been reached.

Solution: $x_1 = 1$, $x_2 = 0$

Max $z = 10(1) + 11(0) = 10$

8. Maximize: $z = x_2 - 3x_3 + 2x_5$

subject to the constraints:

$3x_2 - x_3 + 2x_5 \leq 7,$

$-2x_2 + 4x_3 \leq 12,$

$-4x_2 + 3x_3 + 8x_5 \leq 10,$

$x_2, x_3, x_5 \geq 10.$

Solution: Equivalently, max $z' = -x_2 + 3x_3 - 2x_5$

where $z' = -z$

Introducing s_1, s_4 and s_6 as slack variables, the constraint equations become:

$s_1 + 3x_2 - x_3 + 2x_5 = 5,$

$-2x_2 + 4x_3 + s_2 = 12,$

$-4x_2 + 3x_3 + 8x_5 + s_3 = 10,$

$z' + x_2 - 3x_3 + 2x_5 = 0.$

Write down the equation in the form of a table known as simplex table:

Starting Simplex Table

Basic variable	Solution constants $b(= x_b)$	x_2	x_3	x_5	Min. Ratio x_b/x_k, $x_k > 0$
s_1	7	3	−1	2	7/−1
s_2	12	−2	④	0	12/4 ←
s_3	10	−4	3	8	10/3
z'	0	1	−3 ↑	2	

To identify the Pivot column (least negative entry in the last row). To locate the Pivot row least positive ratio of the constants to values in the marked Pivot column) The least positive ratio is: $\dfrac{12}{4} = 3$

Pivot Element = 4: We write new Simplex table:

Change Pivot to $\dfrac{1}{\text{Pivot}}$. Divide Pivot row by + Pivot and Pivot column by—Pivot. Interchange the variables of Pivot row and Pivot column.

	x_b	x_2	s_2	x_5
s_1	.	.	$-1/-4$	.
x_3	3	$-1/2$	$1/4$	0
s_3	.	.	$-3/4$	.
z'	.	.	$3/4$	.

$$7 \rightarrow 7 - \frac{12 \times (-1)}{4} = 7 + 3 = 10$$

$$3 \rightarrow 3 = \frac{(-2) \times (-1)}{4} = 3 - \frac{1}{2} = \frac{5}{2}$$

$$2 \rightarrow 2 - \frac{0 \times -1}{4} = 2$$

$$10 \rightarrow 10 - \frac{12 \times 3}{4} = 1$$

$$-4 \rightarrow -4 - \frac{(-2) \times (3)}{4} = -4 + \frac{6}{4} = \frac{-10}{4} = \frac{-5}{2}$$

$$8 \rightarrow 8 - \frac{0 \times (-3)}{4} = 8$$

$$0 \rightarrow 0 - \frac{12 \times (-3)}{4} = 9$$

$$1 \rightarrow 1 - \frac{(-2) \times (3)}{4} = 1 + \frac{6}{4} = \frac{10}{4} = \frac{5}{2}$$

$$2 \rightarrow 2 - \frac{0 \times (-3)}{4} = 2$$

So, we have the next Simplex table.

	x_b	x_2	s_2	x_5
s_1	10	5/2	$1/-4$	2
x_3	3	$-1/2$	$1/4$	0
s_3	1	$-5/2$	$-3/4$	
z'	9	5/2	$3/4$	2

Thus, optimal solution: $x_2 = 0$, $x_3 = 3$, $x_5 = 0$
Max $z' = 9$ or in $z = -9$

9. Maximize: $z = 5x_1 + 3x_3$
subject to the constraints:

$x_1 + x_2 \le 2,$

$5x_1 + 2x_2 \le 10,$

$3x_1 + 8x_2 \le 12,$

$x_1, x_2 \ge 0.$

Introducing the slack variables we get the new 'Objective function' as

$$z = 5x_1 + 3x_2 + 0x_3 + 0x_4 + 0x_5 \qquad [1]$$

And the constraint equations as:

$$x_1 + x_2 + x_3 + 0x_4 + 0x_5 = 2$$
$$5x_1 + 3x_2 + 0x_3 + 0x_4 + 0x_5 = 10 \qquad [2]$$
$$3x_1 + 8x_2 + 0x_3 + 0x_4 + x_5 = 12$$

We now present the constraint equations in Matrix form:

$$\begin{bmatrix} 1 & 1 & 1 & 0 & 0 \\ 5 & 2 & 0 & 1 & 0 \\ 3 & 8 & 0 & 0 & 1 \end{bmatrix} \begin{bmatrix} x_1 \\ x_2 \\ x_3 \\ x_4 \end{bmatrix} = \begin{bmatrix} 2 \\ 10 \\ 12 \end{bmatrix}$$

$$\mathbf{A} \qquad \mathbf{x} = \mathbf{b}$$

First Simplex Table

Non-zero basic variable	c_b	c_j / Solution values $b(= x_b)$	$c_1=5$ Real variables x_1	$c_2=3$ x_2	$c_3=0$ Slack variables x_3	$c_4=0$ x_4	$c_5=0$ x_5	Min. Ratio $(x_b/x_k), x_k > 0$
			Coefft. Matrix		Basis Matrix			
x_3	$c_3 = 0$ 2		1	1	1	0	0	2/1
x_4	$c_4 = 0$ 10		5	2	0	1	0	10/5
x_5	$c_5 = 0$ 12		3	8	0	0	1	12/3
$x_1=x_2=0$	$z = 0$		$-5 \uparrow$	-3	0	0	0	δ_j
	$z = c_b x_b$		$\delta_1 = -5$	$\delta_2 = -3$	$\delta_3 = 0$	$\delta_4 = 0$		

Compute the ratio: $\left[\dfrac{2}{1}, \dfrac{10}{5}, \dfrac{12}{3}\right] = [2, 2, 4]$ The minimum ratio (or smallest ratio) of these is two along the first row of the initial simplex table. We next choose the most negative value (or least negative coefft) of δ_j ($\delta_j = c_b x_b - c_j$) Here it is $(-5) \uparrow$ in the first column (of real variable). That is x_1 – column. So, x_1 will enter the basis (x_3). Thus, the first row and the first column will intersect at 'the element 1'. This element is called the key element of Pivotal element which indicates that the current table must be transformed in such a way that the 'Key element' becomes '1' and all other element in that column become zero.

This is done as follows:

We consider the intermediate coefficient matrix of the initial Simplex table. (i.e., after dividing each element of 2nd row by the key element '1')

		$c_1 = 5$	$c_2 = 3$	$c_3 = 0$	$c_4 = 0$	$c_5 = 0$	
	x_b	x_1	x_2	x_3	x_4	x_5	
R_2	2	1	1	1	0	0	
R_3	10	5	2	0	1	0	
R_4	12	3	8	0	0	1	
	$z = 0$	-5	-3	0	0	0	$\delta_j \leftarrow$

Apply $\boxed{R_2 \rightarrow R_2 - 5R_1,\ R_3 \rightarrow -3R_1\ \ R_4 \rightarrow R_4 + 5R_1}$

x_b	x_1	x_2	x_3	x_4	x_5	
2	1	1	1	0	0	
0	0	-3	-5	1	0	
6	0	5	-3	0	1	
$z = 10$	0	2	5	0	0	$\delta_j \leftarrow$

Hence, we have the following:

Second Simplex Table

			$c_1 = 5$	$c_2 = 3$	$c_3 = 0$	$c_4 = 0$	$c_5 = 0$	
Basic Variables	c_b	x_b	x_1	x_2	x_3	x_4	x_5	
x_1	$c_1 = 5$	2	1	1	1	0	0	
x_4	$c_4 = 0$	0	0	-3	-5	1	0	
x_5	$c_5 = 0$	6	0	5	-3	0	1	
$x_2 = 0$	$z = 10$					0	0	
	$z = c_b x_b$		0	2	5	0	0	$\delta_j \leftarrow$

$z = c_b x_1 = (5, 0, 0)(2, 0, 6) = (5 \times 2) + (0 \times 0) + (0 \times 6) = 10$

$\delta_1 = c_b x_1 - c_1 = (5, 0, 0)(1, 0, 0)\ -5 = (5 \times 1) + (0)\ (0) - 5 = 0$

$\delta_2 = c_b x_2 - c_2 = (5, 0, 0)(1, -3, 5) - 3 = (5 \times 1) + (0 \times -3) + (0 \times 5)\ -3 = 2$

$\delta_3 = c_b x_3 - c_1 = (5, 0, 0)(1, -5, -3)\ -0 = (5 \times 1) + (0 \times 5) + 0\ (-3)\ -0 = 5$

$\delta_4 = c_b x_4 - c_1 = (5, 0, 0)(0, 1, 0) - 0 = (5 \times 0) + (0 \times 1) + (0 \times 0) - 0 = 0$

$\delta_5 = c_b x_5 - c_1 = (5, 0, 0)(0, 0, 1) - 0 = (5 \times 0) + (0 \times 0) + (0 \times 1) - 0 = 0$

From the second Simplex table, it is evident that all δ_j's, where $\delta_j = c_b x_j - c_j = z_j - c_j$ are positive and hence an optimum solution has been reached. Thus, an optimum basic feasible solution to the given L.P.P. is $x_1 = 2$, $x_2 = 0$,

$\therefore$ Max $z = 5(2) + 3(0) = 10$ by [1]

Method (2):

10. Maximize: $z = 5x_1 + 3x_2$

subject to the constraints:

$x_1 + x_2 \le 2$,

$5x_1 + 2x_2 \le 10$,

$3x_1 + 8x_2 \le 12$,

$x_1, x_2 \ge 0$.

Step (1): Introducing the slack variables and constraint equations become

$x_1 + x_2 + s_1 = 2$,

$5x_1 + 2x_2 + s_2 = 10$,

$3x_1 + 8x_2 + s_3 = 12$,

$z - 5x_1 - 3x_2 = 0$

Step (2): Writing the system of equations above, in the form of a table known as Simplex table.

Starting (Initial) Simplex Table

Basic variable	Solution constants $(b = x_b)$	x_1	x_2	Min. Ratio
s_1	2	☐1	1	2/1
s_2	10	5	2	10/5
s_3	12	3	8	12/3
z	0	−5 ↑	−3	

Identify the Pivot column (least negative entry in the last row). To locate the Pivot row (least positive ratio of the constants to value in marked Pivot column) The least positive ratio is 2.

Step (3) Pivot Element −1: To write a new Simplex table, change Pivot to $\dfrac{1}{\text{Pivot}}$.

Divide Pivot row by + Pivot and Pivot column by − Pivot, interchange the variables of Pivot row and Pivot column.

Basic Variable	Solution constants $(b = x_b)$	s_1	x_2
x_1	2	1	1
s_2	.	−5	.
s_3	.	−3	.
z	.	5	.

The remaining elements are:

$$\text{Previous element} = \left\{ \text{Previous value} - \frac{\text{Element in Pivot row} \times \text{Element in Pivot column}}{\text{Pivot}} \right\}$$

They are:

$$10 \rightarrow 10 - \frac{2 \times 5}{1} = 0, \quad 2 \rightarrow 2 - \frac{1 \times 5}{1} = -3,$$

$$0 \rightarrow 0 - \frac{2 \times -5}{1} = 10, \quad -3 \rightarrow -3 - \frac{1 \times (-5)}{1} = 2$$

Step (4): So, we have new Simplex table which shows the improvements:

Second (Final) Simplex Table

Basic Variable	Solution constants $(b = x_b)$	s_1	x_2
x_1	2	1	1
s_2	0	−5	−3
s_3	6	−3	5
z	10	5	2

Since last row does not contain negative values, as optimum solution has been reached. The Optimal solution is: $x_1 = 2$, $x_2 = 0$, $\therefore$ Max $z = 5(2) + 3(0) = 10$

11. Maximize: $z = 3x_1 + 2x_2$
    subject to the constraints:
    $x_1 + x_2 \leq 4$,
    $x_1 - x_2 \leq 2$,
    and $x_1, x_2 \geq 0$.

Solution: Introducing the slack variables, we get the new 'Objective function' as

$$z = 3x_1 + 2x_2 + 0x_3 + 0x_4 \qquad [1]$$

And the constraint equations as:

$$x_1 + x_2 + 1x_3 + 0x_4 = 4$$
$$x_1 - x_2 + 0x_3 + 1x_4 = 2 \qquad [2]$$

We present the constraint equations [2] in Matrix form:

$$\begin{bmatrix} 1 & 1 & 1 & 0 \\ 1 & -1 & 0 & 1 \end{bmatrix} \begin{bmatrix} x_1 \\ x_2 \\ x_4 \end{bmatrix} = \begin{bmatrix} 4 \\ 2 \end{bmatrix}$$

First Simplex Table

	c_j:		3	2	0	0	
Non-zero basic variable	c_b	Solution values $b(= x_b)$	Real variables		Slack variables		Min. Ratio $(x_b/x_{kj}, x_k > 0$
			x_1	x_2	x_3	x_4	
			Coefft. Matrix		Basis	Matrix	
x_3	0	4	1	1	1	0	4/1
x_4	0	2	[1]	−1	0	1	2/1
$x_1 = x_2 = 0$	$z = c_b x_b = 0$		−3 ↑	−2	0	0	$\delta_j = 0$ Initial value of δ_j

Compute the ratio $\left[\dfrac{4}{2}, \dfrac{2}{1}\right]$ i.e., $[4, 2]$. The minimum ratio (or smallest ratio) of these is two which is along the second row of the initial simplex table. We now choose the most negative value (or least negative coefft) of δ_j ($\delta_j = c_b x_j - c_j$) Here it is $(-3)\uparrow$ in the first column (of real variable). That is x_1 – column. So, x_1 will enter the basis (x_4). Thus, the second row and the first column (of real variables) will intersect at 'the element 1'. This element is called the 'Key element' which indicates that the current table must be transformed in such a way that the key element becomes '1' and all other elements in that column becomes zero.

This is done as follows:

We consider the intermediate coefficient matrix of the initial Simplex table. (e.g., after dividing each element of 2ⁿᵈ row by the key element '1')

	c_j	3	2	0	0	
	x_b	x_1	x_2	x_3	x_4	
R_1	4	1	1	1	0	
R_2	2	1	−1	0	1	
R_3	$z = 0$	−3	−2	0	0	$\delta_j \leftarrow$

Apply

R$_1$ → R$_1$ − R$_2$
R$_3$ → R$_3$ + 3R$_2$

x_b	x_1	x_2	x_3	x_4	
2	0	2	1	−1	
2	1	−1	0	1	
z = 6	0	−5	0	3	δ_j

Hence, we have the following:

Second Simplex Table

Non-zero basic variable	c_b	c_j Solution values $b(= x_b)$	7 x_1	5 x_2	0 x_3	0 x_4	Min. Ratio (x_b/x_k), $x_k > 0$
x_3	0	2	0	2	1	−1	2/2 ← Key row
x_1	3	2	1	−1	0	1	(negative ratio is not considered)
$x_1 = x_2 = 0$		$z = c_b x_b = 0$	0	−5 ↑	0	3	← $\delta_j \geq 0$

We find this table, the improved basic feasible solution is read as:
$$x_1 = 2, \quad x_2 = 0, \quad x_3 = = 2, \quad x_4 = 0$$

The improved value of z = 6 because minimum ratio (smaller ratio) of $\left[\frac{2}{2}, \frac{2}{-1}\right]$ is $\frac{2}{2} = 1$, (negative ratio is not considered). Thus, the Pivotal element is '2' which indicates that the current table must be transformed in such a way that the key element becomes 1 and all other element in that column become 0. The intermediate coefficient Matrix of the second Simplex table (e.g., after dividing each element of first row by the key element 2) is:

	x_b	x_1	x_2	x_3	x_4	
R$_1$	1	0	1	1/2	−1/2	
R$_2$	2	1	−1	0	1	
R$_3$	z = 6	0	−5	0	3	δ_j ←

Apply

R$_1$ → R$_1$ − R$_2$
R$_3$ → R$_3$ + 3R$_2$

1	0	1	1/2	−1/2	
3	1	0	1/2	1/2	
z = 11	0	0	5/2	1/2	δ_j ←

Hence, we have the following:

Third (Final) Simplex Table

Non-zero basic variables	c_b	Solution values $b(= x_b)$	x_1	x_2	x_3	x_4	
x_2	2	1	0	1	1/2	−1/2	
x_1	3	3	1	0	1/2	1/2	
		$z = c_b x_b = 11$	0	0	5/2	1/2	δ_j

The optimum solution: $x_1 = 3$, x_2, $= 1$, Max $z = 11$

(Since all δ_j's are non-negative) $\delta_j = c_b x_j - c_j$

12. Maximize: $z = 3x_1 + 5x_2 + 4x_3$
subject to the constraints:
$2x_1 + 3x_2 \le 8,$
$2x_2 + 5x_3 \le 10,$
$3x_1 + 2x_2 + 4x_3 \le 15,$
and $x_1, x_2, x_3 \ge 0.$

Introducing the slack variables we get the new 'Objective function' as
$$z = 3x_1 + 5x_2 + 4x_3 + 0x_4 + 0x_5 \qquad [1]$$
$$2x_1 + 3x_2 + 1x_3 + 0x_4 = 8$$
$$2x_2 + 5x_3 + 0x_4 + x_5 = 10$$
$$3x_1 + 2x_2 + 4x_3 + 0x_4 + 0x_5 + x_6 = 15$$

Starting (Initial) Simplex Table

Non-zero basic variables	c_b	Solution values $b(= x_b)$	c_j 3	5	4	0	0	0	Min. Ratio $(x_b/x_k), \; x_k > 0$
			Real variables x_1	x_2	x_3	Slack variables x_4	x_5	x_6	
x_4	0	8	2	3	0	1	0	0	8/3 ←
x_5	0	10	0	2	5	0	1	0	10/2
x_6	0	15	3	2	4	0	0	1	15/2
$x_1 = x_2 = x_3 = 0$	$z = c_b x_b = 0$		−3	−5	−4	0	0	0	←$\delta_j = 0$

We choose the most negative value (or least negative coefficient) of δ_j,
$(\delta_j = c_b x_j - c_j)$

Here it is (-5) in the second column of (Real variables). Compute the ratio $\begin{bmatrix} \dfrac{8}{3}, \dfrac{10}{2}, \dfrac{15}{2} \end{bmatrix}$. The minimum (or smallest) of these is $\dfrac{8}{3}$ which is along the first row of the initial Simplex table.

Thus, the Key element is 3, which indicates that the current table must be transformed in such a way that the 'Key element' becomes 1 and all other element in that column become 0.

This is done as follows:

The intermediate coefficient Matrix of the initial Simplex table, e.g., (i.e., after dividing each element of 1st row by the key element 3).

x_b	x_1	x_2	x_3	x_4	x_5	x_5	
8/3	2/3	1	0	1/3	0	0	
10	0	2	5	0	1	0	
15	3	2	4	0	0	1	
							$\delta_j \leftarrow$

Apply

$$R_2 \longrightarrow R_2 \longrightarrow 2R_1; \qquad R_3 \longrightarrow 2R_1; \quad R_4 \rightarrow R_4 + 5R_1$$

R_1	8/3	2/3	1	0	1/3	0	0
R_2	8/3	–4/3	0	5	–2/3	1	0
R_3	29/3	5/3	0	4	–2/3	0	1
R_3	40/3	1/3	0	–4	5/3	0	0

Hence, we have the following Second Simplex table.

Second Simplex Table

	c_j		3	5	4	0	0	0	
Non-zero basic variables	c_b	xb	x_1	x_2	x_3	x_4	x_5	x_6	Min. Ratio
x_4	0	8/3	2/3	1	0	1/3	0	0	—
x_5	0	14/3	–4/3	0	5	–2/3	1	0	14/3/5 ←
x_6	0	29/3	5/3	0	4	–2/3	0	1	29/3/4
$x_4 = x_2 = x_3 = 0$ ↓	$z = 40/3$		1/3	0	–4 ↑	5/3 ↓	0	0	← δ_j

The smallest ratio is $\dfrac{\frac{14}{3}}{5}$ and the most negative value of δ_j is (-4). Thus the key element is found to be 5, which indicates that the current table must be transformed in such a way that the key element becomes 1 and all other element in that column become 0. This is done as follows :

We now consider the intermediate coefficient Matrix of the second Simplex table (i.e., after dividing each element of second row by the key element 5).

	x_b	x_1	x_2	x_3	x_4	x_5	x_5
R_1	8/3	2/3	1	0	1/3	0	0
R_2	14/15	−4/5	0	1	−2/15	1/5	0
R_3	29/3	5/3	0	4	−2/3	0	1
R_4	$z=40/3$	1/3	0	−4	5/3	0 ↓	0

Apply

	x_b	x_1	x_2	x_3	x_4	x_5	x_6	
$R_3 \to R_3 + 4R_2$	8/3	2/3	1	0	1/3	0	0	8/3/2/3
$R_4 \to R_4 + 4R_2$	14/15	−4/5	0	1	−2/15	1/5	0	—
	89/15	41/15	0	0	−2/15	−4/5	1	89/15/41/15
		−11/15	0	0	17/15	4/5	0	*
	$z=265/15$							

Hence, we have the following:

Third Simplex Table

c_j			3	5	4	0	0	0	
Non-zero basic variable	c_b	Solution values $b\,(=x_b)$	x_1	x_2	x_3	x_4	x_5	x_6	Min. Ratio
x_2	5	8/3	2/3	1	0	1/3	0	0	8/3/2/3
$\to x_3$	4	14/15	−4/5	0	1	−2/15	1/15	0	—
$\leftarrow x_6$	0	89/15	41/15	2	4	−2/15	4/5	1	89/15/41/15
$x_1=x_5=x_4=0$		$z=265/15$	−11/15 ↑	0	0	17/15	4/5	0	δ_j ↓

We find from 3rd Simplex table that $\delta_j = z_1 - c_1 = c_b x_b - c_1 = -\dfrac{11}{15} < 0$

The minimum ratio $\begin{bmatrix} \dfrac{8}{3}, & \dfrac{89}{15} \\[2mm] \dfrac{2}{3} & \dfrac{41}{15} \end{bmatrix}$ i.e., $\left[4, \dfrac{89}{41} \right]$.

The smallest is $\dfrac{89}{41}$. Thus, the leading element is $\dfrac{41}{15}$ (in the 3rd row and first column)

We now consider the intermediate coefficient Matrix of the third Simplex table (i.e., after dividing each element of the 3rd row by $\left(\dfrac{41}{15} \right)$ and also subtract suitable multiples. This new 3rd row so found from the other rows in order to get zero at all other places in (x_1). Hence, we have the following fourth Simplex table as:

Fourth (Final) Simplex Table

Non-zero basic variables	c_b	Solution values $b(= x_b)$	Real variables			Slack variables			Min. Ratio (x_b/x_k), $x_k > 0$
			x_1	x_2	x_3	x_4	x_5	x_6	
x_4	0	50/41	0	1	0	15/41	8/41	–10/41	
x_5	0	62/41	0	0	1	–6/41	5/41	4/41	
x_6	0	89/41	1	0	0	–2/41	12/41	15/41	
$x_1=x_2=x_3=0$		$z = c_b x_b$ $= 761/41$	0	0	45/41	24/41	11/41	11/41	$\delta_j \geq 0$

Thus, we find that all $\delta_j \geq 0$ in the table. Hence, the optimal solution is reached. The solution is

$$x_1 = \frac{89}{41}, \ x_2 = \frac{50}{41}, \ x_3 = \frac{62}{41}, \ \text{Max } z = \frac{765}{41}$$

13. Maximize: $z = x_1 - 3x_2 + 2x_3$
   subject to the constraints:

$3x_1 - x_2 + 2x_3 \leq 7$,
$- 2x_1 + 4x_2 \leq 12$,
$- 4x_1 + 3x_2 + 8x_3 \leq 10$,
and $x_1,\ x_2,\ x_3 \geq 0$.

We can easily covert the problem of minimization to maximization problem by taking the objective function as

$$z' = -z \text{ we get}$$

Max $z' = -x_1 + 3x_2 - 2x_3$

Introducing the slack variables, we get the new 'Objective function' as

$$z' = -x_1 + 3x_2 - 4x_3 + 0x_4 + 0x_5 + 0x_6 \qquad [1]$$
$$3x_1 - x_2 + 2x_3 + x_4 + x_5 + 0x_6 = 7$$
$$-2x_1 + 4x_2 + 0x_3 + 0x_4 + x_5 + 0x_6 = 12 \qquad [2]$$
$$-4x_1 + 3x_2 + 8x_2 + 0x_4 + 0x_5 + 0x_6 = 10$$

Starting (Initial) Simplex Table

Non-zero basic variables	c_b	Solution values $b(= x_b)$	Real variables			Slack variables			Min. Ratio (x_b/x_k), $x_k > 0$
c_j			-1	3	-2	0	0	0	
			x_1	x_2	x_3	x_4	x_5	x_6	
x_4	0	7	3	-1	2	1	0	0	—
x_5	0	12	-2	4	0	0	1	0	12/4
x_6	0	10	-4	3	8	0	0	1	10/3
$x_1=x_2=x_3=0$		$z=c_bx_b=0$	1	-3	2	0	0	0	$\leftarrow$ δ_j
			1	-3 $\uparrow$	2	0	0	0	

We choose the most negative value (or least negative coefficient) of δ_j, $(\delta_j = c_b x_j - c_j)$

Here it is (-3) $\uparrow$ in the second column of (real variables). Compute the ratio $\left[\dfrac{12}{4}, \dfrac{10}{3},\right]$ and $\left[\dfrac{7}{-1}\right]$ (negative ratio) which is not considered.

The minimum ratio of these is 3 which is along the second row of the initial Simplex table.

Thus, the Key element is 3 which is along the second row of the initial Simplex table. Thus, the 'key element is 4. which indicates that the current table must be transformed in such a way that the 'Key element' becomes '1' and all other element in that column become 0.

This is done as follows:

The intermediate coefficient Matrix of the initial Simplex table, (e.g., after dividing each element of 2nd row by the key element 4).

	x_b	x_1	x_2	x_3	x_4	x_5	x_6	
R_1	7	3	-1	2	1	0	0	
R_2	3	$-1/2$	1	0	0	1/4	0	
R_3	10	-4	3	8	0	0	1	δ_j

	x_b	x_1	x_2	x_3	x_4	x_5	x_6	
$R_1 \to R_1 + R_2$	10	5/2	0	2	1	1/4	0	
$R_3 \to R_3 - 3R_2$	3	1/2	1	0	0	1/4	0	
	1	−5/2	0	8	0	−3/4	1	$\delta_j \geq 0$

Hence, we have the following improvement:

Second Simplex Table

Non-zero basic variables	c_b	Solution values $b\,(=x_b)$	Real variables			Slack variables			Min. Ratio
			x_1	x_2	x_3	x_4	x_5	x_6	
x_4	0	10	5/2	0	2	1	1/4	0	10/(5/2)
x_2	3	3	−1/2	1	0	0	1/4	0	—
x_6	0	1	−5/2	0	8	0	−3/4	1	—
$x_1=x_5=x_4=0$		$z=c_b x_b=9$	−1/2	0	2	0	3/4	0	$\delta_j \geq 0$

The most negative value (or least negative coefficient of δ_j, ($\delta_j = c_b x_j - c_j$) is $\dfrac{-1}{2}$. The key element is found to be $\dfrac{5}{2}$ which is in the first row and first column and has been shown in second Simplex table.

Now in order to bring x_4 in place of x_1, we must have unity in the position where $\left(\dfrac{5}{2}\right)$ in the second Simplex table and zero at all other places in x_1.

The intermediate coefficient Matrix of the second Simplex table (e.g., after dividing each element of the first row by the key element $\dfrac{5}{2}$).

	x_b	x_1	x_2	x_3	x_4	x_5	x_6
R_1	4	1	0	4/5	2/5	1/10	0
R_2	3	−1/2	1	0	0	1/4	0
R_3	1	−5/2	0	8	0	−3/4	1
R_4	$z = 9$	−1/2	0	2	0	3/4	0

Apply

	x_b	x_1	x_2	x_3	x_4	x_5	x_6
$R_2 \to R_2 + 1/2 R_1$	4	1	0	4/5	2/5	1/10	0
$R_3 \to R_3 + 5/2 R_1$	5	0	1	2/5	1/5	3/10	0
$R_4 \to R_4 + 1/2 R_1$	11	0	0	10	1	1/2	1
	$z = 11$	0	0	12/5	1/5	4/5	0

Thus, we have the next Third (Final) Simplex table as follows:

Third (Final) Simplex table

Non-zero basic variables	c_b	Solution values $b(= x_b)$	Real variables			Slack variables			Min. Ratio (x_b/x_k), $x_k > 0$
			x_1	x_2	x_3	x_4	x_5	x_6	
x_1	−1	4	1	0	4/5	2/5	1/10	0	
x_2	3	3	0	1	2/5	1/5	3/10	0	
x_6	0	11	0	0	10	1	−1/2	1	
$x_3 = x_4 = x_5 = 0$	$z = c_b x_b = 11$		0	0	12/3	1/5	4/5	0	$\delta_j \geq 0$

From this Simplex table, we find that all $\delta_j = c_b x_j - c_j$ are non-negative and hence an optimum solution has been reached.

The optimum solution is:

$$x_1 = 4, \ x_2 = 5 \ \text{and} \ x_3 = 0$$
$$\text{Max} \ z' = -(4) + 3(5) - 2(0) = 11$$
$\therefore$ Required min. $z = -11$
$$(\text{Min} \ z' = -z)$$

14. Maximize: $z = 3x_1 + 2x_2$

subject to the constraints:

$2x_1 + x_2 \leq 7,$
$x_1 + 3x_2 \leq 6,$
$x_1, x_2 \geq 0.$

Solution: Step (1): Introducing the slack variables, and constraints (inequalities) will become equalities as:

$$2x_1 + x_2 + s_1 = 10$$
$$x_1 + 3x_2 + s_2 = 6,$$
$$z - 3x_1 - 2x_2 = 0.$$

Step (2): Writing the system of equations above in the form of a table known as Simplex table.

Starting (Initial) Simplex Table

Basic variables	Solution constants $b(= x_b)$	x_1	x_2	Min. Ratio x_b/x_k, $x_k > 0$
s_1	10	[2]	1	10/2
s_2	6	1	3	6/2
z	0	−3 ↑	−2	

Locate the Pivot column (least negative entry in the last row). To locate the Pivot row (least positive ratio of the constraints to values in the marked Pivot column.

The least positive ratio is $5 = \dfrac{10}{2}$

Step (3): Pivot Element = 2

To write a new Simplex table, change Pivot to $\dfrac{1}{\text{Pivot}}$. Divide Pivot row by + Pivot and Pivot column by − Pivot. Interchange the variables of Pivot row and Pivot column.

		s_1	x_2	
x_1	5	1/2	1/2	.
s_2	.	−1/2	.	.
z	.	3/2	.	.

The remaining elements are given by:

Previous value =

$$\left\{ \text{Previous value} - \frac{\text{Element in Pivot row} \times \text{Element in Pivot column}}{\text{Pivot}} \right\}$$

They are:

$$6 \to 6 - \frac{10 \times 1}{2} = 1; \qquad\qquad 3 \to 3 - \frac{1 \times 1}{2} = \frac{5}{2},$$

$$0 \to 0 - \frac{10 \times (-3)}{2} = 15, \qquad -2 \to -2 - \frac{1 \times (-3)}{2} = -\frac{1}{2}$$

Next, we have a new Simplex table:

Basic variables	Solution constants $b(= x_b)$	s_1	s_2	Min. Ratio
x_1	5	1/2	1/2	5/1/2
s_2	1	−1/2	5/2	1/5/2 ←
z	15	3/2 ↑	−1/2	δ_j

Pivot column

Repeating the process till no negative values appear in the z − row.

Step (4): The (key) Pivotal element $= \dfrac{5}{2}$. Change Pivot to $\dfrac{1}{\text{Pivot}}$. Divide Pivot row elements by $\left(\dfrac{5}{2}\right)$. Pivot column elements by $\dfrac{-5}{2}$. Interchange the variables of Pivot row and Pivot column.

			s_1	s_2	
x_1	.	.		−1/5	.
x_2	2/5	−1/5		2/5	.
z	.	.		1/5	.

Remaining elements are given by

$$\left\{ \text{Previous value} - \frac{\text{Element in Pivot row} \times \text{Element in Pivot column}}{\text{Pivot}} \right\}$$

$$5 \to 5 - \frac{\dfrac{1}{2} \times 1}{\dfrac{5}{2}} = 5 - \frac{1}{2} \times \frac{2}{5} = \frac{2}{5} = \frac{24}{5}$$

$$\frac{1}{2} \to \frac{1}{2} - \frac{\left(\dfrac{-1}{2}\right)\left(\dfrac{1}{2}\right)}{\dfrac{5}{2}} = \frac{1}{2} + \frac{1}{4} \times \frac{2}{5} = \frac{1}{2} + \frac{1}{10} = \frac{5+1}{10} = \frac{3}{5}$$

$$15 \to 15 - \frac{1 \times \left(-\dfrac{1}{2}\right)}{\dfrac{5}{2}} = 15 + \frac{1}{2} \times \frac{2}{5} = \frac{76}{5}$$

$$\frac{3}{2} \to \frac{3}{2} - \frac{\left(-\dfrac{1}{2}\right)\left(\dfrac{1}{2}\right)}{\dfrac{5}{2}} = \frac{3}{2} - \frac{1}{10} = \frac{14}{10}$$

Final (Second) Simplex Table

Basic variables	Solution constants $b(= x_b)$	s_1	s_2	Min. Ratio
x_1	24/5	3/5	−1/5	
x_2	2/5	−1/5	2/5	
z	76/5	14/10	1/5	$\delta_j > 0$

Since the last row contains no negative value, so an optimum solution has been reached; hence the solution is: $x_1 = \dfrac{24\cdot}{5}$, $x_2 = \dfrac{2}{5}$, Max $z = \dfrac{76}{5}$

15. Maximize: $z = 4x - 2y - z$,
    subject to the constraints:
    $2x + 2y + z \le 4$,
    $x - y \le 0$,
    $x \ge 0$, $y \ge 0$, $z \ge 0$

    Solution: Step (1): Introducing the slack variables, we can write the above (inequalities) constraints in the following form:
    $$x + y + z + s_1 = 3$$
    $$2x + 2y + z + s_2 = 4$$
    $$x - y + s_3 = 0$$
    $$z - 4x + 2y + z = 0$$

    Step (2):

Starting (Initial) Simplex Table

Basic variables	Solution constants (x_b)	x_1	x_2	x_3	Min. Ratio x_b/x_k, $x_k > 0$
s_1	3	1	1	1	3/1
s_2	4	2	2	1	4/2
s_3	0	1	−1	0	0/1
z	0	−4 ↑	2	1	

Step (3): To Locate the Pivot column (least negative entry in the last row). To locate the Pivot row (least positive ratio of the constraints to the entry in the marked column or Pivot column).

Step (4): Pivot Element = 1

Change Pivot to $\dfrac{1}{\text{Pivot}}$. Divide Pivot row by + Pivot and Pivot column by − Pivot. The remaining elements are:

$$3 \to 3 - \frac{0(1)}{1} = 3 \qquad\qquad 1 \to 1 - \frac{(-1)\times1}{1} = 2$$

$$4 \to 4 - \frac{0\times2}{1} = 4 \qquad\qquad 2 \to 2 - \frac{(-1)\times2}{1} = 4$$

$$0 \to 0 - \frac{0\times(-4)}{1} = 0 \qquad\qquad 2 \to 2 - \frac{(-1)(-4)}{1} = -2$$

$$1 \to 1 - \frac{0\times-4}{1} = 1 \qquad\qquad 1 \to 1 - \frac{1\times0}{1} = 1$$

$$1 \to 1 - \frac{0\times2}{1} = 1$$

Second Simplex Table

Basic variables	Solution constants (x_b)	s_3	y	z	Min. Ratio $x_b/x_k,\ x_k > 0$
s_1	3	−1	2	1	3/2
s_2	4	−2	4	1	4/4
x	0	1	−1	0	0/−1
z	0	4	−2 ↑	1	

Repeating the process till no negative values appear in the z – row.

Pivot Element = (4):

Change Pivot to $\dfrac{1}{\text{Pivot}}$. Divide the Pivot – row by + Pivot and Pivot column by − Pivot. Interchange the variables in Pivot row and Pivot column.

		s_1	s_2	z
s_1	.	.	−1/2	.
y	1	−1/2	1/4	1/4
x	.	.	1/4	.
z	.	.	1/2	.

$$3 \to 3 - \frac{4 \times 2}{4} = 1$$

$$-1 \to -1 - \frac{2 \times -2}{4} = -1 + \frac{4}{4} = 0$$

$$1 \to 1 - \frac{2 \times 1}{4} = 1 - \frac{1}{2} = \frac{1}{2}$$

$$0 \to 0 - \frac{4 \times -1}{4} = 1$$

$$1 \to 1 - \frac{(-2)(-1)}{4} = 1 - \frac{1}{2} = \frac{1}{2}$$

$$0 \to 0 - \frac{(1)(-1)}{4} = \frac{1}{4}$$

$$0 \to 0 - \frac{4 \times -2}{4} = 2$$

$$4 \to 4 - \frac{(-2)(-2)}{4} = 4 - 1 = 3$$

$$1 \to 1 - \frac{(-2)(1)}{4} = 1 + \frac{1}{2} = \frac{3}{2}$$

Final (Third) Simplex Table

Basic variables	Solution constants $(b=x_b)$	s_3	s_2	z
s_1	1	0	$-1/2$	$1/2$
y	1	$-1/2$	$1/4$	$1/4$
x	1	$1/2$	$1/2$	$1/4$
z	2	3	$1/2$	$3/4$

Since the values of the z – row are all non-negative, so the optimal solution has been reached, the solution is $x = 1$, $y = 1$, $z = 0$,

Max $z = 4\,(1) - 2\,(1) - 0$

$\qquad = 4 - 2 = 2.$

16. Maximize: $z = x_2 - x_1$,

subject to the constraints:

$-x_1 + 2x_2 \le 2,$

$x_1 + x_2 \le 4,$

$x_1 \le 3,$

$x_1 \ge 0, \ x_2 \le 0$

Solution: Step (1): After introducing the slack variables, the constraints become:

$x_1 + 2x_2 + s_1 = 2$

$-x_1 + x_2 + s_2 = 2$

$x_1 + x_3 + s_2 = 4$

$x_1 + s_3 = 0$

Step (2): Writing the system of equation above in the form of a table known as simplex table.

Starting (Initial) Simplex Table

Basic variables	Solution constants $b(= x_b)$	x_1	x_2	Min. Ratio $x_b/x_k, \ x_k > 0$
s_1	2	-1	$\boxed{2}$	2/4
s_2	4	1	1	4/1
s_3	3	1	0	3/0
z	0	$+4$ $\uparrow$	-1 $\uparrow$	

Identify the Pivot column (least negative entry in the last row). To locate the Pivot row (least positive ratio of the constraints to values in the marked Pivot column.

The least positive ratio is $\dfrac{2}{2} = 1$

Step (2): Pivot Element = 2

To write a new Simplex table, change Pivot to $\dfrac{1}{\text{Pivot}}$. Divide Pivot row by + Pivot and Pivot column by – Pivot, interchange the variables of Pivot row and Pivot column.

464 *Advanced Engineering Mathematics*

		x_1	s_2
x_2	1	−1	1/2
s_2	.	.	−1/2
s_3	.	.	0
z	.	.	1/2

Remaining elements are replaced by:

$$4 \rightarrow 4 - \frac{2 \times 1}{2} = 2,$$

$$1 \rightarrow 1 - \frac{(-1) \times 1}{2} = 1 + \frac{1}{2} = \frac{3}{2},$$

$$3 \rightarrow 3 - \frac{2 \times 0}{2} = 3,$$

$$1 \rightarrow 1 - \frac{(-1) \times 0}{2} = 1$$

$$0 \rightarrow 0 - \frac{2 \times (-1)}{2} = 1$$

$$1 \rightarrow 1 - \frac{(-1)(-1)}{2} \quad 1 - \frac{1}{2} = \frac{1}{2}$$

We have, the next improvement in the next simplex table as:

Second Simplex Table

		x_1	s_1
x_2	1	−1	1/2
s_2	2	3/2	−1/2
s_3	3	1	0
z	1	1/2	1/2

Since the last row contains no negative elements, stop at this stage. An optimum solution has been reached. Solution: $x_1 = 0$, $x_2 = 1$,
Max $z = 1 - 0 = 1$

Repeating the process till no negative values appear in the z − row.

Pivot Element = 4:

Change Pivot to $\dfrac{1}{\text{Pivot}}$. Divide the Pivot – row by + Pivot and Pivot column by – Pivot. Interchange the variables in Pivot and Pivot column.

		s_1	s_2	z
s_1	.	.	–1/2	.
y	1	–1/2	1/4	1/4
x	.	.	1/4	.
z	.		1/2	

$$3 \to 3 - \frac{4 \times 2}{4} = 1,$$

$$-1 \to -1 - \frac{2 \times -2}{4} = -1 + \frac{4}{4} = 0 \ ,$$

$$1 \to 1 - \frac{2 \times 1}{4} = 1 - \frac{1}{2} = \frac{1}{2},$$

$$0 \to 0 - \frac{4 \times (-1)}{4} = 1$$

$$1 \to 1 - \frac{(-2)(-1)}{4} = 1 - \frac{1}{2} = \frac{1}{2}$$

$$0 \to 0 - \frac{(1)(-1)}{4} = \frac{1}{4}$$

$$4 \to 4 - \frac{(-2)(-2)}{4} = 4 - 1 = 3$$

$$1 \to 1 - \frac{(-2)(1)}{4} = 1 + \frac{1}{2} = \frac{3}{2}$$

Final (Third) Simplex Table

Basic variables	Solution constants (x_b)	s_3	s_2	z
s_1	1	0	–1/2	1/2
y	1	–1/2	1/4	1/4
x	1	1/2	1/2	1/4
z	2	3	1/2	3/4

Since the values of the z – row are all non-negative, so the optimal solution has been reached, the solution is $x = 1$, $y = 1$, $z = 0$,

Max $z = 4\,(1) - 2\,(1) - 0$

$\qquad = 4 - 2 = 2$

EXERCISES

Using Simplex Method solve the following L.P.P.

1. Minimize $\quad z = 5x_1 + 3x_2 + 8x_3$
    subject to $\quad 2x_1 + 6x_2 - x_3 \le 4,$
    $\qquad\qquad -x_1 + 5x_2 - 3x_3 \le 1,$
    $\qquad\qquad 5x_1 - x_2 - 6x_3 \le 3,$
    $\qquad\qquad -3x_1 - 3x_2 + 7x_3 \ge 6$
    $\qquad\qquad x_1, x_2, x_3 \ge 0$

    Ans: $\quad x_1 = 0, x_2 = 0.962$
    $\qquad\qquad x_3 = 1.270, z = 13.024$

2. Minimize $\quad z = 5x_1 + 6x_2$
    subject to $\quad 2x_1 + 5x_2 \ge 1500$
    $\qquad\qquad 3x_1 + x_2 \ge 1200$
    $\qquad\qquad x_1 \ge 0, \; x_2 \ge 0$

    Ans: $\quad x_1 = 346.154, x_2 = 161.54$
    $\qquad\qquad x_3 = 161.54, z = 2700$

3. Maximize $\quad z = 3x_1 + 2x_2$
    subject to $\quad x_1 + 2x_2 \le 430$
    $\qquad\qquad 3x_1 + x_2 \le 460$
    $\qquad\qquad x_1, \; x_2 \ge 0$

    Ans: $\quad x_1 = 153.33, x_2 = 0$
    $\qquad\qquad z = 460$

Big - M method

In this method, we require the following steps to be ·followed in the solution of Linear Programming Problem.

Step (1): The objective function is to be maximized i.e. the requirement is Max (z)

Step (2): The constraints may be any of the following:

$$\left\{\begin{matrix} \geq & = & \leq \\ \geq & = & = \\ \geq & = & \geq \end{matrix}\right\}$$

Step (3): R.H.S must be positive.

Step (4): We add the artificial variable if the constraint is of the form $\geq$ and surplus variable is subtracted.

Example: $x_1 + x_2 \geq 50$; then

$$x_1 + x_2 - s_1 + A_1 = 50$$

Step (5): If the constraint is of the $=$ type, we add the artificial variable on L.H.S.

If $2x_1 + x_2 = 5$, then $2x_1 + x_2 + A_1 = 5$

Step (6): If A_1, A_2, A_3 etc. are the artificial variables that enter into solution space, then eliminate the corresponding column in the simplex table in the next iteration.

EXAMPLES

1. Solve the following L.P.P.

Min $z = 2x_1 + x_2$ such that

$5x_1 + 10x_2 - x_3 = 8$, $x_1 + x_2 + x_3 = 1$

$x_1, x_2, x_3, \geq 0$.

Solution: Introducing the artificial variables, the constraints can be written as:

$$5x_1 + 10x_2 - x_3 + A_1 + 0A_2 = 8, \ x_1 + x_2 + x_3 = 1$$
$$x_1 + x_2 + x_3 + 0A_1 + A_2 = 1$$

and maximise $z = -2x_1 - x_2 + 0x_3 - MA_1 - MA_2$

c_b	x_b	c_j b	-2 x_1	-1 x_2	0 x_3	$-M$ A_1	$-M$ A_2	Ratio
$-M$	A_1	8	5	10	-1	1	0	8/10 ←
$-M$	A_2	1	1	1	1	0	1	1
	$z_j = \sum c_j x_i$		$-6M$	$-11M$	0	$-M$	$-M$	
	$z_j - c_i$		$-6M+2$	$-11M+1$	0	0	0	

c_b	x_b	b	x_1	x_2	x_3	A_2	Ratio
-1	$x2$	8/10	1/2	1	$-1/10$	0	-8
$-M$	$A2$	1/5	1/2	0	11/10	1	2/11 ←
	$z_j=$		$-\dfrac{M-1}{2}$	-1	$\dfrac{1-11M}{10}$	$-M$	
	$z_j - c_j$		$-\dfrac{M+3}{2}$	0	$\dfrac{1-11M}{10}$	0	

c_b	x_b	b	x_1	x_2	x_3	Ratio
-1	x_2	9/11	12/22	1	0	
0	x_3	2/11	5/11	0	1	
	$\sum x_i c_i =$		$-12/22$	-1	0	
	$z_j - c_j =$		32/22	0	0	

Since all $z_j - c_j > 0$

$\therefore$ Solution: $-\{x_2 = 9/11;\ x_3 = 2/11;\ x_1 = 0\}$

$\therefore$ Min $z = 2x_1 + x_2 = 0 + \dfrac{9}{11} = \dfrac{9}{11}$

2. Minimize $z = 10x_1 + 6x_2 + 2x_3$

subject to $-x_1 + x_2 + x_3 \geq 1$

$3x_1 + x_2 - x_3 \geq 2$

$x_1,\ x_2,\ x_3 \geq 0$

Solution: Introducing slack and surplus variables, we can write the constraints as

$$-x_1 + x_2 + x_3 - s_1 + A_1 + 0s_2 + 0A_2 = 1$$

$$3x_1 + x_2 - x_3 + 0s_1 + 0A_1 - s_2 + A_2 = 2$$

and Max $z = -10x_1 - 6x_2 - 2x_3 + 0s_1 + 0s_2 - MA_1 - MA_2$

$x_1, x_2, x_3, s_1, s_2, A_1, A_2 \geq 0$

where M is very large (i.e. big M)

| c_b | x_b | b | -10 | -6 | -2 | 0 | 0 | $-M$ | $-M$ | Ratio |
			x_1	x_2	x_3	s_1	s_2	A_1	A_2	
$-M$	A_1	1	-1	$\boxed{1}$	1	-1	0	1	0	$1 \leftarrow$
$-M$	A_2	2	3	1	-1	0	-1	0	1	2
	$z_j = \sum c_j x_i$	$-2M$	$-2M$	0	M	M	$-M$	$-M$		
	$z_j - c_i$	$-2M+10$	$+6$	2	M	M	0	0		

Now, we choose the most negative column. Here, it is $(-2M+6)^{th}$ column and hence we choose this as the pivot column, and the pivot row as one which has '1' in the ratio column (least positive ratio).

| c_b | x_b | b | -10 | -6 | -2 | 0 | 0 | $-M$ | Ratio |
			x_1	x_2	x_3	s_1	s_2	A_2	
-6	x_2	1	-1	1	1	-1	0	0	$-ve$
$-M$	A_2	1	4	0	-2	1	-1	1	$1/4 \leftarrow$
	z_j		$6-4M$	(-6)	$(-6+2M)$	$(6-M)$	(M)	$(-M)$	
$z_j - c_j$	$16-4M$		0 $\uparrow$	$-4+2M$	$6-M$	M	0		

Since A_1 is replaced by x_2 in $c_b.x_b$ column, let us not consider A_1 in this iteration and $(16-4M) th$ column is the most negative column.

| c_b | x_b | b | -10 | -6 | -2 | 0 | 0 |
			x_1	x_2	x_3	s_1	s_2
-6	x_2	$5/4$	0	1	$1/2$	$-3/4$	$-1/4$
-10	x_1	$1/4$	1	0	$-1/2$	$1/4$	$-1/4$
	$z_j =$		-10	-6	2	7	4
	$z_j - c_j =$		0	0	4	7	4

We have eliminated A_2 column as it has been replaced and since all $(z_j - c_j) > 0$, (non-negative), we do not proceed to the next iteration (cannot) and values are $x_1 = \dfrac{1}{4}; \ x_2 = \dfrac{5}{4}; \ x_3 = 0$ from column B.

$\therefore$ Min $z = 10x_1 + 6x_2 + 2x_3 = \dfrac{10}{4} + \dfrac{6 \times 5}{4} + 2 \times 0 = \dfrac{40}{4} = 10$

3. Maximize $z = 3x_1 + 2x_2 + x_3$
subject to $-3x_1 + 2x_2 + 2x_3 = 8$
$-3x_1\ 4x_2 + x_3 = 7$
$x_1, x_2, x_3 \geq 0.$

Solution: Introducing the artificial variables A_1, A_2 we can write the constraints as:

$$-3x_1 + 2x_2 + 2x_3 + A_1 + 0A_2 = 8$$
$$-3x_1 + 4x_2 + x_3 + 0A_1 + A_2 = 7$$

and Max $z = 3x_1 + 2x_2 + 2x_3 - MA_1 - MA_2$

c_b	x_b	b	3 x_1	2 x_2	1 x_3	$-M$ A_1	$-M$ A_2	Ratio
$-M$	A_1	8	-3	2	2	1	0	4
$-M$	A_2	7	-3	4	1	0	1	7/4 ←
	$z_j = \sum c_i x_i =$		$+6M$	$-6M$	$-3M$	$-M$	$-M$	
	$z_j - c_i$		$+6M-3$	$-6M-2$ ↑	$-3M-1$	-0	0	

c_b	x_b	b	3 x_1	2 x_2	1 x_3	$-M$ A_1	Ratio
$-M$	A_1	9/2	$-3/2$	0	3/2	1	3
2	$x2$	7/4	$-3/4$	1	1/4	0	7
	$z_j = \sum c_i x_i$	$\dfrac{3M-3}{2}$	2	$\dfrac{-3M+1}{2}$	$-M$		
	$z_j - c_j$	$\dfrac{3M-9}{2}$	0	$\dfrac{-3M-1}{2}$	0		

c_b	x_b	b	x_1	x_2	x_3	Ratio
1	x_3	3	-1	0	1	-3
2	x_2	1	$-1/2$	1	0	-2
	$z_j = \sum c_i x_i$	-2	2	1		
	$z_j - c_j$		-5 ↑	0	0	

We find that both the ratios are negative we stop the process as we cannot proceed further. Hence the solution is unbounded.

Dual Simplex method

Dual simplex method is applicable to those Linear programming problems that start with infeasible but otherwise optimum solution. The method may be summarized as follows:

Step 1: Objective function is equal to minimization (i.e. min z) If Max z, multiply by negative sign.

Step 2: All the constraints (inequalities) are converted to ($\leq$) type irrespective of R.H.S value.

Step 3: Only slack variables are to be added to constraints.

Step 4: Prepare the dual simplex table.

Step 5: Find $c_j - z_j$ where c_j and z_j are calculated as in ordinary simplex method.

Step 6: Choose the key now, as one which is having most negative 'b' value. If all 'b' are positive, solution is reached, if not, proceed to next step.

Step 7: Determine $\min \theta$ value,

where $\theta = \left| \dfrac{c_i - z_j}{a_{ij}} \right|$ provided a_{ij} is negative value in key row.

Step 8: Choose the column containing minimum as the key column and proceed to next iteration until 'b' values become positive.

EXAMPLES

1. Use dual Simplex Method to solve the following L.P.P.

Maximize: $z = 2x_1 - x_2 + x_3$

subject to: $x_1 + x_2 - 3x_3 \leq 8, \; 4x_1 - x_2 + x_3 \geq 2$

$$2x_1 + 3x_2 - x_3 \geq 4, \; x_i \geq 0$$

Solution: Since the given problem is for maximize (z) so we make it minimize (z) by multiplying by (-1) sign and convert the constraints to $\leq$ form. Hence, the standard form of the given problem is:

minimize: $z = 2x_1 - x_2 + x_3$

subject to: $x_1 + x_2 - 3x_3 + s_1 + 0s_2 + 0s_3 = 8$

$$-4x_1 + x_2 - x_3 + 0s_1 + s_2 + 0s_3 = -2$$

$$-2x_1 - 3x_2 + x_3 + 0s_1 + 0s_2 + s_3 = -4$$

and minimize z: $-2x_1 + x_2 - x_3 + 0s_1 + 0s_2 + 0s_3$
$$x_1, \ x_2, \ x_3, \ s_1, \ s_2, \ s_3 \geq 0$$

The current basic solution is $s_1 = 8$; $s_2 = -2$; $s_3 = -4$ which is infeasible. It is displayed in the dual simplex table.

Initial Iteration:

			−2	1	−1	0	0	0	
c_b	x_b	b	x_1	x_2	x_3	s_1	s_2	s_3	Current Solution
0	s_1	8	1	1	−3	1	0	0	8
0	s_2	−2	−4	1	−1	0	1	0	−2
0	s_3	−4	−2	−3	1	0	0	1	−4 ←
$z_j = \sum c_b x_i$		0	0	0	0	0	0	0	
$z_j - c_j$			−2	1	−1	0	0	0	
$\theta = \left\| \dfrac{c_i - z_j}{a_{ij}} \right\|$			1	1/3					

First iteration:

c_b	x_b	b	x_1	x_2	x_3	x_1	s_2	s_3	Current Solution
0	s_1	20/3	1/3	0	−8/3	1	0	1/3	20/3
0	s_2	−10/3	−14/3	0	−2/3	0	1	1/3	−10/3 ←
1	x_2	4/3	2/3	1	−1/3	0	0	−1/3	4/3
$z_j = \sum c_b x_i$			2/3	1	−1/3	0	0	−1/3	
$c_i - z_j$			−8/3	0	−2/3	0	0	1/3	
$\theta = \left\| \dfrac{c_i - z_j}{a_{ij}} \right\|$			4/7 ↑	−	1	−	−	−	

Final iteration:

c_b	x_b	b	x_1	x_2	x_3	s_1	s_2	s_3	Current Solution
0	s_1	145/21	0	0	−57/21	1	1/4	5/14	145/21
−2	x_1	5/7	1	0	1/7	0	−3/14	−1/14	5/7
1	x_2	6/7	0	1	−9/21	0	1/14	−5/14	6/7

We find that the values of 'b' are all positive

$$x_1 = \frac{5}{7}; \, x_2 = \frac{6}{7}$$

Substituting the values of x_1 and x_2 in the equation for maximize $z = 2x_1 - x_2 + x_3$

we get Maximize $z = 2\left(\dfrac{5}{7}\right) - \dfrac{6}{7} = \dfrac{4}{7}$

2. Solve the given problem using Dual Simplex method (DSM).

Given minimize: $z = 3x_1 + 2x_2 + x_3 + 4x_4$

Subject to: $2x_1 + 4x_2 + 5x_3 + x_4 \geq 10$

$3x_1 - x_2 + 7x_3 - 2x_4 \geq 2$

$5x_1 + 2x_2 + x_3 + 6x_4 \geq 15$

and $x_i \geq 0$

Solution: Rewrite the given constraints to $\leq$ type so we have

$$-2x_1 - 4x_2 - 5x_3 - x_4 \leq -10$$

$$-3x_1 + x_2 - 7x_3 + 2x_4 \leq -2$$

$$-5x_1 - 2x_2 - x_3 - 6x_4 \leq -15$$

Adding slack variable, we have

$$-2x_1 - 4x_2 - 5x_3 - x_4 + s_1 + 0s_2 + 0s_3 = -10$$

$$-3x_1 + x_2 - 7x_3 + 2x_4 + 0s_1 + s_2 + 0s_3 = -2$$

$$-5x_1 - 2x_2 - x_3 - 6x_4 + 0s_1 + 0s_2 + s_3 = -15$$

and minimize $= 3x_1 + 2x_2 + x_3 + 4x_4 + 0s_1 + 0s_2 + 0s_3$

We prepare the table

c_b	x_b	b	$3x_1$	$2x_2$	x_3	x_4	s_1	s_2	s_3
0	s_1	−10	−2	−4	−5	−1	1	0	0
0	s_2	−2	−3	1	−7	2	0	1	0
0	s_3^-	−15	−5	−2	−1	−6	0	0	1
	$z_j = \sum c_b x_i$		0	0	0	0	0	0	0
	$c_i - z_j \Rightarrow$		3	2	1	4	0	0	0
	$\theta = \left\|\dfrac{c_i - z_j}{a_{ij}}\right\|$		3/5	1	1	2/3	−	−	−

c_b	x_b	b	x_1	x_2	x_3	x_4	s_1	s_2	s_3
0	s_1	−4	0	−16/5	−23/5	7/5	1	0	−2/5
0	s_2	7	0	11/5	−32/5	28/5	0	1	−3/5
3	x_1	3	1	2/5	1/5	6/5	0	0	−1/5
$z_j = \sum c_b x_i$			3	6/5	3/5	18/5	0	0	−3/5
$c_i - z_j$			0	4/5	25	2/5	0	0	3/5
$\theta = \left\| \dfrac{c_i - z_j}{a_{ij}} \right\|$			−	1/4	2/23	-	-	-	3/2

c_b	x_b	b	x_1	x_2	x_3	x_4	s_1	s_2	s_3
1	x_3	20/23	0	16/23	1	−7/23	−5/23	0	2/23
0	s_2	289/23	0	153/23	0	29/23	−32/23	1	−1/23
3	x_1	65/23	1	6	0	87/23	1/23	0	−5/23

From the table, $x_3 = \dfrac{20}{23}$; $x_1 = \dfrac{65}{23}$ min $z = \dfrac{215}{23}$

3. Solve the given problem by Dual Simplex method.

Subject to Min $z = 2x + 3y$,

$3x + 4y \geq 5$,

$4x + 5y \geq 7$,

$x + 2y \leq 4$

Solution: Rewriting the given constraints to $\leq$ type, so we have

$-3x - 4y \leq -5$

$-4x - 5y \leq -7$

$x + 2y \leq 4$

$-3x - 4y + 0s_1 + 0s_2 + 0s_3 = -5$

$-4x - 5y + 0s_1 + 0s_2 + 0s_3 = -7$

$x + 2y + 0s_1 + 0s_2 + 1s_3 = 4$

also Min $z = 2x + 3y + 0s_1 + 0s_2 + 0s_3$

We prepare the following table

c_b	x_b	b	2 x	3 y	0 s_1	0 s_2	0 s_3
0	s_1	-5	-3	-4	1	0	0
0	s_2	-7	-4	-5	0	1	0
0	s_3	4	1	2	0	0	1
	$z_j = \sum c_b x_i$		0	0	0	0	0
	$c_i - z_j$		2	3	0	0	0
	$\theta = \dfrac{\left|c_i - z_j\right|}{a_{ij}}$		1/5	3/5	-	-	-

c_b	x_b	b	x	y	s_1	s_2	s_3
0	s_1	1/4	0	-1/4	1	-3/4	0
0	y	7/4	1	5/4	0	-1/4	0
0	s_3	9/4	0	3/4	0	1/4	1

$$y = \frac{7}{4}; \ z = \frac{7}{2}$$

4. Min $z = 10x_1 + 6x_2 + 2x_3$
   subjected to $-x_1 + x_2 + x_3 \geq 1$
   $3x_1 + x_2 - x_3 \geq 2, \ x_i \geq 0$

   Solution: Min $z = 10 \times 1 + 6 \times 2 + 2 \times 3 + 0s_1 + 0s_2$
   We require $\leq$ type, we have to multiply by negative sign
   $$x_1 - x_2 - x_3 \leq -1$$
   $$-3x_1 - x_2 + x_3 \leq -2$$
   $$x_1 - x_2 - x_3 + 0s_1 + 0s_2 = -1$$
   $$-3x_1 - x_2 + x_3 + 0s_1 + 0s_2 = -2$$

c_b	x_b	c_j b	10 x_1	6 x_2	2 x_3	0 s_1	0 s_2
0	s_1	-1	1	-1	-1	1	0
0	s_2	-2	-3	-1	1	0	1
	$z_j = \sum c_B x_i \Rightarrow$		0	0	0	0	0
	$c_i - z_j \Rightarrow$		10	6	2	0	0
	$\theta = \dfrac{\left|c_i - z_j\right|}{a_{ij}}$		10/3	6	-	-	-

–2 is least negative entry in the column b.

Hence, the row containing –2 is the key row (note here key row is first selected) a_{ij} are elements in key row having negative value (positive values are not considered)

Example: In x_3 column , $a_{ij} = 1$ so θ is not considered for that column. Since $\dfrac{10}{3}$ is the min θ make it as key column.

c_b	x_b	c_i b	10 x_1	6 x_2	2 x_3	0 s_1	0 s_2
0	s_1	–5/3	0	–4/3	–2/3	1	1/3
10	x_1	2/3	1	1/3	–1/3	0	–1/3
	$z =$		10	10/3	–10/3	0	–10/3
	$c_i - z_j$		0	8/3	+16/3	0	10/3
	$\theta =$		-	2	8	-	-

Divide pivot row by pivot element.

i.e., (–3), the remaining elements are :

New element = old row element – (pivot element) (key column element)

c_b	x_b	b	10 x_1	6 x_2	2 x_3	0 s_1	0 s_2
6	x_2	5/4	0	1	1/2	–3/4	–1/4
10	x_1	1/4	1	0	–1/2	+1/4	–1/4
	$z_j =$		10	6	–2	–2	–4

$$x_1 = \frac{1}{4} \; ; \; x_2 = \frac{5}{4}$$

$$\text{Min } z = \frac{10}{4} + \frac{30}{4} = 10$$

Duality

An important discovery in the early development of L.P.P. was the concept of duality and its division into important branches.

It is discovered that every L.P.P. has associated with it another L.P.P. The original L.P.P. is called "Primal" while the other is called its "Dual". If the optimal solution to one is known, then the optimal solution of the other is readily available.

Sometimes, a situation may arise where the dual is easier to solve than the primal. The important properties of duality are :

(a) The dual of a dual is primal.

(b) The number of constraints in one is equal to number of variables in other and vice versa.

(c) If there exists a finite optimal solution for one of the problem, then the other also has a finite optimal solution which will be the same.

(d) If one of the problem has no feasible solution, the other has unbounded solution.

(e) If there is an equality in primal the dual variable corresponding to it is unrestricted in sign and vice versa.

EXAMPLES

1. A reputed computer centre offers two kind of services namely "regular service" and "special services". Each hour on regular service brings a contribution of Rs.250 and that on special service is Rs.500. Special services only requires skilled labourers and maximum of 100 hours/week of time is available. Both the services require computing time and a maximum of 400 hours of computing time is available per week. The hourly operational cost of regular and special services are Rs.100 and Rs.250 respectively. The weekly budget for meeting operating expense is Rs. 80, 000. The centre has to allot a minimum of 200 hours/week for "Regular service". How should the centre allot its time for two services to maximize the total contribution ?

[VTU March/April 1999 CSE]

Solution: Let x_1 denote the number of hours for regular service/week.

Let x_2 denote the number of hours for special service/week.

Hence maximize $z = 250x_1 + 500x_2$ (by data)

Now special services require skilled labour and a maximum of 100 hours/week is available.

$$x_2 \leq 100 \qquad\qquad [1]$$

and since both require computing process and maximum of 400 hours is available per week.

$$x_1 + x_2 \leq 400 \qquad\qquad [2]$$

By data , operational costs of both have to be limited to a maximum of 80,000 we have

$$100x_1 + 250x_2 \leq 80,000 \qquad\qquad [3]$$

Centre has to allot a minimum of 200 hours for regular service, we have

$$x_1 \geq 200 \qquad\qquad [4]$$

$x_1, x_2 \geq 0$ (non-negativity rule)

$x_2 \leq 100$

so $x_2 = 100$

$x_1 + x_2 \leq 400$ [5]

$x_1 + x_2 = 400$

$x_1 = 0$	$x_1 = 400$
$x_2 = 400$	$x_2 = 0$

[6]

$100x_1 + 250x_2 = 80,000$

$x_1 = 0$	$x_1 = 800$
$x_2 = 320$	$x_2 = 0$

[7]

$x_1 \geq 200, \ x_1 = 200$ [8]

	x_1	x_2	$z = 250x_1 + 500x_2$
B	200	100	100,000
C	300	100	125,000
A	200	0	50,000
D	400	0	1,00,000

$(x_1 = 300; \ x_2 = 100; \quad \text{Max } z = 1,25,000)$

The graphical representation is as shown below.

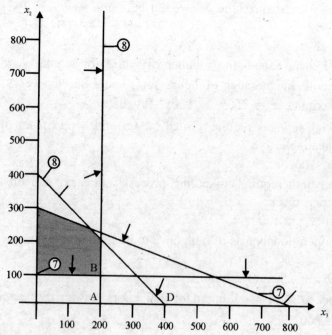

2. A furniture maker has 6 units of wood and 28 hours of free time in which he will make decorative screens. 2 models have sold well in the past. So he will restrict himself to those two. He estimates that model 1 requires 2 units of wood and 7 hours of time. While model 2 requires 1 unit of wood and 8 hours of time. The prices of the two models 1 and 2 are Rs.120 and Rs.80 respectively. How many screens of each model should the furniture maker assemble if he wishes to maximise his sales revenue?

(V.T.U March/April 1998)

Solution: By data, we use the following denotations.

Let x_1 denote the number of screens of model 1.

Let x_2 denote the number of screens of model 2.

	Wood	Time	Prices in Rs.
Model 1 (x_1)	2	7	120
Model 2 (x_2)	1	8	80
	≤ 6	≤ 28	

Max: $z = 120x_1 + 80x_2$ (maximize his sales revenue)

Let the wood requirements be: $2x_1 + x_2 \leq 6$

and for time requirements be: $7x_1 + 8x_2 \leq 28$

$(x_1, x_2 \geq 0$, non–negativity rule)

As usual, ordinary Simplex method to solve, we have

Maximize: $z = 120x_1 + 80x_2 + 0s_1 + 0s_2$

$$2x_1 + x_2 + s_1 + 0s_2 = 6$$

$$7x_1 + 8x_2 + 0s_1 + s_2 = 28$$

and $\quad x_1, x_2, s_1, s_2 \geq 0$

c_b	x_b	c_j b	120 x_1	80 x_2	0 s_1	0 s_2	Ratio
0	s_1	6	2	1	1	0	$6/2 = 3$
0	s_2	28	7	8	0	1	$28/7 = 4$
	$z_j = \sum c_b x_i$		0	0	0	0	
	$z_j - c_i =$		-120	-80	0	0	

c_b	x_b	b	x_1	x_2	s_1	s_2	Ratio
120	x_1	3	1	1/2	1/2	0	6
0	s_2	7	0	9/2	−7/2	1	14/9
	$z_j = \sum c_b x_i$		120	60	60	0	
	$z_j - c_j =$		0	−20	60	0	

c_b	x_b	b	x_1	x_2	s_1	s_2	Ratio
120	x_1	20/9	1	0	8/9	−1/9	
80	x_2	14/9	0	1	−7/9	2/9	
	$z_j = \sum c_b x_i$		120	80	400/9	40/9	
	$z_j - c_j =$		0	0	400/9	40/9	

$$\therefore \text{ Solution: } -\left(x_1 = \frac{20}{9};\ x_2 = \frac{14}{9}\right)$$

$$\text{Max: } z = 120\left(\frac{20}{9}\right) + 80\left(\frac{14}{9}\right) = 266.6 + 124.4 = 391$$

3. A manufacturer of leather belts make 3 belts A, B, C processed on 3 machines M_1, M_2, M_3. Belt A requires 2 hours on M_1, 3 hours on M_3, Belt B requires 3 hours on M_1, 2 hours on M_3. Belt C requires 5 hours on M_1, 4 hours on M_2 and 15 hours on M_3. There are 8 hours of working in a day on M_1, 10 hours/day on M_2, 15 hours/day on M_3. Profit from A is Rs.3/unit, from B is Rs.5/unit, from C is Rs. 4/unit. What should be the daily production of each type of belts to maximize profit?

Solution: By data, use the following denotations.

Let x_1 denote the number of belts of A.

Let x_2 denote the number of belts of B.

Let x_3 denote the number of belts of C.

$\therefore$ Max $z = 3x_1 + 5x_2 + 4x_3$

and 8 hours is the time for M_1

$\therefore$ $2x_1 + 3x_2 + 5x_3 \leq 8$ [1]

10 hours is the time for M_2

$0x_1 + 2x_2 + 4x_3 \leq 10$ [2]

Finally 15 hours for M_3, we have

$3x_1 + 2x_2 + 15x_3 \leq 15$ [3]

$(x_1,\ x_2,\ x_3 \geq 0,\ \text{non-negativity rule})$

As usual, use ordinary Simplex method to solve.

Max $z = 3x_1 + 5x_2 + 4x_3 + 0s_1 + 0s_2 + 0s_3$

$2x_1 + 3x_2 + 5x_3 + s_1 + 0s_2 + 0s_3 = 8$

$0x_1 + 2x_2 + 4x_3 + 0s_1 + s_2 + 0s_3 = 10$

$3x_1 + 2x_2 + 15x_3 + 0s_1 + 0s_2 + s_3 = 15$

c_b	x_b	b	x_1	x_2	x_3	s_1	s_2	s_3	Ratio
0	s_1	8	2	3	5	1	0	0	8/3
0	s_2	10	0	2	4	0	1	0	5
0	s_3	15	3	2	15	0	0	1	15/2
$z_j = \sum c_b x_i$		0	0	0	0	0	0	0	
$z_j - c_j =$		−3	−3	−5	−4				

c_b	x_b	b	x_1	x_2	x_3	s_1	s_2	s_3	Ratio
0	x_2	8/3	2/3	1	5/3	1/3	0	0	
0	s_2	14/3	−4/3	0	2/3	−2/3	1	0	
0	s_3	29/3	5/3	0	35/3	−2/3	0	1	
$z_j = \sum c_b x_i$		10/3	5	25/3	5/3	0	0		
$z_j - c_j =$		1/3	0	13/3	5/3	0	0		

Solution: $x_2 = 8/3$; so Max $z = 40/3$

4. A company can advertise its products using radio and TV stations. Its budget limits the advertisement expenditure to 10,000/ month. Each minute of radio advertisement cost Rs. 50 and each minute of TV advertisement costs Rs. 1000. The company would like to use radio at least twice as much as TV. Past experience shows that each minute of TV advertisements generates 25 times as much sales as each minute of radio advertisements. Determine the optimum allocation of monthly budget to radio and TV advertisement using graphical method.

Solution: By data, we have to maximize the sales.

Let x_1 be the number of minutes of radio usage.

Let x_2 be the number of minutes of TV usage.

Maximize $z = x_1 + 25x_2$

and $50x_1 + 1000x_2 \leq 10,000$ [1]

($\because$ its budget limits to 10,000 / month)

Since company uses radio at least, twice as much

as TV, we have

$$\left.\begin{array}{l} x_1 \ge 2x_2 \\ x_1 - 2x_2 \ge 0 \end{array}\right\} \qquad\qquad [2]$$

$(x_1, x_2 \ge 0$, non-negativity rule)

$$\left.\begin{array}{l} 50x_1 + 1000x_2 \le 10,000 \\ 50x_1 + 1000x_2 = 10,000 \end{array}\right\} \qquad\qquad [3]$$

when $\left.\begin{array}{l} x_1 = 0 \\ \text{then } x_2 = 10 \end{array}\right\}$ $\left.\begin{array}{l} x_1 = 200 \\ x_2 = 0 \end{array}\right\} \Rightarrow (0,10); (200,0)$ are the points

$\therefore \quad x_1 - 2x_2 \ge 0$

$\quad x_1 - 2x_2 = 0$

when $\left.\begin{array}{l} x_1 = 0 \\ \text{then } x_2 = 0 \end{array}\right.$ $\left.\begin{array}{l} x_1 = 200 \\ x = 100 \end{array}\right\} \therefore (0,0); (200,100)$ are the points

Consider points

	x_1	x_2	$z = x_1 + 25x_2$
A	0	10	250
B	20	9	245
C	0	0	0

$\therefore x_1 = 0, x_2 = 10$; Max $z = 250$

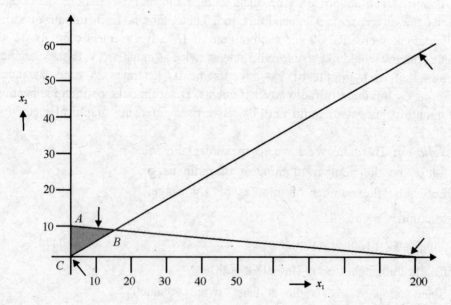

5. A company produces 2 types of belts A and B. Profits of the 2 types are Rs. 3 and Rs. 4 per belt respectively. Each type of belt A requires twice as much time as belt B. If all the belt were of type A, the company can produce 1000 belts/day. But leather supply is limited to 800 belts/day. Belt A requires a fancy buckle and only 400 fancy buckles are available/day. Belt B can be produced to a maximum of 700/ day. How should the company manufacture to maximize the profit?   [B.E, Feb, 1996, CSE]

Solution: Let x_1 denote the number of belts of type A.

Let x_2 denote the number of belts of type B.

Profit $= 3x_1 + 4x_2$

$$\Rightarrow \quad z = 3x_1 + 4x_2 \tag{1}$$

Equation [1] is to be maximized. As the problem involves profit.

Max $z = 3x_1 + 4x_2$. Since leather supply limits to 800/day.

We have $x_1 + x_2 \le 800$ [2]

Since 400 fancy buckles are produced per day and each belt of type A requires a fancy buckle, we have maximum belts of type A to be 400

i.e., $x_1 \le 400$ [3]

Since belt B can be produced upto 700 per day , we have

$$x_2 \le 700 \tag{4}$$

Since each belt of type A requires twice the time required for type B (or the time required for type B is $\frac{1}{2}$ the time required for type A) and a maximum of 1000 belts of type A can be produced if only A is produced, we get

$$x_1 + 0.5x_2 \le 1000 \tag{5}$$

$(x_1, x_2 \ge 0$, non-negativity rule)

Consider equation $x_1 + x_2 \le 800$

Now $x_1 + x_2 = 800$ [6]

is a straight line and the equation is satisfied by all points below it. Now, to plot the line we have

when $x_1 = 0$; $x_1 = 800$

then $x_2 = 800$; $x_2 = 0$

$\therefore \quad$ (0,800) and (800,0) are the points.

Similarly $x_1 = 400$ is another line   [7]

and $x_2 = 700$ is   3rd line   [8]

Finally $x_1 + 0.5x_2 = 1000$ [9]

when $x_1 = 0$; $x_1 = 1000$

then $x_2 = 2000$; $x_2 = 0$

$\therefore$ (0, 2000) and (1000, 0) are the points.

Let us consider the graph shown below:

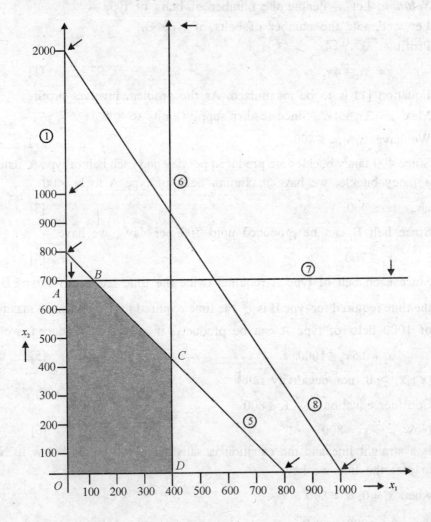

From the graph, we have to consider the points which are inside all straight line. Since all are $\leq$ type, the common area is shown and shaded. In the common area, we calculate at each point x_1, x_2 values and z values.

The points are

	x_1	x_2	Profit $z = 3x_1 + 4x_2$
A	0	700	2800
B	100	700	3100
C	400	400	2800
D	400	0	1200

It is required to maximize the profit, we have to consider point B.

$x_1 = 100$; $x_2 = 700$

Profit $= 3 (100) + 4(700) = 300 + 2800 = 3100$

Degeneracy in Linear Programming Problem

In linear programming, we have an important theorem, which states that, the optimal solution to a linear programming problem with 'n' variables and 'm' constraints, ($n > m$) will have a maximum of 'm' non-zero variables.

This statement implies that an optimum solution can have less than m non-zero variables. In such a case, we say that the solution to L.P.P. is degenerate. For that matter, every solution with less than 'm' non-zero variables, either optimal or otherwise is called a degenerate solution the accompanying status of the L.P.P. is called Degeneracy.

Method to Resolve Degeneracy.

We suggest the following steps in the Simplex procedure, in such situations:

Step 1: Select the rows containing ties.

Step 2: Write the coefficients of the slack variables and divide each coefficient by the coefficient in the Pivot column.

Step 3: By comparing the result ratios column by selecting the smallest ratio, for the departing variable.

Illustration: Let us consider the L.P.P.

Maximize $z = c_1x_1 + c_2x_2 + c_3x_3 + c_4x_4$

$$a_{11}x_1 + a_{12}x_2 + a_{13}x_3 + a_{14}x_4 = b_1$$

Subject to $\quad a_{21}x_1 + a_{22}x_2 + a_{23}x_3 + a_{24}x_4 = b_2$

$$a_{31}x_1 + a_{32}x_2 + a_{33}x_3 + a_{34}x_4 = b_3$$

Here n = number of variables = 4

m = number of constraints = 3

Hence, a situation in which a solution with less than 3 non-zero variables is being considered, is said to be characterized by Degeneracy.

EXAMPLES

1. Maximise $z = 3x_1 + 5x_2$

$$x_1 + x_3 = 4$$
$$x_2 + x_4 = 6$$

Subject to the constraints $3x_1 + 2x_2 + x_5 = 12$

$$x_1, x_2, x_3, x_4, x_5 \geq 0$$

Does degeneracy occur in this problem?

Solution: We prepare the starting simplex table as follows:

			3	5	0	0	0	
c_b	x_b	b	x_1	x_2	x_3	x_4	x_5	Min Ratio
0	x_3	4	1	0	1	0	0	-
0	x_4	6	0	1	0	1	0	6
0	x_5	12	3	2	0	0	1	6
			0	0	0	0	1	
$z_j = \sum c_b x_i$		0	0	0	0	0	0	
$z_j - c_j$			-3	-5	0	0	0	

Since the minimum ratios are the same, this is an indication of degeneracy. So, arrange the columns in such a way that initial identity matrix comes first.

			0	0	0	3	5		
c_b	x_b	b	x_3	x_4	x_5	x_1	x_2	Min Ratio $\dfrac{x_3}{x_2}$	$\dfrac{x_3}{x_2}$
0	x_3	4	1	0	0	1	0		
0	x_4	6	0	1	0	0	1	0	1/1
0	x_5	12	0	0	1	3	2	0	0/2

| c_b | x_b | b | 0 | 0 | 0 | 3 | 5 | Min Ratio |
			x_3	x_4	x_5	x_1	x_2	
0	x_3	4	1	0	0	1	0	
0	x_4	0	0	1	$-1/2$	$-3/2$	0	
5	x_2	6	0	0	1/2	3/2	1	
$z_j = \sum c_b x_i$			0	0	5/2	15/2	5	
$z_j - c_j$			0	0	5/2	9/2	0	

Since $z_j - c_j \geq 0$, an optimal solution has been reached

Solution set: $x_3 = 4$; $x_2 = 6$; $x_4 = 0$

Max $z = 3x_1 + 5x_2 = 3(0) + 5(6) = 30$

2. Maximize $z = 3x_1 + 9x_2$

Subject to the constraints

$x_1 + 4x_2 \leq 8$

$x_1 + 2x_2 \leq 4$

$x_1, x_2 \geq 0$

Solution: Let $s_1 \geq 0$ and $s_2 \geq 0$ be slack variables, then the problems, becomes

Max $z = 3x_1 + 9x_2 + 0s_1 + 0s_2$

Subject to constraints

$\qquad x_1 + 4x_2 + s_1 + 0s_2 = 8$

$\qquad x_1 + 2x_2 + 0s_1 + s_2 = 4$

| | c_j | | 3 | 9 | 0 | 0 | |
c_b	x_b	b	x_1	x_2	s_1	s_2	Min Ratio
0	s_1	8	1	4	1	0	8/4
0	s_2	4	1	2	0	1	4/2
$z_j = \sum c_b x_i$			0	0	0	0	
$z_j - c_j$			-3	-9	0	0	

Thus, there is a tie between first and second row. This is an indication of degeneracy. So, arrange the columns in such a way that the initial identity matrix comes first, then the starting table becomes

c_j			0	0	3	9	
c_b	x_b	b	s_1	s_2	x_1	x_2	Min Ratio
0	s_1	8	1	0	1	4	1/4
0	s_2	4	0	1	1	2	0/2

c_b	x_b	b	s_1	s_2	x_1	x_2	Min Ratio
0	s_1	0	1	−2	−1	0	
9	x_2	2	0	1/2	1/2	1	
$z_j = \sum c_b x_i$				0	9/2	9/2	9
$z_j - c_j$					9/2	3/2	0

Since $z_j - c_j \geq 0$ optimal solution has been reached.

3. Given Simplex table

		c_j:	7	5	0	0	
Non-zero basic variable	c_b	Sol. values x_b	x_1	x_2	x_3	x_4	Min. Ratio $(x_b/x_k, x_k > 0)$
s_3	0	8	1	4	1	0	8/4 = 2
x_4	0	4	1	2	0	1	4/2 = 2
	$z = 0$		−3	−9	0	0	

We find that the first and second rows have the same minimum ratio. So there is a tie in selecting the departing variables from the basis, that is both the slack variables s_1 and s_2 may leave the basis. This causes the problem of degeneracy in the given L.P.P. To break the tie the coefficients of slack variables are taken and they are divided by the corresponding coefficients of the key rows.

Arrange the columns x_1, x_2, s_1 and s_2 in such a way that starting identity matrix appears first. Then the initial Simplex table becomes

		c_j	7	5	0	0	
Basic variable	c_b	Sol. values x_b	s_1	s_2	x_1	x_2	Min. Ratio $(x_b/x_k, x_k > 0)$
s_1	0	8	1	0	1	4	$s_1/x_2 = 1/4$
s_2	0	4	0	1	1	2	0/2 ←
	$z = 0$		0	0	−3	−9	$\delta_j \geq 0$

Compute corresponds to the second row → Pivot Element = 2. We can now improve the Simplex table in the usual manner.

4. Given Simplex table

Basic variable	Solution values	$b (= x_b)$	s_1	s_2	s_3	x_1	x_2	Min. Ratio $(x_b/x_k, x_k > 0)$
s_1	0	12	4	3	1	0	0	12/4
s_2	0	8	4	−1	0	1	0	8/4
s_3	0	8	−1	0	0	0	1	8/4
z	0		−2 ↑	−1	0	0	0	

The second and third rows have the same minimum ratio. So there is a tie in selecting the (outgoing vector) departing variables from the basis, e.g., both the slack variables s_2 and s_3 may leave the basis. This causes the problem of degeneracy in the given L.P.P. To break the tie the coefficient of slack variables are taken and they are divided by the corresponding coefficient of the key as follows:

Arrange the columns in such a way that the starting identity matrix comes first then the initial Simplex table becomes.

Basic variable	Solution values $b(= x_b)$	Values	s_1	s_2	s_3	x_1	x_2	Min. Ratio (s_1/x_1)	(s_2/x_2)
s_1	0	12	1	0	0	4	3	—	—
s_2	0	8	0	1	0	4	−1	0/4	1/4
s_3	0	8	0	0	1	4	−1	0/4	0/4
z	0	0	0	0 ↓	−2 ↑	−2		$\delta_j \leftarrow$	

Compute Min $\left[-\dfrac{0}{4}, \dfrac{0}{4}\right] \to$ again compute Min $\left[-\dfrac{1}{4}, \dfrac{0}{4}\right] = 0 \to$ corresponds to the 3rd row → Pivot Element = 4.

We can now improve the Simplex table in the usual manner.

5. Given Simplex table

Non-zero basic variable	c_b	c_j Solution values $b(= x_b)$	40 x_1	25 x_2	10 x_3	0 x_4	0 x_5	0 x_6	Min. Ratio
x_4	0	100	5	1	4	1	0	0	20
x_5	0	120	2	3	2	0	1	0	60
x_6	0	80	4	1	2	0	0	1	20
	$z = c_b x_b - c_j$		−40 ↑	−25	−10	0	0	0	

We find that first and third rows have the same minimum ratio. So there is a tie in selecting the departing variables from the basis. To break the tie the coefficient of slack variables are taken and they are divided by the corresponding coefficients of the key rows as follows:

	x_4	x_5	x_6
x_5	1/5	0/5	0/5
x_6	0/4	0/4	1/4

Comparing the ratios in the first column we find that x_6 yield the smaller ratio x_6 is the departing variables.

Note: **1. Degenerate:** A basic feasible solution is said to be degenerate if one or more of the basic variables are zero.

2. Non-degenerate: If all m basic variables are positive and the remaining n variables are zero, then the basic feasible solution is said to be non-degenerate.